FUNDAMENTALS OF IMMUNOLOGY

FUNDAMENTALS OF IMMUNOLOGY

Fourth Edition

William C. Boyd

Professor of Immunochemistry
Boston University, School of Medicine

INTERSCIENCE PUBLISHERS

a division of John Wiley & Sons   NEW YORK • LONDON • SYDNEY

Preface

This is an introduction to the study of immunity, in both its practical and theoretical aspects, which means it is also an introduction to immuno-chemistry. Since the first edition appeared, the continued demand for the book has encouraged the author and publishers to believe it answers a real need. Consequently, in preparing this new version, the basic plan has not been greatly changed. However, so much has been learned about the subject since 1943 that extensive changes, calling with each edition for a complete rewriting, have had to be made, and very few pages of the original text appear here. For the third edition some reorganization of the material presented seemed necessary, and this is described in the preface to that edition. The principal changes of that sort in the present version involve putting the material on statistical methods, with some additional material, in a chapter to itself (Chapter 17), and writing a new chapter on immunological tolerance and intolerance and tissue transplants (Chapter 12).

The book is addressed primarily to the same two audiences as before: students and research workers. It is thought that it will continue to be of value also to those practicing physicians who are interested in the principles of immunology, especially as this edition, like the third, includes a discussion of the application of immunological methods, in testing for susceptibility and immunity, in prophylaxis, in diagnosis, and in treatment, of nearly all the more important human infections. Physicians may also find the four chapters on hypersensitivity useful.

Fundamentals of Immunology is still intended as an introduction to the subject and not a comprehensive review. Consequently, no attempt is made to cover all the topics completely or to cite all the pertinent literature. In general the references given have been chosen from a number of possible citations, and, whenever feasible, papers, monographs, books, and reviews were selected which are either important landmarks or which contain numerous references to other important papers. This should make it relatively easy for the student who wishes to do so to explore any particular branch of the subject further and to build up his own bibliography. In spite of adherence to this principle of parsimony, however, some of the collections of references have become fairly extensive. Since these lists are designed to help the reader quickly find the reference he desires, rather than to present him with a series of puzzles, the items are arranged alphabetically by author, although this involved considerably more work on my part. For the same reason I have avoided *ibid., loc. cit.,* and similar mystic symbols.

This book could never have been written, nor adequately revised, without consulting extensively other books, and many journals, dealing with this and related fields. I am glad to record here my particular debt, in some cases going back many years, to certain works: *Traité de l'Immunité,* by Jules Bordet (Masson et Cie., Paris). *The Chemistry of Antigens and Antibodies,* by John Marrack (H. M. Stationery Office, London), *The Specificity of Serological Reactions,* by Karl Landsteiner (C. C Thomas Co., Springfield; Harvard University Press, Cambridge), *The Principles of Bacteriology and Immunity,* by W. W. C. Topley and G. S. Wilson (Fifth Ed. by G. S. Wilson and A. A. Miles) (William Wood Co., Baltimore), *The Bacterial Cell,* by R. J. Dubos (Harvard University Press, Cambridge), *Bacterial and Mycotic Infections of Man,* edited by R. J. Dubos and J. G. Hirsch (J. B. Lippincott Co., Philadelphia), *Viral and Rickettsial Infections of Man,* edited by F. L. Horsfall and I. Tamm (J. B. Lippincott Co., Philadelphia), *Communicable Diseases,* by F. H. Top (C. V. Mosby Co., St. Louis), *The Report of the Committee on the Control of Infectious Diseases* of the American Academy of Pediatrics, *The Report on the Control of Communicable Diseases of Man* of the American Public Health Association, and *Die Immunitätsforschung,* by R. Doerr (Springer-Verlag, Vienna). The successive volumes of the *Journal of Immunology* (Williams and Wilkins, Baltimore), and *Advances in Immunology* (Academic Press, New York and London) have been of great assistance. Grateful acknowledgment is made of permission to quote in several instances from various of these publications.

I am much indebted to friends and colleagues who have read and criticized all or part of the manuscript while it was in the course of preparation. The result has been to make the book much less imperfect, but it must be admitted that I have occasionally exercised the privilege of not necessarily following my consultants' advice, and they are not responsible for any errors of fact or interpretation that the book may still contain. I am particularly indebted to my wife, who read the entire manuscript and the galley proofs, and whose suggestions resulted in improvement of the clarity of the exposition at numerous points. I am very grateful to my student, Mrs. Yang Cha Kim, who undertook the unrewarding tasks of doing the references and helping with the Index. My best thanks are due William and Elizabeth Finley, in whose hospitable home I prepared the Index.

Each chapter is preceded by an appropriate (more or less) quotation. Translations of the quotations in languages other than English are given in an Appendix.

WILLIAM C. BOYD

Contents

CHAPTER 1

Immunity and Immunology

1. Biological Background

The evolution of immune mechanisms began when the evolution of
life began. It may help give us proper perspective if we think back for a
moment to this era in time. Biologists today generally believe that life
originated when the earth still had its primitive atmosphere of methane,
ammonia, water, and hydrogen. According to Muller (87) the first living
units were the complex molecules of nucleic acid we call genes. Everything subsequent is the creation of the genes. Mutant genes would be
favored by natural selection if their products happened to include biological tools, such as enzymes, that are useful for the survival and multiplication of the genes. Wald (122a) suggests that fermentative (*i.e.,* anaerobic) processes developed first, then photophosphorylation, followed by
photosynthesis, which used the hexosemonophosphate cycle to produce
adenosine triphosphate (ATP). This started the process of oxygen
production that has resulted in our own oxygen-rich atmosphere.

One thing is certain; the essence of life is the ability to reproduce, and
the elaborate catabolic and metabolic abilities of the organisms we know
today must have been later developments.

"Protoplasm" may have come into existence very gradually, in the form
of chemical products of the chemical action of the aggregate of genes,
including the genes that had suitably mutated.

Once the process of reproduction had begun, a new phenomenon, that
of *competition,* would exhibit itself; for an organism capable of reproduction must necessarily be able to reproduce itself at a higher rate than

1

the mean rate which is requisite just to stabilize numbers over a short period of time. This higher reproductive rate is needed, because climatic and other conditions may vary, the supply of food may diminish, or other unfavorable conditions may arise, any one of which may drastically reduce the numbers of a population. Unless the population has a capacity to recoup its losses and make good its diminished numbers, it is only a matter of time until it will be wiped out. Since the hypothetical organisms from which all life that we know is supposed to be descended did not die out, they doubtless were capable of reproduction on a more rapid scale than was needed merely to preserve the same number of individuals from year to year, or from generation to generation. But, as soon as larger numbers of individuals are produced, the phenomenon of competition begins, because the food supply—the supply of substances which the young organism may assimilate and turn to its own uses—is finite on a finite planet; and besides, it is unlikely that the first living organisms would have been able to make use of, or even reach, the food of more than a local area of the earth's surface. Before long there will be more organisms than there is food supply to support them, and competition among the organisms for the food supply, or even merely for space in which to live, will begin.

As soon as competition begins, we may suppose that evolution has also begun; for competition between organisms, coupled with the fact that organisms occasionally vary in an inheritable way from the ancestral type, brings evolution about. As a result of evolution, new or more complex organisms may be produced; or the new organisms may perhaps be equally simple but capable of assimilating a slightly different type of foodstuff, or they may have other modifications. Our archeological record indicates that life, originating doubtless in shallow waters adjacent to the land, gradually spread through the waters and eventually emerged onto the dry land, finally producing, through evolution, the terrestrial forms with which we are all familiar.

As soon as different forms or species were produced, there would begin, in addition to the competition which had previously existed between different individuals all of the same kind for food supplies, competition between individuals of different species. Each organism would have to take part in what scientists of the nineteenth century called the "struggle for life." Biologists have shown that this struggle for life is indeed a much more bitter and relentless one than a casual examination of the situation might lead one to suppose. No holds are barred, and no slight adaptive change or useful device, within the scope of the possibilities of living matter, which makes for survival will be overlooked in the long run.

There are a number of ways in which different organisms and different species may compete with each other. In the first place, they may simply want to occupy the same space; in other words, to live on the same half-acre of land or in the same milliliter of sea water. If there is room there for only so much living matter, only a limited number of individuals will be able to occupy this location. Second, and usually a more crucial limitation, is the finite character of the food supply. In the case of plant life, the food supply now consists of carbon dioxide from the air, plus minerals and organic matter in the soil. Any amateur gardener who has observed the way an undesirable sort of grass may take over a whole area formerly occupied by some other plant, considered useful or ornamental by man, will realize the intensity of the struggle for food supply and the completeness with which one variety of living organism may gain ascendancy over the other. Sometimes, in an area where formerly hundreds or perhaps thousands of individuals per square yard of a certain species could be found, five years later not a single individual can be discovered.

At some stage of evolution, one or more species must have made the momentous discovery that a very convenient source of food consists of the tissues of other organisms. Perhaps dead organisms were utilized at first, but it would be but a short step to the consumption of living organisms. The whole of the animal kingdom depends upon eating plant life in some form or other—directly or indirectly—and thus obtains the protein which it needs to build up its tissues and the carbohydrate or fat to provide energy for its activity. It is only the green plants and certain other vegetable organisms which can synthesize these substances from inorganic materials (which include carbon dioxide).

Once the importance and desirability of eating the other fellow was discovered, evolution had the opportunity to take a further step, whereby an animal accustomed to eating plant life could also develop the taste for eating other animals. The new taste might eventually supplant the old vegetarian habits completely. A lion eats no plant life; its usual food consists of large herbivorous mammals. (Of course we do not mean to imply that evolution had to wait for the animals as we now know them to be differentiated to develop this step of one form's eating other or like forms.)

It was probably not very late in the history of evolution that another and about equally important discovery was made. Instead of simply eating other individuals and thus obtaining nourishment, certain organisms can learn to live with or upon other organisms and obtain nourishment, either by eating portions of the tissues or by absorbing food which would otherwise be utilized by the host. This may or may not result in the death of the host. Organisms that live upon another organism and depend upon it for a source of nourishment are known as parasites. Evolution has operated on the parasite as well as upon other living organisms, and the world as we know it contains many examples of extremely accurate adaptations of the parasite to its host. The parasite may in many cases become smaller, and thus less conspicuous and better able to find lodgment in the tissues of the host. It may become, in some respects, simpler—morphologically or chemically—thereby undergoing a process which we usually refer to as degeneration. The evolution of parasites is discussed in (117a).

While parasites were developing, however, the organisms which they made their prey were, in the evolutionary sense, not idle themselves. Whatever the first forms of life on earth may have been, we find at the present time that all organisms have provided themselves with some membrane or sheath to protect themselves against invasion from the outside. In many cases, skin and various kinds of armor have also been developed. The porcupine has devloped a coat of quills which must be very effective in preventing any carnivorous animals from eating him, judging by the results when a dog attempts to attack a porcupine. Quills and other defensive armor would be quite effective against large predatory animals but less effective against smaller organisms which had become parasites, and which either were from the beginning or had become so small as to be invisible to the eye. Such organisms would be able to find their way into the tissues of the host either through natural openings of the body or by actually boring a path, as is done by the free-swimming form of certain parasites, such as *Schistosoma*. This process has gone on to such an extent that it may be safely said that probably no organism of any considerable complexity exists which is not subject, at some stage of its existence, to the attack of some sort of parasite or microorganism.

There are two classes of parasitic organisms of predominant concern to us, which we call bacteria and viruses. Some think the latter may have evolved by degeneration from the former. The nature of these forms of life will be discussed later on in this book. Suffice it to say here that they are small organisms, invisible to the eye without artificial aid, which may on occasion invade the tissues of suitable hosts. When such an invasion occurs, we speak of it as an infection.

Now just as organisms develop protective devices such as spines or armor to protect themselves against being eaten, so also have they, in practically all cases that we know about, developed protective devices against parasites, including the tiny organisms called bacteria and viruses. Some of these protective devices consist of relatively impermeable membranes, such as skin and the mucous membranes of the higher animals. Others include, apparently, the ability to alter the body temperature to one unsuitable to the would-be invader. There must be a great many other such devices. For, just as the parasite is capable, in the course of evolution, of evolving in a manner so as to be able to invade a different host, or to invade the same host more effectively, the host is capable of evolving in such a way that it can resist invasion. The production by artificial selection of plant resistance to various plant diseases such as the rust disease of wheat, etc., is but an imitation of this natural process.

Furthermore, another somewhat accidental factor must operate. In the course of adapting to a certain host, a parasite may automatically lose its adaptation to other hosts, for the adaptation required may involve some physical or chemical change, such as the alteration of one of its enzymes to make it specifically capable of hydrolyzing some particular compound found in the tissues of the desired host. The new enzyme may not work so well against chemical substances found in other organisms. Or a parasite may lose, in the course of evolution, the capacity to produce some vitamin or other substance essential to its metabolism, because it finds this substance in the tissues of the particular host or hosts it is currently living on. Changes of this sort result in specialization. But such changes may deprive the parasite of certain more general abilities which enabled it to invade, though perhaps less successfully, a number of different hosts. It may become completely specialized to a single host, and then, should it find this particular host unavailable, it will die. Organisms to which it is not adapted will be, as we say, immune to attacks of this parasite—that is, they will not be affected by it. This is the correct use of the word "immune," which in its original meaning implies complete freedom or exemption from some certain thing. Thus, pigs are immune to smallpox, and the rat seems to be absolutely immune to diphtheria.

But we shall seldom use the word immune in the strict sense here. We are going to be interested, not in absolute immunity, but in degrees of refractoriness to infection, and the use of the word "immunity" in this way has become accepted terminology. Immunity is only one of the weapons in the basic struggle for life, and denotes the *resistance* which an organism offers against aggression by a parasite. The study of immunity, in the sense in which we are going to use the word, is only a branch of biology, and it could even be maintained that it is only a branch of ecology.

An interesting treatment of disease from the point of view of the biologist has been given in a book by Burnet (12). Burnet points out that there is good reason to think that, even within historical times, there have been changes in certain human diseases, which represent an adaptation either of the host to the parasite, or of the parasite to the host, or perhaps both. He points out that in the majority of cases the best adaptation has been reached when the parasite causes the host comparatively little damage and does not kill it, but is able to perpetuate itself by passing from one host to another, either directly or indirectly. From the point of view of the parasite, of course, the object is to keep the amount of living matter, organized in a way characteristic of the parasite, as great as possible. The organization of the molecules in a particle of influenza virus, for example, is different from the organization of the molecules in one of the cells of *Homo sapiens*. Burnet believes that diseases like herpes simplex (cold sores or fever blisters), which cause the host very little trouble, and in which the virus seems to persist from year to year for long periods of time, represent about the optimum adaptation of the parasite to the host. He considers poliomyelitis, a disease which seems to have been diminishing in severity in recent times in America, Europe, and Australia, to be an example of a disease in the process of evolution (13). Simon also believes that "peaceful coexistence" between organisms is the rule, rather than the exception, in nature (112).

2. Immunity

As we have just pointed out, the subject we propose to study here is not covered by the word immunity in its original meaning. What we are really interested in is degrees of resistance to disease, and particularly in how we may artificially increase inadequate resistance (44,119). The study of the procedures we use and of the mechanisms by which resistance is increased is usually called *immunology*. The study of the diagnostic and experimental procedures connected with this problem is usually called *serology*, because they involve the use of serum. Other subjects, such as blood grouping and forensic precipitin tests, are included under immunology, although, for example, the existence of blood groups in man seems to be, on the whole, a perfectly normal phenomenon without much relation to disease. (See, however, p. 23.) But the procedures used and the mechanisms involved are essentially the same as those developed in research on immunity.

Immunology includes also the study of a phenomenon which is the reverse of increased resistance, namely, hypersensitivity. We shall discuss this problem in Chapters 8, 9, and 11.

It is impossible to study resistance thoroughly without touching also on problems of virulence and invasiveness, and the properties and physiological action of various antigens. Also, we cannot confine our studies to the immunity of individuals, but we must consider the subjects in sample groups. This means that immunity is closely related to epidemiology, and that we cannot draw valid conclusions from such grouped data without properly controlled experiments which, in many cases at least, must be evaluated statistically (28). However, in a book the size of the present one, we shall be unable to do more than touch on some of these peripheral aspects of our subject.

Immunology is a practical science, concerned with methods of diagnosing or preventing disease or influencing its course, mostly by using serums and vaccines. This restriction serves to delimit the subject somewhat, and we shall not discuss here problems of preventing disease by avoiding contact or eliminating the disease agent or its carriers, considering such problems to belong rather to public health and epidemiology. Also no discussion of the chemotherapeutic methods which have become so important in clinical medicine will be attempted. Progress along this line has lessened the importance of biological therapy in some cases, but not in all. Such facts as the increasing frequency with which sulfa-resistant (113,126) and penicillin-resistant microorganisms are being isolated (33), and the rapid development of resistance to streptomycin by the tubercle bacillus, just as trypanosomes have in the past become "drug-fast," suggest in any case that chemotherapy will not soon replace immunological methods completely. Other limitations of chemotherapy are suggested by the increasing frequency of mycotic infections in patients treated with antibiotics (67).

We shall, however, say a few words about processes that seem to have mechanisms similar to those of immune reactions, such as hypersensitivity and transplant rejection, and even a word about the plant proteins that mimic the action of the immune substances called antibodies.

3. Inflammation

Inflammation is a fundamental phenomenon occurring in higher animals (80). It involves lymphatic structures, vascular channels, and the locally affected tissues. It is initiated by a disturbance in fluid exchange, which markedly deranges the normal capillary circulation. One of the major changes is an increase in capillary permeability. This is readily demonstrable by the local seepage of material deliberately introduced into the circulation. Diazo dyes, ferric chloride, graphite particles, and bacteria will readily concentrate from the circulation into acutely inflamed foci (78).

Eyring and others (61,31) have offered a physicochemical explanation of inflammation. According to them, the first of the sequence of responses which constitute inflammation is a wave of destruction of cells primarily native to the interstitial connective tissue. Cell materials, including histamine, are released. These products act as inflammatory stimuli. One of the first and most striking changes is the swelling of the endothelial cells of the capillaries, which is accompanied by increased capillary permeability. The degree of swelling seems to be proportional to the extent of the local tissue injury and may not always be noticeable after extremely mild stimulation.

Accompanying, or just preceding, this change in the endothelial cells, the ground substance, which embeds the capillaries and the injured cells, changes to a more fluid sol-like state. Within minutes following these changes the endothelial cells acquire a sticky surface and leukocytes and platelets begin to adhere to them.

Subsequently there is a marked vasodilatation, the capillary walls become highly permeable, and localized edema and leukocyte migration into the surrounding interstitial substance occur. In this way, the highly phagocytic polymorphonuclear neutrophilic leukocytes mobilize at the site of injury, and the processes of further proteolysis and phagocytosis begin.

Menkin (79,81) believed that there is liberated into exudates in inflamed areas a substance, not directly related to histamine, which is thermostable and diffusable through a cellophane membrane. (In immunology, "thermostable" means resistant to heating at 55° to 60°C. for 30 to 60 minutes.) It seems to be a peptide, but a prosthetic group may be attached. This peptide-like substance, which has been called leukotaxine, not only increases capillary permeability but also induces the migration of polymorphonuclear leukocytes through the capillary wall.

Eyring et al. (61,31) did not think it is necessary to assume that different chemical substances have specific functions in the inflammatory response. They attempted to explain the phenomena by changes of permeability of the cell membranes, since cells in their more permeable state are sticky.

According to Eyring et al. any stress, such as that resulting from overwork, from toxins, from drugs, or from the bursting of normal cells by radiation or burns, or from invading viruses or bacteria, which causes the cells to spend too much time in the "active" (permeable) state, will set up this destructive chain reaction.

Increased capillary permeability allows the free passage of plasma proteins from the circulation into the extracapillary spaces. Fibrinogen is converted to fibrin with the release of thrombokinase following injury to cellular structures. A network of fibrin is formed in tissue distended by edema, and lymphatic channels become plugged with fibrin, thus inducing a lymphatic blockade. This tends to prevent the dissemination of infectious material or microorganisms from the focus of inflammation. The migration of leukocytes into the area serves further to wall off the invading microorganisms, which will be dealt with, if the infection does not spread further, by phagocytosis (see below).

A protein-like *leukocytosis-promoting* factor is believed to be liberated from injured cells. It not only induces a discharge of immature leukocytes from the bone marrow but also causes marked hyperplasia of elements of the bone marrow.

Inflammation is a manifestation of severe cellular injury. The injury seems partly due to the liberation of another substance in the exudate which has been termed necrosin. Menkin (79,81) outlined his concept of the process as follows:

1. Disturbance in local fluid exchange.
    a. Increase in capillary permeability.
    b. Initial increase in lymph flow.
2. Localization of the irritant (fixation).
3. Migration of the leukocytes.
    a. Influx of polymorphonuclear leukocytes.
    b. Other cytological changes dependent on the local pH.
    c. Leukocytosis in the circulation.

This sequence of events favors the localization and ultimate disposal of the irritant. If this is accomplished, repair of the injured area begins.

It is not possible to measure accurately the extent of resistance which an animal may develop locally as the result of inflammation, although Menkin used the degree of retention of a dye as a rough measure of the retentive efficiency of the inflammatory process.

The mechanism of inflammation was reviewed by various authors in a book edited by Jasmin and Robert (60).

4. Phagocytosis

An amoeba gets its food simply by engulfing particles of foreign substance and absorbing the useful portion. An amoeba can deal thus with living microorganisms, and in so doing it provides itself with a most effective defense against them. It might be suspected that such a handy form of defense would not be totally lost in the course of evolution, and in fact in the 1880's Metchnikoff discovered that within the more complicated organisms there exist simple cells capable of ingesting and disposing of particulate matter. This phenomenon is called *phagocytosis* (Fig. 1-1) and represents the great clearing mechanism of the blood. Its effectiveness is graphically shown in Figure 1-2, based on experiments of Freeman, Gordon, and Humphrey (39).

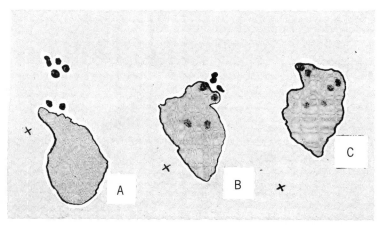

Fig. 1-1. Process of phagocytosis of six pneumococci by a phagocyte. Pictures at intervals of 2 minutes. (*A*) A pseudopod is in contact with two of the pneumococci, whose swollen capsules are shown. (*B*) Two more organisms are being engulfed, while the first two (now minus capsules) are shown within the phagocyte. (*C*) All the pneumococci have been phagocyted. The x marks the position of some untouched organisms which thus serve as a stationary landmark. Modified from Wood, Smith, and Watson (128).

When dyes and suspensions are injected intravenously into an animal, quite often they are not eliminated in the urine or bile (as are, for instance, phenolphthalein and its derivatives), but are deposited in various organs such as the spleen, liver, lymph nodes, and bone marrow, and they may remain there in recognizable form for weeks. For a review of the literature see Cappell (19,20).

Investigation has shown that these dyes are stored inside certain cells which the histologist calls histiocytes, but some immunologists, following Metchnikoff, call them macrophages. These cells have a characteristic distribution throughout the body and may be divided into two main types: sessile and wandering. The most active of the sessile (fixed) histiocytes are found in specialized areas of the vascular or lymphatic endothelium. Chiefly important are the endothelial cells of the capillaries of the liver (Kupffer cells), of the sinuses of the spleen, of the venous sinusoids of the bone marrow, of the capillaries and medullary sinusoids of the adrenals, of the capillaries of the pituitary, and of the sinuses of the various lymph glands of the body. The reticulocytes, which are disposed about the reticulum fibers in the interstices of the tissues, are somewhat less active. Wandering histiocytes occur in all the tissue

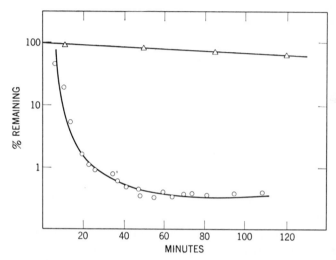

Fig. 1-2. Clearance of heat-aggregated protein from the blood stream, in normal rats (lower curve) and in rats whose reticuloendothelial system had been swamped ("blocked") by injection of foreign particles (India ink) (upper curve). The heat-denatured protein was detected by its radioactive iodine label (39).

spaces and to some extent in the blood, especially in vessels in internal organs.

There is abundant evidence that the activity of some free and some fixed cells in the blood and tissues is an important part of the mechanism of immunity (82).

The similarities in behavior of these cells have led to their being classified together, as a system of cells all with the same special function, in spite of their wide separation in the body. Aschoff's classification (3,4) is summarized in the accompanying table (see p. 12).

Howard (56) states that the term reticuloendothelial system is best regarded as a collective term for the various groups of mononuclear phagocytic cells. He does not think there is much point nowadays in following Aschoff's classification in its entirety.

Reticuloendothelial System

Sessile histiocytes (sessile macrophages)		Wandering histiocytes (wandering macrophages)	
Less active	Very active		
Reticular cells of spleen	Endothelium of liver capillaries (Kupffer cells)	Tissue histiocytes (tissue macrophages)	Blood histiocytes (blood macrophages)
lymphatic glands and tissues	spleen sinuses		
thymus	lymph sinuses marrow sinuses adrenal capillaries pituitary capillaries		

There may be some division of labor in the reticuloendothelial system, in that some parts may be more active in removing aged or fragmentary red corpuscles or leukocytes, whereas others tend to specialize more in removing bacterial or other smaller particles. Species differences are also found in the relative activity of the various regions. It will be seen later that species differences are also found in the behavior of organs with respect to anaphylaxis and to antibody-producing power.

There is, in addition, another class of phagocytic cells, the polymorphonuclear leukocytes of the blood. They do not take up "vital" stains in the same way as the cells of the reticuloendothelial system, but under certain conditions do actively remove particulate material from the circulation. These are the microphages of Metchnikoff. The neutrophiles are active, and the basophiles slightly active; there are conflicting reports as to the activity of the eosinophiles.

This same mechanism which has been observed to free the blood stream from inert particles is also the chief factor in freeing it from bacteria. If bacteria are injected into the blood stream, they disappear rapidly from the circulation and are found to be taken up by the reticuloendothelial cells, especially those of the liver, spleen, and bone marrow.

Mechanism of Phagocytosis

The wandering cells are doubtless brought into contact with particles in the circulation by collisions. But phagocytes can also crawl by amoeboid motions, and it has been found that they are positively attracted to living and dead bacteria and to certain kinds of inert particles. This is called chemotropism or chemotaxis.

Ingenious and plausible experiments have been made (33,34,86,8) to account for the ingestion of particles by the phagocyte in physicochemical terms. Modern studies, however, have shown (63) that phagocytosis is strictly dependent on anaerobic glycolysis (see 56), and is therefore an active physiological process.

When antibody combines with foreign microorganisms, it renders them more susceptible to phagocytosis. Wood (128,127) reported findings which suggest that, even in the absence of antibody, phagocytosis is of the first importance in removing bacteria from the blood. These experiments, carried out primarily with the encapsulated microorganisms pneumococci and Frierländer's bacillus, showed that with such organisms phagocytosis by polymorphonuclear leukocytes in the circulation is an important clearing mechanism. Following the intravenous injection of such bacteria, the circulating polymorphonuclear leukocytes, which normally roll freely along the vessel walls, were seen to become attached to the endothelium of the capillaries, arterioles, and venules. The adherent granulocytes promptly became motile and thus potentially phagocytic. This intravascular cellular response appeared to cause a rapid mobilization of a vast number of active phagocytes within the blood stream. Polymorphonuclear leukocytes thus mobilized on the walls of the blood vessels were shown to be capable of phagocyting fully encapsulated Friedländer's bacilli in the absence of antibody. The polymorphonuclear leukocytes were seen to phagocyte the organisms by first trapping them against the walls of the vessels or against adjacent leukocytes. Bacteria caught in the interstices of the small thrombi were likewise readily phagocyted. It was found that phagocytosis could take place on the surfaces of various inert rough surfaces such as moistened filter paper, cloth, and fiber glass, but not on smooth materials such as cellophane, albumin, glass, and paraffin. Because of the important role of surfaces this sort of phagocytosis, for which antibody is not required, was called "surface phagocytosis." Unlike phagocytosis aided by opsonins, surface phagocytosis does not take place when the cells are floating free in a fluid medium.

Wood reported that of the species of encapsulated bacteria tested (pneumococci, Friendländer's bacilli, beta hemolytic streptococci, and staphylococci), only one, pneumococcus type III, was resistant to this nonantibody form of phagocytosis. He believed that if it were not for this mechanism, operating in the lungs, lymph nodes, and blood stream, untreated patients infected with such well-armored microorganisms as pneumococci or Friedländer's bacilli would invariably die before antibodies could come to their rescue.

Before investigating the nature of the substances in serum which favor phagocytsis, we may pause to ask if the phagocytes themselves are altered in any way as an animal becomes immune. Kahn (62) and Lurie (69) believed they are; and Metchnikoff, although he recognized the "stimulating" effect of serum, conceived the phagocytes themselves to possess different degrees of activity in normal and immune states of the animal.

Lurie (69) carried out experiments in which normal and immune guinea pigs received injections of tubercle bacilli, and bits of lymph node or bone marrow from the infected animals were transplanted to the anterior chamber of the eyes of normal rabbits. This permitted the observation of the bacilli *in vivo* in the transplanted cells. The cells from the immune animals inhibited growth of the tubercle bacilli; those from the normal animals did not. Careful experiments did not demonstrate that antibody had anything to do with this phenomenon.

Lurie (70) showed that the mononuclear phagocytes of the tuberculous animal exhibit increased physiological activity, and have an increased phagocytic activity, not only for tubercle bacilli, but for unrelated particulate matter such as carbon and collodion particles. This increased activity was a property of the cells themselves and not dependent upon the presence of normal or immune serum. Lurie believed that this increased physiological activity may explain several facts: the increased capacity of the tuberculous animal to form antibodies, the intensification of preanaphylactic sensitization to antigens in general and the increased proteolytic activity of the liver. This same enhancement of cell activity, specifically oriented, explains the greater destruction or inhibition of growth in the mononuclears of immunized animals.

Suter and Ramseier (116) summarize more recent evidence that the phagocytes are altered as immunity develops.

Not only is the local mobilization of leukocytes one of the mechanisms of immunity, but there also seems to be an increased production of leukocytes. Leukocytosis, as it is called, following an invasion of microorganisms or foreign cells, is especially marked in immune animals; it can also be provoked to a lower degree by nonspecific stimuli, such as the injection of broth, peptone, and certain vegetable toxins.

Gay and Morrison (43), Cannon and Pacheco (16) have described an early large outpouring of mononuclear cells in the areas of the immune animal subjected to reinvasion. This suggests that the entire process is speeded up so that the polymorphonuclear stage is brief and the mononuclear cells are mobilized more readily.

"Opsonic" Action of the Serum

It was found by Denys and Leclef (23) that the destruction of bacteria

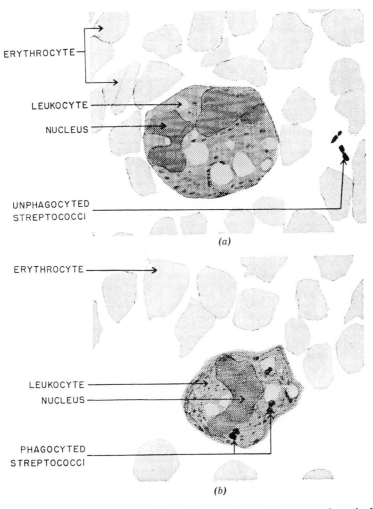

(a)

(b)

Fig. 1-3. (a) Smear of defibrinated blood from patient with puerperal sepsis due to hemolytic streptococci, mixed with drop of a young culture of streptococci. (b) Preparation as above, plus a drop of serum from an immune person. Phagocyted streptococci seen within leukocyte. (Drawings made by the author from photomicrographs by Dr. Charles Janeway.)

by phagocytosis was powerfully increased when immune serum was added to the leukocytes of either a normal or an immunized animal (see Fig. 1-3). This was confirmed by later workers, and since then investigations of phagocytosis have concentrated chiefly on the role of the serum.

The antibodies facilitating phagocytosis of bacteria were called "bacteriotropins." The word "opsonins" (from ὀψώνης, a purveyor of fish or dainties) was coined by Wright and Douglas for these then purely hypothetical substances.

Even today the exact nature and chemistry of the opsonins is largely unknown, Antibody is certainly a factor, but there seem to be several other types or systems of serum components involved (116). One of these is heat labile, and appears to be complement, involving all four components (see Chapter 7). A factor called "coopsonin," associated with a protein of molecular weight over 50,000, has been described as essential for phagocytosis of group A streptococci *in vitro* (115). Suter and Ramseier (116) suggest that this factor might be similar to, or identical with, the phagocytosis-promoting factor of Tullis and Surgenor (121).

According to Nelson (88), treponema and bacteria coated with specific antibody and complement (*C'*) adhere to normal erythrocytes, and this adherence may lead to an enhancement of phagocytosis. Nelson (90) calls this the immune-adherence phenomenon.

Importance of Phagocytosis

Phagocytosis is of decisive importance in the animal's resistance to many diseases. In spite of the fact that the cooperation, so to speak, of serum antibody is required, in some diseases, recovery would be impossible without phagocytosis. The general importance of the phenomenon was stated by Bordet (10) to be shown by:

1. The strict parallelism between the vigor of phagocytosis and the degree of resistance. There seem to be no examples of recovery without the intervention of phagocytes.

2. The sterilizing power of the body fluids for many pathogenic bacteria is negligible; even when raised by infection it is not sufficient to explain the complete destruction of the relatively large numbers of microorganisms which can be taken care of by the animal.

3. The natural or acquired properties to which microorganisms owe their virulence are essentially antiphagocytic mechanisms. Harmless organisms are easily captured and destroyed by phagocytosis; dangerous organisms resist—indeed it is because they resist that they are dangerous.

4. Inoculation of pathogenic microorganisms is less dangerous when it is made into a region rich in phagocytes. Thus inoculation of pigeons, normally refractory to anthrax, by injecting the bacilli into the aqueous humor of the eye where leukocytes are mobilized only slowly, will produce the disease. The longer the bacteria have to multiply before leukocytic response, the more serious the infection; also in this time the invading organisms may be able to make protective adaptations. Preliminary treatment tending to mobilize leukocytes increases resistance to infection. It has even been claimed that injection of leukocyte extracts has protective and curative power.

5. Any influence that interferes with phagocytosis diminishes resistance proportionally. Tetanus spores are easily phagocyted, but concomitant injection of substances toxic for leukocytes, such as lactic acid or quinine, favors infection. Even sterile, inert material may make the spores more dangerous by distracting the phagocytes from the real struggle. It is also apparent from medical and surgical experience that wounds and bruises, as well as cold, starvation, and poor general condition, favor infection.

6. Very generally a favorable turn of an infection is accompanied by an increase in the number of leukocytes. Immunized animals generally show a leukocytosis, which persists for a long time.

It is natural to suppose that when a microorganism is ingested by a phagocyte it is either already dead or dies at once, and such bacteria are sometimes killed (93), sometimes within a few minutes (58), but this is not always the case. Indications have been found that, in some cases, in susceptible animals pathogenic microorganisms remain viable for some time after being taken up by the phagocytes. Rous and Jones (106) showed that phagocyted typhoid bacilli survived in the cells and were protected from the action of lytic antibody. Fothergill, Chandler, and Dingle (38) found evidence suggesting that ingested influenza bacilli remain viable. Work by Lyons (71) showed that toxigenic strains of staphylococci are not killed by the leukocytes which ingest them. Indeed *Myco. tuberculosis* and certain *Brucella* species have been observed to multiply within the macrophages (58).

Some virulent bacteria seem to be liberated again after ingestion, perhaps after they have killed the phagocytes (see below). These are exceptions to the general rule, however, and the great mass of data shows that phagocytes can and often do kill ingested organisms, and in many cases the swelling, granulation, fragmentation, and lysis can easily be observed microscopically. Pneumococci have been observed to be phagocyted and destroyed. A number of workers such as Ørskov and collaborators (73), Cannon and co-workers (18,22) showed by actual cultivation experiments, using, for example, groundup tissues from the animals, that ingestion of the bacteria actually resulted in death of the bacteria. Also, numerous test tube experiments show that leukocytes kill bacteria. Some organisms are almost completely resistant to the action of serum, even if complement is present, but nevertheless succumb to phagocytosis (24,42).

Leukocytes contain many enzymes (37), but this does not suffice to account for their power of killing ingested microorganisms, for only one of the enzymes thus far demonstrated, lysozyme, has any bactericidal power, and it lyses only certain nonpathogenic bacteria. It has been suggested that the contents of the vacuole which surrounds the ingested bacteria are sufficiently acid to kill them, but this is by no means certain.

Hirsch (52) reported that polymorphonuclear leukocytes contain a principle which kills a number of kinds of bacteria (enteric organisms for example) which are not killed by lysozyme. This protein is not identical with lysozyme. It is not active against Grampositive cocci. This principle is now called phagocytin.

Resistance of Bacteria to Phagocytosis

In many cases it has been found that virulent forms of bacteria are more resistant to phagocytosis. There are various factors causing this. The type-specific polysaccharides in the capsule of the pneumococcus (see Chapter 4) seem to help defend the organism against phagocytosis (32). In themselves they are not attractive to leukocytes and apparently they are not harmful. But a pneumococcus will not be phagocyted until antibody combines with it and renders the surface "attractive" to the phagocytes. Since the polysaccharides are continually being cast off into the surrounding fluids in soluble form, and since they have been shown to combine with antibody which would otherwise coat the bacterial surface, they thereby render this antibody unavailable for defense. In other organisms a relation between susceptibility to phagocytosis and possession by the cell body of a certain substance (antigen) has been shown. An example is the "Vi antigen" of Felix, discussed in Chapter 4.

A number of microorganisms, including streptococci, staphylococci, and pneumococci, produce substances having a destructive action on leukocytes. These substances are called *leukocidins*. They probably aid the bacteria in their struggle with the leukocytes.

It has been shown that venoms (25,26) and certain pathogenic bacteria (21,83,85,104) contain a "spreading factor" (53,74) which has been identified with the enzyme hyaluronidase (75), which causes depolymerization of a mucopolysaccharide, hyaluronic acid (84), which is found in the skin. According to Duran-Reynals (27) the degree of invasiveness of bacteria is largely determined by the amount of the spreading factor present, and the successive phases of infection induced by invasive bacteria include (3) the hydrolysis of the mucoid ground substance of the connective tissue, which otherwise acts as a physiological obstacle to the spread of the infection, and (4) a spreading primarily through the interstitial system of the connective tissue. Hyaluronidase could therefore well be called "invasin." Invasiveness is, however, not synonymous with virulence, and with some microorganisms (*e.g.*, streptococci) poor correlation has been observed between virulence and the production of spreading factor.

Haas (47) considered that he had demonstrated in plasmas of mammals, birds, and fish a counterenzyme, which he called antivasin I. Bacteria and venoms, however, contain an enzyme proinvasin I, which rapidly inactivates antivasin I. A second protective enzyme, antivasin II, was reported by Haas to be present in normal plasma. It is thought to act by destroying provasin I. Other bacterial and plasma enzymes have been postulated.

Measurement of Phagocytic Power

Since phagocytic power is a useful index of the degree of resistance of the animal to infection, methods of measurement are important. Unfortunately the technic is difficult, and it is difficult to obtain absolutely reliable results. For this reason measurement of antibody content seems likely to remain the easier method of estimating immunity and is the one generally used.

Leukocytes and phagocytosis are discussed by Berry and Spies (8) and Tullis (120).

5. Kinds of Immunity

After successfully counterattacking and driving back an invading microorganism or other pathogen, a host is likely to display more resistance than before to attacks of this particular disease agent. This is one of the types of resistance we call acquired immunity. But even before contact with a pathogen, an animal may have a relative or even an absolute immunity, which we call constitutional, innate, or natural immunity. This is no doubt the most important kind of immunity, and it is this which keeps us as human beings from coming down with canine distemper, or bots, or tobacco mosaic disease, or a thousand others. Nevertheless, it is about this kind of immunity that we know least, and we can do little to increase it. The pages immediately following represent what we have to say about it in the present book.

Natural Immunity.

Natural immunity can vary from complete insusceptibility to a disease, as in the case of a human being and rabbit snuffles, to a degree of resistance so slight that nearly every individual exposed will contract the disease, as with measles and typhus. Even with these diseases, however, there may be degrees in the severity of the attack. Measles, in our population at least, is usually a mild disease, whereas typhus is a serious disease with a high mortality. It is partly merely a matter of terminology whether we say, in such a case, that one pathogen is more virulent than the other, or that human beings are less resistant.

We do not know much about the mechanisms of this natural resistance. A brief outline of what we do know is given in Section 12. We say it is innate or constitutional, meaning it is inherited, and in the case of complete immunity this is simply a truism. A rat inherits his immunity to diphtheria just as he inherits the other characteristics which make him a rat. And so far as we know, every rat gets this absolute immunity. When the degree of resistance is less, we might expect to find within the same species individual differences in immunity which depend on heredity and which we could therefore expect to study genetically. For any study of the mechanism of inheritance is impossible unless we have inherited *differences* to study.

Salmonella typhimurium, as its name implies, produces a fatal typhoid-like disease in mice, but only food poisoning in man, whereas *Salmonella typhi* produces the potentially fatal typhoid fever in man and is essentially nonpathogenic for mice.

A nonantibody humoral factor in resistance, called ablastin, has been described in anthrax (5), trypanosome infection (117), and others. Ablastin seems to have the property of inhibiting multiplication of the infecting organisms.

6. Genetics of Natural Resistance

If innate resistance is inherited, we might expect to find some races or strains of a species more resistant than others to certain diseases, since the essential basis of distinction into races is differences in the frequencies of various genes. There is no doubt that such racial differences in susceptibility do exist. The greater resistance to anthrax of Algerian sheep, as compared to European sheep, is well established, and some breeds of mice, rats, guinea pigs, and other animals are much more susceptible than others to some infections (99). The Rockefeller (PRI) strain of mice are 100 per cent resistant to yellow fever; the Swiss strain are 100 per cent susceptible (108). Webster and his associates (125) succeeded in breeding up almost at will strains of mice either more or less susceptible to various agents. Inherited resistance in mice has been demonstrated to louping ill, Russian Spring-Summer virus, and St. Louis encephalitis virus. A particularly simple example of genetically determined resistance in animals was studied by Sabin (108), who found that the striking difference between Swiss and PRI mice to the 17D strain of yellow fever virus was apparently determined by a Mendelian pair of genes. (See Table 1-1.)

TABLE 1-1

Inheritance of Resistance of Mice to 17D Strain of Yellow Fever Virus (108)

	Observed			Theoretical	
Mice used	Number of mice inoculated	Mortality (per cent)	Genetic formula of mice used for breeding	Genetic formula for progeny	Expected mortality (per cent)
Swiss (S)	300	100	aa × aa	aa	100
PRI (R)	100	0	AA × AA	A	0
F_1 (S × R)	51	0	aa × AA	Aa	0
F_2 (F_1 × F_1)	213	28.2	Aa × Aa	AA + 2Aa + aa	25
Backcross:					
F_1 × R	79	0	Aa × AA	Aa + AA	0
F_1 × S	90	50	Aa × aa	Aa + aa	50
F_2 (susceptible) × S	21	100	aa × aa	aa	100

The mice were tested by intracerebral injection of approximately 10000 LD_{50} of the virus. The theoretical genetic formulas and expected percents mortality are calculated on the assumption that the PRI mice are homozygous for a dominant gene for resistance (A) and the Swiss mice homozygous for a recessive gene for susceptibility (a).

Natural resistance of mice to virus diseases seems to involve at least two factors, a genetically determined mechanism, possibly enzymatic, which inhibits the multiplication of the virus, and other differences which we call, with a vagueness at present still unavoidable, differences of the mouse's tissues in vulnerability to the virus (108).

Animals resistant to one pathogen may nevertheless be fully susceptible to another. Mice that were resistant to St. Louis encephalitis were not resistant to the viruses of vesicular stomatitis, rabies, and lymphocytic choriomeningitis (108).

Racial differences in susceptibility in man doubtless exist also but are harder to verify because of the complexity of the situation. In some cases apparent innate differences in susceptibility are really due to differences in habits or living conditions or to immunity acquired from mild, inapparent infections during childhood. It seems likely, however, that some aboriginal peoples were much more susceptible, on first contact, than we are to diseases introduced by the Europeans, such as measles and tuberculosis.

Russell and Salmon (107) have presented evidence that the Welsh are racially more susceptible to tuberculosis than are the English. Negroes are more susceptible to tuberculosis than white persons (105). The data of Hopkins (55) suggest a heredity factor in susceptibility to leprosy.

The much greater incidence of tuberculosis in the co-twin of a pair of identical twins, one of whom has developed tuberculosis, is enough to show that there is a strong generic component in susceptibility or resistance to this disease (Table 1-2).

TABLE 1-2

Tuberculosis in Relatives of Tuberculous Patients (14)

Relation to "index case"	Percentage with tuberculosis
One-egg twin	87
Two-egg twin	25.6
Other brother or sister	25.5
Marriage partner	7

We know of another way in which known genetic differences can operate to bring about differences in susceptibility to a disease. In some parts of Africa, and, less commonly, elsewhere, there is a human gene that causes the production in its possessors of an abnormal hemoglobin, called sickle cell hemoglobin or hemoglobin S. It was given this name because erythrocytes containing this kind of hemoglobin, when deprived of oxygen (as in a sealed cover-slip preparation), shrink into fantastic shapes sometimes reminiscent of sickles. It seems to be all right to be heterozygous for this sickle cell gene (*i.e.*, to have only one dose of it), but homozygous individuals (persons with two doses) generally develop a serious anemia, and die before puberty. There is thus considerable selective pressure against the gene. How has it managed to persist in these populations? Allison (2) presented evidence that probably answers this question.

Allison noticed that the frequency of the sickle cell gene was highest in those parts of Africa where falciparum malaria was most severely endemic. He reasoned that perhaps the gene, in single dose (heterozygous), conferred increased resistance to malaria on the individual possessing the gene, and tested this idea by deliberately exposing, by injection of infected blood or by infected mosquito bite, 15 heterozygous (sickle cell) natives, and 15 "normal" (nonsickle cell) natives. All of the normals came down with malaria, in some cases so severe that it had to be stopped by chemotherapy, and only two of the sickle cell volunteers developed malaria, and in both cases the attack was light.

It is apparent that the sickle cell gene, although a disadvantageous gene in the homozygous state, confers a greater resistance to falciparum malaria in the heterozygous state, and is thus advantageous. The advantage evidently overweighs the disadvantage, and the gene persists. In fact, there is evidence suggesting that it is becoming more common in some populations.

This genetic mechanism, the production of greater resistance to a disease by a gene that at first sight does not seem to have anything to do with infection, may be much more common that had been realized, and is an example of the polymorphisms that evolution produces in man (and other species), and an example of a mechanism by which such polymorphisms are maintained.

Malaria is also concerned with other human polymorphisms (68).

Although natural immunity is inherited, like many other hereditary characteristics it can be influenced by other factors, such as the age of the animal, sex, hormonal status, nutrition, and environment. For instance, cortisone may convert a nonparalytic poliomyelitic infection of a monkey into a severe prostrating paralysis (108). It has been found that the administration of antibiotics may depress the immune response (114). Other hormonal effects are discussed by Humphrey and White (58). There is some evidence that vitamin deficiencies may lower natural resistance. Exposure to lower temperatures may increase susceptibility, especially to respiratory infections.

The lower resistance of very young and very old animals is well known (15,29,109,118,7,46). Sex is usually less influential but sometimes plays a definite role.

An extreme example of the variation in susceptibility with age is provided by the diseases that, though they are relatively mild in the grownup or child, are very damaging to the fetus. German measles (rubella) may produce in the fetus, during the first three months of pregnancy, permanent defects such as cataract, deafness, and heart lesions. The protozoon *Toxoplasma gondii* is much more likely to cause severe disease if acquired in fetal life.

7. Disease and Blood Groups

Evidence has been accumulating that disease may be affecting the frequencies of genes which have no immediately obvious influence on the production of hereditary disease or resistance to infection. The pioneers in this field were Aird and co-workers (1), who observed in patients with peptic ulcer and cancer of the stomach significant departures from the ABO blood group frequencies of the general population (Table 1-3). At

the same time, the blood group distribution of patients with other malig-
nancies were found to be normal (see results for cancer of the colon and
rectum in Table 1-3). The results of Aird *et al.* suggested that, if their

TABLE 1-3

Association between Blood Groups and Disease (1)
(Blood Group Frequencies Shown in Per Cent)

Blood group	Peptic ulcer (3,011 cases)		Cancer of stomach (2,745 cases)		Cancer of colon and rectum (2,599 cases)	
	Control	Disease	Control	Disease	Control	Disease
O	47.00	55.40	46.78	42.95	46.07	44.79
A	40.99	34.67	41.38	46.19	41.78	43.63
B	8.98	7.44	8.79	7.76	8.94	8.66
AB	3.03	2.49	3.05	3.10	3.21	2.92

series were typical, persons of blood group O are about 35 per cent more
likely to develop peptic ulceration requiring hospital treatment than are
persons of other blood groups. It was subsequently found that the O-ulcer
association is more marked for duodenal than for gastric ulcer. Later
workers found similar associations between the ABO blood groups and
certain other diseases, but most diseases showed no such association. The
subject has been reviewed by Roberts (102,103). Until recently, no disease
was found to be associated with any blood group system other than the
ABO blood group system, but in my laboratory we observed an apparent
correlation between the Rh blood group system and ulcerative colitis (11).

8. Natural Selection

The reader might well ask the question: If natural selection is acting
in man, and genes conferring greater resistance to disease are being
favored, why haven't we all become so resistant that we simply don't get
disease any more?

A good question, but there are probably a number of good answers.
First, however, let us note that none of the correlations between blood
groups and disease, thus far observed, really indicate a strong action of
natural selection. The number of persons who die from such diseases
(100) before performing their reproductive function is too small. The
associations between blood groups and disease known at present are probably merely proof that the blood group genes *can* be acted on by natural
selection.

Even in the case of diseases where there is reason to think the observed mortality does suggest a significant selective action, we must remember that deleterious genes can be continually recruited by mutation. For example, although there is no reason to doubt that the gene for hemophilia is being eliminated from human populations by the great disadvantage it confers on males who carry it, there is reason to think that the gene is continually being produced again. The evidence from the study of the European royal families seems to indicate that such a mutation occurred in the person of Queen Victoria and was transmitted by her female descendants and the disease appeared in male members of various families, notably the Spanish and Russian royal houses.

If a gene is continually being eliminated by selection and continually being produced by mutation, an equilibrium between these two opposing forces will result. Sewall Wright (129) derived a simple formula for this:

$$q = \sqrt{(\mu/k)}$$

where μ is the mutation frequency, q the frequency of the mutated gene, and k the selection coefficient. The frequency of the gene that can be maintained by mutation is higher than might be supposed. For example, if the mutation frequency is 3×10^{-5}, which is not at all unusual, and the selection coefficient is 0.001, which used to be taken, at any rate, as a very reasonable selective coefficient, one finds q, the frequency of the deleterious gene, equal to 0.17, or nearly 20 per cent.

Another reason why selection has not made us completely resistant to all diseases is connected with the fact that probably most of the genes causing hereditary diseases are recessives, and selection acts very slowly to eliminate recessive genes, particularly when their frequency is already low (54). Nearly forty years ago Hogben (54) pointed out that even if we could exercise the most drastic imaginable selection, such as sterilization of all homozygotes, against a rare recessive gene, such as the one causing diabetes or the one causing Friedrich's ataxia, the reduction in the incidence of the disease would be small even if our "eugenics" program went on for a period of time equal to the length of the whole Christian era.

One reason selection has not made us all completely resistant to all diseases is that this is just one of the things nature won't permit. Natural selection is wonderful and has produced the organisms, species, and races we see today, but there are limits to what it can do, and we should no more expect it to make us completely resistant to disease than to expect it to make us so resistant to high temperatures that we can stick our fingers into the flame of a Bunsen burner without having them burned.

One is reminded of another attempt to beat nature's game, when plant breeders had the bright idea of crossing the cabbage and the radish to get a hybrid with the foliage of the cabbage and the root of the radish. This would be a great economic step forward. The cross worked beautifully, and they obtained a luxuriant, hardy and prolific plant, but it had the foliage of the radish and the root of the cabbage.

There are reasons for this. If you try to beat the game and make an animal completely resistant to every disease, or even *completely* resistant to any one disease, you will generally find you have done something else that is not so good. An example of something similar is provided by experiments in which it was found that if you make a microorganism resistant to a certain antibiotic, you will find that, although it may have become resistant to certain other antibiotics (generally the ones with a similar mode of action), it has also become less resistant to other antibiotics. From the point of view of the microorganism, becoming more resistant is good and becoming less resistant is bad.

There are other examples. In the domestic goat, for instance, breeders have been selecting for a number of years for hornlessness. Horns were not considered a desirable attribute of goats, and the breeders selected quite successfully for goats without horns. But it was noticed a number of years ago that at the same time they got herds with a high percentage of animals that were intersexes and consequently sterile. This was a disadvantage from the point of view of both the goat breeder and the goat (6).

Another example of the fact that selection in one direction may produce unexpected undesirable effects in another is the case of abdominal chaetae of *Drosophila*. These experiments had to be terminated in all cases because the experimental strains of *Drosophila*, whether they had been selected for more chaetae or for fewer, became sterile in the long run and died out.

It becomes understandable, therefore, that while selection can indeed improve the resistance of an organism to a certain disease, it may do this, beyond a certain point at least, at the price of producing undesirable effects in other ways.

There are several reasons why this happens. One reason, already mentioned, is that genes are pleiomorphic, that is, they may affect more than one characteristic of an organism. So if you increase the frequency of a gene which has the effect of producing resistance to a disease, or increase it too much, the gene may begin to produce some effect you never noticed before, and there may be undesirable consequences such as sterility, lowered resistance to some other disease, or something of the sort.

Another reason for this is that all organisms, including man, are made what they are by a delicately balanced system of genes that interact in a complex way. If you change the frequency of one of these genes, the effects of some of the others becomes different. The effects of most genes depend partly upon the environment, and one of the most important parts of this environment is the background provided by the other genes that the organism possesses. Waddington (122) attempted to visualize this situation by his ingenious picture of the "epigenetic landscape."

Therefore, the extent to which natural selection can increase the frequency in a given population of a gene for resistance to some disease, which of course depends, among other things, on the severity of the disease and the extent to which it is endemic, depends also on the genetic composition of the local population.

Another factor which often, perhaps usually, limits the extent to which we can increase the frequency of a given gene in a population is the phenomenon of balanced polymorphism. Fisher (36) showed in his classical book, *The Genetical Theory of Natural Selection,* that if two alleles are acting in a population (whence it is termed "polymorphic"), and the heterozygote happens to have a selective advantage over both of the homozygotes such that the three genotypes that occur with frequencies p^2, $2pq$, and q^2 have relative selective advantages in the ratio a:b:c, then there will be an equilibrium such that the ratio of the two gene frequencies

$$p/q = (b - c)/(b - a).$$

In such a situation appreciable frequencies of a gene which is deleterious or even lethal in homozygous dose may be maintained in the population. Natural resistance to infections was discussed by various workers in a symposium held at the New York Academy of Sciences (76). It was reviewed in 1959 by Shilo (111).

9. Acquired Immunity

There are two principal ways in which an organism may acquire immunity. One kind of immunity results from recovery from an infection or an artificial inoculation. This kind is called active immunity and will be our chief concern here. The other is passive immunity, which is merely transmitted to an animal, either naturally from the mother through the placenta or in the colostrum (or in the case of birds, in egg yolk), or artificially by injection of serum or other proteins derived from an immune animal.

We shall outline the mechanism of acquired immunity in Section 13, and most of the rest of this book will be devoted to the discussion of certain of these mechanisms.

We may now make a classification of the various kinds of immunity. It is very logical but not particularly informative.

   I. Innate immunity (constitutional or racial).

      1. Active: (a) natural; (b) artificial.

   II. Acquired immunity.

      2. Passive: (a) natural (congenital); (b) artificial.

We shall, on the whole, be more interested here in active than in passive immunity.

10. Grades of Immunity

Immunity, in our sense of the word, can exist in varying degrees. It is rather rare to find an animal absolutely without resistance to an infection that often occurs in that species. In the case of common fatal infections, this is obvious, for such an animal, inevitably contracting the disease, would already have succumbed before we had the opportunity to observe him. In the case of some diseases with which the ordinary individual has very little contact, such as psittacosis and tularemia, the resistance of the average person is very low, and at first almost every laboratory worker who worked with these diseases contracted them.

The infectiousness of any given disease depends, of course, not only on the host but also on the invading organism. Some diseases are enormously more infectious than others, and some are much more serious when contracted. We shall be forced here to neglect the interesting question of intrinsic virulence in various organisms and strains of organisms, and to consider it a branch of bacteriology and not of immunology.

Topley and Wilson (119) classified grades of immunity (to bacterial diseases) as follows (slightly modified):

1. Completely susceptible. (All or almost all infected individuals will develop fatal bacteremic infections. Local lesions infrequent and minimal.)

2. Low-grade immunity. (Fatal bacteremic infections less common. Local lesions more frequent and more pronounced. A small but increasing number of latent infections.)

3. Medium immunity. (Bacteremia and death much less frequent. Local lesions common and relatively extensive. Latent infections more frequent.)

4. High-grade immunity. (No deaths, bacteremia infrequent and when found slight and transient. Local lesions less frequent and when found less extensive. Latent infections most frequent or on decline.)

5. Complete immunity (if it exists). (The animal is completely resistant to any attack of the infectious agent.)

In prophylactic treatment of human beings, we are often satisfied if we can achieve immunity of grades *3* or *4*.

11. Measurement of Immunity

A number of immunological procedures are directed toward the end of measuring resistance, and these will be discussed in the appropriate place. Here a few general remarks may be made.

As a rule it is difficult or impossible to measure the resistance of an individual animal. For suppose we give a measured dose of the active disease-producing agent, or of some toxic product of the agent, and observe what happens. If the animal dies, its resistance was less than that of animals which can tolerate this dose. But how much less? To this question we have no answer, nor can we obtain one, for the animal is now gone. If we start with a smaller dose, which the animal successfully resists, we cannot proceed to determine its resistance precisely by trying successively larger doses, since the first dose will have altered the resistance which we wanted to measure.

A possible way out of this dilemma consists in testing simultaneously a large number of individuals, all with the same history, employing different doses. Then from the different numbers which succumb to each dose, we can estimate, subject to some uncertainty, the average degree of resistance. This matter will be discussed under a more appropriate heading in Chapter 17.

With human beings we often wish we could determine the degree of resistance of an individual, so that we may know if he is susceptible to a given disease, and thus may need prophylactic immunization (if this is in our power), or ought to be warned to avoid sources of infection. It would also be desirable to be able to give the individual an estimate of the degree of his susceptibility. If we knew the complete mechanism of immunity and could measure in a given person all the pertinent factors, our information might make it possible to give a person a diagnosis of the degree of his immunity.

Suppose for example, that we knew that immunity to a certain disease was due *solely* to the increase in amount of some one well-characterized protein constituent in the blood. If we could measure the concentration of this protein accurately, we could make determinations for it on groups of individuals and then correlate this information with their average resistance. From the results we could say that a certain level of this protein constituent in the blood (allowing perhaps for some random variation) meant a certain degree of immunity. This test could be performed on any person, and it would be possible to predict with considerable accuracy whether or not he would succumb to infection, and perhaps even how severe an attack he would have, assuming that we could predict he would eventually recover.

The actual situation, as will be seen below, is mostly not so simple, but there are some cases of a slightly different nature where analogous methods can really be applied. In the standardization of type I antipneumococcal sera, Heidelberger, Sia, and Kendall (50) showed that a close parallel existed in these sera between the amount of protein that was specifically precipitable by the type 1 specific pneumococcal polysaccharide and the number of mouse protection units. Walter, Schenkein, and Sutliff (124) found in the serum of immunized volunteers a good correlation between the amount of antibody (see below) N per ml. specifically precipitable by pneumococcus polysaccharides and the number of protective units per ml. for mice, except in the weaker sera. In the average and stronger than average sera, 1 mg. of antipolysaccharide N corresponded to about 200 to 700 mouse units (their mouse unit protected mice against challenge with 100,000 MLD of living pneumococci). The concentration of circulating antipneumococcus antibody needed to confer immunity in man is not exactly known, but 10 μg./ml. *cures* pneumonia in rats (49), and the ordinary response in man to immunization with pneumococcus polysaccharides (2 to 60 μg. antibody N/ml. serum) confers immunity for at least 6 months (112). Therefore we may conclude that, if we analyze the serum of an individual and find as much as 5 μg. of specific antipneumococcus antibody N per ml, we shall be justified in stating that this person is probably immune to pneumonia caused by pneumococcus of this particular type. Skin tests (*e.g.,* the Schick test, Chapter 15) can also sometimes give information as to the state of immunity of the individual.

12. Mechanisms of Natural Immunity

First of all, of course, most pathogens never get a lodgment within our tissues, but are kept out by the barriers of the skin and mucous membranes, and no infection results. These surfaces not only act as mechanical barriers but seem to possess in addition considerable bactericidal power. If a drop of culture of a pathogen is placed on the skin and simultaneously another drop placed on a glass slide, it is found by making subcultures that most of the bacteria in the drop placed on the skin are dead after 10 minutes or so, whereas those on the glass surface are still viable. It is not known precisely to what this bactericidal action is due, but the action of the lactic and fatty acids present has been suggested as one of the possibilities. According to Hellat (51), however, the self-disinfecting powers of the skin are mostly merely the result of the drying to which microroganisms on the surface are exposed.

The moist surfaces of the respiratory and urogenital surfaces catch many of the microorganisms which reach them, and the cilia of the respiratory epithelium constantly sweep trapped particles outwards, thus providing a mechanical cleansing device. It has been said that the majority of organisms in the air are stopped in the anterior nares, where the numerous hairs act as a filter. The moist films of these surfaces also possess bactericidal and virucidal properties. These properties are due partly to the so-called natural antibodies present (p. 54), but also to substances such as lysozyme (first recognized by Fleming, the discoverer of penicillin), a basic protein which functions as a mucolytic enzyme and which can attack the capsules of certain bacteria; an antianthrax polypeptide; antivasin, an enzyme which inactivates hyaluronidase; and other protective enzymes. Antiviral substances are also found; they seem to be substrates in normal tissues and body fluids which combine with the tissue-combining receptors of the virus.

The egg white of the hen also contains a lysozyme. It is a single polypeptide chain of 129 amino acids folded through 4 bridges through the cystine residues, and the entire amino acid sequence is known (61a).

In the majority of bacterial respiratory infections the infectious microorganism is essentially restricted to the surface. The primary site of localization of a number of viruses seems to be on the superficial epithelium of the respiratory tract.

The gastrointestinal tract possesses, in addition to the usual epithelial protection, bactericidal enzymes, as does the saliva. The stomach is highly acid and also contains enzymes. The intestinal contents contain enormous numbers of bacteria, but the intestinal mucosa contains such effective antibacterial factors that infection by way of the intestinal mucosa is uncommon. All of these normal bacteria are potential sources for antibiotics against other organisms.

Even if bacteria pass the natural barriers of the body, they do not always set up an infection. The tissues of some animals, for reasons we do not understand, are simply insusceptible to the toxins of some microorganisms. Frogs and toads, for example, are not affected by any amount of diphtheria toxin or tetanus toxin, and rats are very resistant.

When living virulent microorganisms have gained entrance to the body, they are met by the defenses of inflammation and phagocytosis, already discussed. Bacteria which enter the circulation are promptly removed by phagocytes in the lungs, in the lymph nodes, and in the circulation itself.

In addition to the phagocytic mechanisms, there are other specific and nonspecific humoral mechanisms. So-called normal antibodies, which may be partly immune antibodies formed in response to previous subclinical attacks and partly globulins which accidentally happen to have sufficient affinity for certain microorganisms to enable them to combine, will speed up and intensify phagocytosis. There are also other substances in serum which are active. Von Behring demonstrated a heatstable component which is bactericidal for Gram-positive organisms, which he called beta-lysin. Pettersson (93) demonstrated two factors which are responsible for the antimicrobial action of heated serum. One, called the activating factor, is adsorbed to the susceptible bacterium; the second is not. Different species may show great differences in the antimicrobial action of their serum, depending upon the microorganisms used for testing.

The serum lipides seem to be related to the virucidal properties of serum (91). It is possible that they act merely in conjunction with the "normal" antibodies.

Some experiments have suggested that the nonspecific bactericidal power of serum is related to certain enzymes in the blood (91). Another natural bactericidal substance is a basic polypeptide which kills *Bacillus anthracis* (9). Another agent, *antivasin*, is discussed on page 19.

Pillemer (95–98) believed he had found a new protein constituent of normal serum, which he called properdin, which was essential for the bactericidal power possessed by such serum. The cooperation of complement or certain complement components, and magnesium ions, is required for bacteriolysis, for properdin alone is inactive. Unlike antibodies, properdin is nonspecific. It participates in such diverse activities as the destruction of bacteria, the neutralization of viruses, and the lysis of certain red cells.

Nelson (89), after an intensive study of the subject, concluded that properdin merely represents the combined action of complement (see Chapter 7) together with low levels of antibody present in normal sera which can cross-react with antigens contained in zymosan. More recent work (56) suggests the view that properdin represents a group of antibodies that are heat labile IgM globulins of the 19S type (see Chapter 2).

Other body fluids contain antimicrobial substances. Saliva contains lysozyme, and other antimicrobial factors which may be related to the bacterial flora.

Antimicrobial factors have also been found in the genitourinary tract secretions, milk, etc.

In 1957 another mechanism of resistance, to virus infections, was discovered. This is the production of *interferon*. It had been known for many years that an animal or tissue infected with one virus was likely to resist infection with a second virus, even if the new virus was antigenically quite unrelated to the first. This resistance seems to be due to the presence of an agent called by Isaacs and Lindemann interferon, which seems to be a product of the cells of the host, not the virus. It is remarkably stable to acid. It is a protein with a molecular weight of 20,000 to 30,000, and is species specific rather than virus specific, that is, interferon from the cells of one animal species is most effective in preventing virus multiplication in cells of that species, but will prevent the growth of a number of different viruses.

Interferon seems to be a defense against foreign nucleic acids, whether of virus or other origin (59).

There are other processes which aid the resistance of the infected body. They include changes of body temperature, as in the fever which follows so many infections, changes in concentration of certain tissue metabolites, and changes in the oxygen tension in the tissues. The growth of many pathogens is markedly retarded at temperatures of 40° to 41°C. (104° to 106°F.). The maintenance of normal oxygen tension in the tissues protects against invasion by tetanus bacilli or clostridia, and these organisms gain a foothold only in areas devitalized by injury so that vascular or atmospheric oxygen is cut off. This illustrates the inadvisability of tight bandaging of cuts and other injuries.

The tubercle bacillus, on the other hand, requires a good deal of oxygen for its development; this may account for its frequent predilection for the lungs.

Many observers (40,44,77,80,94) have reported that local treatment with certain agents, even with nonspecific irritants, which provoke inflammation, will increase resistance temporarily.

Natural resistance and nonspecific factors in immunity are discussed by Perla and Marmorston (92), Raffel (99), Nungester (91), and Howard (56).

13. Mechanisms of Acquired Immunity

There seem to be four ways in which *increased resistance* to a disease can be effected in an animal. (*1*) There may be some increase in the nonspecific factors of resistance, such as a decrease in the permeability of the skin and mucosa (see above). (*2*) The tissues may be altered in such a way that they become intrinsically resistant. (*3*) Mobile cellular elements (phagocytes) may be made available more quickly to fight off the invading organisms. (*4*) Soluble substances which tend to protect against the infection (antibodies) may be secreted into the blood and tissue fluids.

Tissue Immunity (Cellular Immunity)

By tissue immunity we mean an alteration in the tissues themselves, aside from (*3*) the mobilization of cellular defenses in the blood and fluids, and (*4*) the production of soluble defense substances such as antibodies, which makes them more resistant to specific infection. Not all workers are agreed that such a type of immunity exists; others have written whole books on the subject.

A priori, it would seem entirely possible that tissue immunity, as defined above, and as distinct from complete tissue invulnerability (p. 20), could exist; evidence that it does has been presented by Elberg (30) and Suter and Ramseier (116).

It is certainly true that tissue cells can participate in the immunological response; this is shown by the development of hypersensitivity of the de-layed type, which, as we shall see in Chapter 9, seems to take place entirely independently of humoral antibodies. It is difficult to see, however, how any alteration of the fixed tissue cells can affect the fate of invading bacteria, since, as pointed out by various authors (101,99), the bacteria occupy the tissue *spaces* and not the interior of the (fixed) cells. Those who advocate tissue immunity as part of the mechanism of acquired immunity have never been able to offer any explanation as to the manner in which the cells are supposed to overcome the bacteria. Even in the case of a virus infection (fowlpox) in which the infectious agent inhabits the interior of the tissue cells, Goodpasture, Douglas, and Anderson (45) were unable to demonstrate the existence of tissue immunity.

There is a lipoidal cellular toxin of the cholera vibrio which increases the permeability of isolated intestinal strips. This toxin is antigenic, and animals will form antibodies against it, but the antibodies do not protect the intestinal strips from the permeability-increasing effects of the toxin. But strips removed from immunized animals are resistant to this toxic effect. It might be thought that the mucosal cells of the intestine had acquired a resistance to the toxin, but an alternative explanation is that there are intracellular antibodies within the macrophages of the intestinal wall, and this is the explanation which Burrows *et al.* themselves advanced.

In favor of the idea that apparent examples of tissue immunity are at least in some cases due to antibodies are the observations of Cannon and Sullivan (17); and Walsh, Sullivan, and Cannon (123) found evidence that certain parts of animals which had experimentally been brought directly in contact with *Salmonella schottmuelleri* tended to have a greater concentration of antibodies than even the spleen and liver, suggesting perhaps that at least part of the local resistance was due to antibodies.

Antibodies

Animals that are exposed to infection produce in the blood and tissue fluids soluble substances which tend specifically to prevent or cure infection. These are called *antibodies* (because they are *bodies* acting *against* introduced substances), but the term, as we have seen, is not restricted to substances with a protective function. The substances that call forth the production by the animals of antibodies are called *antigens* (because they cause animals to *generate* the antibodies). There is a certain element of circularity in these definitions, which we shall not bother to remove, for the reader will acquire a better notion of what antibodies and antigens are by reading the following chapters than from any definition.

A substance which can act as an antigen is said to be antigenic. Some substances and mixtures which are not antigenic, or are only slightly so, are, however, often referred to as antigens, because they *react* with antibodies. This inconsistency in nomenclature is not as confusing as might appear at first. Some writers have recently begun replacing the term antigenic by *immunogenic*. To the present writer this seems unfortunate, for the unwary reader might suppose that immunogenic substances made the animals, to which they were administered, immune. This, in many cases, they do not do. They may merely result in the production of antibodies to harmless antigens not connected with resistance to any disease (*e.g.*, egg albumin or human serum albumin in rabbits), they may be present naturally as part of the individual's biological makeup (*e.g.*, the isoagglutinins in man), or they may actually make the individual more, not less, susceptible to further exposure to the same antigen (*e.g.*, antigens producing hypersensitivity).

Immunity vs. Hypersensitivity

The changes that occur in an organism in response to an infection may enable it to throw off the infection, and are beneficial in the sense that resistance to subsequent infections of the same type will be greater. The mechanism of these changes, however, is evidently so general that they can be provoked by influences other than infectious agents. Noninfectious, dead microorganisms may cause such changes, and even apparently harmless substances may sometimes cause alterations in the reactions of the tissues or the substances in the circulation. An animal may become highly reactive ("hypersensitive") to certain harmless substances (Chapter 8). Burnet (12) suggested that the basic mechanism of all reactions of an organism to foreign substances consists in the recognition by the tissues of the organism of the differences between "self" and "not-self." You do not (usually) become hypersensitive to any of your own blood proteins, and your stomach, although it will digest tripe, refuses (usually) to digest itself—so long as you are alive. The defenses which an organism puts up against infection may therefore have something in common with the processes of digestion, just as Metchnikoff thought.

Not all antibodies are concerned with infection. The injection of many substances not even derived from disease-producing organisms will call forth the production of substances which have all the general characteristics of antibodies, and which can be observed to react with the injected antigen in some recognizable way. Since there is every reason to believe that these substances are of the same nature as antibodies concerned with disease and that they are produced by the same mechanism, they are also called antibodies, and the substances which cause their production are called antigens.

Such "pseudo-defense" measures, in the case of usually harmless substances such as ragweed pollen, may set up a mode of reaction which is actually deleterious to the organism (Chapter 8). We can only suppose that on the whole the benefits of possessing the immunity-sensitization mechanism outweigh the harm, or otherwise the device would not have survived during the long course of evolution.

Effects of Cortisone and ACTH

There is currently considerable interest in the effect of cortisone and ACTH on immunity, and we may make a few remarks on the subject in this chapter.

Little is known about the peripheral utilization of the adrenal hormones, but Sayers (110) surmised that they regulate some aspects of metabolism in practically every cell of the body, for nearly every organ is affected by withdrawal of adrenal cortical hormones, and injection of these hormones has widespread effects throughout the body.

The favorable effects which cortisone and ACTH have on rheumatoid arthritis and other "collagen diseases" led to their trial in a variety of infections. The results have been the reverse of encouraging (65) because:

1. Cortisone and ACTH usually depress the resistance of laboratory animals to a wide variety of bacterial, viral, protozoal, and fungal agents.

2. They may activate latent infections or render animals susceptible to fatal infection by ordinary nonpathogenic inhabitants of the respiratory or intestinal tract.

3. Resistance is depressed whether it is innate (hereditary) or acquired.

4. Pathogens are often induced to multiply more extensively, are disseminated more widely, and local inflammatory responses are diminished.

5. Infected animals receiving cortisone or ACTH may succumb to smaller doses of an infectious agent than do animals not receiving these hormones.

6. When ACTH or cortisone is given together with antibiotics it generally reduces the effectiveness of the antibiotics. (In a few cases the survival of infected animals seemed to be prolonged by cortisone (65).)

Several possible mechanisms of this lowering of resistance have been suggested: inhibition of the inflammatory process by decreasing capillary

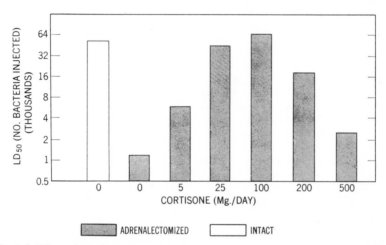

ADRENALECTOMIZED   INTACT

Fig. 1-4. Effect of cortisone on pneumoccocal infection in mice. Mice were given a dose of antibody sufficient to protect half of the normal mice against the injection of 50,000 virulent organisms, in other words the LD_{50} was 50,000 (see Chapter 17). For adrenalectomized mice the LD_{50} was much less, but increased as the dose of cortisone was increased. It decreased again as the dose was increased still further. From (64).

permeability, with a resulting decrease of blood serum proteins in and around the infected tissue; decrease of infiltration of phagocytes; inhibition of antibody formation; possible decrease in the activity of the fixed phagocytic cells of the reticuloendothelial system.

Despite early reports to the contrary, there is little reason to believe that ACTH or cortisone increases antibody production or release. On the contrary, they have been definitely shown to inhibit the antibody response in rabbits, rats, mice, and guinea pigs (65). Since the rate of disappearance of passively administered antibody is not influenced, it seems probable that the hormones interfere with antibody synthesis. In addition to this, other mechanisms may also be interfered with (65). Cortisone has been found to lower resistance to viruses and to depress the ability of the reticuloendothelial system of the rat to remove bacteria from the blood (91).

Cortisone in small doses may increase resistance, but depress it in larger doses (Fig. 1-4).

References

1. Aird, I., H. H. Benthall, J. A. Mehigan, and J. A. Fraser Roberts, *Brit. Med. J.*, **2**, 315 (1954).
2. Allison, A. C., *Trans. Roy. Soc. Trop. Med. Hyg.*, **48**, 312 (1954).
3. Aschoff, L., *Ergeb. Inn. Med. Kinderheilk.*, **26**, 1 (1924).
4. Aschoff, L., *Lecture on Pathology*, Hoeber, New York, 1924.
5. Ascoli, A., *Z. Physiol. Chem.*, **48**, 315 (1906).
6. Asdell, S. A., *Science*, **99**, 124 (1944).
7. Baumgartner, L., *J. Immunol.*, **27**, 407 (1934).
8. Berry, L. J., and T. D. Spies, *Medicine (Paris)*, **28**, 239 (1949).
9. Bloom, W. L., *et al.*, *J. Infect. Diseases*, **80**, 41 (1947).
10. Bordet, J., *Traité de l'Immunité*, Masson, Paris, 1939.
11. Boyd, W. C., M. Heisler, and E. Orowan, *Nature*, **190**, 1123 (1961).
12. Burnet, F. M., *Biological Aspects of Infectious Diseases*, Macmillan, Cambridge, 1940.
13. Burnet, F. M., *Virus as Organism*, Harvard University Press, Cambridge, 1945.
14. Burnet, F. M., *Natural History of Infectious Disease*, Harvard University Press, Cambridge, 1953.
15. Burnet, F. M., and F. Fenner, *The Production of Antibodies*, Macmillan, Melbourne, 1949.
16. Cannon, P. R., and G. A. Pacheco, *Am. J. Pathol.*, **6**, 749 (1930).
17. Cannon, P. R., and F. L. Sullivan, *Proc. Soc. Exptl. Biol. Med.*, **29**, 517 (1931–32).
18. Cannon, P. R., F. L. Sullivan, and E. F. Neckermann, *J. Exptl. Med.*, **55**, 121 (1932).
19. Cappell, D. F., *J. Pathol. Bacteriol.*, **32**, 595 (1929).
20. Cappell, D. F., *J. Pathol. Bacteriol.*, **33**, 429 (1930).
21. Chain, E., and E. S. Duthie, *Brit. J. Exptl. Pathol.*, **21**, 324 (1940).
22. Culbertson, J. T., *J. Immunol.*, **29**, 29 (1935).
23. Denys, J., and J. Leclef, *La Cellule*, **11**, 177 (1895).
24. Dubos, R. J., *The Bacterial Cell in Its Relation to Problems of Virulence, Immunity and Chemotherapy*, Harvard University Press, Cambridge, 1945.
25. Duran-Reynals, F., *Compt. rend. soc. biol.*, **99**, 6 (1928).
26. Duran-Reynals, F., *J. Exptl. Med.*, **69**, 69 (1939).
27. Duran-Reynals, F., *Bacteriol. Rev.*, **6**, 197 (1939).
28. Edsall, G., *J. Immunol.*, **67**, 167 (1951).
29. Edsall, G., in *The Nature and Significance of the Antibody Response*, A. M. Pappenheimer, ed., Columbia University Press, New York, 1953.
30. Elberg, S. S., *Bacteriol., Rev.*, **24**, 67–95 (1960).
31. Eyring, H., and T. F. Dougherty, *Am. Scientist*, **43**, 457 (1955).
32. Felton, L. D., and G. H. Bailey, *J. Infect. Diseases*, **38**, 131 (1926).
33. Fenn, W. O., *J. Gen. Physiol.*, **4**, 373 (1922).

34. Fenn, W. O., in *The Newer Knowledge of Bacteriology and Immunology*, E. O. Jordan and J. S. Falk, eds., University of Chicago Press, Chicago, 1928.
36. Fisher, R. A., *The New Systematics*, Oxford University Press, Oxford, 1930.
37. Florey, H., *Lecture on General Pathology*, Saunders, Philadelphia, 1954.
38. Fothergill, L. D., C. A. Chandler, and J. H. Dingle, *J. Immunol.*, **32**, 335 (1937).
39. Freeman, T., A. H. Gordon, and J. H. Humphrey, *Brit. J. Exptl. Pathol.*, **39**, 459 (1958).
40. Gay, E. P., in *The Newer Knowledge of Bacteriology and Immunology*, E. O. Jordan and I. S. Falk, eds., University of Chicago Press, Chicago, 1928.
41. Gay, E. P., et al., *Agents of Disease and Host Resistance*, Charles C Thomas, Springfield, Illinois, 1935.
42. Gay, E. P., and A. R. Clark, *Proc. Soc. Exptl. Biol. Med.*, **27**, 995 (1930).
43. Gay, E. P., and L. F. Morrison, *J. Infect. Diseases*, **33**, 338 (1923).
44. Giddings, N. J., *Science*, **95**, 553 (1942).
45. Goodpasture, E. W., B. Douglas, and K. A. Anderson, *Arch. Pathol.*, **30**, 212 (1940).
46. Grasset, E., *Publs. S. African Inst. Med. Res.*, **24**, 1171 (1929).
47. Haas, E., *J. Biol. Chem.*, **163**, 63, 89, 101 (1946).
48. Hahn, L., *Biochem. Z.*, **315**, 83 (1943).
49. Heidelberger, M., et al., *J. Exptl. Med.*, **83**, 303 (1946).
50. Heidelberger, M., R. H. P. Sia, and F. E. Kendall, *J. Exptl. Med.*, **52**, 477 (1930).
51. Hellat, A., *Studies on the Self-Disinfecting Power of the Skin*, Helsinki, 1948.
52. Hirsch, J. G., Paper presented at conference on the plasma proteins and cellular elements of the blood, The Protein Foundation, Cambridge, Mass., January 5, 1956.
53. Hoffman, D. C., and F. Duran-Reynals, *J. Exptl. Med.*, **53**, 387 (1931).
54. Hogben, L. T., *Genetic Principles in Medicine and Social Sciences*, Williams and Nongate, London, 1931.
55. Hopkins, R., *Symposium Series, Am. Assoc. Advan. Science*, **1**, 112 (1938).
56. Howard, J. G., *Mod. Trends Immunol.*, **1**, 86–106 (1963).
58. Humphrey, J. H., R. G. White, *Immunology for Students of Medicine*, F. A. Davis, Philadelphia, 1963.
59. Isaacs, A., *Sci. Am.*, **209**, 46–50 (1963).
60. Jasmin, G., and A. Robert, eds., *The Mechanism of Inflammation*, Acta., Montreal, 1953.
61. Johnson, F. H., H. Eyring, and M. J. Polissar, *The Kinetic Basis of Molecular Biology*, Wiley, New York, 1954.
61a. Jollès, J., J. Jauregui-Adell, I. Bernier, and P. Jollès, *Biochim. Biophys. Acta*, **78**, 668–689 (1963).
62. Kahn, R. L., *Tissue Immunity*, Charles C Thomas, Springfield, Illinois, 1936.
63. Karnovsdy, M. L., *Physiol. Rev.* **42**, 143 (1962).
64. Kass, E. H., *Ann. N. Y. Acad. Sci.*, **88**, 108 (1960).
65. Kass, E. H., and M. Finland, *Ann. Rev. Microbiol.*, **7**, 361 (1953).
66. Kiser, J. S., H. Lindh, and G. C. de Mello, *Ann. N. Y. Acad. Sci.*, **66**, 312–328 (1956).
67. Kligman, A. M., *J. Am. Med. Assoc.*, **149**, 979 (1952).
68. Knudson, A. G., *Genetics and Disease*, Blakiston Div., McGraw-Hill, New York 1965.
69. Lurie, M. B., *J. Exptl. Med.*, **75**, 247 (1942).
70. Lurie, M. B., *Am. J. Med.*, **9**, 591 (1950).
71. Lyons, C., *Brit. J. Exptl. Pathol.*, **18**, 411 (1937).
72. MacLeod, C. M., et al., *J. Exptl. Med.*, **82**, 445 (1945).

73. Madsen, T., *Lecture on the Epidemiology and Control of Syphilis, Tuberculosis, and Whooping Cough, and Other Aspects of Infectious Disease,* Wood, Baltimore, 1937.
74. McLean, D., *J. Pathol. Bacteriol.,* **34,** 459 (1931).
75. McClean, D., and C. W. Hale, *Nature,* **145,** 867 (1940).
76. McDermott, W., *et al., Ann. N. Y. Acad. Sci.,* **66,** 233–414 (1956).
77. Menkin, V., *Physiol., Rev.,* **18,** 366 (1938).
78. Menkin, V., *The Dynamics of Inflammation,* Macmillan, New York, 1940.
79. Menkin, V., *New Engl. J. Med.,* **229,** 511 (1943).
80. Menkin, V., *Science,* **101,** 422 (1945).
81. Menkin, V., *Newer Concepts of Inflammation,* Charles C Thomas, Springfield, Illinois, 1950.
82. Meyer, K. F., *J. Immunol.,* **64,** 139 (1950).
83. Meyer, K., *et al., J. Exptl. Med.,* **71,** 137 (1940).
84. Meyer, K., and J. W. Palmer, *J. Biol. Chem.,* **114,** 689 (1936).
85. Meyer, K., R. Dubos, and E. M. Smyth, *J. Biol. Chem.,* **118,** 71 (1937).
86. Mudd, S., M. McCutcheon, and H. Lucke, *Physiol. Rev.,* **14,** 210 (1934).
87. Muller, H. J., *Science,* **121,** 1 (1955).
88. Nelson, R. A., *Science,* **118,** 733 (1953).
89. Nelson, R. A., *J. Exptl. Med.,* **108,** 515 (1958).
90. Nelson, D. S., *Advan. Immunol.,* **3,** 131–180 (1963).
91. Nungester, F., *Ann. Rev. Microbiol.,* **8,** 363 (1954).
92. Perla, D., and J. Marmorston, *Natural Resistance and Clinical Medicine,* Wood, Baltimore, 1941.
93. Pettersson, A., *Z. Immunitätsforsch.,* **102,** 432 (1943).
94. Pfeiffer, R., and Issaeff, *Z. Hyg. Infektionskrankh.,* **17,** 355 (1894).
95. Pillemer, L., *et al., Science,* **120,** 279 (1954).
96. Pillemer, L., *Trans. N. Y. Acad. Sci.,* **17,** 526 (1955).
97. Pillemer, L., Paper presented at conference on the plasma proteins and cellular elements of the blood, The Protein Foundation, Cambridge, Mass., January 5, 1956.
98. Pillemer, L., *et al., Science,* **122,** 545 (1955).
99. Raffel, S., *Immunity,* Appleton-Century-Crofts, New York, 1953.
100. Reed, T. E., A study of eight blood group systems and reproductive performance, abstract, *Proceedings of the Second International Conference of Human Genetics, Rome 1961,* Paper **83,** Amsterdam, Excerpta Medica, 1961.
101. Rich, A. R., *The Pathogenesis of Tuberculosis,* 2nd ed., Charles C Thomas, Springfield, Illinois, 1951.
102. Roberts, J. A. Fraser, *Brit. J. Prevent. Soc. Med.* **11,** 107 (1957).
103. Roberts, J. A. Fraser, *Brit. Med. Bull.,* **15,** 129 (1959).
104. Roertson, W. van B., *et al., J. Biol. Chem.,* **133,** 261 (1940).
105. Roth, R. B., *Am. Rev. Tuberc.,* **38,** 196 (1938).
106. Rous, P., and F. S. Jones, *J. Exptl. Med.* **23,** 549 (1916).
107. Russel, W. T., and G. Salmon, *J. Hyg.,* **34,** 380 (1934).
108. Sabin, A. B., *Ann. N. Y. Acad. Sci.,* **54,** 936 (1952).
109. Sabin, A. B., *et al., Proc. Soc. Exptl. Biol. Med.,* **63,** 135 (1947).
110. Sayers, G., *Physiol. Rev.,* **30,** 241 (1950).
111. Shilo, M., *Ann. Rev. Microbiol.,* **13,** 255–275 (1959).
112. Simon, H. J., *Attenuated Infection,* J. B. Lippincott, Philadelphia, Montreal, 1960.

113. Spink, W. W., and J. J. Vivino, *Science,* **98,** 44 (1943).
114. Stevens, K. M., *J. Immunol.,* **71,** 119 (1953).
115. Stollerman, G. H., M. Rytel, and J. Ortiz, *J. Exptl. Med.,* **117,** 1–17 (1963).
116. Suter, E., and H. Ramseier, *Advan. Immunol.,* **4,** 117–173 (1964).
117. Taliaferro, W. H., *Bacteriol. Rev.,* **12,** 1 (1948).
117a. Taylor, A. E. R., ed., *Evolution of Parasites,* Blackwell, Oxford, 1965.
118. Thomsen, O., and K. Kettel, *Z. Immunitätsforsch.,* **63,** 67 (1929).
119. Topley, W. W. C., and G. S. Wilson, *The Principles of Bacteriology and Immunity,* 5th ed., by G. S. Wilson and A. A. Miles, Wm. Wood, Baltimore, 1964.
120. Tullis, J. L., ed., *Blood Cells and Plasma Proteins,* Academic Press, New York, 1953.
121. Tullis, J. L., and D. M., Surgenor, *Ann. N. Y. Acad. Sci.,* **66,** 368–390 (1956).
122. Waddington, C. H., *The Strategy of the Genes,* Allen and Unwin, London, 1957.
122a. Wald, G., *Proc. Nat. Acad. Sci.,* **52,** 595 (1964).
123. Walsh, T. E., F. L. Sullivan, and P. R. Cannon, *Proc. Soc. Exptl. Biol. Med.,* **29,** 675 (1931–32).
124. Walter, A. W., E. L. Schenkein, and W. D. Sutliff, *J. Exptl. Med.,* **83,** 321 (1946).
125. Webster, L. T., *J. Exptl. Med.,* **57,** 793 (1933).
126. Wilson, A. T., *Proc. Exptl. Biol. Med.,* **58,** 130 (1945).
127. Wood, W. B., *Harvey Lectures Ser.,* **47,** 72 (1953).
128. Wood, W. B., M. R. Smith, and B. Watson, *J. Exptl. Med.,* **84,** 387 (1946).
129. Wright, S., *The New Systematics,* J. S. Huxley, ed., Clarendon, Oxford, 1940.

CHAPTER 2

Antibodies and Antibody Specificity

1. Chemical Constitution of Blood, Plasma, and Serum

Our first concern will be with those soluble protective substances that the immune animal produces in its blood.

First, a few words concerning this important fluid itself. Blood consists of a liquid portion, called plasma, in which float a number of different kinds of cells, including the oxygen-transporting red cells and the various kinds of white cells, or leukocytes, already discussed. If blood is drawn from an animal and prevented from clotting by the addition of an anti-coagulant, such as sodium citrate, lithium oxalate, or heparin, the cells can be centrifuged off and the plasma obtained.

If blood is allowed to clot, certain constituents of it unite to form a fibrous mass which traps the cells, forming a firm, jelly-like clot. This clot, on standing, will shrink, and a clear yellowish fluid, called serum, separates. Serum is similar in composition to plasma, but differs somewhat, chiefly in the absence of the fibrinogen (a protein making up about 6 per cent of all the plasma proteins), which has entered into the composition of the clot.

It is the serum which interests us as immunologists. Serum contains a number of inorganic dissolved substances, various more or less simple organic compounds, some containing nitrogen, and a large number of the high molecular weight nitrogenous compounds called proteins. The great majority of these serum proteins can be placed in one of two classes, originally based on solubility characteristics, called albumins and globulins. Albumins were defined as soluble in water and in half-saturated ammonium sulfate solutions. Globulins were thrown out of solution by half-saturation with ammonium sulfate. Some globulins were insoluble in water and were called euglobulins ("true globulins"), and some were

* Translations of mottos not in English will be found in the Appendix.

water-soluble and were called pseudoglobulins. Since the time of the studies which led to this classification other differences between the two classes have been found. The serum globulins, in general, are larger molecules than serum albumin, and ordinarily have lower net electric charges per molecule.

These serum proteins have a number of important functions (313). They are important nutritionally, they act as buffers to help maintain the pH of the blood at physiological levels, they exert osmotic pressure which maintains and stabilizes the blood volume, and they are involved in the transport of hormones, lipides, and other substances. The albumins are especially important for the osmotic effect, the globulins for their transport function. But one of the most important, perhaps the most important, functions of the globulins is the defensive action which certain of them exert against infection. These globulins are called antibodies. The ways in which they differ from "normal" globulins will be discussed below.

2. One Antibody, Many Manifestations

It could easily be imagined that the only way of detecting antibodies would be by their power of neutralizing infectious agents or rendering them susceptible to destruction. This seems to be true of some antibodies, notably those against certain viruses, and in such cases the technic of demonstration does depend on the neutralizing effect which the antibodies have.

Fortunately for us, however, antibodies in many cases react with the antigen in a way that is or can be made visible in the test tube. Thus antibodies have been observed to cause swelling of capsules of microorganisms against which they are directed, to cause lysis (solution) of microorganisms and foreign cells, to cause agglutination (sticking together) of organisms and cells to kill microorganisms, to cause the formation of a precipitate when mixed with soluble antigen, to opsonize (see Chapter 1) microorganisms so they can be phagocyted, to neutralize toxic products of bacteria (or other toxins), and to sensitize animals passively to various antigens. In addition, in most of these reactions, complement will, if present, enter into combination with the antibody–antigen compound (see Chapter 7), and this factor is requisite for lysis and killing.

Originally a separate name was given to the hypothetical cause of each different serological phenomenon, so that we had names such as lysin, bacteriolysin, hemolysin, amboceptor, agglutinin, hemagglutinin, bactericidin, precipitin, opsonin, tropin, bacteriotropin, antitoxin, sensitizer. Eventually it occurred to immunologists (6,65,331) that it might be possible for the same antibody to perform all or most of these functions, and thus the number of hypothetical entities required was drastically reduced. This theory has been called the "unitarian" view. It is now realized, in any case, that many of these reactions, such as precipitation and agglutination, represent only the secondary effects of the primary immunochemical reaction between antibody and antigen.

The unitarian view was a much-needed simplification, but as originally stated it went too far, as many reforms do. It stated that a single pure antigen would produce only one variety of antibody (332) and that this antibody, brought into contact with the antigen in appropriate form, under appropriate conditions, could agglutinate, precipitate, fix complement, lyse, opsonize, etc. Now there is no doubt that one and the same antibody can do all or at least many of these things (54,71,133,166). Heidelberger and Kabat (133), for example, found that type-specific agglutinin and precipitin in type I antipneumococcus horse serum were present in identical amounts by weight, and a removal of some of one caused a quantitatively identical decrease in the other. Doerr and Russ (71) found the anaphylactic sensitizing effect of a precipitating serum to be quantitatively proportional to the precipitin content, and Chow, Lee, and Wu (54) found that immunologically pure precipitin from rabbit sera would protect mice from an otherwise fatal dose of type I pneumococcus, or produce passive anaphylaxis, or fix complement, in addition to precipitating its homologous polysaccharide.

However, there can be little doubt now that one and the same antigen *may* give rise to antibodies that exhibit differences in behavior. In fact the antibody molecules in an immune serum are generally rather heterogeneous (p. 52) and some react more rapidly and more firmly with the antigen than do others. A certain amount of antibody which will unite with the antigen but which will not cause precipitation is often found. Kuhns and Pappenheimer (179) found that antitoxin produced in allergic human beings is generally different from that produced in normal individuals, being nonprecipitating but skin-sensitizing, whereas that produced by normals is precipitating but nonsensitizing (*cf.* 165).

In allergic patients skin-sensitizing antibody is often present. Therapeutic injection of the allergen may increase the production of the antibody these patients possess, but Loveless (191) suggested that the clinical benefits might be due to a different sort of antibody which was also produced following the injection of the allergen. This antibody has a binding action on the antigen and apparently blocks its union with the sensitizing antibody. For this reason it is called "blocking" antibody. Kuhns

(178) also found such antibody in the serum of allergic patients injected with toxoid.

Two kinds of hemagglutinating antibodies are also often observed, especially in the Rh system (320,255). One of these will agglutinate erythrocytes that possess the appropriate receptors, if the cells are suspended, as is usual, in 0.9 per cent NaCl solution. The other kind of antibody will combine with the erythrocytes in saline but will not cause any agglutination. This combination prevents agglutination of these cells by the ordinary agglutinating antibody, and antibodies of this second kind are therefore called "blocking" antibodies. (Note that they are entirely different from the "blocking" antibodies of allergy.) These "blocking" Rh antibodies will agglutinate Rh+ cells if the latter are suspended in 25 per cent serum albumin, or if the cells are previously treated with a proteolytic enzyme such as trypsin, papain, or ficin, or if the antibody-coated cells are treated with an antibody to the antibody (Coombs test). Since these "blocking" antibodies do not cause agglutination under ordinary conditions, they have also been called "incomplete" or "univalent" antibodies. There is good evidence that they are not univalent (see below).

The physicochemical differences which underlie the differences in behavior of these different sorts of antibodies are still not fully understood. See, however, p. 80.

Another manifestation of the action of antibody is represented by certain types of hypersensitivity reactions (see Chapters 8 and 9). Hypersensitivity of the delayed type cannot be transferred by serum, but specific cutaneous sensitivity to tuberculin was transferred by Chase (49) in unsensitized guinea pig by the injection of leukocytes isolated from peritoneal exudates produced in sensitized guinea pigs.

Lawrence (186) transferred cutaneous hypersensitivity to tuberculin in man by the intradermal injection of viable leukocytes isolated from the peripheral blood of tuberculin-positive human beings.

Later Chase (51) was able to transfer cutaneous sensitivity to picryl chloride in guinea pigs by injecting washed splenic cells or cells teased from lymph nodes. Circulating antibody also appeared in the injected animals, but Chase stated that the two effects are separable. Harris and Harris (120) reported similar work.

Antitoxin has been found as soon as 18 hours after animals have received well-washed cells from an animal previously injected with toxoid. It seems likely that this antitoxin comes from the injected cells. Later on a separate rise in antitoxin level in the circulation of the injected animals was observed, beginning about the 12th day. This was interpreted as the result of active immunization resulting from the presence of toxoid in the injected cells, a conclusion strengthened by the fact that the animals which had received the injection of cells responded to a later injection of toxoid with a secondary response (p. 91).

The general question of antibody reactions mediated through cells is discussed by Chase (51) and Lawrence (187).

3. Modes of Behavior

In most cases study has not revealed any differences between antibodies and globulins normally present in the blood which are great enough to enable the presence of antibodies to be recognized chemically. The presence of globulin in unusual amounts, particularly of "euglobulin" (as determined by salting out) or gamma globulin (determined by electrophoresis), probably indicates the presence of more antibody than usual and certain electrophoretic or ultracentrifugal components of horse sera are greatly increased when the horse is immunized with certain antigens (p. 59). Some immune sera do not seem chemically different from normal sera, however, and it has in fact been questioned if there is any such thing as "normal" gamma globulin (p. 100). The chemical methods cannot detect the presence of very small amounts of antibody, and in addition the methods suffer from a much more serious drawback; they are not specific, for they do not tell us *which* antibodies are present. Therefore the best methods for the recognition of antibodies depend upon the characteristic behavior which they exhibit when brought in contact with the antigen under the appropriate conditions. Examination for protective power, by injecting animals with mixtures of antiserum and infective agent, is in some cases the only method at our disposal, and consequently has to be used. It has the merit that it tests for the thing we are interested in, immunity, since we know that this is dependent on the properties of the blood. It is, however, wasteful of experimental animals and time-consuming, and even when large numbers of animals are used, it is still subject to some residual uncertainty (see Chapter 17). Some antibodies are directed against toxic products (toxins) produced by the infective organism, and will neutralize these substances, rendering them harmless. The presence of these antibodies can be tested for by mixing the serum with the toxin (freed from the microorganisms), and then testing the toxicity of the mixture on suitable susceptible animals. This method has some of the disadvantages of the previous one, but, similarly, in some cases it is still the best method available.

In view of the technical difficulties of the direct test on animals, and because other antibodies that interest us seem to have little protective power, and because we find it instructive to study, in experimental investigations, antibodies to noninfective and nontoxic substances and cells, it is fortunate that we have in most cases other ways of recognizing the presence of antibodies.

An antibody directed towards a soluble constituent of a microorganism, or against other soluble antigens, will usually, when mixed in appropriate concentration with a solution of the antigen, produce a precipitate. Such precipitates, which contain both antibody and antigen, when made, for example, with toxin and antitoxin in appropriate amounts, are found to be neutral (*i.e.,* nontoxic) and to have a definite composition. Since this procedure can be carried out in the test tube, it offers great advantages over tests requiring animals. In addition it is rapid, easily seen, and well suited for demonstration. It is natural that this *precipitin reaction* (see Fig. 2-1) has become one of the most extensively used of the immunological reactions.

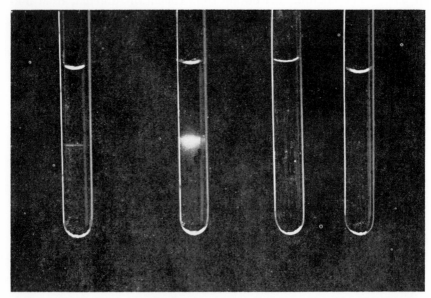

Fig. 2-1. Photograph of precipitin tests. These tests were carried out by the interfacial technic in which a short column of antiserum is placed in the bottom of the tube, and a layer of diluted antigen placed on top of this. The reaction, if any, occurs at the junction in the form of a "ring" (actually a plane) of precipitate. The illustration shows, reading from left to right, weak positive reaction, strong positive reaction, negative reaction, negative reaction. (Photograph by the author.)

It has also been found that antibodies directed against a microorganism or a foreign cell will often, when mixed in suitable concentration with a suspension of these cells, cause them to stick together in clumps. This is called *agglutination,* and provides a rapid and striking method of detecting antibodies (see Fig. 2-2).

Conglutinin is the name given by Bordet and Streng to a heat-stable component of bovine serum which combines with cells that have been treated with antibody and complement, and causes a rapid strong agglutination, often followed by lysis. Doerr (70) gives a complete historical account of the phenomenon. Wiener (318,320) applied the term "con-

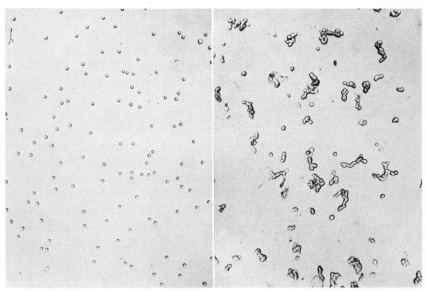

Fig. 2-2. Photomicrographs of agglutination. On the right, unagglutinated erythrocytes; on the left, erythrocytes agglutinated by action of agglutinating antibody. (Photographs by the author.)

glutination" to the clumping which takes place when red cells are exposed to "blocking" (nonagglutinating) antibodies in the presence of plasma, concentrated serum albumin, or globulin, or various mixtures of these. Wiener did not call this phenomenon agglutination. Some workers have objected to Wiener's use of the term conglutination for such hemagglutination, since complement is not involved here, but the usage has been defended by Wiener (320) and Doerr (70).

In some cases the antibody (aided by complement) is observed to bring about the death of the microorganism responsible for its production (bactericidal effect). Such antibodies can cause partial or complete solution of the cells against which they are directed. This is called *lysis* and requires the cooperation of other substances found in serum (complement).

In some cases the antibody has the power of causing the capsule of the microorganism to swell visibly (German, *Quellung*), and thus provides a convenient method of recognizing its presence.

We have seen that combination of antibody with microorganisms seems in many cases either essential to, or of enormous importance for, *phagocytosis*. Therefore, by treating the organisms with the serum and then exposing them to the action of leukocytes, the presence of antibody can be detected.

Some antibodies combine with their antigens without producing any visible change. If the antibody–antigen compound is capable of combining with complement, as is usually the case, the reaction causes complement to disappear from the serum (*complement fixation*). This also is not accompanied by any visible change, but may be detected indirectly by adding an antibody–antigen system which, in the presence of complement, but not without it, will produce some visible phenomenon (lysis). This is the basis of the classical Wassermann test, where the presence of the syphilitic "reagin" (antibody) is detected by adding an antigen with which it will react, if it is present, causing added complement to be taken up at the same time. Then sheep erythrocytes and antisheep lysin are added. If lysis of the sheep cells takes place, this shows that complement is still present in the serum and no reaction took place with the Wassermann antigen, and consequently no "reagin" was present; if lysis does not take place, it indicates the presence of "reagin" and presumably of syphilitic infection. See Chapter 7.

Immunized animals often become hyperreactive to the antigen ("sensitive" or "allergic"). In many cases the antibody in their circulation is capable, if injected into a normal animal, of making the latter sensitive also (passive *sensitization*). This can be detected by appropriate tests of the passively sensitized animal and provides another indirect way of demonstrating antibodies.

4. Specificity

It is a very old observation that, although recovery from a disease may give an individual a longer or shorter period of immunity to this disease, it does not protect him against other unrelated diseases. If antibodies are one of the main bases of immunity, we should expect that they would also show this selective action, and this is the case.

Antibodies that neutralize diphtheria toxin (antitoxins) will give protection against diphtheria and, by neutralizing the toxin produced subsequent to their injection, will facilitate the recovery of a patient with diphtheria; they are of no use in streptococcal infection or syphilis. Diphtheria antitoxin will produce a precipitate when mixed in the proper proportions with diphtheria toxin; it will not precipitate tetanus toxin. Antibodies can apparently recognize the difference between proteins from different species, and between different proteins of the same species, and each can single out its own antigen. There is a limit, however, even to the astonishing precision of serological specificity. When homologous proteins or carbohydrates of related species are used, the antibodies for one antigen may react also with another, though usually less strongly. These are called cross reactions. In some cases, particularly with carbohydrates, cross reactions may occur with substances of quite a different biological origin.

The specificity of serological reactions, extraordinarily sharp but still limited, was well defined by Landsteiner (180) as "the disproportional action of a number of similar agents on a variety of related substrata." This definition seems the best that has been proposed, although it would also include many chemical reactions, as might be expected if serological specificity were fundamentally chemical in its nature, which we now believe.

This definition carries with it consequences that often seem surprising to those not familiar with serological research. For instance, if we test an antibody against a number of related antigens, which we may call X, Y, Z, and W, the beginner would not perhaps say the antibody was specific for Y unless it reacted strongly with antigen Y and not at all with antigens W, X, or Z. But if the antigens are closely related, we may find that what actually happens is that the antibody reacts best with antigen Y, but reacts weakly with antigens X and Z also. In such a case serologists still say the antibody is specific for antigen Y. This is a relative statement. It is relative because we base it on the *degree* to which the antibody reacts with the various antigens, not requiring it to react solely with only one of them, and relative because we may not have tested all the antigens with which this antibody might react. For all we know, it might react still more strongly with one we have not thought of testing, say antigen V. If we tested V, and found it did in fact react better than Y, we should then change our statement to say that the antibody is specific for antigen V (or for V and Y, depending on the difference in the strength of the two reactions).

The same usage of the word "specific" applies to the inhibition reaction (see Chapter 3). If we test a number of simple chemical compounds, say D, E, F, G, and H, for their power of inhibiting a certain antibody (*i.e.*, preventing it from precipitating, or agglutinating, its antigen), and found that the strongest solutions we have of substances D, E, G, and H (say 0.2M) do not prevent the antibody–antigen reaction, whereas substance F, even at a concentration as low as 0.005M does inhibit, we should say substance F specifically inhibits the antibody in question. So far so good. But what might puzzle the beginner is that if we found that substance F inhibited at a concentration of 0.001M, substances D and H did not inhibit even at 0.2M, and substances E and G inhibited at concentrations of about 0.05, we should still say that substance F specifically inhibits the antibody–antigen reaction.

Much of what we know about the specificity of antibodies has been learned by the study of antibodies to proteins which have had coupled to them relatively simple compounds of known composition. Antibodies to simple, known, introduced groups (haptens) could often thus be obtained, and a study of their reactions was extremely informative. We shall discuss methods of altering antigens chemically in the next chapter.

The most outstanding investigator in this field was Karl Landsteiner, and the second edition of his classic book (181) will long be the best source of information for the student of the specificity of antibodies and antigens. In a textbook such as the present, it would be both impossible and undesirable to cover the subject of specificity in the complete way Landsteiner did.

5. Nonhomogeneity

As will be seen in Chapter 3, antibodies to conjugated antigens may exhibit three types of specificity: one directed towards the hapten, one toward the protein carrier, and occasionally, apparently, against both simultaneously. We could treat the antibody of each of these classes as if it were a homogenous substance, each molecule possessing the same specificity. However, this is not the case. As a rule an antiserum against a given antigen contains a diversity of antibodies not all alike (38,181,287, 148,216,217,162).

By absorption of antisera against conjugated proteins, with unconjugated homologous protein or with heterologous protein coupled with homologous hapten, it can be demonstrated that the antihapten and antiprotein antibodies are distinct. This of course is not surprising. At least three anticarbohydrate antibodies can be demonstrated in antiserum to type VIII pneumococcus by cross reaction with type III polysaccharide.

One of these, amounting to at least two-thirds of the total, is rigidly type-specific and does not cross-react with type III polysaccharide at all. Separate antibodies for different parts of the hapten of some conjugated antigens have been demonstrated and may be present in other instances (5,148,205,209). There is hardly any doubt that if a large complicated hapten were used, particularly one containing acidic groups, distinct antibodies to different portions of the hapten could regularly be detected.

Antisera to native proteins when absorbed with heterologous related proteins, are shown to contain antibodies with different cross-reactive powers (59,149,185).

In the majority of cases the difference in the antibodies does not seem to mean that there are present just two or three separate antibodies sharply directed towards different parts of the molecule, but rather that the antibody molecules present vary among themselves in the extent to which they are directed towards the whole hapten (see p. 127) or towards the part which serves as the antigenic "determinant." Therefore, although we must assume a multiplicity of antibodies (183), we should think of them, not as several distinct species, but rather as "a large family, with varying degrees of deviation from a mean." (22).

Pauling, Pressman, and Grossberg (238) made a similar and more precise suggestion. In their opinion, the free binding energies of the different antibody molecules (for the determinant that induced their formation) are distributed according to the Gauss error function.*

It is likely that some of the more weakly reactive molecules reflect the structure of the determinant very imperfectly, and that the more "avid" molecules have more faithfully reproduced the essential electronic configuration (in reverse, we must assume) of the original structure (121). The nature and size of the antigenic determinants in protein antigens is discussed in the following chapter.

Before we go on, it may perhaps be said that the heterogeneity of antibody response is one of its striking characteristics. The different molecular classes of antibody (see below) all show variations in their binding affinity for their antigens, even within one class. It has even been shown that antibodies to a single antigenic determinant (hapten) vary considerably among themselves, and not all of them are even precipitable by the immunizing conjugated antigen (213,284).

---

* This is the well-known "normal distribution" formula of statistics,

$$f(x) = [1/\sigma\sqrt{(2\pi)}]\exp{(-x^2/2\sigma^2)}$$

where σ, called the standard deviation, is a measure of the "dispersion" or degree of heterogeneity of the population whose composition is summarized by the curve. See Chapter 17.

In addition to antibody which produces good precipitation or agglutination, it is often possible to demonstrate in a serum a "low-grade" antibody which will not do this, but which will combine with the antigen or with the compound of the antigen and good antibody. The possible ways in which this low-grade antibody differs from "good" antibody were discussed above (p. 53).

We should also mention that the specificity of antibodies often apparently becomes less as immunization is continued, as is shown by the increase in strength and extent of cross reactions (181). To some extent this may be due to increased antibody concentration in the sera from later bleedings, but some observations suggest that it may be caused partly by the production of antibodies which have been described as of greater combining capacity (181). Qualitative changes in combining power may also be observed between early and late antibodies, for it has been shown, in at least one case, that the later antibodies could combine with a related antigenic determinant with which the antibodies at first produced showed no reaction (152).

The individuality of the animal producing the antibody must also play a considerable role. It is common knowledge that not all rabbits respond in the same way to a given antigen. Bodily and Eaton (20) found wide variations in the specificity of the immune response of human beings to various strains of influenza A virus.

To sum up what we know about the specificity of antibodies, we may say: antibodies can be sharply specific and can distinguish minute differences in chemical or spatial configuration. Differences which are slight from the chemical point of view tend to be slight serologically, and in some cases, especially with neutral antigenic determinants, antibodies fail to distinguish marked chemical differences. Antibodies clearly must contain spatial differences corresponding to the differences of the stereoisomeric substances they can differentiate. In some cases the specificity of antibodies is of a relatively low order, and they may be specific for a part of the molecule only, or even for certain radicals, such as the arsonic acid group ($-AsO_3H_2$) or ($-SO_3H$) (180). Antibodies may be directed towards more than one determinant in the molecule, and even those directed towards one determinant evidently vary to some extent around a main pattern. Antibodies will react with simple chemical compounds as well as with proteins and other complex antigens.

6. Normal Antibodies

In the blood of animals that have not been immunized, and so far as we know have not had the disease in question, there may occur substances that react with a certain infectious agent or with products derived from it. Also of frequent occurrence are substances acting on the erythrocytes of other species, or even on erythrocytes of different individuals of the same species. These substances are so much like antibodies in their behavior that they are called normal or natural antibodies.

Some of the "normal" antibodies are probably real immune antibodies, formed in response to an infectious agent which, however, failed to produce the disease, perhaps because too small a dose gained entrance, but which did produce a latent or subclinical infection, or at any rate some antibody. This has been pretty well proved in the case of "normal" antitoxin for diphtheria (74) and in certain other cases (7,155,259). There is also the possibility that in some cases the antibody production has been in response to organisms which did not enter by the usual portal of infection, and this was affirmed for tetanus antitoxin by Ramon and Lemétayer (260). Ingalls (158) found normal rabbit serum to agglutinate, in low titer, many bacteria isolated from rabbit intestines.

In the globulin fraction II + III separated from pooled normal human plasma by the Harvard group (57), antibodies, in addition to the isohemagglutinins, could be demonstrated to: diphtheria toxin, dysentery bacilli, herpes virus, human and swine influenza virus, lymphocytic choriomeningitis virus, scarlatinal toxin, streptococcus toxin, typhoid H and O antigens, and vaccinia virus.

It is also likely that some of the "normal" antibodies are produced in response, not to the organism with which we observe them to react, but to some related organism, or to some unrelated organism which contains a common antigen. This seems to be the origin of the antisheep hemolysins which may appear in rabbits as a consequence of invasion by bacteria like *Pasteurella cuniculicida* which contain the Forssman antigen (Chapter 4). The presence of related antigens in food is probably also sometimes a factor. The Forssman antigen (p. 195) is heat-stable and present in various plant and animal foods, so that slight absorption from the gastrointestinal tract would provide a continual stimulus to the production of anti-Forssman antibodies.

However, it is not certain that all normal antibodies can be accounted for in this way. Some seem to be definitely physiological. Some occur regularly in all individuals of a species, and not at all in individuals of another species which should have had equal opportunity to come in contact with the antigen which would naturally be considered the stimulus, were these antibodies really of immune origin. Landsteiner (180) suggested that most of the normal hemagglutinins and hemolysins acting on the blood of foreign species were of spontaneous origin. This idea is supported by the lower degree of specificity often exhibited by these normal antibodies, which are sometimes but poorly absorbed by the very cells on which they act and may act on more than one antigen (206).

Another class of normal antibodies comprises the isoagglutinins of the human blood groups (Chapter 5). It is true that it has been suggested that these are the result of antigenic stimulus by antigens, chemically related to the blood group antigens, which occur in bacteria and animal parasites (319), but it was suggested earlier that they are genetically determined, the anti-A being merely another product of the action of the gene B, and the anti-B of gene A (97). This latter view has been somewhat strengthened by the report of Filitti-Wurmser *et al.* (93) that there are actually several different normal human anti-B agglutinins depending on the genotype (Chapter 5) of the individual in whose serum they occur. This is based on studies of the heat of reaction (see Chapter 6) and molecular weight determinations. The anti-B agglutinin has a heat of reaction of 16, 6.5, 1.7, 9, or 3 kcal. per mole, depending on whether it is from an individual of genotype A_1O, A_1A_1, OO, A_2 (probably A_2O), or A_3 (doubtless A_3O). The sedimentation constants of the anti-B from the first three of these are reported to be 15.5, 11, and 6.5. Another conclusion from this work is that the isoagglutinin in the blood of an individual of any particular genotype is homogeneous, at least in regard to heat of reaction and chemical affinity, which would thus differentiate these antibodies from immune antibodies (p. 52). A mixture of the anti-B from genotypes A_1A_1 and OO is quite distinguishable from the anti-B from genotype A_1O.

This work has been confirmed (see Chapter 6). However, other types of experiment may suggest that it nevertheless does not prove that the human isoagglutinins are genetically determined in the sense suggested above.

Experiments with germ-free chicks suggest that the agglutinins for human B erythrocytes that normal chicks possess or develop are the result of stimulation by antigens in their food and perhaps in bacteria that inhabit the gastrointestinal tract. Many workers [*e.g.,* Springer (289a)] believe that the human isoagglutinins have a similar origin.

In this connection it is of interest that germ-free animals are observed to have very low gamma globulin levels and hypoplastic lymphoid tissue. On the removal of these animals to a contaminated environment, their gamma globulin increases and their lymphoid tissue assumes a normal appearance.

It seems possible, then, that the inception and continuation of production of the human isoagglutinins is not genetically determined. The *differences* between the various isoagglutinins observed by the Wurmsers of course might be; in other words, individuals of different groups and genotypes may manufacture different isoagglutinins in response to the stimulus that starts such production. It must be admitted that this is at present a purely hypothetical suggestion, but in light of what we now know about antibody production there is nothing inherently improbable about it.

Specificity of Normal Antibodies

Some of the normal antibodies of animal blood exhibit considerable specificity, and if they are the result of subclinical infections or other inapparent antigenic stimulus this is not surprising. Others, however, are only relatively specific, and Landsteiner (181) showed that one such substance might react with a number of different antigens. There are, therefore, not present in blood as many distinct proteins as there are observed reactivities with antigens.

Even the specificity of the lectins, although good in some instances, is generally not absolute. The anti-A from Lima beans, when purified and concentrated, reacts weakly with B cells also, and the anti-B from *Sophora japonica* (176) reacts sufficiently with group A cells to render it unsatisfactory as a blood grouping reagent. A number of plants contain agglutinins which react with A and B cells and weakly or not at all with O. All of these phenomena illustrate the soundness of Landsteiner's definition (p. 51) of specificity.

7. Electric Charges and Electrophoretic Mobilities

Since proteins contain acidic groups, such as carboxyl, sulfhydryl, and phenolic hydroxy groups, which may be negatively charged in alkaline solution, and basic groups such as the guanidinium group in arginine, the imidazolium group in histidine, and the ϵ-ammonium group in lysine, which may be positively charged in acid solution, they ordinarily carry a net charge. The magnitude of this charge varies with the protein and the distance of the pH of the solution from the isoelectric point of the protein. As a consequence, protein molecules not at their isoelectric point will move in an electric field, the direction and rate depending on their net charge, which in turn depends on the pH. Antibodies behave in this respect like other proteins.

The movement of the boundary, or more accurately, concentration gradient, is observed, as in the ultracentrifuge, by optical methods which visualize the rate of change of concentration along the axis of migration, or in other words, the *slope* of the concentration curve. This is illustrated in Fig. 2-3, modified from Lundgren and Ward (192).

The development by Tiselius of a practical apparatus for the determination of rates of electrophoresis under controlled conditions enabled proteins to be characterized by a new method, based on their rate of migration

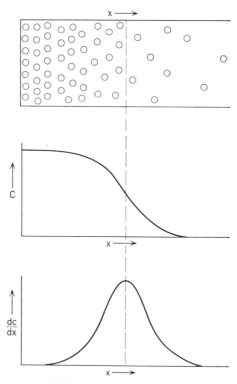

Fig. 2-3. Diagrammatic representation of manner in which concentration gradient is photographed in electrophoresis apparatus (or in ultracentrifuge).

in an electric field of known strength. This rate varies with the charge on the molecules at the *p*H in question. Use of the Tiselius apparatus has sometimes allowed the separation of proteins which were apparently homogeneous. On the other hand, the observation that a preparation shows only one boundary in the electrophoresis apparatus does not prove that it contains only a single protein. The number of distinguishable mobilities is limited, and quite different particles have also been observed to migrate at approximately the same rate.

Normal horse serum shows components with at least four different electrophoretic mobilities; in order or decreasing mobilities these are the albumin, and three globulin components designated as α, β, and γ globulins (306). Rabbit serum shows four components of approximately the same mobilities as the components of horse serum (Fig. 2-4). All of the globulins, α, β, and γ, are in reality mixtures. The right-hand side of Fig. 2-4 shows that the antibodies in the rabbit serum being examined in that experiment had the mobility of the gamma globulins.

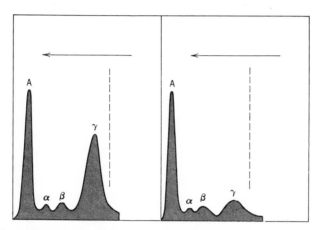

Fig. 2-4. Electrophoretic pattern of an immune rabbit serum. Right-hand diagram, after removal of antibody.

The early determinations of the electrophoretic mobilities of antibodies were carried out by Tiselius and Kabat (307), van der Scheer *et al.* (275) and others.

In man, rabbit, and monkey, immune sera did not at first show any electrophoretic component not found in normal sera, but in the horse antiprotein sera a new component (T, or β_2),* between the β and γ components, appeared after immunization. Small amounts of this component are present in normal horse serum, but the amount is increased on immunization.

In practice, comparison of electrophoretic patterns and of the areas under the respective peaks, rather than determination of actual electrophoretic rates, usually proves sufficiently informative.

When horses are immunized by subcutaneous injections of certain toxoids, or of rabbit serum albumin, egg albumin, hemocyanin, and the

* It is now realized that the different designations, T, β_2, and γ_1 all refer to one and the same electrophoretic mobility (237).

like, the resultant antibodies are primarily pseudoglobulins, and electrophoretic examination of the sera frequently shows an increase in the β_2- (or γ_1)-globulin component. But antibodies produced in the horse by repeated intravenous injections of bacteria, pneumococcal nucleoprotein, bacterial polysaccharides, and rabbit globulin are primarily euglobulins (water-insoluble). Electrophoretic examination of such sera frequently shows an increase in the γ-globulin, although the β_2-globulin may increase somewhat also. The antitoxins of the horse have been found mainly in the γ_1 (or β_2), although considerable amounts were present in the γ_2. Most of the horse antibody to *Hemophilus pertussis* was found in the γ_2 component (287). Marked influence of the route of injection in guinea pigs was found by Glover and Bishop (103).

Earlier workers reported that horse antidiphtheria toxin could exhibit the characteristics of either a $\beta(\beta_2)$- or a γ-globulin. These two kinds of antitoxin showed definite differences in serological behavior. Electrophoretically pure β_2 (or γ_1 or T) antitoxin flocculates more slowly than the γ antibody, and has a lower L_+/L_f ratio (terms explained on p. 679). The precipitate formed by the most rapidly flocculating mixture of antibody and toxin contains, when β_2 antitoxin is used, only half as much antibody per unit of toxin as when γ antitoxin is used (171,172). Beta$_2$ antitoxin has a higher electrophoretic mobility at pH 8.6, and a higher carbohydrate content, than the gamma of the same serum.

Human antitoxin is primarily associated with the γ_2-globulin fraction, in some individuals, with the γ_1, in others (179). Most individuals have some of both.

Rabbit antibody seems generally to have an electrophoretic mobility corresponding to that of the γ-globulins.

In 1953 a valuable technique for the study of immunoproteins was introduced by Grabar and Williams (115). The material to be studied, serum for example, is placed in a well in a layer of agar on a glass plate, and an electric field established. The proteins migrate in this field at different rates, much as in the Tiselius apparatus. The water of the gel moves towards the cathode, dragging protein, especially the slow gamma globulin, along with it. After the electrophoresis, antiserum (against whole serum, for example) is placed in a trough or troughs cut parallel to the line of electrophoretic migration. The antibodies in the antiserum produce precipitates with the partially or completely separated components of the electrophoresced mixture, producing arcs of precipitate whose shape and distance from the starting point are characteristic (*cf.* 41,114).

8. Relation of Electrophoretic Components to Fractions Obtained by Salting Out

Before the development of the Tiselius apparatus, it was common to characterize serum proteins by their solubility behavior, especially in concentrated solutions of salts such as sodium and ammonium sulfate. There is no simple exact correspondence between globulin fractions so obtained and the components of different electrophoretic mobilities. However, Cohn *et al.* (56) and Svensson (298) reported that there is a general parallelism between solubility and mobility, so that if relatively low salt concentrations are used, the slower moving component (γ) is precipitated completely before all of the faster components are. As a rule, however, globulin fractions thrown down by salting out consist of mixtures of components of all three mobilities. In particular the α- and β-globulins come down over a rather wide range of salt concentrations.

It has also been the practice of some workers to precipitate a "euglobulin" fraction from serum by dialysis (usually at physiological pH) against distilled water or by electrodialysis. Svensson (298) found that euglobulin so prepared generally contains all the electrophoretic components of total globulin; he thought that there was no clear correlation between mobility and water insolubility.

9. Molecular Weights

Since antibodies are globulins, they may be expected to have molecular weights appropriate to globulins. The available evidence, based on ultracentrifugal determinations (297), supports this prediction.

From the rate at which protein molecules sediment in artificial gravitational fields of the order of 200,000 to 300,000 times gravity, a value called the sedimentation constant can be calculated. This is usually abbreviated s_{20}, and expressed in units called svedbergs (1 svedberg has the dimensions of 10^{-13} second (79). If the diffusion constant D, and the partial specific volume $\bar{v}$ are known, the molecular weight is given by the equation

$$M = RTs_{20}/D(1 - \bar{v}\rho),$$

where R is the gas constant, T the absolute temperature, and ρ the density of the solvent.

The partial specific volumes of most proteins are between 0.70 and 0.75. The density of the solvent is usually nearly 1.00. This leaves the diffusion constant, D, which is actually the most difficult of all the necessary values to determine. It is customary to calculate, from measurements of sedimentation constant and diffusion constant, or in other ways (297,79), a "dissymmetry constant," or "frictional ratio," f/f_0 which is an index of the deviation of the molecule from sphericity. It can be shown that if we take $\bar{v} = 0.75$, $\rho = 1.00$, we have

$$M = 5150 \times (s_{20} \times f/f_0)^{3/2}$$

approximately. If the molecule were spherical, $f/f_0 = 1$ and this would reduce to

$$M = 5150 \times (s_{20})^{3/2}.$$

Since f/f_0 is actually always greater than 1.00, it can be seen that the use of this formula will give a minimal estimate of the molecular weight.

Molecular weights may be calculated conveniently by the nomogram of Wyman and Ingalls (330).

In order to appreciate the changes which occur on immunization, it is necessary to have some knowledge of the ultracentrifugal behavior of normal serum. Serum is a very complex mixture of proteins, but it is found that human or rabbit serum shows two main components in the sedimentation diagram, with sedimentation constants (s_{20}) of about 4.5 and 7.1. These correspond to the albumin and the globulins (see Table 2-1).

Antibodies are always found in the globulin fraction of serum, never in the albumin. Antibody activity seems to be found in three classes of globulins. The majority of the activity is due to a protein with a sedimentation constant of 7S, and this comprises 85–90% of the total. The second component, with a sedimentation constant of 19S, has been called

TABLE 2-1

Sedimentation Constants and Calculated Molecular Weights of Normal Serum Proteins

Species	Protein	Sedimentation constant, s_{20}	Partial specific volume, v	Frictional ratio, f/f_0	Molecular weight	
					Minimum (assuming spherical shape)	Corrected for asymmetry
Horse	Albumin	4.46	0.748	1.27	48,500	70,000
"	Globulin	7.1	0.745	1.44	98,000	167,000
"	"	18	0.74	2.0	394,000	930,000
Rabbit	Albumin	—	—	—	—	—
	Globulin	6.5	(0.745)	1.6	85,000	165,000
Man	Albumin	4.6	0.733	1.28	51,000	69,000
	Globulin	7.2	0.739	1.38	99,500	156,000

variously gamma-1M, beta-2M, and 19S-gamma. It has a much higher molecular weight, a greater electrophoretic mobility at pH 8.6, and contains about five times as much carbohydrate as the 7S antibody. See Table 2-2. The third component, gamma-1A or beta-2A, was detected after Grabar and Williams (115) introduced the technique of immuno-electrophoresis. It then became clear that another protein was present, antigenically related to the 7S and 19S gamma-globulins, but different in some respects.

TABLE 2-2

Characteristics of the Immunoglobulins
[Modified from Humphrey and White (157)]

Immuno-logical component	Electro-phoretic mobility	Sedimen-tation constant	Molecular weight	Carbo-hydrate content	Effect of breaking S—S bonds
IgG	From slowest γ to β or even α	7S	160,000	1.5–3%	None[a]
(These share antigenic determinants)					
IgM(β_2M or γ_1 globulin)	Fast γ- or β-globulin	19S	ca. 900,000	ca. 10%	Breaks into smaller units

[a] If peptide linkages are also broken the molecule falls apart.

It has been suggested that these proteins be called collectively *immuno-globulins* (143) and that the 7S, 19S, and gamma-1A fractions be referred to as IgG, IgM, and IgA, respectively. It seems likely that this notation will be generally adopted.

All species examined have IgG and IgM in their blood, but so far IgA has been demonstrated with certainty only in human serum. It has been suggested, however, (277,141) that the β_2-globulin, sometimes called T, that contains most of the antitoxic activity of the serum of a horse strongly immunized to diphtheria or tetanus toxoid, may be the equine equivalent of IgA. A rather similar protein has been reported in the serum of hyperimmunized guinea pigs (55).

At first there was some doubt whether the IgA fraction of the immune globulins contained any antibodies, but it now seems probable that the reagins (see p. 42) are associated with this fraction (55). We now know it is associated with a number of other types of antibody. In man, IgA has potent isoagglutinin activity (261,158a). IgA seems to be found preferentially in mucous secretions, and may be the immunoprotein active in defending linings of body cavities against foreign invaders.

Evidently the primary response to an antigen results in the synthesis of 19S gamma globulin (IgM), also called macroglobulin (289). This molecule consists of two kinds of polypeptide chain, a light chain (L_M) which may be common to antibodies of all classes, and a heavy chain (H_M) that is characteristic of the 19S antibody.

As immunization proceeds, the lymphoid tissue begins to produce 7S antibody (IgG). It is still not understood why this change in antibody

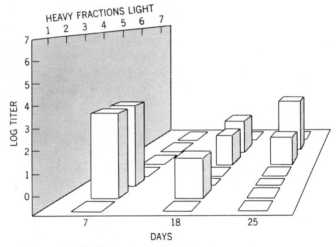

Fig. 2-5. Variations in heavy and light antibody as immunization progresses. (Courtesy Dr. Robert Schwartz.)

size takes place, but it could conceivably be related to the mechanism that Najjar (211) has been suggesting, and supporting with experimental evidence for some years, namely that the body's response to antibody–antigen complexes is different from its response to antigen alone. Uhr (310) suggests that the IgM antibody is "the first line of defense," consisting of molecules capable of being produced promptly in large numbers, a kind of antibody that can readily "coat" particulate antigens such as bacteria, but which is relatively inefficient in binding soluble antigens such as toxins. The 7S system, Uhr suggests, may be represented at first by a relatively small population of cells not capable of an immediate vigorous response, but able eventually to synthesize a more efficient antibody over

2. ANTIBODIES AND ANTIBODY SPECIFICITY

longer periods of time, and able to participate in the development of a persisting "immunological memory."

There is evidence that the synthesis of 19S antibodies is inhibited by the presence of 7S antibodies (271,94).

The way the size distribution of antibodies in the blood changes during immunization is shown in Fig. 2-5, based on work of Dr. Robert Schwartz (278).

Two forms of light chain (Type I and Type II) are recognized as occurring in man. The World Health Organization (48) has proposed designating these by the Greek letters kappa and lambda, and calling the immunoglobulins containing them Type K and Type L, respectively. The heavy chains they propose calling gamma, alpha, and mu. The way this proposal corresponds to current usage is shown below.

Present usage		World health proposal	Molecular formulae
7Sγ	type I	γGK or IgGK	$\gamma_2\kappa_2$
7Sγ	type II	γGL or IgGL	$\gamma_2\lambda_2$
γ_1A	type I	γAK or IgAK	$\alpha_2\kappa_2$
γ_1A	type II	γAL or IgAL	$\alpha_2\lambda_2$
γ_1M	type I	γMK or IgMK	$(\mu_2\kappa_2)n^{\circ}$
γ_1M	type II	γML or IgML	$(\mu_2\lambda_2)n^{\circ}$

n° in this case may be 6.

All six of these types of immunoglobulin have been shown to contain activity (87).

10. Size and Shape of Antibody Molecules

Perrin (240) showed that frictional ratios within the observed range could be produced by either of two kinds of asymmetry in the molecule, prolateness (cigar shape) or oblateness (disk shape). A study of the relaxation times of protein molecules (240) suggests that actual protein molecules are prolate spheroids. For this case Perrin found

$$f/f_0 = \frac{(1 - \rho^2)^{1/2}}{\rho^{2/3} \ln \left[\dfrac{1 + (1 - \rho^2)^{1/2}}{\rho} \right]}$$

where ρ is the ratio of the minor (b) to the major semi-axis (a), and ln means the logarithm to the base e.

From the experimentally determined values of f/f_0 the corresponding ratio b/a can be calculated. If we let $n = a/b$, the volume of a prolate ellipsoid is given by

$$V = 4\pi n b^3/3.$$

This must equal the volume of one molecule of the protein, which is

$$V = M\bar{v}/N,$$

where $\bar{v}$ is the partial specific volume of the protein and N is Avogadro's number.   Consequently, if in any given case we know the molecular weight and the frictional ratio, we can calculate $a/b = n$ from Perrin's equation, put the two expressions for V equal to each other, and solve for b, which gives us the dimensions of the protein molecule, assuming that it is a prolate ellipsoid of the indicated degree of asymmetry.   The results of such calculations, following those of Neurath (215) are shown in Table 2-3.

TABLE 2-3

Dimensions (Major and Minor Axes) of Some Antibody Molecules, with Normal Gamma Globulin and Serum Albumin for Comparison, Calculated from Frictional Ratios (f/f_0)

Source of antibody	Antigen	Molecular weight ($\times 10^{-3}$)	$\bar{v}$	f/f_0	Dimensions, $2a \times 2b$ (in A)	
					Unhydrated	Hydrated (0.2 g. H_2O/g. prot.)
Horse	Pneumococcus	920	0.715	2.0	945 × 47.0	897 × 54.5
Pig	"	930	0.744	2.02	981 × 47.3	928 × 54.7
Cow	"	910	0.725	1.98	930 × 47.4	882 × 55.0
Horse	Diphtheria toxin	165[a]	0.736	1.4	277 × 37.3	254 × 43.9
"	" "	90[b,c]	0.745	1.3	192 × 33.3	170 × 39.9
"	" "	90[d]	0.749	1.23	168 × 35.7	146 × 43.1
Rabbit	Pneumococcus	157	0.745	1.4	273 × 36.8	251 × 43.3
"	Ovalbumin	165	0.745	1.6	363 × 32.7	338 × 38.2
Monkey	Pneumococcus	157	(0.745)	1.5	315 × 34.3	291 × 40.2
Man	"	195	(0.745)	1.5	339 × 36.9	313 × 43.2
"	(Normal gamma globulin)	156	0.739	1.38	263 × 37.1	241 × 44.0
"	(Normal serum albumin)	69	0.733	1.28	169 × 30.8	151 × 36.8

Values of $\bar{v}$ in parentheses are assumed values.

[a] Published as 184×10^3 owing to error in diffusion constant (232).

[b] Published as 113×10^3 owing to error in diffusion constant (232).

[c] Water-soluble fraction after treatment with pepsin.

[d] Crystallized preparation obtained after trypsin treatment of antitoxin–toxin precipitates.

It makes some difference whether or not it is assumed that the protein molecule is hydrated in solution.   It is simpler to assume that it is not, and those who have previously published calculations of the dimensions of antibody molecules have made this assumption.   Oncley (228) has pointed out that it is more likely that protein molecules in solution carry with them a certain amount of bound water. If we assume, with Oncley, that a fair value for this water of hydration is 0.2 g. H_2O per gram protein, we obtain the dimensions shown in the last column of Table 2-3.

The difference made by hydration is mainly in the minor axis (thickness) of the molecule, and the difference in length is probably not great enough for the question to be decided by any other sort of measurement. It is of some interest, however, to note that estimates of the length of

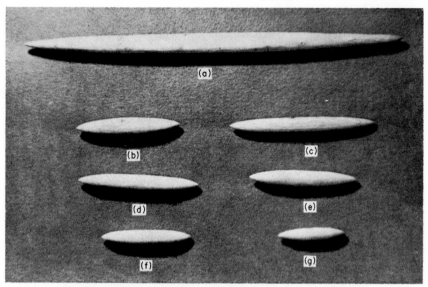

Fig. 2-6. Models of typical antibody molecules with serum albumin for comparison. (a) Horse antipneumococcus antibody; (b) horse antitoxin; (c) rabbit antipneumococcus antibody; (d) human antipneumococcus antibody; (e) rabbit antipneumococcus antibody; (f) human gamma globulin; and (g) human serum albumin. (Models made and photographed by the author.)

horse antipneumococcus and human gamma globulin by the method of double refraction of flow (228) agree better with the calculations for the unhydrated molecules.

The probable shape of antibody molecules has an important bearing on theories of antibody formation and antibody–antigen combination (see below, pp. 349 and 353).

Figure 2-6 shows a photograph of models of typical antibody molecules, with human serum albumin for comparison. The models were made on the basis of the dimensions of unhydrated molecules shown in Table 2-3.

Actual photographs (Fig. 2-7) suggest that the ends of antibody molecules are probably not as tapered as in the ellipsoids of revolution used as models. The taper is retained in models mainly because of the difficulties of treating mathematically the problems of hydrodynamic flow around a solid with blunt ends.

Malkiel (197) made electron micrographs of the precipitate of tobacco mosaic virus and its (rabbit) antibody, and found the molecules separated by a definite constant space, presumably the length of an antibody molecule. He estimated this distance as 270 A., in good agreement with the dimensions calculated above. More recently Hall *et al.* (119) and

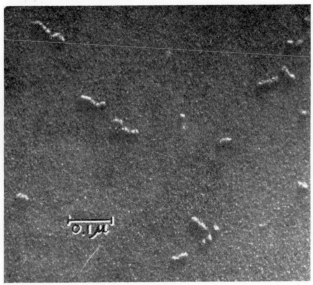

Fig. 2-7. Electron micrographs of rabbit antibody molecules. (Photograph by Dr. C. E. Hall.)

Höglund (55) and Almeida *et al.* (1), using the increased resolution of modern electron microscopes, have obtained photographs of antibody molecules whose estimated dimensions are also in good agreement with those calculated. One of Hall's photographs is shown in Fig. 2-7.

The properties of some typical human antibodies are shown in Table 2-4. Since most workers now think that the specifically reactive portion of the antibody molecule constitutes only a small portion of the whole, these findings are not surprising. It is therefore also not surprising that antibodies made to different antigens do not seem themselves to be different when they are injected into other animals as antigens (168).

TABLE 2-4

Properties of Some Human Antibodies [Modified from Humphrey and White (157)]

Antibody for	Stimulus	Electro-phoretic behavior	Sedimenta-tion constant (svedbergs)	Molecular weight
Pneumococcus (capsular polysaccharide)	Pneumonia	γ_2(slow)	7.4	190,000
Diphtheria toxin	Immunization	γ_2	ca. 6.7	160,000
Tetanus toxin	"			
Salmonella H	"	γ_2	ca. 6.8	160,000
" O	"	γ_1	18–19	900,000 1,000,000
Mumps virus	Disease			
Measles "	"	γ_2	ca. 6.8	160,000
Pollen reagins	Pollen inhalation, etc.	γ_1	ca. 6.8 or 18–19	160,00 or 900,000
Pollen blocking antibodies	"Desensitization" injections	γ_2	6.8	160,000
Rh (incomplete or blocking)	Sensitization in pregnancy	γ_2	ca. 6.8	160,000
Rh (saline agglutinating)	"	γ_1	18–19	900,000
A or B isoagglutinogens	?	γ_1	18–19 or 16	900,00 or 600,000
(Cold hemagglutinins)	Waldenström's macroglobulinemia	γ_1	16–19	330,000– 350,000
Wasserman reagin	Syphilis	γ_1	18–19	900,000
Rheumatoid factor	Rheumatoid arthritis	γ_1	22	>1,000,000
L.E. factor (see p. 538)	Lupus erythematosis	γ_1 or $_2$	7 or 19	160,00 or 900,000

11. Action of Enzymes on Immunoglobulins

Antibodies can be split by some proteolytic enzymes without losing their specificity. IgG from all species studied can be split by papain into three approximately equal-sized pieces. The two combining groups of the antibody remain, one on each of two apparently identical fragments. These two fragments have electrophoretic mobilities similar to those of the parent antibody (55). The third piece is quite different in nearly every way. For instance, unlike antibody, it can easily be crystallized (144). When prepared from rabbit antibody this portion is called III.

If instead of papain pepsin at pH 5 is used, one piece of molecular weight of about 100,000 is obtained, plus some smaller peptides. This 100,000 fragment will still precipitate with antigen. It can be split into two equal halves by reduction with thiol (220). Each of these halves has a combining group for the antigen, but will not precipitate it, and is very similar to the I and II pieces produced by papain. It therefore seems that the I and II pieces are held together by a disulfide bond that is split by the cysteine used to activate the papain (47).

12. Reduction of Immunoglobulins

Reduction of antibody liberates sulfhydryl groups without changing the activity. If the sulfhydryl groups are reacted with iodoacetamide and the mixture dialyzed against acetic acid, the molecule separates into com-

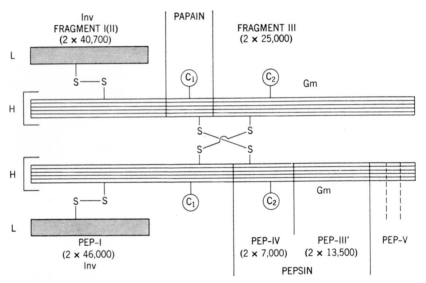

Fig. 2-8. Diagram showing supposed relationship of pepsin-digestion fragments (Pep-I, Pep-IV, Pep-III', and Pep-V) to the papain fragments I and III and to the heavy (H) and light (L) chains. C_1 and C_2 are carbohydrate moieties. The supposed positions of the papain and pepsin cleavages are shown. Each inter-heavy-chain disulfide bond is asymmetric with respect to its half-cystine groups. Measured molecular weights are given in parentheses. The value for Pep-IV is approximate and based on the mass recovery from a known quantity of γ-globulin; it does not include the contribution of the carbohydrate. The location of the Gm and Inv allotypic specificities (p. 72) is shown. From (55, 296a, and 310a).

ponents (55). The larger component is called H (heavy) and the smaller L (light). On the basis of such studies diagramatic structures for rabbit IgG such as that shown in Fig. 2-8 have been proposed (250,55,296a,310a).

Edelman's (94a) ideas of antibody structure and the sequence of steps by which it can be degraded to the various chains and fragments are illustrated schematically in Fig. 2-9. Note that the combining group, symbolized by the V-shaped groove in the ends of the molecule, involves both the heavy (γ) and light (κ or λ) chains. These ideas are also discussed by Nossal (224).

Immunoglobulins of all types, of all species tested, contain carbohydrate, as indeed do most proteins. Since evolution has selected structures,

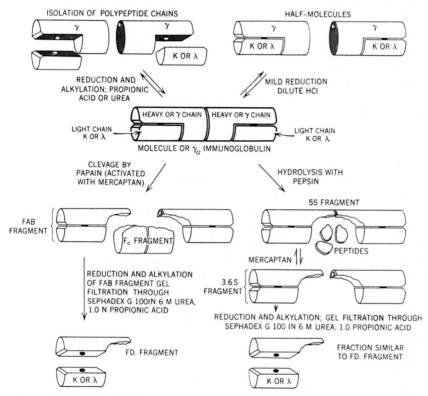

Fig. 2-9. Edelman's model of the γG immunoglobulin molecule and the sequence of steps leading to its degradation to the various chains and fragments. Disulfide bonds (—S—S—) and half-cystine residues are shown as small disks between the chains. Redrawn from Fougereau and Edelman (94a), with permission.

even on the molecular level, for usefulness, one supposes that this carbohydrate has some function. It is not likely, however, that the carbohydrate has anything to do with the antigen-combining power of the antibody. In the first place, there is no known mechanism by which carbohydrate attached to a protein could specifically influence the protein's combining power.   In the second place, papain pieces I and II can be obtained practically free of carbohydrate, but with their full power of combination with antigen (55).   The carbohydrate seems to be attached to the H chains.

13. Allotypy

Certain proteins of various species exist in more than one antigenic form, and injection of one of these varieties into an animal that does not possess it may cause the formation of antibodies.   These different antigenic forms, so far not distinguished by the usual physicochemical and chemical criteria, are called *allotypes*.

Rabbit gamma globulin exists in at least six different forms, and these differences seem to be hereditary.   A uniform notation has been proposed for these allotypes and the genes controlling them (72).

The existence of the *Gm* groups in man, discovered by Grubb (118) and studied by a number of workers (266) suggest the existence of such allotypes in man.

The *Gm* groups were discovered during work on the "rheumatoid arthritis factor."   This factor behaves like an antibody to human globulin, and will react with it in a visible way when the globulin is adsorbed on a surface or in some way made highly insoluble.   This reaction is inhibited by gamma globulin from some individuals but not others.   There are at least four *Gm* groups in human populations that can be distinguished in this way, and the differences are hereditary.   The differences seem to be present in 7S gamma-globulins but not in 19S, and to be associated with the "inert" part of the molecule (piece III) (see Fig. 2-8).

Another gamma-globulin locus for which allotypic variation is known is the *Inv* locus, which controls differences in the light chains, which is common to all classes of antibodies (see Fig. 2-8).   At present, only a few alleles are known at the *Inv* locus, but a large number have been detected at the *Gm* locus (296a).

Allotypes and blood groups (Chapter 5) are both examples of the polymorphisms that the complex forces of evolution create and maintain apparently in all species.

14. Chemical Nature and Analyses of Antibodies

Analyses of antibodies for amino acids have shown that their compositions are very much the same.   All the available evidence, furthermore, indicates that antibodies differ very little from ordinary serum globulins in chemical composition.

Some antibodies have some slight distinctive chemical and physical properties, however, as is shown by a number of observations. It has been found that the antipneumococcus antibody in horse serum has an isoelectric point of about 4.8 (307), whereas the isoelectric point of normal horse serum globulin ranges around 5.7 (137). (In the rabbit, antipneumococcus antibodies seem to have an isoelectric point of about 6.6, not far from that of normal rabbit globulins (101,137).

The antipneumococcus antibodies in horse serum usually have a much higher molecular weight than the majority of the horse serum globulins, although a small amount of globulin with this molecular weight is also found in normal horse serum, and probably also in human serum (see p. 63). Different antibodies have been found to vary in resistance to high pressures (23), heat, acid, or alkali (174,181). For instance, agglutinins for the flagellar antigens of the typhoid bacillus are more resistant to heat than are the antibodies to the somatic O antigens. Some antibodies seem to be more resistant than are normal globulins to the action of proteolytic enzymes (234,246,321).

In their susceptibility to the action of many denaturing and destructive agents, antibodies closely resemble proteins in general. Antibodies are generally said to be heat-stable in contrast, for example, to complement, which is heat-labile. These statements refer to heating to 56°C. However, antibodies in some sera, particularly human sera, may be considerably altered by heating to 56°C. for 4 hours. Kuhns and Pappenheimer (179) found that this treatment destroyed the skin-sensitizing power of the nonprecipitating type of human antitoxin, although this antibody remained capable of "blocking" the wheal and erythema produced by injecting into the skin mixtures of unheated antitoxin and toxoid. Heating to 56°C. for 4 hours destroyed the precipitating power of the precipitating type of antitoxin, but did not convert it into the skin-sensitizing type of antibody. Antibodies are usually destroyed by alcohol at room temperature, but in the cold this destructive action is much less marked. In fact, if the solutions are cooled and kept cold (about 0° to −10°C.), alcohol can be used to precipitate and fractionate antibodies (57). (See p. 82.)

15. Nature of Combining Groups of Antibodies

The fact that no striking chemical differences between antibodies or between antibody and normal globulin have yet been found suggests that the portion of the antibody molecule responsible for its specific combining properties cannot be very large. This idea is supported by the evidence, to be discussed in the next chapter, that the portion of the antigen with which an antibody combines is relatively small, at least compared with the size of a protein molecule. From experiments of Landsteiner and van der Scheer (184), Campbell and Bulman (40) computed that the specific combining site of an antibody is not larger than 700 square angstrom units (700 A.^{2}). Winkler (323) has suggested that the combining group of an antibody is a peptide containing not more than three or four amino acids.

It is believed that van der Waals forces are among the most important in the union between antibody and antigen. Since these are very short-range forces, being inversely proportional to the seventh power of the distance, the combining groups of antibody and antigen probably come into intimate contact to produce union as firm as that actually observed. (The free energy change $-\Delta F$ is of the order of 5 to 9 kcal. per mole. See Chapter 6.) Hooker and Boyd (151) suggested that the combining group of the antigen might fit into a cavity in the antibody. Pauling made a similar suggestion. Figure 2-11 shows Pauling's conception of antibody cavities corresponding to o-, m-, and p-aminoarsonic acid.

To what extent such a cavity in the antibody is merely schematic and to what extent it is real is not yet decided. The concept has certainly proved useful in thinking about antibody-antigen reactions.

Porter (248) found that a specific precipitate of ovalbumin and rabbit gamma globulin contained more histidine which was unreactive with Sanger's reagent, as opposed to reactive histidine, than did the gamma globulin alone. This could be interpreted as showing that an imidazole group was involved in the specific combining group of the antibody, or alternatively, since the ratio of antibody to ovalbumin in the precipitate was 3:1, that three iminazole groups of the ovalbumin were blocked by combination with antibody.

Pressman and Sternberger (253) found that the specific combining groups of antibody to p-azobenzoate or p-azobenzenearsonate ions, which are ordinarily destroyed by iodination, were protected when in combination with their homologous hapten. This seems to show that there is a grouping within these specific combining groups which is altered by iodination. This could be tyrosine or histidine, which would be oxidized. Pressman et al. (254) later produced evidence suggesting that the amino acid involved is tyrosine. Wagley et al. (311) suggested, from their observations on peroxidase inactivation of anti-Rh agglutinins, that the active groups of antibodies may contain tyrosine residues.

Singer (283) found that some of the groups of antialbumin antibody were protected from acetylation when the antibody was combined with its antigen, suggesting that amino groups form part of the combining groups

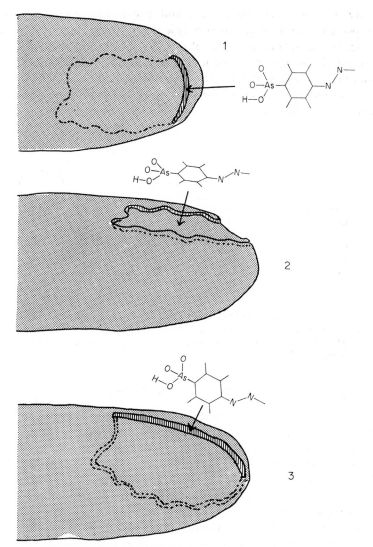

Fig. 2-10. Schematic drawings of three possible types of cavities (determinants) in antibody molecule: (1) invagination; (2) shallow trough; (3) slit trench.

of the antibody. Singer suggests that probably one ϵ-amino group of lysine is involved. *Cf.* Epstein and Singer (85a).

It has been shown that free amino groups are essential for the reactivity of some antibodies, at least (rabbit antiovalbumin and horse antipneumococcus). In the case of rabbit antiovalbumin the disulfide group seems unessential (249).

A number of years ago Hooker and Boyd (151) suggested that the correspondence of antibody to antigenic determinants might result in the presence in the antibody surface of a cavity specifically adapted in shape and size to the antigenic determinant and published illustrative drawings; this idea has also been put forward by Pauling (239). Drawings showing how such cavities could be adapted to *o-*, *m-*, and *p*-azophenylarsonic acid hapten groups are shown in Fig. 2-11, modified from Pauling and Itano (237).

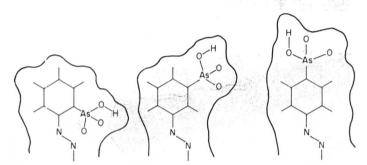

Fig. 2-11. Van der Waals outlines of *o-*, *m-*, and *p*-abozenzenearsonates. [From L. Pauling and H. A. Itano, eds., *Molecular Structure and Biological Specificity*, American Institute of Biological Sciences, Washington, 1957 (237) by permission of the editors and publishers.]

16. Valence of Antibodies

It is common to speak of a polyvalent vaccine, which contains more than one strain of a virus or microorganism, or of a polyvalent serum, which contains antibodies to more than one strain. The antibodies in such a serum are separate and distinct.

When we speak of the valence of an antibody we mean the number of specific combining groups for antigen which are present on one and the same antibody molecule.

The evidence available at present indicates that the valence of precipitating antibodies is two, or perhaps sometimes three (the large antibody molecules produced by the horse, pig, etc., constitute a special case). Some of the more convincing evidence follows.

Pappenheimer, Lundgren, and Williams (233) studied the products of the reaction of diphtheria toxin and horse antitoxin in the ultracentrifuge, and from the amounts of reagents added and the areas under the three peaks (representing free toxin, free antitoxin or pseudoglobulin, and the toxin–antitoxin complex) Pappenheimer later (231) calculated molecular ratios of toxin to antitoxin of 1.5 to 1, 2.1 to 1, and 1.6 to 1. Pappenheimer, Lundgren, and Williams (233) concluded that "the maximum valence of antitoxin for toxin is definitely greater than one and at most two."

Oncley et al. (229) determined by the ultracentrifuge the molecular composition of compounds of human serum albumin and horse antibody in the region of antigen excess, and found a limiting ratio of antigen to antibody of 2.00.

Singer and Campbell (285), using lightly iodinated bovine serum albumin as antigen, and rabbit antibovine serum albumin as antibody, made an ultracentrifugal and electrophoretic study of the soluble antibody–antigen complex that forms when an antigen is in excess (p. 354), and concluded that the principal complex was mostly AG_2. (A = antibody, G = antigen.)

Becker (14) by ultracentrifugal and diffusion determinations found for the antibody–antigen complex in the region of excess a value of 350,000, which corresponds to an average value of $AG_{1.8}$, suggesting that the antibody is bivalent.

From an electrophoretic study of the compounds formed with excess antigen (crystalline horse serum albumin and crystalline bovine serum albumin) and antibody, Marrack et al. (201) obtained evidence that antibody is bivalent. They suggested that the second valence of the antibody molecule is weak, and is reinforced, especially when antibody is in excess, by a nonspecific attraction due to the fact that the polar groups of the antibody are brought into opposition, and attract each other instead of water molecules.

Plescia et al. (245) estimated the ratio of antigen to antibody, in preparations made by dissolving the precipitate of human serum albumin and its (rabbit) antibody in excess antigen, by electrophoretic determination of the amount of free antigen, and calculation of the antigen–antibody ratio from the combined antigen. As the amount of antigen was increased, the limiting value for the human albumin system was effectively two (2.04). The bovine albumin system yielded a somewhat higher value, but the authors warn of difficulties in the analyses in the region of extreme antigen excess.

Eisen and Karush (82) plotted the reciprocal of the number of moles of hapten [p-(p-hydroxyphenylazo)phenylarsonic acid] per mole of antibody $(1/r)$ against the reciprocal of the free hapten concentration $(1/c)$, and by extrapolating $1/c$ to zero, obtained values of $1/r$ of 0.5 ± 0.05, thus indicating a valence of two for antibody.

Figure 2-12, taken from Goldberg and Williams (104) illustrates how the antibody valence found in various studies tends to a maximum valence of two.

These experiments seem to show that much antibody, at any rate, is bivalent. Is there any evidence that some antibody is trivalent, or multivalent, or that any is merely univalent?

Here we are on much less certain ground, but it does not seem likely there are any such antibodies.

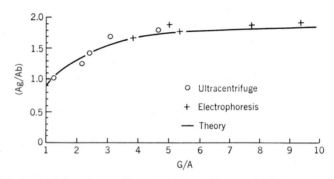

Fig. 2-12. Valence of antibody. From Goldberg and Williams (104).

When Heidelberger and Kendall (135) found antibody to ovalbumin which by itself would not precipitate but which could be carried down with precipitates made with ovalbumin and "good" antibody, it was natural to assume that this was because this "low grade" antibody had but a single combining group, and to call it univalent. Pappenheimer (230) found a nonprecipitating antibody in the serum of a horse immunized with crystalline ovalbumin. Then believing it must be univalent, he called it "incomplete," implying that it was antibody which for some reason had not developed its proper complement of two combining groups.

Nonprecipitating antibody of high titer has been demonstrated in the serum of certain allergic patients (178,179,231), and it has been suggested that such antibody is univalent.

Pappenheimer, although he believed some antibody may be univalent (232), also pointed out (231) that mere failure to precipitate or agglutinate is not sufficient proof that an antibody is truly univalent. Several workers [refs. in Nisonoff and Pressman (217)] have found that acetylation of antibodies may cause them to lose their power of precipitating with the antigen, and Nisonoff and Pressman (218) were able to show that in the case studied by them the combining power of the hapten had not been much affected. Horse antibody to a hapten has been found that is nonprecipitating but could be shown to be divalent and to have an even higher affinity for the hapten than did the precipitating antibody (175). It would have been better, obviously, to have used, instead of the question-begging term "univalent," the term "nonprecipitating" or "nonagglutinating" for such antibodies.

When anti-Rh antibodies were found which could combine with red cells without agglutinating them, they were called "incomplete" antibodies by Race, and Wiener has published diagrams in which they are represented as merely half an ordinary antibody molecule, with one instead of two combining groups. This was certainly a simple and obvious theory to explain the action of this new kind of antibody, but few of the Rh workers seem to have asked themselves if any other theory could explain the observations equally well, or if any experimental evidence existed that the "incomplete" (or "blocking") antibody were truly univalent.

Arguments against the theory that nonagglutinating antibody is univalent come from the observation (231) that such antibody will agglutinate cells suspended in plasma, albumin, normal globulin, or mixtures of these (see p. 284), or will agglutinate trypsinized cells. It is hard to see how treatment of the cells with trypsin, or the addition of albumin, could increase the valence of the antibody which is added later. It is now generally believed that these antibodies are bivalent (256,243,333,324).

Pirofsky and Cordova (243) suggest that "incomplete" erythrocyte antibodies, though bivalent, are unable to bring about agglutination because their tertiary (Fig. 2-13) structure somehow blocks at least one of their specific combining groups. They believe that the reason proteolytic enzymes (Chapter 5) make it possible for such antibodies to cause agglutination is that the enzymes change the tertiary structure in such a way as to remove the steric obstruction, and even suggest that antiglobulin sera and solutions of macromolecules such as serum albumin may act in a similar way.

Not only do most, perhaps all, antibody molecules possess two specific combining groups, but these groups seem practically always, perhaps always, to have the same specificity. It might have been expected that when more than one antigen was administered, or especially when an antigen possessing two or more antigenic determinants (and most antigens probably do) was given, antibody possessing one combining group for one of the antigenic determinants and one combining group for another would be produced. There is no good evidence that such antibody is ever formed (219).

It is probable that the antigen-combining sites of the antibody are on the H chain, but conclusive evidence is not yet available (55).

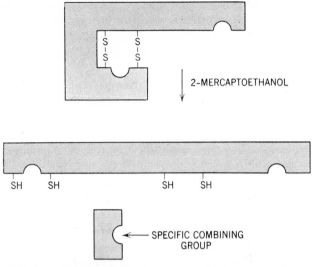

Fig. 2-13. Pirovsky and Cordova's idea how one combining group of 7S anti-Rh antibody might be prevented by steric hindrance from combining with erythrocytes, and hypothetical mechanism by which 2-mercaptoethanol converts "incomplete" to "complete" antibody (242a) .

17. Species Differences

Knowing that antibodies are merely slightly modified serum globulins, we should not expect that antibodies from different species directed towards the same antigen will show any particular similarity, but should rather expect these antibodies to show the differences characteristic of the plasma proteins of the animals which produced them. This has been found to be the case. We have already mentioned the formation of large amounts of high molecular weight antipneumococcus antibodies by the horse, cow, and pig, as opposed to the production by man, rabbit, and monkey of antibodies having predominantly the same molecular weight as normal globulin.

Antibodies also show species differences in regard to complement fixation. Horsfall and Goodner (153) found that with encapsulated pneumococci as antigen, guinea pig complement was fixed when the antibody was from rabbit, guinea pig, sheep, or cow, but not when it was from horse, man, mouse, cat, dog, or goat. These results are shown in tabular form by Kabat (167). Horse antibody did not fix guinea pig complement when the antigen was pneumococcus polysaccharide, C-substance, or polysaccharide from *Hemophilus influenzae,* but did with pneumococcus protein. Rabbit serum fixed guinea pig complement with all of these but C-substance. Dingle *et al.* (67) found species differences in this respect when they tested antisera to *H. influenzae* from horse, rabbit, and guinea pig, using complement from these animals.

The guinea pig often is a poor producer of precipitating antibodies, but it has been found (67) that immunization of these animals with *Hemophilus influenzae*, though practically no demonstrable agglutinins or precipitins were produced, gave sera with a surprisingly effective bactericidal power *in vivo*, suggesting that antibody was present, but, perhaps because of its physical characteristics, not able to precipitate or agglutinate.

The solubility behavior of antibodies is generally the same as that of the class of serum proteins to which they belong; but here, too, species differences are found.   Rabbit antibodies to proteins seem generally to appear first in the fraction of the globulins precipitated in 13.5 per cent sodium sulfate solution ("euglobulin"); then as immunization progresses they are found also in the fraction precipitated between 13.5 and 17.4 per cent ("pseudoglobulin I"); and only in powerful sera, as a rule, are they found in the fraction precipitated between 17.4 and 21.5 per cent sodium sulfate concentration ("pseudoglobulin II") (27).   During immunization these globulin fractions in the rabbit tend to increase in roughly this order.   In the horse, antibodies to toxins and other subcutaneously injected proteins tend to fall chiefly in the pseudoglobulin fraction, and the results of Reymann (262) suggest that it is this fraction which increases most on immunization.

Most horse antiprotein antibodies, such as antitoxin, differ from horse anticarbohydrate antibodies or rabbit, guinea pig, monkey, or human antibodies, in the way in which they react with antigen (58).   This difference is brought out by studies on the velocity of flocculation (21), or on the amount of precipitate formed by the addition of various amounts of antigen to a constant amount of serum (75).   In either case the difference is found to consist in the fact that an excess of the horse antiprotein antibody inhibits; that is, it slows down the rate of flocculation, and if present in sufficient amount, prevents the formation of a precipitate altogether (21,35).   Boyd (21) suggested that this difference depends at least partly upon the solubility differences just referred to; this suggestion will be discussed in Chapter 6.   It was also found that rabbit antibodies, if a large number of sera were examined, showed similar but less marked differences among themselves, suggesting that the various antibodies might differ in solubility.

Antitoxin in horse serum is usually found to some extent in all three globulin fractions as they are separated by salting out, and variations in its distribution among the fractions are found, even in the sera of the same animal examined by the same method at different times (99,189). The findings depend partly on the method of protein precipitation used. In the goat it seems that diphtheria antitoxin has chiefly the properties of a euglobulin (11). Felton (90) found the antipneumococcal antibodies in horse serum to be of euglobulin character.

It is a noteworthy fact that immune antibodies are never found to be albumins, no matter what their species origin.

Since antibodies are serum proteins, if they are injected into animals they are capable of acting as antigens and have the characteristic specificity of the serum proteins they so closely resemble. Conversely, it has been found that antibodies are precipitated specifically by antisera to the serum globulins of the proper species (150,288).

Rabbit antipneumococcus antibodies are more resistant to alkali than horse antibodies (167). Rabbit and horse antitoxins are more resistant to heat (56°C.) than are the human and guinea pig antitoxins (203). However, purified antibody (γ-globulins) can be heated to 56°C. without any effect whereas heating the crude serum would make it nonprecipitating (232). It is evident that the effect of heat is not a simple destruction of antibody. Perhaps in crude serum some complex formation takes place which renders the antibody incapable of precipitating.

Species differences in the electrophoretic mobilities of antibodies have been discussed in Section 7.

18. Methods of Purification

Methods of purifying antibodies fall into two main classes: (1) methods depending on the physical and chemical properties of antibodies; and (2) methods depending on the immunological properties.

(1) The nonspecific methods are generally procedures for separating the γ-globulins from the albumins and the other globulins. The purity of the resulting preparation depends mainly on the proportion of the γ-globulins that consist of the antibody desired.

Fractionation by precipitation with sodium or ammonium sulfate has generally been used for separation of the γ-globulin, and Campbell and Bulman (40) state that they still find this method the most convenient. Felton (89) and others employed alcohol in the cold for this purpose, and during World War II the Harvard group carried out extensive studies of this method. If proper equipment is available for working at low temperatures, this method offers many advantages and is inherently more powerful (302,156).

The Harvard group separated plasma proteins into four main fractions: I, containing most of the fibrinogen; II + III, containing most of the gamma globulin; IV, mostly α- and β- and some γ-globulin; and V, largely albumin. Reworking of the fractions and modifications of the procedures allowed these fractions to be split up still further. As a result, relatively pure γ-globulin prepared from pooled human plasma is commercially available, and contains many of the antibodies which occur in such pools of human blood.

The degree of purification obtained by such methods is much greater (*ca.* 12-fold) when the starting material is human or rabbit plasma or serum than when horse serum is processed. In the latter case the purification is only $2^1/_2$- to 3-fold.

In the commercial purification of antitoxins, a preliminary treatment with enzymes (see p. 69) before ammonium sulfate fractionation is sometimes used.

We have seen (p. 60) that certain antibodies are euglobulins, and Felton (89) and Northrop and Goebel (222) took advantage of this fact to separate out horse antipneumococcus antibodies in fairly pure state.

Gamma globulins can be separated from other serum proteins by electrophoresis, and small amounts of antibody can be concentrated in this way. Antibodies which are large molecules (*e.g.*, horse antipneumococcus) can be concentrated in the ultracentrifuge, and "heavy" and "light" antibodies can be separated by density gradient centrifugation. The amounts which can be handled by these methods are too small to be of much practical importance.

(2) The method by which antibody preparations of the highest purity to date have been obtained depends on their specific immunological characteristics. If the precipitate or "agglutinate" resulting from the reaction of an antiserum and its antigen is washed several times with adequate amounts of saline, the remaining compound consists almost entirely of antibody and antigen (plus small amounts of lipoids, complement, etc.). When it is possible to cause the reaction by which the compound was formed to reverse partially, free antibody may be obtained from such preparations.

A number of methods have been employed to set free some of the antibody. Dilute acid or alkali has been found effective in some cases; sodium chloride and glycine have been used, and in the case of agglutinated erythrocytes, warming and centrifuging while warm leaves free agglutinin in the supernatant (182). Acid dissociation has been used by Haurowitz *et al.* (127,128), Campbell *et al.* (39), and Campbell and Lanni (42).

Heidelberger, Kendall, and Teorell (136) were able to obtain purified antibody from precipitates made with horse antipneumococcus antibody and specific pneumococcus polysaccharide, by treating the precipitates with salt solutions of concentrations ranging from 0.1 to 1.79M. High salt concentrations shift the equilibrium, freeing antibody which can then be separated from the precipitate by centrifuging. Chow, Lee, and Wu (53) obtained purified antibody by dissolving the precipitate in dilute alkali and then adding acid to adjust the pH to about 9.5. A precipitate appeared, and the mixture was allowed to stand in the cold overnight; then sufficient acid and NaCl were added to make the mixture isotonic and bring the pH to 7.6. Centrifugation gave a solution containing 40 to 60 per cent of the antibody, which was 80 to 90 per cent precipitable by the specific polysaccharide.

Another method, applicable in certain cases, is to destroy the antigen in the specific antibody–antigen complex without damaging the antibody, or at least without serious damage to it. Ramon and Locke, Main, and Hirsch thus recovered antitoxin from toxin–antitoxin precipitates; Sumner and Kirk (173,295) obtained antibody from urease–antiurease precipitates by making the urease insoluble by treatment with acid.

Some of the best early results were obtained with horse antipneumococcus antibody. Felton (91) dissolved the precipitates made with antibody and the specific polysaccharide in calcium or strontium hydroxide. The polysaccharide was then precipitated by addition of calcium or strontium chloride and phosphate with adjustment of the pH; the antibody remained in solution. It could be further purified by precipitation through dialysis and resolution in salt solution.

Parfentjev (234) found that treatment of diphtheria antitoxic serum with pepsin, until 70 to 80 per cent of the protein was rendered noncoagulable by heat, resulted in considerable purification, giving a product a high proportion of which was specifically antitoxic (see 315). Similar treatment of horse antipneumococcus serum destroyed practically all the mouse protective power, although considerable precipitating power remained (276). It was found by Grabar (108) that digested horse antipneumococcus (types I and II) antibody combines with twice as much polysaccharide per milligram of antibody nitrogen as does the normal antibody. Petermann and Pappenheimer (241) found, no matter what the molecular weight of the antibody in the starting material for this product, a sedimentation constant of 5.2, suggesting a final molecular weight of less than 100,000.

Sternberger and Pressman (293) have reported a method for the purification of antibody which they state will have general applicability. The method involves the treatment of the antigen with diazotized p-aminobenzenarsonic or o-aminobenzoic acid. The coupling does not destroy the native reactivity of the antigen. This coupled antigen is then reacted with its antibody in the usual way to form a precipitate. By treatment of the washed precipitate with saturated calcium hydroxide solution and calcium aluminate, the azo-antigen is precipitated, leaving the antibody. The yields were fairly low, less than 20 per cent, but the antibody was of fair purity. This method is obviously of limited used with antibodies which are very susceptible to denaturation at high pH. A better general method has been proposed by Singer, Fothergill, and Shainoff (286). It involves treating the protein antigen with N-acetylhomocysteine, which introduces a number of sulfhydryl groups, but does not seriously affect the ability of the antigen to precipitate with its antibody. The washed specific precipitate is dissolved in a glycine–H_2SO_4 buffer at pH 2.4 and the bifunctional organic mercurial, 3,6-bis(acetoxymercurimethyl)-dioxane is added. The sulfhydrylated antigen is crosslinked and thus polymerized by the mercurial by the formation of $-S-Hg-Hg-S-$ bonds, and precipitates, leaving most of the antibody in solution.

Another method which may have wide applicability has been reported by Campbell (43). It depends upon reducing the antigen to an insoluble state by coupling to finely ground cellulose through an azobenzyl ether linkage. The material was then used in the form of an absorption column and the antiserum run through this. The antibody could be eluted from the column with acid (final pH 3.5). Yield and purity were calculated to be 100 per cent, and the material of the column could be used again. Campbell (200) also used the commercially available p-aminobenzylcellulose, Cellex-PAB, for coupling to the antigen. The antibody was dissociated by use of a glycine–HCl buffer of pH 3.0. The yield was 46–70 per cent, and 83 per cent of the recovered protein was precipitable with the specific antigen.

Isliker (160) has developed a method of purification of antibodies using an absorption column of resin to which antigen has been irreversibly coupled. Stroma from human red cells were mixed with sodium tetraborate and formaldehyde and mixed with a suitable resin. Normal isoagglutinins absorbed on a column of this coupled resin could be partially eluted by solutions of N-acetyl-D-glucosamine and D-galactose, and the resin could be used again.

By treatment of the specific precipitate of horse antipneumococcus type I antibody and its polysaccharide antigen with acid potassium phthalate and subsequent fractionation with ammonium sulfate. Northrop and Goebel (222) obtained a preparation of antibody completely precipitable by its homologous antigen. Part of this preparation could be crystallized in poorly formed rounded rosettes, but this part was not any purer than the remainder and the process was accompanied by the formation of some insoluble protein.

Anti-hapten antibodies can generally be separated from the specific precipitate by use of an excess of free hapten. If the hapten–protein complex used in making the precipitate is relatively insoluble, the solubilized antibody can be separated and dissociated from the hapten by dialysis or use of a column of material such as Sephadex (crosslinked dextran). Karush and Marks (169) and Bassett, Beiser and Tanenbaum (12) have used such methods.

Pope (246) studied the effect of varying conditions, pH, time of digestion, etc., on the isolation of antibody, by digestion with proteolytic enzymes, and found that antibodies are readily split by short digestion into an inactive portion, which is easily denatured by heat, and an active portion, which is more resistant. The practical value of such methods depended largely on the elimination of nonspecific, antigenic proteins which they brought about. The active portions remaining seem to be nonantigenic, or at least poor antigens, so that the danger of sensitizing a patient to horse serum, and possibly of causing serum sickness or anaphylactic shock, was diminished.

Northrop (221) reported the preparation of diphtheria antitoxin in a form which satisfies the criteria for a pure protein, by digesting away the toxin of a toxin-antitoxin precipitate with trypsin. The resulting antitoxin preparation has been obtained in several instances as crystals. The purified antitoxin was completely precipitable by diphtheria toxin. The homogeneity and freedom from denaturation of this preparation were probably due to the use of concentrated solutions during as much of the process as possible. Some modification of the antitoxin by the enzyme had probably taken place, however. Rothen (268) found that antitoxin purified by means of enzymes had a sedimentation constant of 5.5, whereas that which had not been so treated had a sedimentation constant of 6.9. This probably indicates that the enzyme-treated material has a somewhat lower molecular weight.

Pope (247) does not believe that Northrop's product was homogeneous, in spite of its crystallizability and constant solubility, as he has isolated antitoxin with a 50 per cent higher specific activity per gram of protein. Pope used the antigens of toxin-free cultures of diphtheria to remove nonantitoxin antibodies from pepsin-treated antitoxin. Pope's material was repeatedly treated with proteolytic enzymes.

19. Formation of Antibodies

Place of Formation

Ever since White (316) and Coons (63) demonstrated the fact immuno-histochemically, it has been known that plasma cells may contain specific antibody. Thus it seemed likely that antibody was synthesized here. Since then several lines of evidence have confirmed this idea:

(*a*) The appearance of plasma cells in tissue that has been stimulated antigenically is followed by an elevation of the antibody level in the circulation (86,214) and in the stimulated tissue (177,96). (*b*) The absence of plasma cells is correlated with lower levels, or absence, of circulating antibody (280). (*c*) Plasma cell tumors make specific gamma globulins (251). (*d*) Plasma cells possess the morphologic equipment (microsomes and ribosomes) that is known to be capable of producing protein that reaches the circulation (33). This equipment is casually related to the synthesis of antibody (84).

Unfortunately, the histological origin of the plasma cells is still unsettled. The ultrastructure of the plasma cell is unique and does not suggest any relation to the lymphocyte or the macrophage. Some believe these are all derived from a common ancestral cell (86,116), some believe they are from perivascular advantitial cells (2), and some from lymphoid cells (296), but no conclusive evidence has been produced. For serologists the question is perhaps a secondary one anyhow.

How typical plasma cells look is well shown by color photographs in an article by Nossal (224).

Other types of cell have been found to contain gamma globulin or antibody. In the thoracic duct lymph and in the spleen of antigenically stimulated animals there are found a few cells, cytologically indistinguishable from small lymphocytes. A few of these (less than 1 per cent) have antibody in their cytoplasm (88). In human liver a cell has been found that under the electron microscope seems to be a phagocyte and which contains gamma globulin (273). Gamma globulin has also been observed in other types of cells, but whether it was synthesized there or taken up from the circulation (88) is not known.

Immunological and morphological evidence exists that there are at least two types of plasma cells involved in antibody formation, one apparently producing 7S gamma globulin, and one producing 19S gamma globulin (88).

There is good evidence that the site of antibody synthesis in the cell is in the rough ergastoplasm, between the parallel double membranes. Using Singer's ferritin protein conjugate technique, Rifkind *et al.* (265) demonstrated the presence of gamma globulin in these structures, and, using ferritin as an antigen, De Petris *et al.* (64) demonstrated antibody there. No evidence exists that antibody is synthesized in any of the other organelles of the cell (88), although Coons *et al.* (63) observed the *presence* of antibody in the nuclei of a few lymphoid cells in immunized mice.

It is known that particulate antigens are taken up by the phagocytes (Chapter 1). Even today little is known of what happens between this event and the manufacture of antibody. Harris (126) suggested that after phagocytosis, the antigen might be digested and soluble antigen released. Recent studies (327,100) on the fate of bacterial antigen taken up by macrophages tend to confirm this. Gill and Cole (100) suggest that it may be the macrophage that provides the stimulus for antibody formation by modifying particulate antigen and that it may be the macrophage that recognizes the difference between "self" and "non-self." Fishman's work suggests that, after ingesting antigen, macrophages release an RNA-ase sensitive material (probably either RNA or an RNA-antigen complex) that stimulates a second line of cells (lymphocytes?) to develop into plasma cells.

Soluble antibody–antigen complexes are evidently also taken up by the cells of the reticuloendothelial system, and can be shown, by the fluorescent antibody technique, to be present in the Kupffer cells of the liver (15).

The site of antibody formation depends to a considerable extent upon the site of injection of the antigen (122). If the antigen is injected in such a way that it is localized in a certain part of the body, antibodies are formed at the site of injection and in the regional lymph nodes. Thus injection of an antigen into the foot pad of a rabbit leads to the formation of antibody in the popliteal lymph nodes and the appearance of antibodies in the lymph which drains the lymph node (291). Even the secondary response following the injection of a second dose of antigen remains localized, for White (317) found that rabbits injected in the left foot pad with diphtheria toxoid and in the right with ovalbumin produced, when injected after an interval of 7 months with a mixture of both antigens, anti-diphtheria toxoid in the lymph node of the left foot pad and anti-ovalbumin in the right.

If an antigen is injected intravenously, so that it spreads throughout the whole body, the evidence indicates that antibody formation is in the spleen and lymphoid tissue (204).

Antibody formation is not limited to intact organisms. The organs and tissues of immunized animals are able to continue the production of antibodies *in vitro* (122,305,291).

Study of antibody formation by single cells from doubly immunized animals [refs. (195,225)] reveal that the great majority of the cells form only one of the antibodies, and only 1–2 per cent of the active cells form both.

Although many attempts have been made to induce antibody formation by adding antigen to cells *in vitro,* it is by no means certain that this has ever been accomplished (291).

Burnet introduced the term "immunologically competent cells" to include all cells of the body able to respond to an antigenic determinant, whether by producing antibody, developing the delayed type of hypersensitivity, or rejecting homografts.

The thymus was long considered a superfluous organ like the human appendix. More recently, however, it has been discovered [review in (106)] that in the mouse the thymus is a key source of cells or humoral substances (207), or both, essential to the normal maturation of the peripheral lymphoid tissues and to the development of normal immunological capabilities. A similar situation, but sometimes not so marked, exists in other species, and it is supposed that the thymus is essential in man, since patients who are immunologically deficient (hypogammaglobulinemic and lymphopenic) often have vestigial thymuses almost completely lacking in lymphoid tissue. The patients are unusually susceptible not only to bacterial infections but, unlike patients who are merely "agammaglobulinemic," to virus and fungus diseases. Also, some children with the disease ataxia-telangiectasia, who are unusually susceptible to infection of the sinuses and lungs, have been found at autopsy not to have a thymus (106).

It has been shown that in rats thymectomized early in life there is partial or complete suppression of several types of immune response, such as delayed hypersensitivity (skin sensitization to tuberculin), experimental allergic encephalomyelitis, and skin homograph [Chapter 12 (rejection, 312)].

Effect of Various Factors on Antibody Formation

The ability of animals to form antibodies depends on their genetic constitution, age, sex, and hormonal status. Young infants are deficient in antibody-forming power (38,78), and there is some evidence that the ability to form antibodies falls off in old age (117,13,304,269).

There have been many studies of the effects of cortisone (11-dehydro-17α-hydroxycorticosterone) and ACTH (anterior adrenocorticotropic hormone). Since the adrenal cortex and cortisone may influence phagocytic activity, depress inflammatory response, and possibly depress the functions of the reticuloendothelial system, it is apparent that the effect on immune processes can be great. In some cases, certainly, treatment with cortisone lowers resistance to infection, as with tuberculosis, favoring a wider distribution of lesions.

Malkiel and Hargis (199) found that ACTH caused a marked diminution, and cortisone an almost complete suppression, of precipitin production in rabbits being injected with bovine serum albumin. Hayes (129) found that cortisone delayed local antibody formation in loose connective tissue of mice. Patients with pneumococcal pneumonia, or those vaccinated with pneumococcal polysaccharides while being treated with cortisone or ACTH, proceeded to produce antibodies. However, antibodies present from a previous vaccination were decreased as much as 25 per cent by cortisone. On the whole the effect of these substances on the immune processes seems unfavorable. The marked alleviatory action of cortisone and ACTH in rheumatoid arthritis (p. 538) may actually be another example of this, if this disease is, as suggested in Chapter 13, possibly the result of the development of "autoantibodies" against the patient's own tissues.

The effect of adrenocortical hormones in infection and immunity was reviewed by Kass and Finland (170).

Chloramphenicol inhibits antibody production, probably by interfering with the messenger RNA necessary for protein synthesis (3).

X-radiation of animals prior to or near the time of immunization will interfere with antibody production, but radiation given a few days after injection has much less effect (202,70). If antigen is injected at the time of irradiation, or in some cases up to 12 hours later, antibodies may be produced, although somewhat delayed in appearance (299,257). Nitrogen mustard has been found to suppress antibody formation (242,290). The temperature at which animals are kept may influence antibody production. Ipsen (159) found mice to develop better immunity to tetanus toxoid at 35°C. than at 25° or 6°C.

It would seem logical that antibodies, being proteins, would not be formed as well by nutritionally depleted persons, but experimental studies show on the contrary that such persons are capable of producing antibody as well as or better than well-nourished controls, and studies made on prisoners of war do not suggest deficient antibody production (8). If protein deficiency is maintained long enough, however, ability to synthesize antibody is impaired (45,46,325,326).

Rate of Formation and Destruction

Antibody does not appear at once in the circulation following exposure of the animal to an antigen, nor does the animal become at once immune. Instead there is a latent period, during which time the immune mechanism is probably elaborating the antibodies which will appear later. The time required for the production of immunity may depend on the amount of antigen administered (208). Ehrlich (80) found that the immunity of mice to ricin, induced in this case by feeding, set in suddenly on the sixth day. In general, after a single injection of an antigen, there is a sudden appearance of antibody in the blood at the end of a period of several days (4), although traces of antibody have been reported 8 to 10 hours after injection of antigen (122). The concentration then increases, reaching a maximum in about a week. After this time, if no further injections are given, the concentration begins to fall off, rapidly at first, more gradually later, although weeks or years may elapse before the antibody content of the circulation falls to zero.

If another injection is given before this happens, the antibody present is temporarily almost or completely neutralized, but quickly begins to increase again as the introduced antigen is eliminated and new antibody is manufactured, usually to reach a higher level then before (Fig. 2-14). This may be repeated a number of times and the antibody level and the rapidity with which it is restored increase, until a limit is reached. The time which

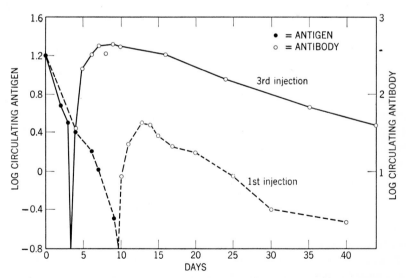

Fig. 2-14. Curves of fall in circulating antigen and rise in circulating antibody in rabbit injected with isotopically labeled bovine serum albumin, showing difference in primary and secondary response in the same animal. From Dixon, Maurer, and Deichmiller (68).

must elapse before subsequent injections fail to result in a final higher antibody level varies from a matter of weeks (27) to months, depending on the species. Antibody in immunized animals does not usually remain at high levels without periodic injections, but Pappenheimer (232) found nonprecipitating antitoxin to remain remarkably high for months in allergic individuals injected with toxoid, and Heidelberger *et al.* (131) found that antipneumococcus antibodies, produced in response to pneumococcus polysaccharide, persisted at presumably protective levels for considerable periods of time.

The highest level of antibody which can be produced by injections by the ordinary routes depends upon the antigen and upon the animal. Within a given species, some individuals are better antibody producers than others. With rabbits which have been injected repeatedly, it is likely that the highest concentration of antibody is present in the blood about 5 to 7 days after the last injection. If injections are continued too long, the resulting antibody level of the blood may begin to decline. This may require only weeks for rabbits, or years with horses.

The absolute rate at which the organism can turn out antibody molecules is still uncertain, but in view of Bjørneboe's observation (19) of immune rabbits in which all the globulin of the blood consisted of antibody, it seems that the rate may be at least as great as that at which the body can replace the globulins as they disappear at the normal rate from the blood. It has been observed (193) that a dog weighing 11 kg. can easily produce 13 g. of plasma proteins per week, or about 170 mg. per kg. of body weight per day. The rate of production by the antibody-forming tissues themselves is much greater than this. In experiments with rabbit tissues (spleen, lymph node) removed at the height of the secondary response, rates of antibody production in the range 256–1900 mg. per kg. of tissue were observed, and transplanted lymph nodes in man have produced 10 g. antibody per kg. of tissue (291). The time required for the synthesis of an antibody molecule may be only a few minutes (291).

Studies with isotopically labeled amino acids (123) have shown that these amino acids are incorporated into antibodies at about the same rate as into normal serum globulins, but they do not become part of the preformed antibodies in passively immunized animals. Antibodies are therefore formed from the free amino acid pool of the cell (291).

Evidence has been presented which indicates clearly (140,268) that the longer persistence of antibody in the circulation of actively as opposed to passively immunized animals is due to the continued production of antibody.

Studies with isotopically labeled homologous antibodies and normal globulins (68,123) show that antibodies are rapidly destroyed, just as they are rapidly formed. The half-life of an antibody molecule is apparently influenced by the metabolic rate of the animal, and by the gamma globulin level at the time. In man the average half-life of an antibody molecule is 15 days, in the cow, 21 days, in dogs, 8 days, in rabbits, 5 days, in guinea pigs, 4.5–6 days, and in mice 2 days. In immunized animals still producing antibody, this destruction affects the observed levels only slowly, when the rate of production of new antibody begins to fall off.

The Anamnestic Reaction

When a specific antibody has once been produced by an animal as a result of contact of the tissues with a foreign protein, the amount of circulating antibody gradually decreases with the passing of time after contact ceases until, at length, none at all can be detected. If, now, the antigen enters the tissues again, the specific antibody will appear in the circulation and will reach a given level in a much shorter time than was required following the first contact (263). It was recognized long ago by von Pirquet (244) that when anaphylactic hypersensitivity has once been established, it will gradually wane if there is no further contact with the antigen, but reintroduction of the antigen causes the hypersensitive state to appear again in a decidedly shorter time than was required at first. Bacterial hypersensitiveness is also rapidly returned to a high level by fresh contact of the tissues with the specific bacteria (9,322). This is called the anamnestic ("recollection") reaction (44).

The term is also applied to renewed production of antibodies following contact with related antigens. A number of workers have also reported renewed production of antibody following injection of quite unrelated antigens (61,73,308 and even of nonantigenic substances (227,314). Modern work has not supported such claims.

The anamnestic response shows that the body has an "immunological memory." It was formerly supposed that this was simply the persistence of antigen, or fragments of antigen, in the antibody-forming cells, but more recent studies have made this doubtful. For one thing, plasma cells, now thought to be the principal site of antibody formation, have a limited life span, and it is not easy to visualize the transmission of antigen or antigen fragments from a cell that has taken it up to a daughter cell. For another, the antibody produced during the secondary response is frequently different, e.g., 7S instead of 19S.

Antigen can persist in the body in detectable amounts for at least 100 days (146), and it has been calculated from observed rates of disappearance that about a microgram of some antigens would be present in the liver of an injected rabbit after 3 years. Antibody production, however, can go on as long as 8 years after an injection of antigen (157). It thus still seems uncertain whether immunological memory is due to the persistence of antigen.

Smithies (289) has recently suggested another mechanism that is perhaps more plausible. Since it has been shown that many viruses can alter the genetic constitution of the bacteria they attack, and recent work with the Rous sarcoma virus shows that an RNA virus can even induce a cell transformation that is DNA mediated (303), Smithies postulates that the acquisition of immunological memory is due to the insertion of some of the nucleic acid of the replicating "antibody virus" into the genetic material of the cell in which the antibody virus is being replicated. He postulates further that (a) the transduction involves sufficient portions of both the L_M and H_M genes to bring about preservation of the specificity of the antibody combining site; (b) there are several different genetic receptors in such cells, each carrying information for the synthesis of the invariant portions of the class of antibody concerned, such as IgG, IgA, etc.; (c) this genetic material does not contain information for the synthesis of specific combining groups, until this information is transduced into it by the antibody virus.

Mechanism of Antibody Formation

We must now ask ourselves: How does the body manage to produce relatively large amounts of globulin molecules, so precisely adapted to combining with definite chemical groupings?

It is not easy to answer this question. A number of hypothetical mechanisms of antibody formation have been proposed, of which we may mention (a) the cast-off receptor theory of Ehrlich, (b) the template theory of Haurowitz, (c) the template theory of Pauling, (d) the "trained enzyme" theory of Burnet, and (e) the "natural selection" theory of Jerne, and (f) the "clonal selection" theory of Burnet (see below).

(a) According to the theory of Ehrlich, antibodies are simply natural preformed receptors of the body cell for various chemical groupings. When the number of such chemical groupings coming in contact with the cell is increased (antigenic stimulus), an excess of such receptors is formed. Some are cast off into the circulation and constitute circulating antibody. This theory was given up when it was found that antibodies could be formed against artificial groupings with which the organism had never come in contact in the course of its evolution and for which it could hardly be expected to possess preformed receptors.

(b) According to Haurowitz (123), a template, which (as the result of the presence of a molecule of antigen) reflects in reverse the significant portions of the structure of the antigen held in the expanded configuration by polar forces of a molecule of nucleic acid, attracts to itself molecules of amino acids from which a duplicate of itself is built up and cast off into the circulation. This theory seems to require the persistence of small amounts of antigen throughout antibody formation, although this might not strictly be a necessary part of the theory.

(c) Pauling's theory (235) was a modification of that of Haurowitz and differs mainly in Pauling's supposition that preformed normal globulin, becoming unfolded ("denatured") at the ends of the polypeptide chain (he assumed that they have accessible to them a number of about equally stable folded configurations), fold up (are "renatured") on contact with a molecule of antigen and thus become specific antibody. This theory definitely presupposed the persistence of antigen.

Although Pauling (236) claimed to have made antibody *in vitro* (125) in confirmation of his theory, this claim was never confirmed, and the theory was abandoned when it was found that antibody is not formed from pre-existing gamma globulin, but synthesized *de novo* from the amino acid pool of the body (291).

(d) Burnet and Fenner (38) suggested that enzymes involved in the destruction of normal body constituents become adapted to acting on similar molecules of foreign substances, are self-reproducing, and continue to multiply after the elimination of the antigen. Antibodies are supposed to be enzymatically inactive partial replicas of these adapted enzymes. Burnet has abandoned this theory in favor of his "clonal selection theory" (see below).

(e) Jerne (163) suggested that globulin molecules of a very wide variety of configurations and therefore of specific reactivities are continually being produced by the body. Some of these molecules happen to have configurations complementary to surface groups of some antigens; these are the "natural antibodies." When an antigen enters the circulation, it combines with those molecules which happen to have the corresponding specificity. These combinations are phagocyted and transported to the antibody-forming cells. There the antigen is dissociated and probably discarded, and the cell—for reasons not specified—proceeds to make more globulin molecules like those just introduced. The casting off into the circulation of these new specific globulins constitutes the phenomenon of antibody rise.

Jerne's theory, in spite of having been proposed fairly recently, has found considerable favor. Talmage (300,301) considers it essentially similar to the theory of Ehrlich but suggests that the replicating elements are cells rather than extracellular protein.

(f) The clonal selection theory, developed by Burnet (36,37) and Lederberg (188), is a modification of Jerne's theory.

According to Burnet, antigen combines with specific receptors on the surface of lymphocytes and thereby stimulates these particular cells to settle down and multiply in an appropriate tissue. The result of this replication of selected cells is the production of more of the type of globulin molecule with which the antigen combined in the first place.

Burnet and Lederberg both assume that the antibody-forming cells are "hypermutable," i.e., that normally there are frequent changes in the types of globulin molecules a cell is genetically capable of producing. Thus, all possible types of gamma globulin molecules would generally be represented in the circulation *with the exception of* those produced by those cells that happened to combine with antigen while they were still immature; this is supposed to result in the elimination of such cells. This additional assumption is made to account for "acquired immunological tolerance."*

Any attempt to revive the Ehrlich theory must take account of the objection that antibodies can be formed to antigens for which the body can hardly be expected to have preformed natural receptors. Talmage (301) tries to do this by supposing that sharp specificity, when observed, results from a mixture of globulin molecules, not all alike, each with some degree of specificity for the antigen or hapten. With the help of a diagram (Fig. 2-15) and by thermodynamic calculations he tries to show how the "information" and net specificity of a combination of different globulin molecules could be greater than those of any one type of globulin alone. Talmage suggests that the average "monospecific" serum contains ten to 100 different kinds of globulin molecules and points out that on such a basis the assumption of about 5000 different possible natural globulins could account for approximately 3×10^{120} different specificities. Since this number is larger than the number of electrons the universe is supposed to contain, Talmage believes it is satisfactorily large. In fact, Haurowitz (124) estimated that not more than 50,000 different antibodies exist.

Of the theories just discussed, the theories of Ehrlich, Pauling, and Haurowitz are what are now called "instructional" theories, and the theories of Burnet and Jerne are "selectional" theories. Opinion seems to be veering in the direction of the "selectional" theories.

Haurowitz (264), Campbell (270), Nossal (223) and Sterzl (294), how-

---

* When animals are injected with an antigen during fetal life, or in some cases shortly after birth, they may be incapable of responding immunologically to this antigen as adults (see Chapter 12).

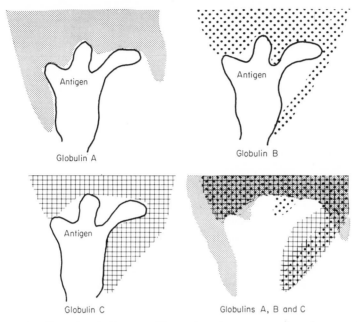

Fig. 2-15. Two-dimensional diagrams illustrating the concept that the contained information and net specificity of a combination of three different globulin molecules may be greater than that of one globulin alone. [Redrawn from Talmage (301).]

ever, have presented evidence that continued antibody production is possible only in the presence of persisting antigen. These authors, especially Haurowitz, strongly favor the instructional theories.

The present writer must admit to a prejudice in favor of the older ideas of antibody formation [cf. (125a)]. Like Haurowitz, I find it "difficult to believe that the body should contain preformed antibodies against azophenylarsonate, azophenyltrimethylammonium ions, and other artifacts of the chemical laboratory." So in spite of the present vogue of the "selection" theories, I incline to believe that they will ultimately prove invalid.

Smithies (289) has proposed a hypothesis that combines features of both types of theory. He suggests that: (a) Variability in the structure of antibodies arises by rearrangements in the nucleic acids corresponding to the genes controlling the polypeptides of the immunoglobulins formed during the primary response to the antigen. (b) These rearranged nucleic acids govern the synthesis of many forms of "antibody viruses" (molecules containing nucleic acid with coded information for antibody of a particular specificity). (c) Immunological tolerance is established when antibody viruses encounter an antigen that can combine with their protein portion in an environment in which virus replication cannot begin. (*d*) Antibody viruses escaping destruction are transferred to cells taking part in the primary immune response. (*e*) Primary exposure of the intracellular viruses to an antigen causes those viruses that react with the antigen to proliferate (selective phase of the process). (*f*) Cells in which the virus is replicating can be transformed, mediated by virus-derived nucleic acid (instructive phase of the process). (*g*) The transformed cells divide and can mediate the anamnestic response when reexposed to the proper antigen.

The fetus is ordinarily a poor producer of antibodies, and were there no mechanism for transferring maternal antibodies to the fetus, it would generally not have protective antibodies at first. In hogs, cows, sheep, mice, and rats, the newborn get their first antibodies from the colostrum that the mother's mammary glands secrete before milk production begins. In primates, immunoglobulins diffuse across the placenta from the maternal circulation, and the fetus is born with antibodies derived from its mother (106). There is some evidence that the fetus can, under some conditions, make some sorts of immune response (282).

It is not fully understood why the fetus cannot produce antibodies, but it may be connected with the poor development of its lymphoid tissue (106). Not only does the fetus not produce antibodies, but it may become unable ever to produce antibodies to antigens to which it is exposed. Such a state is called "immunological tolerance," and is seen for instance in the tolerance for mutual tissue grafts shown by members of cattle twins, which often have a single chorion and thus a common circulation. Such twins will accept skin grafts from each other, but reject grafts from their parents or other siblings (16). Burnet and Fenner (38) postulated that it is in this way that an animal's own antigens are usually not antigenic for it, being somehow recognized as "self." Tolerance has been reviewed by Chase (52).

However, immunological tolerance, though it is easier to produce in fetuses or the newborn, can be produced in adult animals, especially in some species (106), and seems to be a result of overloading the antibody-forming tissues with antigen. It is thus apparently similar to the phenomenon of "immunological paralysis" discovered by Felton (92). (These workers discovered that, although small doses of pneumococcus polysaccharide would immunize mice to pneumococcus of the serological type in question, larger doses not only did not immunize but made the animal incapable for many months of being immunized to that type.)

Eisen and Karush (83) have proposed an interesting hypothesis to account for tolerance. They suggest that the dimolecular antibody–antigen complex Ab-Ag can stimulate the immunologically competent cells to produce more antibody, but that neither Ag nor Ag-Ab-Ag can do so. This would explain why large doses of antigen would produce tolerance or paralysis, which would persist as long as there was enough antigen to convert all the antibody present into Ag-Ab-An.

The initial Ab needed to form the Ab-Ag that starts the process of antibody formation would be "natural" antibody to that antigen, as in Jerne's theory (p. 95).

Najjar (212) suggested that antibody production is one phase of a continuing physiological process that has as its object the production of specific globulins for the protection of the membrane of the cells that produce them.

20. Normal Globulin

Since antibodies are globulins, we should expect the serum globulins to increase during immunization, and this is almost always the case, particularly with the γ-globulin (see references in 27). Van den Ende (85) found that the amount of γ-globulin in normal rabbit serum was too small to incite the formation of any antibody for this fraction when whole rabbit serum was injected into guinea pigs, whereas injection of immune serum readily produced antibodies for the γ-globulins. These antibodies reacted also with the γ-globulins of normal serum.

Bjørneboe (18,19) found that the agglutinin produced in rabbit serum, during immunization with pneumococci, was quantitatively identical with the increase in serum protein. In other cases, the increase in serum globulins has been found to be somewhat greater than the antibody produced. Liu, Chow, and Lee (190) wrote: "At most $2/3$, usually $1/2$ of the increase in globulin in a rabbit's serum, on immunization with pneumococci is accounted for by the antibody." Boyd (27) found that the antibody amounted to roughly 40 to 70 per cent of the increase in globulin, and stated: "That this increase in globulins is . . . closely connected with antibody production is indicated by several facts. The increase in globulin, though greater than the amount of antibody produced, still tends to parallel the content of antibody. . . . Injection of gelatin which produces little or no detectable antibody, produces little or no increase in the various globulin fractions." Bjørneboe (19) found that in hyperimmunized rabbits (more than 10 mg. antibody nitrogen per milliliter) all the globulin in the serum was antibody; in other words, all the "normal" globulin had been replaced by antibody.

It seems not impossible that the increase in γ-globulins consequent on immunization, over and above what is known to be antibody, may be largely or perhaps completely of two additional fractions: *first* (the minor one?), antibody to other antigens to which the animal has previously responded—the "anamnestic phenomenon"—of which there are probably a great many, and *second,* antibody directed towards the antigens actually injected, but of such poor quality or avidity (see p. 341) that it either fails to give any demonstrable reaction with the antigens, or is washed off the precipitate or "agglutinate" while the latter is being prepared for analysis, and consequently escapes classification as "antibody." It is not impossible that in amount this latter fraction is fully equal to or greater than the detected antibody.

It was suggested by Boyd (27) that all globulins formed, or at least all γ-globulin, might be antibody, and Grabar (111) and Haurowitz (122) have supported this idea. Unfortunately, it is not an easy hypothesis to test experimentally.

Grabar (110,109,113) has suggested further that the role of gamma globulins is to combine more or less specifically with various substances, such as metabolic products, hormones, products of cell breakdown; and finally with antigenic substances entering the body through wounds, through the gastrointestinal and respiratory tracts, through infection; and with substances deliberately introduced parenterally (vaccinations). Grabar calls this function that of carrier (*transporteur*) and compares it with the lipide-carrying role of the β-globulins. According to this view, immune antibodies would simply be γ-globulins specifically adapted to combine with and transport certain antigens.

A consequence of this view is that γ-globulins ought to contain antibody-like molecules of varying degrees of specificity capable of combining with various substances. The finding of globulins which react like antibodies to gelatin (p. 121) might be an example of this.

Agammaglobulinemia

The serum of certain individuals contains no gamma globulin or a very small amount (252,77,60,105,279). Such persons are found experimentally to be unable to produce circulating antibodies. This condition seems to be a definite clinical entity, featured by (*1*) a history of recurrent bacterial infections, (*2*) absence of acquired antibodies, (*3*) lack of iso-hemagglutinins, (*4*) no (or extremely little) gamma globulin, (*5*) failure of long-term antibiotic therapy to furnish protection, and (*6*) favorable response to protective injections of gamma globulin.

The question whether agammaglobulinemia is a congenital defect of the antibody-forming tissues or is acquired has not been definitely answered. Janeway (161) hinted at the possibility of sex-linked inheritance since so far all the clear-cut cases have been in males, but in some cases the recurrent bacterial infections began so late in life, *e.g.*, at the age 26, that the condition seems to be an acquired one.

The existence of such a disease might be thought to strengthen the suggestion that all gamma globulin is antibody of a sort, since the patients are deficient, not in some particular antibody or even in all antibodies, but in total gamma globulin, but even this evidence is far from conclusive. A more interesting and equally puzzling question is: how do persons who are unable to manufacture any antibody survive to adulthood at all? Some workers have suggested (105) that these individuals would in fact not have survived before the days of sulfa drugs and antibiotics, and it has also been suggested that in some patients the condition is acquired rather than congenital. It is of interest that Good (105) reports that the recurrent infections which characterize the history of the patients with agammaglobulinemia are *bacterial* infections, and the patients have recovered in the normal way from virus infections such as chickenpox, poliomyelitis, mumps, and measles. Since no virus-neutralizing antibodies are found in the blood of such persons, this suggests that antibodies do not play so important a role in combating virus infections as they do in combatting bacterial disease.

21. Measurement of Concentration

In view of the importance of antibodies for immunity, it is important to have methods of determining them quantitatively.

If we assume, as seems entirely reasonable, that there is a certain limiting concentration, below which an antibody would not be active, or at least not produce any visible effect of the type we are testing for, we can obtain a rough index of antibody concentration by diluting the immune serum until we find the highest dilution which still gives a reaction, any higher dilution being negative. This end point can be based upon any of the activities of the antibody in which we are interested, protection *in vivo*, or neutralization, precipitation, agglutination, complement fixation, etc., *in vitro*. If this limiting dilution is x, we may assume the concentration of antibody in the serum is x times the lowest concentration which will exhibit the activity we have tested for. If we have a serum containing a known concentration of antibody, or a serum arbitrarily selected as a standard, which has a limiting active dilution of y, we may state that the concentration of the unknown serum is x/y times that of the standard. Although it is not a good use of the term, chemically speaking, it is customary to call these limiting dilutions *titers*.

It has been found that the activity of the precipitins in a serum does not persist if the serum is diluted very much, and the custom arose of determining, not the limiting dilution of the antiserum, but the limiting dilution of the *antigen* which would give a visible precipitate with the serum, and calling this the titer. This has been used as a measure of the strength of the serum, although it is clear that it can hardly test the concentration of the antibody except in a very rough way (181,147,272). However, the method is rapid and easy to apply, and gives a gratifying impression that something is being measured. Actually there is reason to believe it does measure something, possibly the "avidity" (see p. 341) of the antibody, and it has a real value in selecting the best of a batch of precipitating sera. A good precipitating serum will give a positive reaction with an antigen present in a concentration as low as 10^{-5} mg. per milliliter. Such a sensitive reaction is very suitable for work such as forensic examination for human blood. For this and for other reasons the method of determining limiting dilutions will continue to be used for some time.

Such limiting dilution methods are very crude. It is customary to make the dilutions successively double, and since it is often difficult to decide which of two tubes shows the last trace of reaction, this means there can be an error of 50 per cent, or 100 per cent, depending on how you look at it, in our estimate of the titer. It is possible to make the dilutions in finer steps, but this is hard to do accurately, involves the use of a lot of glassware, and often merely makes the problem of deciding between two tubes still more difficult. Therefore, if limiting dilution methods can be replaced by something more precise, this should be done. In some cases, however, as with certain antivirus sera, limiting dilution methods are all we have.

In determining the neutralizing power of an antiserum for its antigen, additional complications may result from the fact that antibody and antigen combine in multiple proportions, and the amount of antitoxin, for example, which is needed to neutralize a given amount of toxin completely may be not two, but many, times as great as the amount required to half-neutralize that amount of toxin. This will be appreciated by a glance at a typical neutralization curve for such a case, as Fig. 6-13 in Chapter 6. The methods developed by Ehrlich in the early days of immunology illustrate this point.

First an arbitrary unit of toxin, the amount which, injected subcutaneously, is sufficient to kill in 4 to 5 days a guinea pig weighing 250 g. (minimal lethal dose, MLD), was established. Most toxins contained many such units per milliliter, so a "normal" solution was designated as one containing 100 MLD per milliliter. Then the amount of antitoxin needed to neutralize this was determined. Antitoxin proved to be more stable than toxin, so a certain dried antitoxin serum was set up as the reference standard. Then new batches of toxin were titrated against this.

Unexpected difficulty was encountered, because the quantitative course of serological reactions was at that time unknown, and horse antitoxin has a very broad equivalence zone. Since 100 MLD of toxin are just neutralized by 1 unit of antitoxin, Ehrlich and other chemists of the time expected that 101 MLD, mixed with 1 unit of antitoxin, would produce a mixture having 1 MLD of toxin in excess, and consequently would kill a guinea pig. Instead such a mixture was found to be substantially neutral, and the amount of toxin which had to be mixed with 1 unit of antitoxin in order to make it lethal to a guinea pig was some 140 to 150 MLD. This was considered puzzling and led to a complicated set of theories about toxin-antitoxin reactions, which happily we need not go into here.

Cohn and Pappenheimer (58) pointed out that antitoxin from other animals shows a much more narrow zone of neutralization, and state that "if Paul Ehrlich had used a species other than the horse to study the toxin-antitoxin reaction, he would not have defined the many units and hypothetical varieties of toxin which have since been so confusing to the student."

For such an important determination as antitoxic power, the determination of the neutralizing dose (L_0) was not accurate or definite enough, since there was no experiment giving a sharp end point. It proved better and more reproducible to determine for each new toxin the amount which, when mixed with a unit of the preserved standard antiserum, would kill a 250-g. guinea pig in 4 to 5 days. Thus the L_+ dose, where $+$ was originally a cross signifying the death of the animal, was established. New batches of antitoxin could be standardized by reference to this temporarily standardized toxin, using the same end point. This is somewhat similar to the use of an intermediate unstable, standard solution in volumetric titration, except that the end point in our case is not neutrality, but a mixture sufficiently toxic to kill.

The amount of an unknown antitoxic serum which gives the same amount of neutralization (allowing death of a guinea pig in 4 to 5 days) with the L_+ dose of toxin as does the standard antitoxin can be assumed to have the same curative power, allowing for variation between different guinea pigs. Such allowance can be made, and the accuracy of our estimates of the potency of the new serum can be judged, if statistical methods are applied to the planning and interpretation of the experiment. These methods are discussed in Chapter 17, where examples of such titrations are given.

A modern technic more economical of animals titrates the neutralizing effects of antitoxin by injecting small amounts of mixtures of toxin and antitoxin into the skin of a rabbit. In this way many different doses can be tested on one animal.

When Ramon (258) discovered that antitoxin would precipitate toxin when the two reagents were mixed in the proper proportions, this made possible an *in vitro* method of titrating antitoxin and of comparing unknown antisera with a standard without the use of animals. This method is of course much more rapid and economical than the Ehrlich method, and may actually give a better estimate of the actual amount by weight of antibody present than does the earlier technic. However, since the quality ("avidity") of antitoxin in different lots may vary, and because not all the precipitating antibodies present are antitoxin, the Ramon method may not necessarily give as good an estimate of the actual protective power of a serum.

Ramon made the important observation that mixtures of toxin and antitoxin precipitated at different rates, depending on the absolute concentrations and on the proportions in which the two reagents were mixed; and that that mixture which precipitated fastest indicated the proportions in which to mix antitoxin with toxin in order to obtain a neutral mixture. The amount of toxin which gives most rapid flocculation with one standard unit of antitoxin is called the L_f dose. It is not usually the same as the L_0 dose determined by using animals, but is usually somewhat smaller. It has been found to represent 0.00042 to 0.00048 mg. toxin nitrogen, or some 30 to 40 MLD. Unknown sera are titrated against the freshly standardized toxin by the same technic. This method is used in many laboratories for preliminary titration, but it has not displaced the Ehrlich method for final standardization.

In 1926 a valuable observation of much the same sort was made by Dean and Webb (66). They found that with the system they were using (horse serum as antigen and rabbit anti-horse-serum antibody), mixtures with antigen and antibody in different proportions precipitated at different rates. They found that the most rapid precipitation (flocculation) occurred, using any given concentration of antiserum, with one certain concentration of antigen. Tubes containing less than this amount of antigen went more slowly, as did tube containing more. Irrespective of the absolute dilutions, the dilution of antigen in the fastest tube, divided by the dilution of antiserum, was a constant, which Dean and Webb called the ratio of optimal proportions. They found that, in their system, this tube contained a neutral mixture (*i.e.*, neither antigen nor antibody, or only traces of both, in the supernatant fluid), after the precipitate had settled out. This is not always true of other systems, but precipitates made at the optimal proportions point contain antibody and antigen in a ratio which is roughly constant for any given system (28,29). Most, and frequently all, of the antigen is precipitated at this point, so, knowing the amount of antigen added and the ratio of antibody to antigen in precipitates made with this system, we can calculate the amount of antibody in a measured amount of serum. Even without all these data, a comparison of the strength of different sera is possible by determining their optimal proportions points against the same antigen. The procedure will be further discussed in the chapter on antigen–antibody reactions; the technic is given in Chapter 16.

The most accurate method of determining the actual *amount*, as opposed to activity, of antibody in a serum consists in chemical analysis. Since antibodies do not differ in any gross way from other serum proteins, however, the only practical way of doing this is first to separate the antibodies from the unreactive serum proteins by adding a suitable amount of antigen to combine with all the antibody. If the two reagents react to form a precipitate, or if the antigen is particulate (*e.g.*, red cells), this results in the separation of the antibody–antigen complex, which after centrifugation and washing is now ready for analysis.

One difficulty was that in practice the only ways we have of estimating the amount of antibody in such precipitates, or "agglutinates," depend upon its properties as a protein, as for example the micro-Kjeldahl method for protein nitrogen, the use of the Folin-Ciocalteu phenol reagent to determine tyrosine, or the biuret or ninhydrin colorimetric methods (313,167). But the antigen is usually a protein itself or at least contains much protein. Even nonprotein antigens such as the pneumococcal polysaccharides and blood group substances usually contain nitrogen. This means that a simple application of the micro-Kjeldahl method will leave us uncertain how much of the nitrogen is antibody nitrogen, and how much antigen nitrogen.

The way out of this difficulty was found by Wu *et al.* (328,329) who introduced the use of antigen (*e.g.*, iodized albumin) which has a characteristic which enables it to be determined separately (in this case by iodine determinations); and by Heidelberger and Kendall (134), who introduced the use of a nitrogen-free antigen. Later workers have used natural antigens containing iron (34) and copper (198), and more recent workers have employed proteins marked with radioactive tracers (10, 95,123).

When particulate antigens, particularly bacteria or red cell stroma, are used, it is possible to determine the antigen nitrogen by doing a suitable blank, and thus obtain the antibody nitrogen by subtraction (132). This can also be done in the case of precipitates in the region of antibody excess, where all the antigen is precipitated (130,167). By analyses of the supernatants, Heidelberger *et al.* (130,137) were even able to determine the composition of precipitates in the region where not quite all the antigen was precipitated.

The amounts of antibody found in the blood of immunized animals can be quite considerable, amounting to 2 to 2.3 mg. antibody N (12 to 14 mg. antibody protein per milliliter of serum) (27), or in hyperimmunized animals to an average of 2.9 mg. N (18 mg. antibody protein) (274). At least one rabbit has been found to have 6.7 mg. antibody N [42 mg. antibody protein per milliliter in his serum (194)].

The amounts of antibody found in normal human serum are much less than this. They are in fact usually so small that exact determination by these methods is not possible, but they can be estimated, *e.g.*, by neutralization tests in animals, especially after the serum has been concentrated. Immediately after immunization, human beings may show accounts of antibody of the order of 0.075 to 0.26 mg. antibody nitrogen (0.47 to 1.6 mg. antibody protein) per milliliter of serum (131). Hyperimmunized individuals may produce more antibody. Diphtheria antitoxin in human beings injected with toxoid has been found to be over 2 mg. antibody protein per milliliter in several cases (232), and cases have been reported of amounts of antibody of 15 to 30 mg. per milliliter.

Since we have seen (p. 44) that the various antibody functions of an antiserum are often simply various manifestations of the activity of one and the same sort of antibody, it was reasonable to suppose that the agglutinating antibody and protective antibody, in a serum known to have protective action against the microorganism used, might be one and the same, and consequently the amount of agglutinating antibody should be a good measure of the protective potency of the serum. This was found to be true for antipneumococcus sera, so far as could be judged from experiments designed to test it (101). Methods based on this fact have been extensively applied by Heidelberger and collaborators and by others. Goodner, Horsfall, and Dubos (107) recommended them for standardizing antipneumococcus serum.

It has since been found that determinations of the precipitating antibody from antipneumococcus sera, by analyses for nitrogen of precipitates made with the specific carbohydrates, provide an even more convenient measure of the potency of the serum (98). In this case a measure of the precipitin present seemed to be a better index of protective power than did a measure of the antipneumococcus agglutinins [by the quantitative method of Heidelberger and Kabat (132)], for Gerlough, Palmer, and Blumenthal (98) reported that the precipitin found by the above method was identical with protective antibody, whereas some of the agglutinin present did not have any appreciable protective function.

Heidelberger and Treffers (139) estimated the total hemolysin in lytic sera by determining the nitrogen added to sheep stromata suspensions when treated with lysin.   Henriksen and Heidelberger (141) applied a quantitative agglutination procedure to the determination of the amount of antibody in antisera to hemolytic streptococci.

TABLE 2-5

Sensitivity of Various Methods of Detecting or Determining Antibodies [from Grabar (112)]

Method	Micrograms of antibody-N
I. Specific precipitation	
(a) Qualitative	
"Ring" test	3–5
In gels	5–10
(b) Quantitative	
Micro-Kjeldahl	20
Nephelometry (photonreflectometer)	20
Colorimetry (Biuret reagent)	20
" (Folin-Ciolcalteu reagent)	4
II. Bacterial agglutination	
(a) Qualitative	0.05–1.0
(b) Quantitative	10–20
III. Hemagglutination	
(a) Active (blood groups)	0.1–0.2
(b) Passive (adsorbed antigens)	0.003–0.006
IV. Hemolysis	
(a) Active (lytic antibody and complement)	0.0002–0.03
(b) Passive (adsorbed antigen)	0.3
V. Complement fixation	0.1
VI. Flocculation test (syphilis)	0.2–0.5
VII. Anaphylaxis	
(a) Passive (guinea pig)	30
" (uterine muscle)	0.01
(b) Local passive (guinea pig skin)	0.003
" (rat skin)	3
(c) Skin transfer (Prausnitz-Küstner)	0.01
(d) Arthus phenomenon	10
VIII. Toxin neutralization	
(Guinea pig skin)	0.3

Analytical methods suitable for quantitative antibody determination are given by Kabat and Mayer (167). See also Chapter 16.

Although it involves the mention of some technics not discussed until later in this book, we give in Table 2-5 a list of methods of detecting or determining small amounts of antibody, with the approximate limits of sensitivity of each.

A. H. Coons (62) devised an ingenious and very useful technique of labeling antibodies with a fluorescent dye which makes it possible to detect and identify small amounts of microbial and tissue antigens and antibodies against them (cf. 41,210). This technique has been particularly useful in studying antigen and antibody occurrence in cells.

The iron-containing protein from liver, ferritin, also makes a good label for antibodies, because of its visibility in the electron microscope (154).

A quick, sensitive method of detecting antibodies in single cells is the bacterial adherance technique of Mäkelä and Nossal (196).

A very sensitive method of measuring the precipitate produced in antibody–antigen reactions has been proposed by Glick et al. (102).

References

1. Almeida, J., B. Cinader, and A. Howatson, J. Exptl. Med., 118, 327–340 (1963).
2. Amano, S., Ann. Rept. Inst. Virus, Res., Kyoto Univ., A1, 1–47 (1958).
3. Ambrose, C. T., and A. H. Coons, J. Exptl. Med., 117, 1075–1088 (1963).
4. Armstrong, R. R., Proc. Roy. Soc. (London), B98, 525 (1925).
5. Avery, O. T., W. F. Goebel, and F. H. Babers, J. Exptl. Med., 55, 769 (1932).
6. Bail, O., and E. Hoke, Arch. Hyg., 64, 313 (1908).
7. Bailey, G. H., Am. J. Hyg., 7, 370 (1927).
8. Balch, H. H., J. Immunol., 64, 397 (1950).
9. Baldwin, W. R., and L. U. Gardner, Am. Rev. Tuberc., 5, 429 (1921).
10. Banks, T. E., G. E. Francis, W. Mulligan, and A. Wormall, Biochem. J. (London), 48, 180 (1951).
11. Banzhaf, E. J., and W. Famulener, Studies, N. Y. C. Dept. Health, 8, 208 (1914).
12. Bassett, E. W., S. M. Beiser, and S. W. Tanenbaum, Science, 133, 1475–1476 (1961).
13. Baumgartner, L., J. Immunol., 27, 407 (1934).
14. Becker, E. L., J. Immunol., 70, 372 (1953).
15. Benacerraf, B., M. Sebestyen, and N. S. Cooper, J. Immunol., 82, 131–137 (1959).
16. Billingham, R. E., G. H. Lampkin, P. B. Medawar, and L. H. Williams, Heredity, 6, 201–212 (1952).
18. Bjørneboe, M., J. Immunol., 37, 201 (1939).
19. Bjørneboe, M. Z. Immunitätsforsch., 99, 245 (1941).
20. Bodily, H. L., and M. D. Eaton, J. Immunol., 45, 193 (1942).
21. Boyd, W. C., J. Exptl. Med., 74, 369 (1941).
22. Boyd, W. C., Fundamentals of Immunology, 1st. ed., Interscience, New York, 1943.
23. Boyd, W. C., J. Exptl. Med., 83, 401 (1946).
27. Boyd, W. C., and H. Bernard, J. Immunol., 33, 111 (1937).
28. Boyd, W. C., and S. B., Hooker, J. Gen. Physiol., 17, 341 (1934).

29. Boyd, W. C., and S. B. Hooker, *J. Gen. Physiol.*, 22, 281 (1939).
30. Boyd, W. C., and R. M. Reguera, *J. Immunol.*, 62, 333 (1949).
33. Braunsteiner, H., K. Feelinger, and F. Pakesch, *Blood*, 8, 916–922 (1953).
34. Breinl, F., and F. Haurowitz, *Z. Physiol. Chem.*, 192, 45 (1930).
35. Brown, A. M., *Brit. J. Exptl. Pathol.*, 16, 554 (1935).
36. Burnet, F. M., *Australian J. Sci.*, 20, 67 (1957).
37. Burnet, F. M., *The Clonal Selection Theory of Acquired Immunity*, Cambridge University Press, Cambridge, 1958.
38. Burnet, F. M., and F. Fenner, *The Production of Antibodies*, Macmillan, Melbourne, 1949.
39. Campbell, D. H., R. H. Blaker, and A. B. Pardee, *J. Am. Chem. Soc.*, 70, 1293 (1948).
40. Campbell, D. H., and N. Bulman, *Fortschr. Chem. Org. Naturstoffe*, 9, 443 (1952).
41. Campbell, D. H., J. S. Garvey, N. E. Cremer, and D. H. Sussdorf, *Methods in Immunology*, W. A. Benjamin, New York, 1963.
42. Campbell, D. H., and F. Lanni, "The Chemistry of Antibodies," in *Amino Acids and Proteins*, D. Greenberg, ed., Charles C Thomas, Springfield, Illinois, 1951.
43. Campbell, D. H., E. Luescher, and L. S. Lerman, *Proc. Natl. Acad. Sci. U. S.*, 37, 575 (1951).
44. Cannon, P. R., *J. Lab. Clin. Med.*, 28, 127 (1942).
45. Cannon, P. R., W. E. Chase, and R. W. Wissler, *J. Immunol.*, 47, 133 (1943).
46. Cannon, P. R., R. W. Wissler, R. L. Woolridge, and E. D. Benditt, *Ann. Surg.*, 120, 514 (1944).
47. Cebra, J. J., D. Givol, H. I. Silman, and E. Katchalski, *J. Biol. Chem.*, 236, 1720 (1961).
48. Ceppellini, R., et al., *Bull. World Health Organ.*, 30, 447–450 (1964).
49. Chase, M. W., *Proc. Soc. Exptl. Biol. Med.*, 59, 134 (1945).
50. Chase, M. W., *Federation Proc.*, 10, 404 (1951).
51. Chase, M. W., "Immunological reactions mediated through cells," in *The Nature and Significance of the Antibody Response*, A. M. Pappenheimer, ed., Columbia University Press, New York, 1953.
52. Chase, M. W., *Ann. Rev. Microbiol.*, 13, 349–376 (1959).
53. Chow, B. F., K. H. Lee, and H. Wu, *Chinese J. Physiol.*, 11, 139, 155, 163, 169, 175, 183, 193, 201, 211, 223 (1937).
54. Chow, B. F., K. H. Lee, and H. Wu, *Chinese J. Physiol.*, 11, 139 (1937).
55. Cohen, S., and R. R. Porter, *Advances in Immunology*, 4, 287–349, Academic Press, New York, 1964.
56. Cohn, E. J., et al., *J. Am. Chem. Soc.*, 62, 3386 (1940).
57. Cohn, E. J., et al., *J. Clin. Invest.*, 23, 417 (1944).
58. Cohn, M., and A. M. Pappenheimer, *J. Immunol.*, 63, 291 (1949).
59. Cole, A. G., *Arch. Pathol.*, 26, 96 (1938).
60. Collins, H. D., and H. R. Dudley, *New Engl. J. Med.*, 252, 255 (1955).
61. Conradi, H., and R. Bielung, *Deut. Med. Wochschr.*, 42, 1280 (1916).
62. Coons, A. H., *J. Immunol.*, 87, 499–503 (1961).
63. Coons, A. H., E. H. Leduc, and J. M. Connolly, *J. Exptl. Med.*, 102, 49–60 and 61–72 (1955).
64. De Petris, S., G. Karlsbad, and B. Pernis, *J. Exptl. Med.*, 117, 849–862 (1963).
65. Dean, H. R., *Lancet*, 1, 45 (1917).
66. Dean, H. R., and R. A. Webb, *J. Pathol. Bacteriol.*, 29, 473 (1926).
67. Dingle, J. H., L. D. Fothergill, and C. A. Chandler, *J. Immunol.*, 34, 357 (1938).

68. Dixon, F. J., P. H. Maurer, and M. P. Deichmiller, *J. Immunol.,* **72,** 179 (1954).
69. Dixon, F. J., D. W. Talmage, and P. H. Maurer, *J. Immunol.,* **68,** 693 (1952).
70. Doerr, R., *Die Immunitätsforschung,* vol. 4, 221, Springer-Verlag, Vienna, 1949.
71. Doerr, R., and V. K. Russ, *Z. Immunitätsforsch.,* **3,** 181 (1909).
72. Dray, S., S. Dubisi, A. Kelus, E. S. Lennox, and J. Oudin, *Nature,* **195,** 1785–786 (1962).
73. Dreyer, G., and E. W. A. Walker, *J. Pathol. Bacteriol.,* **14,** 28 (1909).
74. Dungal, N., *Brit. J. Exptl. Pathol.,* **13,** 360 (1932).
75. Duran-Reynals, F., *Yale J. Biol. Med.,* **12,** 361 (1940).
76. Edelman, G. M., and B. Benacerraf, *Proc. Natl. Acad. Sci.,* **48,** 1035 (1962).
77. Editorial, *J. Am. Med. Assoc.,* **156,** 1084 (1954).
78. Edsall, G., in *The Nature and Significance of the Antibody Response,* A. M. Pappenheimer, ed., Columbia University Press, New York, 1953.
79. Edsall, J. T., in *The Proteins,* H. Neurath and K. Bailey, eds., Vol. 1B, Academic Press, New York, 1953.
80. Ehrlich, P., *Deut. med. Wochschr.,* **17,** 976 (1891).
82. Eisen, W., and F. Karush, *J. Am. Chem. Soc.,* **71,** 363 (1949).
83. Eisen, H. N., and F. Karush, *Nature,* **202,** 677–682 (1964).
84. Eisen, H. N., E. S. Simms, E. Helmreich, and M. Kern, *Trans. Assoc. Am. Physicians,* **74,** 207–214 (1961).
85. Van den Ende, M., *J. Hyg.,* **40,** 377 (1940).
85a. Epstein, S. Q., and S. J. Singer, *J. Chem. Soc.,* **80,** 1274 (1958).
86. Fagraeus, A., *Acta Med. Scand. Suppl.,* **130,** 204 (1948).
87. Fahey, J. L., and H. Goodman, *Science,* **143,** 588–590 (1964).
88. Feldman, J. D., *Adv. Immunol.,* **4,** 175–248, Academic Press, New York, 1964.
89. Felton, L. D., *Bull. Johns Hopkins Hosp.,* **38,** 33 (1926).
90. Felton, L. D., *J. Immunol.,* **21,** 357 (1931).
91. Felton, L. D., *J. Immunol.,* **22,** 453 (1932).
92. Felton, L. D., and B. Ottinger, *J. Bacteriol.,* **43,** 94–95 (1942).
93. Filitti-Wurmser, S., G. Aubel-Lesure, and R. Wurmser, *J. Chim. Phys.,* **50,** 236 (1953).
94. Finkelstein, M. S., and J. W. Uhr, *Science,* **146,** 67–69 (1964).
94a. Fougereau, M., and G. M. Edelman, *J. Exp. Med.,* **121,** 373 (1965).
95. Francis, G. E., and A. Wormall, Communication to XI International Congress Pure and Applied Chemistry London, July 17–24, 1947.
96. Fuji, H., *Acta Haematol. Japan,* **21,** 701–713 (1958).
97. Furuhata, T., *Japan Med. World,* **7,** 197 (1927).
98. Gerlough, T. D., J. W. Palmer, and R. R. Blumenthal, *J. Immunol.,* **40,** 53 (1941).
99. Gibson, R. B., and K. R. Collins, *J. Biol. Chem.,* **3,** 233 (1907).
100. Gill, F. A., and R. M. Cole, *J. Immunol.,* **94,** 898–915 (1965).
101. Girard, P., and M. Louran, *Comp. rend. soc. biol.,* **116,** 1010 (1934).
102. Glick, D., R. A. Good, L. J. Greenberg, J. J. Eddy, and N. K. Day, *Science,* **128,** 1625–1626 (1958).
103. Glover, T. D., and D. W. Bishop, *Nature,* **198,** 901–902 (1963).
104. Goldberg, R. J., and J. W. Williams, *Trans. Faraday Soc.,* **13,** 226 (1953).
105. Good, R. A., unpublished manuscript, 1955.
106. Good, R. A., and B. W. Papermaster, in *Advances in Immunology,* **4,** 1–115, Academic Press, New York, 1964.
107. Goodner, K., F. L. Horsfall, and R. J. Dubos, *J. Immunol.,* **33,** 279 (1937).

108. Grabar, J., *Compt. rend.*, **207**, 807 (1938).
109. Grabar, J., *Thérapie*, **9**, 163 (1954).
110. Grabar, P., *Les Globulins du Sérum Sanguin*, Editions Desoer, Liège, 1947.
111. Grabar, P., *Ann. Rev. Biochem.*, **19**, 453 (1950).
112. Grabar, P., *Atti Congr. Intern. Microbiol., 6th Congr., Rome*, **2**, 169 (1953).
113. Grabar, P., in *Protides of the Biological Fluids*, H. Peeters, ed., Elsevier, Amsterdam, 1964.
114. Grabar, P., and P. Burtin, *Analyse Immuno-électrophorétique*, Masson, Paris, 1960.
115. Grabar, P., and C. A. Williams, *Biochim. Biophys. Acta*, **10**, 193 (1953).
116. Granboulan, N., *Rev. Hematol. (Paris)*, **15**, 52–71 (1960).
117. Grasset, E., *Publ. S. African Inst. Med. Research*, **24**, 1171 (1929).
118. Grubb, R., and A. B. Laurell, *Acta Pathol. Microbiol. Scand.*, **39**, 390–398 (1956).
119. Hall, C. E., A. Nisonoff, and H. S. Sayter, *J. Biophys. Biochem. Cytol.*, **6**, 407 (1959).
120. Harris, S., and T. N. Harris, *Federation Proc.*, **10**, 409 (1951).
121. Haurowitz, F., *J. Immunol.*, **43**, 331 (1942).
122. Haurowitz, F., *Bio. Rev. Cambridge Phil. Soc.*, **27**, 247 (1952).
123. Haurowitz, F., "Theories of antibody formation," in *The Nature and Significance of the Antibody Response*, A. M. Pappenheimer, ed., Columbia University Press, New York, 1953.
124. Haurowitz, F., *J. Cellular Comp. Physiol.*, **47**, Suppl. 1, 1 (1956).
125. Haurowitz, F., *Ann. Rev. Biochem.*, **29**, 609–634 (1960).
125a. Haurowitz, F., in *Conceptual Advances in Immunology and Oncology*, Hoeber (Harper and Row), New York, 1963.
126. Harris, T. N., and W. E. Ehrich, *J. Exptl. Med.*, **84**, 1957 (1946).
127. Haurowitz, F., and S. Tekman, *Compt. rend., soc. Turque sic. nat.*, **13**, 81 (1947).
128. Haurowitz, F., S. Tekman, M. Bileu, and P. Schwerin, *Biochem. J. (London)*, **41**, 304 (1947).
129. Hayes, S. P., *J. Immunol.*, **70**, 450 (1953).
130. Heidelberger, M., *Bacteriol. Rev.*, **3**, 49 (1939).
131. Heidelberger, M., in *The Nature and Significance of the Antibody Response*, A. M. Pappenheimer, ed., Columbia University Press, New York, 1953.
132. Heidelberger, M., and E. A. Kabat, *J. Exptl. Med.*, **60**, 643 (1934).
133. Heidelberger, M., and E. A. Kabat, *J. Exptl. Med.*, **63**, 737 (1936).
134. Heidelberger, M., and F. E. Kendall, *J. Exptl. Med.*, **50**, 809 (1929).
135. Heidelberger, M., and F. E. Kendall, *J. Exptl. Med.*, **62**, 697 (1935).
136. Heidelberger, M., F. E. Kendall, and T. Teorell, *J. Exptl. Med.*, **63**, 819 (1936).
137. Heidelberger, M., K. O. Pedersen, and A. Tiselius, *Nature*, **138**, 165 (1936).
138. Heidelberger, M. R., H. P. Sia, and F. E. Kendall, *J. Exptl. Med.*, **52**, 477 (1930).
139. Heidelberger, M., and H. P. Treffers, *J. Gen. Physiol.*, **25**, 523 (1942).
140. Heidelberger, M., *et al.*, *J. Biol. Chem.*, **144**, 555 (1942).
141. Henriksen, S. D., and M. Heidelberger, *J. Exptl. Med.*, **74**, 105 (1941).
142. Heremans, J. F., *Clin. Chim. Acta*, **4**, 639 (1959).
143. Hermans, J. F., *Les Globulines Sériques du Systeme Gamma*, Editions Arscia S. A., Brussels, 1960.
144. Hershgold, E. J., F. Cordoba, and D. Gitlin, *Nature*, **199**, 284 (1963).
146. Holub, M., and L. Jaroskova, eds., *Mechanism of Antibody Formation*, Academic Press, New York, 1960.
147. Hooker, S. B., and W. C. Boyd, *J. Immunol.*, **23**, 465 (1932).
148. Hooker, S. B., and W. C. Boyd, *J. Immunol.*, **25**, 61 (1933).

149. Hooker, S. B., and W. C. Boyd, *J. Immunol.*, **26**, 469 (1934).
150. Hooker, S. B., and W. C. Boyd, unpublished data.
151. Hooker, S. B., and W. C. Boyd, *J. Immunol.*, **42**, 419 (1941).
152. Hooker, S. B., and W. C. Boyd, *Proc. Soc. Exptl. Biol. Med.*, **47**, 187–190 (1941).
153. Horsfall, F. L., and Goodner, *J. Immunol.*, **31**, 135 (1936).
154. Hsu, K. C., R. A. Rifkind, *Science*, **142**, 1471–1473 (1963).
155. Hughes, T. P., and W. A. Sawyer, *J. Am. Med. Assoc.*, **99**, 978 (1932).
156. Hughes, W. L., "Interstitial Proteins: the proteins of blood plasma and lymph," in *The Proteins*, H. Neurath and K. Bailey, eds., Vol 2, Part B, Academic Press, New York, 1954.
157. Humphrey, J. H., and R. G. White, *Immunology for Students of Medicine*, F. A. Davis, Philadelphia, 1963.
158. Ingalls, M. S., *J. Immunol.*, **33**, 123 (1937).
158a. Ishizaka, K., T. Ishizaka, E. H. Lee, and H. Fudenberg, *J. Immunol.*, **95**, 197 (1965).
159. Ipsen, J., *J. Immunol.*, **69**, 273 (1952).
160. Isliker, H. C., *Ann. N. Y. Acad. Sci.*, **57**, 225 (1953).
161. Janeway, C. A., L. Apt, and D. Gitlin, *Trans. Assoc. Am. Physicians*, **66**, 200 (1953).
162. Jerne, N. K., *Avidity*, Ejnar Munksgaard, Copenhagen, 1951.
163. Jerne, N. K., *Proc. Nat. Acad. Sci. U. S.*, **41**, 849 (1955).
164. Jerne, N. K., *Ann. Rev. Microbiol.*, **14**, 341–358 (1960).
165. Kabat, E. A., in *The Nature and Significance of the Antibody. Reponse*, A. M. Pappenheimer, ed., N. Y. Acad. Med., New York, 1953.
166. Kabat, E. A., and A. E. Bezer, *J. Exptl. Med.*, **82**, 207 (1945).
167. Kabat, E. A., and M. M. Mayer, *Experimental Immunochemistry*, Charles C Thomas, Springfield, Illinois, 1948.
168. Kabat, E. A., and M. M. Mayer, *Experimental Immunochemistry*, Charles C Thomas, Springfield, Illinois, 1961.
169. Karush, F., and R. Marks, *J. Immunol.*, **78**, 296–303 (1957).
170. Kass, E. H., and M. Finland, *Ann. Rev. Microbiol.*, **7**, 361 (1953).
171. Kekwick, R. A., *Chem. Ind. (London)*, **60**, 486 (1941).
172. Kekwick, R. A., and B. R. Record, *Brit. J. Exptl. Pathol.*, **22**, 29 (1941).
173. Kirk, J. S., and J. Sumner, *J. Biol. Chem.*, **97**, lxxxvii (1932).
174. Kleczowski, A., *Brit. J. Exptl. Pathol.*, **22**, 192 (1942).
175. Klinman, N. R., J. H. Rockey, and F. Karush, *Science*, **146**, 401–403 (1964).
176. Krüpe, M., *Z. Hyg. Infertionskrankh.*, **136**, 200 (1953).
177. Kuge, H., *Acta Haematol. Japan*, **20**, 436–445 (1957).
178. Kuhns, W. J., *J. Exptl. Med.*, **99**, 577 (1954).
179. Kuhns, W. J., and A. M. Pappenheimer, *J. Exptl. Med.*, **95**, 375 (1952).
180. Landsteiner, K., *The Specificity of Serological Reactions*, Charles C Thomas, Springfield, Illinois, 1936.
181. Landsteiner, K., *The Specificity of Serological Reactions*, 2nd rev. ed., Harvard University Press, Cambridge, Massachusetts, 1945.
182. Landsteimer, K., and C. P. Miller, *J. Exptl. Med.*, **42**, 841, 853, 863 (1925).
183. Landsteiner, K., and J. v. d. Scheer, *J. Exptl. Med.*, **63**, 325 (1936).
184. Landsteiner, K., and J. v. d. Scheer, *J. Exptl. Med.*, **67**, 709 (1938).
185. Landsteiner, K., and J. v. d. Scheer, *J. Exptl. Med.*, **71**, 445 (1940).
186. Lawrence, H. S., *Proc. Soc. Exptl. Biol. Med.*, **71**, 516 (1949).
187. Lawrence, H. S., in *Mechanisms of Hypersensitivity*, J. H. Shaffer, G. A. LoGrippo, and M. W. Chase, eds., Little, Brown, Boston, 1959.

188. Lederberg, J., *Science,* 129, 1649–1653 (1959).
189. Ledingham, J. C. G., *J. Hyg.,* 7, 65 (1907).
190. Liu, S. C., B. F. Chow, and K. H. Lee, *Chinese J. Physiol.,* 11, 201 (1937).
191. Loveless, M. H., *Southern Med., J.,* 33, 869 (1940).
192. Lundgren, H. P., and W. H. Ward, "Determination of the molecular size of proteins," in *Amino Acids and Proteins,* D. M. Greenberg, ed., Charles C Thomas, Springfield, Illinois, 1951.
193. Madden, S. C., *et al., J. Exptl. Med.,* 71, 283 (1940).
194. Madden, S. C., and G. H. Whipple, *Physiol. Rev.,* 20, 194 (1940).
195. Mäkelä, O., and G. J. V. Nossal, *J. Immunol.,* 87, 457–463 (1961).
196. Mäkelä, O., and G. J. V. Nossal, *J. Immunol.,* 87, 447–456 (1961).
197. Malkiel, S., *J. Immunol.,* 57, 51 (1947).
198. Malkiel, S., and W. C. Boyd, *J. Exptl. Med.,* 66, 383 (1937).
199. Malkiel, S., and B. J. Hargis, *J. Immunol.,* 69, 217 (1952).
200. Malley, A., and D. H. Campbell, *J. Am. Chem. Soc.,* 85, 487 (only) (1963).
201. Marrack, J. R., H. Hoch, and R. G. S. Johns, *Brit. J. Exptl. Pathol.,* 32, 212 (1951).
202. Maurer, P. H., F. J. Dixon, and D. W. Talmage, *Proc. Soc. Exptl. Biol. Med.,* 83, 163 (1953).
203. Mayer, M. M., *Ann. Rev. Biochem.,* 20, 415 (1951).
204. McMaster, P. D., "Sites of antibody formation," in *The Nature and Significance of Antibody Response,* A. M. Pappenheimer, ed., New York Acad. Med., New York, 1953.
205. Meyer, K., and W. T. J. Morgan, *Brit. J. Exptl. Pathol.,* 16, 476 (1935).
206. Milgrom, F., and Z. Swierczynska, *Schweiz. Zeitschr. Allgemeine Path. u. Bakt.,* 19, 189–204 (1956).
207. Miller, J. F. A. P., *Science,* 144, 1544–1551 (1964).
208. Mohlmann, H., *Z. Immunitätsforsch.,* 101, 269 (1942).
209. Morgan, W. T. J., *Biochem. J. (London),* 31, 2003 (1937).
210. Nairu, R. C., ed., *Fluorescent Protein Tracing,* E. and S. Livingstone, Edinburgh-London, 1962.
211. Najjar, V. A., ed., *Immunity and Virus Infection,* Wiley, New York, 1959.
212. Najjar, V. A., *Physiol. Rev.,* 43, 243–262 (1963).
213. Najjar, V. A., and M. E. Griffith, *Biochem. Biophys. Res. Commun.,* 16, 472–477 (1964).
214. Neil, A., and F. J. Dixon, *A. M. A. Arch. Pathol.,* 67, 643–649 (1959).
215. Neurath, H., *J. Am. Chem. Soc.,* 61, 1841 (1939).
216. Nisonoff, A., and D. Pressman, *J. Immunol.,* 81, 126–135 (1958).
217. Nisonoff, A., and D. Pressman, *J. Immunol.,* 80, 417–428 (1958).
218. Nisonoff, A., and D. Pressman, *Science,* 128, 659–660 (1958).
219. Nisonoff, A., M. H. Winkler, and D. Pressman, *J. Immunol.,* 82, 201–208 (1959).
220. Nisonoff, A., F. C. Wissler, L. N. Lipman, and D. L. Woernley, *Arch. Biochem. Biophys.,* 89, 230 (1960).
221. Northrop, J. H., *Science,* 93, 92 (1941); *J. Gen. Physiol.,* 25, 465 (1942).
222. Northrop, J. H., and W. F. Goebel, *J. Gen. Physiol.,* 32, 705 (1949).
223. Nossal, G. J. V., *Immunology,* 3, 109 (1960).
224. Nossal, G. J. V., *Sci. Am.,* 211, No. 6, 106 (1964).
225. Nossal, G. J. V., and O. Mäkelä, *Ann. Rev. Microbiol.,* 16, 53–74 (1962).
227. Obermayer, F., and E. P. Pick, *Wien. Klin. Wochschr.,* 17, 265 (1904).
228. Oncley, J. L., G. Scatchard, and A. Brown, *J. Phys. Chem.,* 51, 184 (1947).
229. Oncley, J. L., E. Ellenbogen, D. Gitlin, and F. R. N. Gurd, *J. Phys. Chem.,* 56, 85 (1952).

230. Pappenheimer, A. M., *J. Exptl. Med.*, **71**, 263 (1940).
231. Pappenheimer, A. M., ed., *The Nature and Significance of the Antibody Response*, Columbia University Press, New York, 1953.
232. Pappenheimer, A. M., personal communication, 1955.
233. Pappenheimer, A. M., H. P. Lundgren, and J. W. Williams, *J. Exptl. Med.*, **71**, 247 (1940).
234. Parfentjev, I. A., U. S. Patent 2,065,196 (1936).
235. Pauling, L., *J. Am. Chem. Soc.*, **62**, 2643 (1940).
236. Pauling, L., and D. H. Campbell, *J. Exptl. Med.*, **76**, 211 (1942).
237. Pauling, L., and H. A. Itano, eds., *Molecular Structure and Biological Specificity*, Waverly, Baltimore, 1957.
238. Pauling, L., D. Pressman, J., and A. L. Grossberg, *J. Am. Chem. Soc.*, **66**, 784 (1944).
239. Pauling, L., and D. Pressman, *J. Am. Chem. Soc.*, **67**, 1003 (1945).
240. Perrin, F., *J. Phys. radium*, **7**, 1 (1936).
241. Petermann, M. L., and A. M. Pappenheimer, *Science*, **93**, 458 (1941).
242. Phillips, F. S., F. H. Hopkins, and M. L. H. Freeman, *J. Immunol.*, **55**, 289 (1947).
242a. Pirofsky, B., and M. S. Cordova, *Nature*, **197**, 393 (1963).
243. Pirofsky, B., and M. S. Cordova, *Vox. Sanguinis*, **9**, 17–21 (1964).
244. von Pirquet, C. E., *Arch. Internal Med.*, **7**, 259 (1911).
245. Plescia, O. J., E. L. Becker, and J. W. Williams, *J. Am. Chem. Soc.*, **74**, 1362 (1952).
246. Pope, C. G., *Brit. J. Exptl. Pathol.*, **20**, 132, 201, 213 (1939).
247. Pope, C. G., and M. F. Stevens, *Brit. J. Exptl. Pathol.*, **34**, 56 (1952).
248. Porter, R. R., *Biochem. J. (London)*, **46**, 479 (1950).
249. Porter, R. R., "The relation of chemical structures to the biological activity of the proteins," in *The Proteins*, H. Neurath and K. Bailey, eds., Vol. 1, Part B, Academic Press, New York, 1953.
250. Porter, R. R., in *Basic Problems in Neoplastic Disease*, A. Gellhorn and E. Hirschberg, eds., p. 177, Columbia University Press, New York, 1962.
251. Potter, M., and J. L. Fahey, *J. Nat. Cancer Inst.*, **24**, 1153 (1960).
252. Prasad, A. S., and D. W. Koza, *Ann. Internal Med.*, **41**, 629 (1954).
253. Pressman, D., and L. A. Sternberger, *J. Immunol.*, **66**, 609 (1951).
254. Pressman, D., A. Nisonoff, G. Radzimski, and A. Shaw, *J. Immunol.*, **86**, 489–495 (1961).
255. Race, R. R., and R. Sanger, *Blood Groups in Man*, 2nd ed., Blackwell, Oxford, 1954.
256. Raffel, S., *Immunity*, Appleton-Century-Crofts, New York, 1953.
257. Raffel, S., *Immunity*, Appleton-Century-Crofts, New York, 1961.
258. Ramon, G., *Compt. rend. soc. biol.*, **86**, 661, 771, 813 (1922).
259. Ramon, G., and E. Lemétayer, *Compt. rend. soc. biol.*, **116**, 275 (1934).
260. Ramon, G., and E. Lemétayer, *Rev. immunol.*, **1**, 209 (1935).
261. Rawson, A. J., and N. M. Abelson, *J. Immunol.*, **93**, 192 (1964).
262. Reymann, G. C., *Z. Immunitätsforsch.*, **39**, 15 (1924).
263. Rich, A. R., *Physiol. Rev.*, **21**, 70 (1941).
264. Richter, M., S. Zimmerman, and F. Haurowitz, *J. Immunol.*, **94**, 938–941 (1965).
265. Rifkind, R. A., E. F. Osserman, K. C. Hsu, and C. Morgan, *J. Exptl. Med.*, **116**, 423–432 (1962).
266. Ropartz, C., J. Lenoir, and L. Rivat, *Nature*, **189**, 586 (1961).
267. Ropartz, C., P. Y. Roussean, L. Rivat, and J. Lenoir, *Rev. France Etudes Clin., Biol.*, **6**, 374–377 (1961).
268. Rothen, A., *J. Gen. Physiol.*, **25**, 487 (1942).

269. Sabin, A. B., et. al., Proc. Soc. Exptl. Biol. Med., 65, 135 (1947).
270. Saha, A., J. S. Garvey, and D. H. Campbell, Arch. Biochem., 105, 179 (1964).
271. Sahiar, K., and R. S. Schwartz, Science, 145, 395–397 (1964).
272. Saton, T., Z. Immunitätsforsch., 79, 117 (1933).
272a. Schachman, H. K., Ultracentrifugation in Biochemistry, Academic Press, New York-London, 1959.
273. Schaffner, F., and H. Popper, Nature, 196, 684–685 (1962).
274. v. d. Scheer, J., E. Bahnel, F. H. Clarke, and R. W. G. Wycoff, J. Immunol., 44, 165 (1942).
275. v. d. Scheer, J., J. G. Lagsdin, and R. W. G. Wycoff, J. Immunol., 41, 209 (1941).
276. v. d. Scheer, J., R. W. G. Wycoff, and F. H. Clarke, J. Immunol., 41, 349 (1941).
277. Schultze, H. E., "Bildung der Antikörper," 10 Colloquium der Gesellschaft für Physiologische Chemie in Mosbach, Springer, Berlin, 1959, p. 146.
278. Schwartz, R., personal communication, 1965.
279. Seltzer, G., S. Baron, and M. Toporek, New Engl. J. Med., 252, 252 (sic) (1955).
280. Sercarz, E. E., and A. H. Coons, J. Immunol., 90, 478–491 (1963).
281. Shulman, S., L. Hubler, and E. Wifebsky, Science, 145, 815–817 (1964).
282. Silverstein, A. M., Science, 144, 1423–1428 (1964).
283. Singer, S. J., Proc. Natl. Acad. Sci., 41, 1041 (1955).
284. Singer, S. J., Immunochemistry, 1, 15–20 (1964).
285. Singer, S. J., and D. H. Campbell, J. Am. Chem. Soc., 74, 1794 (1952).
286. Singer, S. J., J. E. Fothergill, and J. R. Shainoff, J. Am. Chem. Soc., 82, 565–571 (1960).
287. Smith, E. L., and B. V. Jager, Ann. Rev. Microbiol., 6, 207 (1952).
288. Smith, F. C., and J. Marrack, Brit, J. Exptl. Pathol., 11, 494 (1930).
289. Smithies, O., Science, 149, 151–156 (1965).
289a. Springer, G. F., Klin. Woch., 38, 513 (1960).
290. Spurr, C. L., Proc. Soc. Exptl. Biol. Med., 64, 259 (1947).
291. Stavitsky, A. B., Advances in Immunology, 211–261, Academic Press, New York, vol. 1, 1961.
292. Steinberg, A. G., J. A. Wilson, and S. Lauset, Vox. Sanguinis, 7, 151–156 (1962).
293. Sternberger, L. A., and D. Pressman, J. Immunol., 65, 65 (1950).
294. Šterzl, J., Nature, 183, 547 (1959).
295. Sumner, J., and J. S. Kirk, Z. Physiol. Chem., 205, 219 (1932).
296. Sundberg, R. D., Ann. N. Y. Acad. Sci., 59, 671–689 (1955).
296a. Sutton, E. H., Science, 150, 858 (1965).
297. Svedberg, T., and K. O. Pedersen, The Ultracentrifuge, Oxford University Press, London, 1940.
298. Svensson, H., J. Biol. Chem., 139, 805 (1941).
299. Taliaferro, W. H., Ann. N. Y. Acad. Sci., 69, 745 (1957).
300. Talmage, D. W., Ann. Rev. Med., 8, 239 (1957).
301. Talmage, D. W., Science, 129, 1643 (1959).
302. Taylor, J. F., "The isolation of proteins," in The Proteins, H. Neurath and K. Bailey, eds., Vol. 1, Part A, Academic Press, New York, 1953.
303. Temin, H. M., Proc. Natl. Acad. Sci., 52, 323 (1964).
304. Thomsen, O., and K. Kettel, Z. Immunitätsforsch., 63, 67 (1929).
305. Thorbecke, G. J., and F. J. Keuning, J. Immunol., 70, 129 (1953).
306. Tiselius, A., J. Biol. Chem., 139, 805 (1937).
307. Tiselius, A., and E. A. Kabat, J. Exptl. Med., 69, 119 (1939).

308. Tsukahara, I., Z. *Immunitätsforsch.*, **32**, 410 (1921).
309. Tunis, M., *J. Immunol.*, **92**, 864–869 (1964).
310. Uhr, J. W., *Science*, **145**, 457–464 (1964).
310a. Utsumi, S., and F. Karush, *Biochem.*, **4**, 1766 (1965).
311. Wagley, P. F., I. W. Sizer, L. K. Diamond, and F. H. Allen, *J. Immunol.*, **64**, 85 (1950).
312. Waksman, B. H., B. G. Arnason, and B. D. Janković, *J. Exptl. Med.*, **116**, 187–206 (1962).
313. Walker, B. S., W. C. Boyd, and I. Asimov, *Biochemistry and Human Metabolism*, Williams and Wilkins, Baltimore, 1954.
314. Weichardt, W., and E. Schrader, *Munch. med. Wochschr.*, **66**, 289 (1919).
315. Weil, A. J., I. A. Parfentjev, and K. L. Bowman, *J. Immunol.*, **35**, 399 (1938).
316. White, R. G., *Brit., J. Exptl. Pathol.*, **35**, 365–376 (1954).
317. White, R. G., in *Mechanisms of Antibody Formation*, M. Holub and L. Jaroškova, eds., Pub. House of Czech. Acad. Sci., Prague, 1960, pp. 25–29.
318. Wiener, A. S., *Exptl. Med. Surg.*, **5**, Nos. 2–3 (1947).
319. Wiener, A. S., *J. Immunol.*, **66**, 287 (1951).
320. Wiener, A. S., *Rh-Hr Blood Types*, Grune and Stratton, New York, 1954.
321. Williams, J. W., *Fortschr. Chem. Org. Naturstoffe*, **7**, 270 (1950).
322. Willis, H. S., *Am. Rev. Tuberc.*, **17**, 240 (1928).
323. Winkler, M. H., *J. Theoretical Biol.*, **4**, 237–241 (1963).
324. Winn, H. J., C. D. Matt, and C. S. Wright, *J. Immunol.*, **71**, 261 (1953).
325. Wissler, R. W., R. L. Woolridge, and C. H. Steffee, *Proc. Soc. Exptl. Biol. Med.*, **62**, 199 (1946).
326. Wissler, R. W., R. L. Woolridge, C. H. Steffee, and P. R. Cannon, *J. Immunol.*, **52**, 267 (1946).
327. Wooles, W. R., and N. R. Di Luzio, *Science*, **142**, 1078–1080 (1963).
328. Wu, H., L. H. Cheng, and C. P. Li, *Proc. Soc. Exptl. Biol. Med.*, **25**, 853 (1928).
329. Wu, H., P. P. T. Sah, and C. P. Li, *Proc. Soc. Exptl. Biol. Med.*, **26**, 737 (1929).
330. Wyman, J., and E. N. Ingalls, *J. Biol. Chem.*, **147**, 297 (1943).
331. Zinsser, H., *J. Immunol.*, **6**, 289 (1921).
332. Zinsser, H., J. F. Enders, and L. D. Fothergill, *Immunity: Principles and Application in Medicine and Public Health*, Macmillan, New York, 1939.
333. Zwicker, H., L. Giordano, and R. E. Hoyt, *J. Immunol.*, **69**, 415 (1952).

CHAPTER 3

Antigens

The word "antigen" has been used in two senses, first to denote a substance which, when introduced parenterally* into an animal, will cause the production of antibodies; second, to denote a substance which reacts in a visible way with antibodies. The latter class includes practically all of the first, but the reverse is not so; that is, there are a number of substances which, although they react with antibodies, have not been shown to produce antibodies when injected into animals. A substance is not said to be *antigenic* unless it will cause the production of antibodies or initiate some other "immune" response, such as sensitization.

Antigenicity is not restricted to substances produced by microorganisms and parasites. Protein poisons such as snake venom may cause the production of neutralizing antibodies, and harmless foreign cells such as erythrocytes and innocuous proteins such as ovalbumin will also act as antigens. It is true that the result may not be to make the animal producing the antibodies more resistant, for Portier and Richet (220) discovered that dogs treated with the poisonous extracts of the tentacles of certain sea anemones became more instead of less susceptible, and a guinea pig injected once with ovalbumin, which is in the first instance perfectly harmless, may react fatally to a later injection. Nevertheless there is reason to include these happenings under the general classification of immune phenomena.

Immunity to the poisonous protein of the castor bean (*Ricinus communis*) can be produced by feeding (55) and hypersensitivity to food allergens, which are usually proteins, results from ingestion of the antigen. Proteins degraded by digestive enzymes (or in other ways) to their

---

* That is, outside the digestive tract. This gives an antigen the best chance to act, although some antigens are effective when fed.

117

constituent amino acids or to simple polypeptides are no longer antigenic, so immunization in the above examples evidently results from the absorption of sufficient protein, intact or relatively so, from the gastro-intestinal tract.

1. Conditions of Antigenicity

It is to be hoped that eventually we shall be able to answer the obvious question: what makes a given substance antigenic to a given animal? At present we are far from having a complete answer. If we attempt to generalize from the scanty available data, we may make the following statements (25);

1. Antigens must be foreign to the circulation of the experimental animal, and the more foreign (*i.e.*, the more remote the source taxonomically), the more antigenic a protein will be. The problem of the (usual) unresponsiveness of the organism to its own antigens is discussed in Chapter 12.

Proteins fulfilling very similar functions in different species are similar chemically, and this doubtless accounts for the low antigenicity of such proteins. Hemoglobin from the horse is a poor antigen for rabbits, although the plasma proteins of the horse are good antigens. It is tempting to speculate that the plasma proteins, especially the globulins, have a more specialized role than does the hemoglobin, whose function is much the same in all mammalian species. Once a suitable amino acid sequence for hemoglobin had been hit upon, there was no particular evolutionary reason to change it much.

Similarly, insulin, even from such taxonomically remote animals as the hog and the cow, is seldom an antigen in man (151,104). Insulin fulfills the same function in all the higher animals, and seemingly does not vary much chemically from one species to another.

2. Antigens must have more than a certain minimal degree of complexity and a certain molecular size. This is suggested by the non-antigenicity of the protamines and of the relatively simple molecule of gelatin, and by the high antigenicity of the large molecules of the hemocyanins.

Size alone however does not necessarily mean antigenicity. Glucagon, a pancreatic hormone with a molecular weight of about 3,800, has provoked an antibody response, and foreign insulin, MW about 6,000, will fairly regularly cause antibody production if injected with adjuvants (p. 125), whereas in man dextrans with a MW less than 100,000 are not antigenic.

The importance of particle size in antigenicity is indicated by observations that nonantigenic or weakly antigenic substances can sometimes be made antigenic by adsorbing them on particulate matter such as collodion particles, kaolin, or charcoal (73,130,213,242). Even merely suspending particulate material, especially killed microorganisms, in a solution of an antigen may suffice to enhance the antigenic stimulus so that fair antisera can be obtained against poor antigens such as hemoglobin. Boyd at first employed killed typhoid bacilli, but later the less toxic *Monilia candida* (24). It has been observed that intact microorganisms may produce a better antibody response to a constituent antigen than will the antigen alone (180).

According to Haurowitz (80) another prerequisite for antigenicity is rigid structure of the determinant groups. He believes that the highly specific action of the aromatic diazo compounds is due to the rigidity of their benzene rings, while the inability of the long-chain fatty acids to act as determinant groups is due to the fact that the paraffin chains are easily distorted, and their shape constantly alters.

Various workers have been led to speculate further as to the causes of antigenicity, and some speculations have been the result of comparing gelatin with other proteins. The first suggestion of this sort is due to Obermayer and Pick (189). In a passage which has often been misquoted, they said: "Therefore it seems probable to us that the species specific groupings in the protein molecule are mainly influenced by groups which are connected with the aromatic nuclei of the protein. It hardly has to be mentioned that the aromatic groups in themselves naturally would not suffice to explain the enormous number of possible variations which nature calls for, and that our conception of the role of the aromatic groups is that they are so to speak the center around which the species specific side chains group themselves; the entrance of substituents smooths out these species differences." It is apparent that these authors were more concerned with specificity than with antigenicity, but they have often been cited (248) as suggesting that the possession of aromatic amino acids is requisite for antigenicity.

When proteins are racemized by treatment with alkali, they are no longer antigenic. Since it was found by Dakin and Dudley (43) that such proteins were no longer susceptible to hydrolysis by enzymes, it was suggested that these facts were causally related (240). However, other workers have found (147) that these racemized proteins are not completely resistant to enzyme action. It has also been found that the antigenicity is lost more rapidly than the optical activity (257). Landsteiner (126) pointed out that the alkali might destroy structures significant for the antigenic function at the same time it produced racemization. The lower antigenicity of alkali-treated proteins may possibly be connected also with the smaller size of their molecules; Boyd (16) found that on treatment of crystalline ovalbumin with alkali there was at first a marked rise in optical activity to several times the initial value, followed by a slower fall to a minimum, indicating possibly that the molecule was first split, then racemized.

That racemization does not in itself mean nonantigenicity is indicated by the observation of Landsteiner and Barron (129) that nitration of racemized proteins restored some degree of antigenicity, as, to a less extent, did iodination (109).

It is quite certain that aromatic amino acids in an antigen do not suffice to make it antigenic, and the absence of aromatic acids does not mean that a substance cannot be antigenic. As already mentioned, proteins that have been "racemized" (which probably involves also denaturation or hydrolysis) by treatment with alkali (240) are no longer antigenic, although any aromatic amino acids they may have possessed are still present. Proteins that have been altered to the point that they no longer show the characteristic absorption bands of aromatic rings may still be antigenic (252,226). The pneumococcus polysaccharides, which contain no aromatic groups, are antigenic for men and mice (49). Sulfonated polystyrene (I), although full of aromatic groups, is not antigenic (19).

$$CH_2-CH_2-\left[CH-CH_2-\right]_x-C=CH_2$$

SO$_3$H   SO$_3$H   SO$_3$H

I

Campbell and Bulman (36) suggested that to be antigenic a substance must be at least partly susceptible to the action of hydrolytic enzymes of the injected animal. The general validity of this rule seems doubtful, but the nonantigenicity of sulfonated polystyrene is in accord with it.

Furthermore, nonantigenic proteins can be rendered antigenic by treatments which do not add to their content of aromatic residues. Alkali-treated proteins can be made antigenic again by nitration (129) and iodination (109). Gelatin can be rendered antigenic by coupling it with a variety of chemicals, such as arsanilic acid (99a). It is true that arsanilic acid is an aromatic compound and couples with aromatic groups (tyrosine and histidine) in the protein molecule, but it is doubtful if it is the aromatic character of the introduced group which is important. More likely it is its acidic character (128). Gostev (74) reported being able to make starch antigenic by coupling sulfanilic and arsanilic acids to it.

Haurowitz (79) attributed the nonantigenicity of gelatin to three causes: (1) It is a heat-treated denatured protein and thus has no definite fixed internal structure. (2) It is not deposited in the organism into which it is introduced, but is rapidly excreted. (3) It contains large amounts of glycine, the one amino acid having no side chain in the alpha position. Such linkages allow free rotation around the longitudinal axis and as a result the molecule has no fixed configuration (186). It seems reasonable that an antigen must have a definite configuration for it to be copied (in reverse) by the antibody-forming mechanism.

The role of rigidity had been emphasized by the brilliant work of Sela (235) on synthetic antigens. He believed that as little as 2 per cent of tyrosine, or other rigid antigenic grouping, would be enough to make gelatin a good antigen. He reported that tryptophane, phenylalanine, and possibly cysteine also work. Histidine, methionine, and leucine had not yet been tested (235).

When gelatin is injected it is rapidly excreted from the body. (If it were not it might be a valuable blood substitute or "plasma expander.") But then most antigens soon disappear from the circulation, and apparently the more powerful antigens disappear faster. The very small amount of an antigen which gets trapped by the reticuloendothelial system (see Chapter 2) seems to be responsible for initiating antibody formation. So the disappearance of gelatin from the circulation may not have any bearing on its nonantigenicity, and it would be difficult to prove that small amounts, comparable to the amounts of other, antigenic, proteins are not retained somewhere in the body. Furthermore, the retention of a substance in the body does not always mean it is going to act as an antigen. Gum acacia, used as a blood substitute in World War I, is retained in the body—the liver, apparently—for a very long time, but does not seem to act as an antigen. And mice injected with too large a dose of pneumococcus polysaccharide do not produce detectable antibody, and can not thereafter be induced to produce such antibody by the injection of the proper dose (which is quite small) of the polysaccharide. See p. 510. The only explanation seems to be that they retain some of the polysaccharide in their bodies after the first injection, but this retained polysaccharide, far from being an antigenic stimulus, actually paralyzes the antibody-forming mechanism in so far as this particular antibody is concerned.   See Chapter 12.

We do not yet even understand really how the chemical treatments mentioned above make gelatin antigenic.   We might perhaps speculate in a vague sort of way that the introduced chemical groups in some way *accentuate* the individuality of the gelatin structure, and nitration and iodination do not accentuate it enough.   It may be noted that coupling with o-β-glucosidotyrosine, which makes gelatin antigenic, also increases the antigenicity of the weak antigen insulin (104).

Work of Maurer (see p. 126) suggests that gelatin itself under suitable conditions (*e.g.*, when mixed with adjuvants) can be antigenic, and that small amounts of a protein which behaves like antigelatin antibody are found in numerous sera.   This suggests that gelatin, although certainly a much weaker antigen than many, probably most, proteins, does some-times act as an antigenic stimulus, as antibodies are produced—possibly only under abnormal conditions (see Chapter 11)—to the collagen of the body and these antibodies also react weakly with gelatin.

None of the special theories of antigenicity thus far put forward seem to explain the low antigenicity of insulin and hemoglobin; this is probably accounted for by the chemical similarity of these proteins, whether they are of equine, bovine, or porcine origin, to the corresponding protein of the experimental animal.

By no means all antigens are proteins.   Many years ago Abel and Ford (1) reported antibody production to a toxic glucoside from the mushroom *Amanita phalloides*.   Many carbohydrates are antigenic; the capsular polysaccharides of the pneumococcus are antigenic in man and mice, although not in rabbits and horses (49).   Even alkali-degraded pneumo-coccus polysaccharides may be fully antigenic for man (87).   Antiagar antibodies are commonly obtained when agar-grown microorganisms are injected into animals (48).   Gum acacia and cherry gum act similarly when conjugated with bacterial proteins (48).   The human blood group substances, which are mucopolysaccharides, are antigenic in man, though not in rabbits (Chapter 5).   (The Forssman antigen is discussed in Chapter 4.)   Campbell (35) isolated a nitrogen-free polysaccharide from *Ascaris lumbricoides* that was antigenic.   The high molecular weight bacterial polysaccharide, dextran, which has been suggested as a blood substitute, is an antigen in man (113,163).   Glycogen may be antigenic (84).   Some lipide–carbohydrate–protein complexes are antigenic, with the specificity determined by the carbohydrate portion (see p. 216).   Certain protein–lipide combinations seem to be antigenic (see p. 183).

Aside from proteins, carbohydrates, and lipide–carbohydrate–protein complexes, it has not been definitely established that any other class of compound is antigenic, although other, even simpler, compounds may be haptenic (Chapter 9).

As a rule, an animal's own proteins, or those of another individual of the same species, are not antigenic for it. In immunology this principle has received the name of *horror autotoxicus* (fear of poisoning one's self), which is stated thus: an animal will not produce antibodies to any substance normally found in his own circulation. (See, however, Chapter 2 and Chapter 13.)

Although it is true that no antibodies for the proteins found in the circulation of an animal are ever found, certain immunologists have argued that they are nevertheless produced. If an animal did produce antibodies to its own hemoglobin or plasma proteins, these antibodies would be combined with by the great excess of the antigen constantly present, and the antibody–antigen compound would be promptly removed from the circulation, so that no trace of the antibody would ever be detected. It is thus conceivable that each animal is constantly producing antibodies to its own hemoglobin, serum albumin, serum globulins, and so on, and that these antibodies are removed as fast as they are formed. But it may be argued on broad biological grounds that this is unlikely, for it supposes that each animal is constantly producing a supply of precisely engineered molecules which are promptly eliminated without ever having served any useful purpose. The amino acids which went into the composition of such molecules might be recovered and used again, but the thermodynamic work involved in elaborating them would be permanently lost. It seems likely that natural selection would have eliminated such a wasteful mechanism ages ago.

Proteins and carbohydrates found in an animal's own circulation are thus not generally antigenic for the animal producing them. This rule, if it is a rule, does not apply to substances that are produced by the animal under such circumstances that they do not normally find their way into the circulation. The milk proteins furnish an example. The milk proteins, except possibly the γ-globulins, are not derived directly from the plasma proteins but synthesized by the mammary gland. They are thus foreign to the circulation, and it is not surprising that casein, for example, will act as an antigen when injected into another animal of the same species, or even into the individual that produced it. Lewis (145) was able to cause lactating goats to form antibodies to their own casein. It has even been reported that about one fifth of women who suddenly stop lactating develop antibodies against antigens of their own milk (4a).

Similarly it seems that the proteins of the lens of the eye are autoanti-genic (156), and it has been reported that a guinea pig can be sensitized anaphylactically to the proteins contained in one of its eyes and, after an appropriate interval, shocked by injection of the proteins of the other eye (145).

In line with the nonantigenicity of an animal's own blood proteins, it is found that the proteins from closely related animals, which are chemi-cally much like those of the experimental animal, are nonantigenic, or at any rate poor antigens. In general, proteins are better antigens if they come from organisms that are taxonomically remote from the experimental animal. Most plant proteins, for example, seem to be good antigens. In rabbits, we find that hemocyanin is a powerful antigen in them, whereas horse hemoglobin, for example, is a poor antigen. In fact hemoglobin is such a poor antigen that it has several times been erroneously reported to be nonantigenic. More careful work has established its antigenicity (25,79). Egg albumin from the hen is a good antigen for rabbits, but Hooker and Boyd (101) failed to obtain a response to it in ducks. The proteins of horse serum, notably the albumins, are good antigens for the rabbit and (unfortunately) also for man. The very small amount of horse serum (about 0.01 ml.) which was contained in the toxin-antitoxin mix-tures once used for immunization to diphtheria regularly sensitized more than 25 per cent of the individuals receiving the injections (241).

None of the theories of antigenicity offered seems entirely adequate. Antigens must be foreign to the animal's circulation and must not be too simple in structure; that is about all we can say with confidence.

The possibility that under abnormal conditions the body may form antibodies to constituents of its own tissues, generally to its disadvantage, will be discussed in Chapter 13.

Homogeneity

When referring to antigens it is easy to say that the same antigen was used in two experiments, A and B, but it is by no means easy to be sure that preparations A and B were really identical. Generally we have processed our materials in some way, and although we may think this has not affected them, we are never sure. The writer is not likely to forget the serum sickness caused during World War II by purified (crystalline) bovine serum albumin (See Chapter 9).

Even aside from problems of processing, it is often difficult to be sure that preparations A and B are the same. For the proteins of higher species, at any rate, often vary in antigenic specificity because of allotypy (see Chapter 2). That is, the protein that fulfills an identical function in individuals of a species may exist in more than one antigenically different form. These differences are apparently hereditary and the polymorphism is stabilized by evolutionary forces we do not yet fully understand.

Charge

Landsteiner's work showed the importance of electric charge in antigenicity. However, charge is not essential, for the blood group substances, containing no ionized groups as an essential constituent, are antigenic, and Sela and Fuchs (235a) have produced a synthetic polypeptide devoid of charge that is antigenic.

Synthetic Antigens

Synthetic antigens (polypetides) have been made (239,62,165). Sela believes that the results obtained with them, in addition to suggesting that rigidity of the molecule is an important feature of an antigen, indicate that the antigenically important area of the molecule should be accessible to the cellular site of antibody synthesis, and not hidden in the interior of the molecule.

Adjuvants

Adjuvants are substances which when mixed with antigens improve antibody production or other immune response. They may be antigenic, like killed microorganisms, or nonantigenic, like alum and mineral oil (48,60,51).

The use of such additional substances for the intensification of the antibody response originated with Pasteur (201). Since then a number of adjuvants have been introduced and studied. Ramon (54), for example, mixed tapioca with antigen preparations.

Precipitation of diphtheria toxoid with alum (potassium aluminum sulfate) brings the material into particulate form and purifies it somewhat. The method has also been used with tetanus toxoid, *Pertussis,* and in mixed vaccines. There is good evidence that these alum-precipitated vaccines produce higher antibody titers and longer immunity.

Aluminum hydroxide (alumina cream), also a protein precipitant, has been shown to increase the antigenic stimulus in some cases, as with scarlet fever toxoid. There is evidence that it is even better than alum in the case of diphtheria and tetanus toxoids (172).

Mixtures of mineral oil with aqueous preparations of antigens, emulsified with lanolin, were introduced by Freund (58–69), and have become increasingly popular. During World War II Freund *et al.* (61) were even able to produce immunity to malaria in monkeys by this technic, but the process proved too heroic to apply in man. Heidelberger *et al.* (88) found that the injection of formalized plasmodia, without adjuvants, produced no immunity.

The addition of killed tubercle bacilli to such emulsions greatly increases their adjuvant effect. This is caused by a lipopolysaccharide of the bacillus (228).

Other substances have been used. Salk (234) used calcium phosphate to mix with influenza virus. Staphylococcus toxin has been reported to improve some immunological responses.

Although antigens may sometimes interfere with each other when injected together (see below), there are also numerous cases in which certain combinations of antigens exert an adjuvant effect on each other, especially, apparently, if one produces local inflammation, when given in the doses cutomarily used for human immunization (54).

The mechanism of action of adjuvants is not entirely understood. When they bring the antigen into particulate form they may influence its being taken up by the phagocytes, and such precipitated antigen may persist in the tissues longer. The irritating effect of substances such as alum may be a factor. Ramon (54) many years ago noted the enhancing effect of accidentally induced inflammation at the site of inoculation. The injection of the oil–water–lanolin–tubercle bacilli mixtures of Freund produces a sterile abscess which is irritating and from which the antigen is released slowly, although these facts probably do not wholly explain the effect.

It has been found that when the mouse, which is relatively refractory to anaphylactic sensitization, is injected with certain antigens mixed with *Pertussis* vaccine, sensitization is relatively easily produced (155). Circulating antibodies could not however be demonstrated in such animals, and Malkiel (155) doubted that the *Pertussis* was acting as an adjuvant in such experiments. The phenomenon seems to be as yet unexplained, nor is it known how it is connected with the increase in sensitivity to histamine which injection of *Pertussis* vaccine produces in mice.

2. Competition of Antigens

When a weak and a strong antigen are injected together, the animal may fail to respond to the weaker antigen, particularly if this is present in smaller amount (128,11). This (probably rare) phenomenon has been termed "competition of antigens." It is roughly the converse of the effect obtained with mixtures of antigens which are all good antigens (see above) (3).

3. The Specificity of Antigens

The specificity of antigens resides in the structural peculiarities of their molecules. While it has not been possible in every case to correlate immunological differences in substances, particularly proteins, with their chemical structure, there is no doubt that this is simply because of our ignorance of the detailed structure of these compounds. The dependence of specificity on chemical structure is proved by several lines of evidence. (1) Purified proteins that exhibit chemical differences can nearly always be differentiated serologically (76,101,141,146); (2) carbohydrates related structurally give serological cross reactions (67,71); (3) simple chemical substances (haptens and some allergens) give cross reactions when chemically similar (126); (4) chemical alteration of antigens generally alters their specificity; (5) corresponding proteins of different species which are functionally, and thus probably structurally, related generally cross-react.

The very large number of specifically different antigens need cause no surprise, in view of the power of the antibody-forming mechanism to recognize the smallest shades of chemical difference (see p. 155) and in view of the enormous number of different proteins that can be built up from the known amino acids (5), and the smaller but still enormous number of possible polysaccharides (82).

4. Nature of Antigenic Determinants (Epitopes)

Antibodies can be obtained which are specific for a simple chemical compound (called in this connection a *hapten*) and which precipitate proteins which have had this group introduced into them. In this case we know something about the size and chemical nature of the specific reactive group in the antigen, *i.e.*, it equals the introduced hapten (except in cases where the adjacent portions of the protein molecule seem also to play some role). The location and spacing of the haptens in the conjugated protein molecule, however, remain unknown.

With the natural protein antigens we do not have even this much information to guide us. We certainly cannot suppose that the whole molecule is the antigenic determinant and that every part of it is required for the full specificity. This would not fit with the fact that several molecules of specific antibody can combine simultaneously with a molecule of antigen. The known behavior of protein molecules in solution as globular particles, perhaps prolate ellipsoids, does not allow us to suppose that an antibody can come into effective contact with more than a portion of the antigen molecule. Evidently the antigenic determinant must be only a part of the complete molecule. It has been customary to call the portions of the antigenic molecule, that the antibody-forming mechanism responds to, antigenic determinants. Jerne (108) has proposed the term *epitopes*, and it is to be hoped that this usage will become general.

Attempts have been made to get some idea of the size of such determinants (epitopes) by testing fragments of the molecule obtained by the action of enzymes, etc., for specific reactivity with antibody (usually by the inhibition technic) but with little success. However, it is not certain that the specific determinants of an antigen molecule can ever be identified with any particular fragments of the polypeptide chain alone, for this chain is folded up in a complicated way in the intact molecule, and the determinant might consist of parts of several adjacent chains (158) which in the intact molecule are held together by hydrogen bonds or other forces (see Fig. 3-2).

Landsteiner (127) reported obtaining hydrolysis products of silk, consisting of peptides having molecular weights of about 600 to 1000, which were capable of inhibiting the reactions of precipitin sera for silk. This experiment may perhaps serve provisionally to set an upper limit to the size of the antigenic determinants in natural proteins. It must be recalled, however, that compounds simpler than the actual determinant, but chemically related to it, in studies on conjugated antigens have been observed to inhibit (p. 163).

This work has been confirmed by Cebra (37), who found that tyrosine forms an important part of the antigenic determinant in silk fibroin, but that a considerable length of the glycyl–alanyl chain is also required for detectable specific combination. Dodecapeptides (MW *ca.* 900) were the most active of the peptides compared, giving up to 50 per cent inhibition. Of the octopeptides tested, $Gly(gly_3ala_3)tyr$ (MW *ca.* 600) was the most effective inhibitor and probably represents a major part of the specific antigenic determinant.

There is no reason to believe that the antigenic determinants in proteins are prosthetic groups of carbohydrate or of other nonprotein nature. The surfaces of globular proteins possess negatively charged groups $(RCOO^-)$ from aspartic and glutamic acid residues, and positively charged groups (RNH_3^+) from lysine and arginine residues. In addition, the phenolic hydroxyls of the tyrosine and the imidazole groups of the histidine residues are polar; the work of Landsteiner (128) on "synthetic" antigens showed that the polar groups may be of decisive significance for specificity.

We know proteins to be made up of chains of amino acids, held together by the peptide linkages. If such a chain were stretched out, part of it might look like Fig. 3-1. As proteins are present in solution, they are globular or ellipsoidal in shape, so we must assume the peptide chain is rolled up. Marrack (157) suggested that, considering the importance of the terminal amino acid in the peptide haptens studied by Landsteiner and van der Scheer (see Table 3-5), it is probable that the immunological character of natural proteins is determined by the arrangement of amino acids on the surface of the molecule. This is supported by evidence that

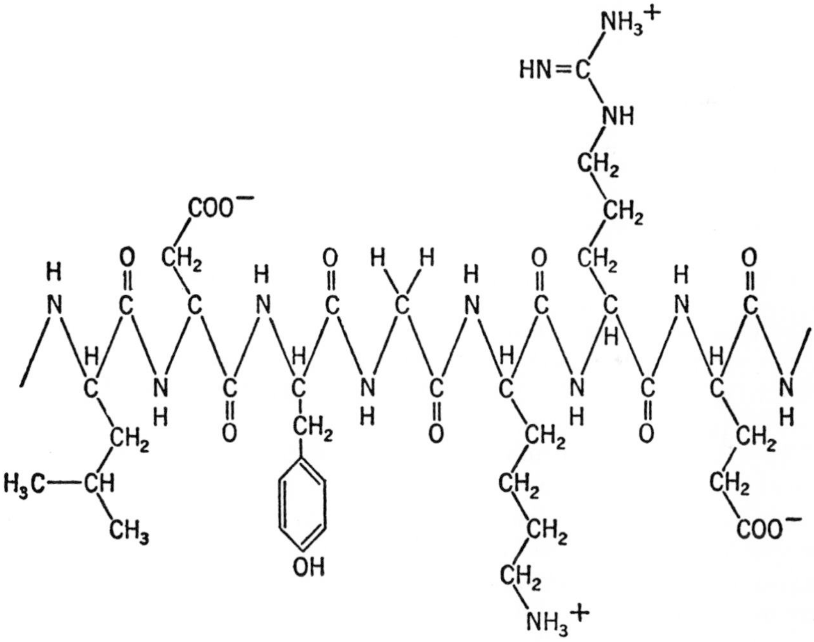

Fig. 3-1. Part of the polypeptide chain of a hypothetical protein.

antigens react as spherical or ellipsoidal molecules (21,23,197) (see Chapter 6). It is also compatible with results (38,232) indicating that monofilms of proteins about 9 A. thick still possess the power of reacting specifically with antibody.

Marrack (157) supposed that several of these amino acid residues acting together constituted an "active patch" on the surface of the antigen, with sufficient polarity to act as a strong combining site, and with a characteristic combination of, and spacing between, the polar groups to make the patch specifically characteristic of the protein in question. He pointed out that such a patch might be more or less completely altered by the molecular rearrangements taking place on denaturation; the latter, as we know, affects specificity and antigenicity. He supposed further that there would be a number of these "active patches" all with the same or very similar specificity (Fig. 3-2).

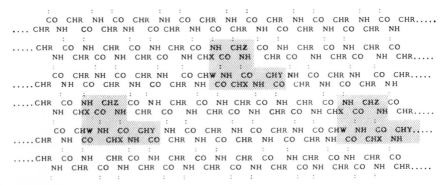

Fig. 3-2. Polypeptide chains represented as folded together and held together by iminocarbonyl hydrogen bonds. R represents amino acid residues (CH_3CH_2—C_6H_5—, etc.). Boxes indicate areas (Marrack's "active patches") where amino acid residues W, X, Y, and Z, which for some reason—perhaps being more polar—are of greater significance for antigenic determinants, recur in the same arrangement at intervals (20).

The role of individual amino acid residues in the antigenic determinants of native proteins has not been established. Possibly any portion of a protein molecule of sufficient size can function as such a determinant, the specificity being determined by the number and arrangement of the various amino acids. Kleczkowski (120) found that when iodine atoms were introduced into all of the tyrosine of horse serum globulin, the ability to combine with the antibody for native horse serum globulin was lost. This would seem to demonstrate that the tyrosine residue is an essential part of the determinant groups of this particular protein (assuming halogenation produced no other important changes). Certain workers (81,119) have obtained results from the study of conjugated proteins which suggest that in horse serum globulin tyrosine forms an essential part of the antigenic determinants. Haurowitz, Sarafian, and Schwerin (79,81) suggested that the determinants consist in fact of a definite arrangement of tyrosine groups, free amino groups, and perhaps other groups, on the surface of the protein molecule. In such determinants polar groups might play a prominent role. Kabat and Heidelberger (114) similarly found the phenolic groups to be an essential part of the antigenic determinants of ovalbumin. Their work indicated, however, that these groups were not essential in bovine serum albumin.

Blumenthal (12) reported that the sulfhydryl groups were not essential to the antigenic determinants of ovalbumin. It has been reported (158) that neither $-NH_2$ nor other ionizable groups (such as $-COOH$ and guanidino) constitute essential parts of the determinants of native proteins.

Pressman and Sternberger (225) found that a hapten when combined specifically with an antibody protected the specific combining sites against the destructive effects of iodination. Since the introduction of small amounts of iodine affects only the tyrosine, histidine, and cysteine residues, it seems that some or all these residues may be essential parts of the specific combining groups. Porter (218) found that, although all the histidine residues of rabbit antibody ovalbumin precipitates were available to combination with fluorodinitrobenzene, one histidine residue of the ovalbumin rabbit antiovalbumin was not available. This seems to indicate that histidine forms part of the combining group of the antibody (or of the antigen).

The studies of Cebra (37) on silk fibroin showed that although an octapeptide, $Gly(gly_3ala_3)tyr$, was a very good inhibitor of the antibody–antigen reaction, a mixture of dodecapeptides was better. Kabat (111) calculated that this establishes a minimum length for the antigenic determinant (epitope) of about 44 A.

Brown et al. (29) were able to obtain peptide fragments by enzymatic digestion of bovine ribonuclease that would inhibit antibody to native ribonuclease. These peptides contained 20 to 24 amino acids and, interestingly enough, did not contain tyrosine (142).

The antigenic determinants of the polysaccharides seem to consist of combinations of two or a few hexose units. Kabat (110) obtained fairly precise information as to the size of the epitope in a carbohydrate antigen, by studying the inhibition reactions of the human antibodies produced against dextran, a large-molecule polysaccharide produced by certain bacteria. Dextran appears to be made up entirely of glucose, predominantly connected by 1-6 linkages (Fig. 3-3). With such a simple antigen the possible antigenic determinants are merely one or more glucose units. Finding out how big an antigenic carbohydrate determinant may have a specifically corresponding antibody determinant is simply a matter of finding out how many glucose units an oligosaccharide must contain to fill the combining site on the antibody. Kabat studied this question by measuring the relative inhibiting power for an anti-dextran serum acting

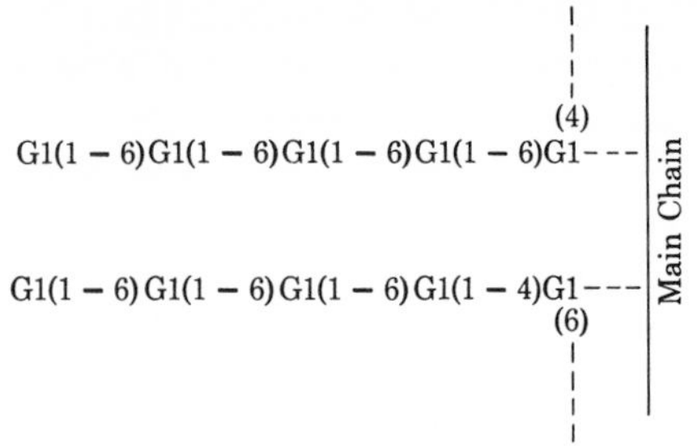

$$\begin{array}{l} \text{(4)} \\ \text{G1(1 - 6)G1(1 - 6)G1(1 - 6)G1(1 - 6)G1---} \\ \\ \text{G1(1 - 6)G1(1 - 6)G1(1 - 6)G1(1 - 4)G1---} \\ \text{(6)} \end{array}$$

Main Chain

Fig. 3-3. Suggested structure of dextran.

on dextran of glucose, isomaltose (two glucose units), isomaltotriose (three glucose units), and larger polysaccharides. The results are shown in Fig. 3-4. It is apparent that isomaltose (two glucose units) is distinctly better than glucose as an inhibitor but that isomaltotriose is much better than either, suggesting that the antibody determinant corresponds to an antigenic determinant of at least three glucose units. Actually, the data suggest that the antibodies can distinguish even isomaltohexaose (six glu-

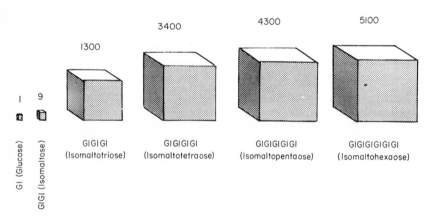

Fig. 3-4. Relative inhibitory power of oligosaccharides for anti-dextran serum acting on dextran (redrawn from data of Kabat, 110).

cose units) from any smaller antigenic determinant, but the difference between the pentaose and the hexaose is not great. Kabat suggests that the hexaose is the largest group capable of entering the cavity in the anti-dextran antibody molecule.

If the hexasaccharide is accepted as the largest group which can totally combine with the combining site of the antibody, the contribution of each glucose residue, starting with the terminal unit, to the total free binding energy between antibody and antigen can be computed. Such calculations are shown in Table 3-1, taken from Kabat (110). It will be seen that the terminal glucose contributes as much as 39 per cent of the total binding energy. The first five units together contribute 98 per cent of the binding energy, leaving only 2 per cent to be contributed by the sixth and later units.

TABLE 3-1

Calculated Contributions to the Free Energy of Combination of Glucoses in Reactive Groups of Dextran (110)

Number of glucose units	Contribution to binding energy, %
5	98
4	95
3	90
2	60
1 (terminal unit)	39

5. Number of Epitopes (Reactive Groups) (Valence) in an Antigen Molecule

Since we do not know the exact nature of the epitopes in natural proteins, we cannot determine accurately how many are present in a single molecule. From analyses of precipitates for antibody and antigen, however, it is possible to determine the maximal number of antibody molecules which can combine with a molecule of antigen; the "valence" of the antigen cannot be less than this. We thus set a lower limit for the valence of the antigen molecule. The following minimal values have been obtained (references in 103):

TABLE 3-2

Calculated "Valence" of Certain Protein Antigens

Antigen	Approx. molecular weight ($\times 10^{-3}$)	Valence
Ovalbumin	43–44	5
Serum albumin	70	6
Diphtheria toxin	70	8
Thyroglobulin	650	40
Busycon hemocyanin	6,500	74
Viviparus hemocyanin	6,500	231

Since the amount of antibody combining with a molecule of antigen tends to depend on the molecular weight of the antigen (21,23), the results for other antigens of molecular weights similar to those in the above table would probably be of the same order of magnitude.

These results are clearly limiting values, or minimal valences, because it is conceivable, and even likely, that there are more reactive groups on the surface of an antigen molecule than can simultaneously be combined with, because the molecules of antibody get in their own way, so to speak (steric hindrance). Also, calculations from the data indicate that when antibody is in excess the surface of each molecule of antigen is completely covered by molecules of antibody (21,23). Unless we are to suppose that the reactive groups which are present are distributed in each case with exactly the right spacing between them to allow all to react before steric hindrance blocks them off, it would seem that there must be more reactive groups present than this minimal number.

In the case of artificial antigens, it is possible to estimate the number of active groups in a molecule of antigen by chemical analysis. This method was applied by Hooker and Boyd (99) to compounds of diazotized arsanilic acid and casein. It was found that preparations containing less than about thirteen introduced groups per molecule would not precipitate with the antiarsanilic antiserum. Similar results were obtained by Haurowitz (77), who showed that a minimum of between ten and twenty introduced groups were needed, and furthermore that the failure of compounds of lower arsenic content to precipitate was not due merely to lessened acidic character. Reactivity and antigenicity are different, for compounds containing fewer introduced groups, down to only one per molecule, were found still able to immunize.

The results obtained with artificial antigens, contrary to those for natural proteins, may give too high a value for the valence, as we cannot be sure that all the introduced groups are on the surface, or if they are that they are in a position to combine with antibody. So the actual number functioning may be less than indicated. Taking account of all these points, we may perhaps surmise that the valence of protein molecules of moderate size is somewhere between five and fifteen (Table 3-2).

Certain nonprotein antigens, such as the pneumococcus polysaccharides, which are polymers of simpler compounds such as aldobionic acid, may contain the combining group repeated many times and are undoubtedly multivalent (157). In some cases we know the size and structure of the determinant groups, but the exact number of combining groups per molecule is in most cases still unknown, since in most cases we do not know the molecular weight of these substances.

6. Effect of Chemical Alteration and Conjugation on Specificity

Almost any decided chemical change in a protein may alter its specificity. It is worth while to survey the various methods which have been used in the study of immunological specificity. These methods may be conveniently considered as falling into two classes: (1) alterations of the protein structure; and (2) coupling of chemical compounds to the protein molecule (conjugation). We may define conjugated antigens as those giving rise to antibodies capable of reacting with the introduced group by itself. This permits in theory a sharp separation of the two types of antigens, although in some cases the requisite information is not available. Conjugation, of course, is usually accompanied by some alteration of the protein molecule itself. However, this is relatively unimportant, as the tests are usually carried out in a way that eliminates any influence of the protein carrier. The advantage of conjugated antigens for our purpose lies in the fact that we know the chemical constitution of the reacting groups and the number of them per molecule of protein.

Alteration

Denaturation. The word denaturation is used to include the mild alterations in proteins which are manifested mainly by loss of solubility in solvents in which the protein was previously soluble. The first theory of protein denaturation, still largely valid, was developed by Wu (256). Mirsky and Pauling (173) later proposed a very similar but somewhat more detailed theory. The modern point of view stems from these two papers; it is believed that the structure of the native corpuscular protein molecule consists of folded or coiled polypeptide chains, which open up on denaturation to give extended chains without gross intramolecular rearrangements involving covalent bond breakdown (150). The "all-or-none" theory of denaturation of Wu has now been superseded by the concept of stepwise denaturation, at some stages of which the reactions involved are reversible.

Proteins can be denatured by strong acids and alkalis, salts of the heavy metals, light, heat, shaking, pressure, adsorption on a surface, and by the action of alcohol, acetone, and substances such as ether and urea.

Denatured proteins may fail to precipitate with antisera to the native protein, or may still precipitate somewhat, depending on the extent of the denaturation. It is interesting that a denatured protein has been found to inhibit the formation of a precipitate by the natural protein and its antiserum, although it itself would no longer precipitate (189,238). This suggests that perhaps some denatured proteins may still be able to react with the antibody, but the reaction for some reason does not result in the formation of a precipitate. It has also been found that injection of a denatured protein may produce antibodies reacting with native as well as denatured protein (171). It would be desirable to repeat these and other observations with greater attention to the possibility that small amounts of undenatured protein were present in the denatured preparations.

Heating most proteins in solution soon destroys their power to react with their antibodies (casein solutions are resistant to heating to 100°C.). But *antigenicity* is not lost, for heated proteins will often produce antibodies when injected. The interesting observation has been made (64) that precipitins for heated proteins will often react with heated proteins of other species. Uwazumi (244) even reported producing precipitins by injecting rabbits with rabbit serum which had been heated to 120°C.

Oxidation. By oxidizing proteins with potassium permanganate, products have been obtained which would immunize; and antibodies were obtained which precipitated with the antigen injected, but not with other proteins so treated, and not with the untreated protein (see 126). Thus species specificity seemed to be preserved, although the immunological nature of the protein was completely altered.

Reduction. Blumenthal (12) found some diminution in the reactivity of serum albumin, but not of egg albumin, after reduction with thioglycolic acid.

Digestion. Destruction of protein antigens by digestion results in a complete loss of their specificity. Pepsin generally causes a protein to lose rapidly the power of precipitating with antisera for the unaltered protein, although Parfentjev (see Chapter 2) has found that antitoxin may retain its antibody activity after treatment with pepsin under appropriate conditions. If a peptic metaprotein is injected, antibodies may be obtained which precipitate the metaprotein and also the unaltered protein (see 126).

Plakalbumin is formed from ovalbumin by the action of enzymes of *Bacillus subtilis* with the release of three peptides, A, B, and C (227). A is a hexapeptide, alanylglycylvalylaspartylalanylalanine, B a tetrapeptide, alanylglycylvalylaspartic acid, and C the dipeptide alanylalanine. Plakalbumin does not precipitate all the antibody from an antiserum against native ovalbumin (116), which might suggest that one or perhaps all of these peptides play some role in the structure of the antigenic determinants of native ovalbumin.

Acid and Alkali. Acids and alkalis react with proteins to form acid and alkali metaproteins. This decreases the antigenic activity, alkalis being much more active in this way then acids. Acid-treated proteins seem to lose their species specificity to some degree, and perhaps acquire the capacity of reacting with antisera for other such proteins (126).

Deamination. Lewis (145) found that treatment of casein with 7 per cent acetic acid and sodium nitrite, a procedure which removed all free amino groups, did not change the more obvious antigenic characteristics of the protein. A yellow, difficultly soluble product was obtained. Maurer and Heidelberger (167) found that removal of about one-third of the free amino groups from egg albumin did not influence its serological specificity.

Substitution Reactions; Formaldehyde. Formaldehyde reacts with the amino groups of amino acids, and probably with those of proteins, rendering them less basic. This fact is made use of in the formol titration of Sørensen. The reactions were discussed in a review by French and Edsall (57). Von Eisler and Lowenstein (56) and Landsteiner and Lampl (131) found that the species specificity of formaldehyde-treated proteins was not much affected.

Toxoids prepared by treating toxins with formaldehyde lose their toxic properties but may retain their antigenicity and precipitability by antibodies virtually unimpaired. Whether or not specificity is lost depends on the pH, total protein concentration, and formaldehyde concentration. This suggests that the groups altered by formaldehyde are essential for the toxic groups of the protein, but not for the groups responsible for its immunological specificity. The two sorts of groups are therefore different.

It may be that the free amino groups are essential to the toxicity and not to the antigenicity, although Hewitt (95) believed that the reaction of formaldehyde with proteins in such cases is different from that with the free amino groups, being slow and irreversible, and involving smaller amounts of formaldehyde. In any case, other treatments which involve reaction with free amino groups, such as treatment with ketene gas, abolish the toxicity of toxin (72,193).

It is of interest that the optical rotation of toxin is not altered by formaldehyde treatment, suggesting that the optically active carbon atoms adjacent to the peptide linkages have not been racemized (52).

Esterification. Landsteiner (126) employed two methods of esterification, treatment of the protein with acid in alcoholic solution and treatment with diazomethane (CH_2N_2). The first method was intended to esterify the carboxyl groups, and the second, in addition to esterifying these, also methylated, on intensive treatment, the hydroxyl, amino, and imino groups. The products were insoluble and had to be tested for serological reactivity by the complement fixation technic. It was found that these esterified proteins had lost their capacity to react with antibodies to the unchanged proteins.

Acylation. Proteins are easily acetylated with acetic anhydride,

$(CH_3CO)_2O$. The behavior of such products is similar to that of the methylated proteins. Landsteiner (126) concluded that the amino and hydroxyl groups are the ones affected. Some cross reaction was found between proteins containing different acyl groups.

It has been found that the type-specific polysaccharide (SI) of type I pneumococci is acetylated in the form in which it occurs in the organisms. The preparations first isolated had been deacetylated by the use of alkali, with the loss of some antigenic properties. It was also found that the deacetylated polysaccharide would not absorb all the protective antibodies from antiserum produced by injecting whole cocci, whereas the acetylated form would (8).

Ketene gas, $CH_2:C:O$, may be used to acetylate proteins.

Benzoyl groups $\left(\langle\bigcirc\rangle CO-\right)$ were introduced into proteins by Medveczky and Uhrovits (169) by treatment with benzoyl chloride. They supposed that the benzoyl groups go first on the carboxyl groups, then on the amino, and finally on the imino and hydroxyl groups. As before, the antigens acquire a new common specificity.

By the action of carbobenzoxy chloride (benzyl chloroformate), $C_6H_5CH_2OCOCl$, Gaunt and Wormall (65) produced carbobenzoxyproteins. The reaction appears to be concerned mainly with the free amino groups. The original species specificity was almost completely destroyed, and the antisera reacted with other proteins similarly treated. The reactions were completely inhibited by carbobenzoxyamino acids, indicating that the specific group is $-NHCOOCH_2C_6H_5$. Phenylcarbamido-amino acids , containing the related group $-CHNHCONHC_6H_5$, also inhibited to a less degree.

Halogenation. Following pioneer work of Obermayer and Pick, iodine and bromine have been introduced into proteins (182). The introduction of chlorine has been attempted; for references see Wormall (255). Iodinated proteins acquire a new specificity, and antisera to them react with other iodoproteins. The brominated proteins are only slightly different from the iodinated proteins, and cross-react with them. Wormall (255) found that 3,5-diiodo- or dibromotyrosine, and to a less extent dichlorotyrosine, would inhibit the reaction of iodoprotein with its antibody. Halogenated imidazole was apparently not tried. Snapper and Grunbaum (236) found that any substance, including thyroxin, containing the

3,5-diiodo-4-hydroxy group, $I \overset{OH}{\diagup\diagdown} I$, is capable of this inhibiting reaction.

Kleczkowski (119) studied quantitatively iodination and its effect on the serological properties of horse serum globulin. He found that the ability to react with and to produce antibodies to native globulin disappeared almost simultaneously when the Folin color value fell to about 30 per cent of the original value, *i.e.*, when all the tyrosine was presumably substituted He calculated that the amount of iodine which entered the molecule (11 per cent) was all accounted for by the tyrosine groups, so there was no reason to suspect other alterations in the molecule. If this is so, we may suppose that tyrosine forms an essential part of the epitopes of native horse serum globulin.

Proteins into which small amounts (in some cases as much as 18 atoms per molecule) of iodine have been introduced act serologically like untreated protein, and are stable (34,224). Advantage has been taken of this to tag antibodies and antigens with radioactive I^{131}.

Nitration. Nitrated proteins, first studied serologically by Obermayer and Pick (see 126), have been investigated by several workers. Nitric acid has usually been used for the nitration; Wormall (255) also used tetranitromethane. The nitroproteins (xanthoproteins) are yellow and have acquired another new common property, for they cross-react serologically. The chemical change is probably the production of mononitrotyrosyl and nitrotryptophanyl groups.

By the method of specific inhibition Mutsaars (182) demonstrated that the serological specificity of the xanthoproteins is due to the nitrotyrosyl group. By testing numerous compounds, he found that the reactivity depends on the presence of nitro and hydroxyl substituents in the benzene ring and a carboxyl group which can be free or esterified. Boyd (16) and Mutsaars (182) found that the nitration of gelatin did not make it antigenic; according to the latter it does not precipitate with immune sera to other nitroproteins, but does inhibit specifically.

In the case of methylated, acylated, halogenated, and nitrated proteins the species specificity is not entirely destroyed, as can be demonstrated by testing with diminishing quantities of antibody, whereupon it is observed that the reactions are stronger with the homologous protein (126).

Diazotization. Proteins do not contain aromatic amino groups; nevertheless, if they are treated with nitrous acid intensely yellow products are formed, which are almost indistinguishable, serologically, from the nitroproteins (133). It is supposed (see 126,255) that the nitrous acid treatment causes the introduction of a diazo group into the tyrosine and tryptophane (and possibly histidine) nuclei (208), and that the intense yellow color is due to the change of the benzene ring of the tyrosine and tryptophane residues to a quinoid structure. This is also thought to explain the color of the nitro derivatives.   This would offer a reasonable explanation of the close similarity between the two classes of compounds.   The serological similarity of the nitro- and diazoproteins has been confirmed in the case of gelatin by inhibition tests (181).

Treatment with Mustard Gas. Berenblum and Wormall (10) treated proteins with mustard gas (I) and with the corresponding sulfone (II):

$$S\Big\langle{\begin{array}{l}CH_2CH_2Cl\\CH_2CH_2Cl\end{array}}\qquad\qquad O_2S\Big\langle{\begin{array}{l}CH_2CH_2Cl\\CH_2CH_2Cl\end{array}}$$

$$\text{(I)}\qquad\qquad\qquad\qquad\text{(II)}$$

In each case a new specificity was conferred, although it was not so striking as in some of the experiments described above.   The two classes of compounds did not cross-react.   Species specificity was retained to a considerable degree, but there may have been some unchanged protein in the preparations.   It is thought that the reaction may involve the free amino groups of the protein.

Treatment with Phenyl Isocyanate. Hopkins and Wormall (104) produced phenylureidoproteins by treatment with phenyl isocyanate $(C_6H_5N{:}C{:}O)$.   The introduced groups go mainly, if not entirely, to the free amino groups of the lysine, as follows:

$$-CH_2NH_2 + O{:}C{:}NC_6H_5 \xrightarrow{pH8} -CH_2NHCONHC_6H_5$$

Although not all the amino groups were substituted, cross reactions with the untreated protein were found to be much reduced, and a new specificity was conferred.   The reactions could be inhibited by compounds of phenyl isocyanate with lysine or ϵ-amino-n-hexoic acid; compounds of other amino acids were less effective.   The antisera reacted weakly with compounds prepared by treating proteins (including gelatin) with diazotized aniline presumably because of the similarity of the groups $-CONHC_6H_5$ and $-N{:}NC_6H_5$.   Injection of the gelatin compound did not produce any antibodies that could be detected.   The p-bromo compounds were also studied, with similar results.

Fluorescent isocyanates and isothiocyanates have been used in the fluorescent labeling of antigens and antibodies in the technique developed by Coons (42) and Nairn (183).

Treatment with β-Naphthoquinone Sulfonate. Fujio (63) reported that injection of proteins treated with this substance, at alkaline reaction, produced antibodies reacting with another unrelated protein similarly treated.   Similarly, anaphylaxis could be induced by sensitizing with one coupled protein, shocking with another.   Fujio considered the reaction to involve the amino groups.

Other Treatments. Wetter and Deutsch (251) studied the effects of acetylation, esterification, iodination, and coupling with diazo compounds of an antigen (ovomucoid), and Grabar and Kaminski (75) studied the effects of conversion of ovalbumin to plakalbumin, diazotization, acetylation, denaturation by heat, shaking, and ultrasonic vibration. Malkiel (154) studied the effects of ultrasonic vibration on tobacco mosaic virus, and concluded that the treatment uncovered other antigenic groups in the molecule.

7. Conjugation

Methods (usually coupling with a diazonium compound) have been employed to attach a new specificity to a protein, and thus create an *artificial conjugated antigen.* Such treatment usually weakens the native specificity of the protein. This may in part be due to other chemical changes accompanying the conjugation, but it seems likely that it is at least partly directly due to the presence of the introduced groups.

Haurowitz, Sarafian, and Schwerin (81) found that the precipitation (by an antipseudoglobulin) of pseudoglobulin (from sheep or horse serum) was prevented by the introduction of about one hundred or more azo groups or iodine atoms per molecule. When less than fifty groups were introduced, no diminution in precipitability was observed.

Conjugated Antigens

The specificity of antigens has been explored in minute detail by numerous workers in the present century, notably by Landsteiner (126). This has been done partly by the study of reactions with related natural proteins, but largely by the use of "conjugated antigens." By the term "conjugated antigen" is meant an antigen which has had a new specificity grafted onto it, as it were, by chemical treatment. It has been found possible to create thus new categories of specificity, so that a chemically conjugated protein will engender antibodies which will react with other unrelated proteins containing the same attached groups.

Treatment with Diazotized Amines

This is the method which was chiefly utilized by Landsteiner in his extensive studies on specificity, although he pointed out that any method leading to the attachment of new groups to the protein would be expected to have the same effect. It has proved on the whole to be the most flexible and useful. An aromatic amine containing the group $\underset{}{\overset{HN_2}{\wedge}}$ is diazotized

by treatment with sodium nitrite and hydrochloric acid, and the diazo-

nium compound $\overset{ClN:N}{\wedge}$ is produced. It will couple with proteins in alka-

line or even neutral solution, giving yellow, orange, or red compounds con-

taining the diazo linkage $\overset{N:N-}{\wedge}$. This results in the introduction of a

new specificity, and may or may not destroy the original specificity completely, depending on the severity of the treatment. This method of introducing groups into proteins has wider possibilities than most of the other
methods, because an aromatic amino group can be introduced into almost
any kind of compound, making it possible then to couple it to an antigenic
protein. Thus we are not restricted to the use of simple aromatic amines
such as aniline and sulfanilic acid, but can make use of more complex
compounds specially synthesized for the purpose, containing any chemical
group we are interested in studying. An example of such a compound is
the p-aminobenzyl ether of the specific polysaccharide of type III pneumococcus. With this last compound, Avery and Goebel (7) were able to
immunize rabbits actively against infection with type III pneumococcus
and to obtain antisera which precipitated the type III polysaccharide,
agglutinated type III pneumococci, and protected mice specifically against
type III infection.

According to Pauly (205–207) diazonium compounds couple with proteins through the histidine and tyrosine, two groups going into each
tyrosine and two into each histidine residue. We can calculate (22) the
number of entering groups per molecule of protein. Actually, Boyd and
Hooker (22) and Boyd and Mover (26) found that in various proteins
considerably more arsenic could be introduced by repeated treatment
with diazotized arsanilic acid (below) than could be accounted for on this
basis.

Introduction of too much hapten may diminish the antigenicity of the
conjugate (27,128).

Affinity Labeling

Singer (253a) described a new approach to the chemical modification of antibodies. He made use of the fact that if a hapten, H, is combined chemically with a structure, X, which is capable of forming a stable covalent bond with some one or several of the amino acids that make up the antibody, then the compound HX will be introduced much more richly into the appropriate amino acids in the region of the specific combining groups of the antibody than elsewhere, because HX is led to attach itself in the first place to the anti-H region for which it has a specific affinity, before the stable covalent bonds are formed. Singer calls this procedure affinity labeling.

Making use of the principle of affinity labeling, Matsubara and Boyd (162a) succeeded, probably for the first time, in modifying by chemical treatment, not indeed an antibody, which they did not try, but a lectin (Chapter 5). Treatment of the anti-A lectin from Sieva lima beans with diazotized p-aminophenyl-N-acetyl-D-galactosaminide greatly increased the agglutinating power of the lectin for group B erythrocytes, while leaving the anti-A activity virtually unimpaired.

Coupling through the Sulfhydryl Groups of Proteins

Pillemer, Ecker, and Martiensen (210) introduced groups into proteins by reducing the disulfide sulfur to sulfhydryl groups and allowing these to react with organic halogen compounds according to the following formula (X represent halogen):

$$ASH + RX \rightarrow ASR + HX$$

This method is specially applicable to keratins because of the high percentage of disulfide sulfur they contain (10 to 15 per cent cystine).

Treatment with Azides

Clutton, Harington, and Mead (40) were able to introduce groups such as:

$$(C_6H_{11}O_5)O\langle\rangle CH_2CHNH_2CO-$$

into proteins through linkage with the free amino groups, by use of the azide of O-β-glucoside-N-carbobenzyloxytyrosine. Clutton, Harington, and Yuill (41) found that this masked the specificity of the original protein entirely, and the new specificity was conditioned by the introduced groups. Gelatin was thus rendered slightly antigenic (see p. 126). The latter authors (41) also succeeded in introducing in a similar way thyroxyl groups into proteins, and obtained slight reactions between the antisera and thyroglobulin. Administration of such antisera protected animals somewhat against the normal physiological effects of later doses of thyroglobulin and thyroxin.

8. Significance of Conjugation Studies

The great significance of the work of Landsteiner on artificial antigens and of its confirmation and extension by others was this: it showed that antibodies could be directed towards groups of known chemical constitution in an antigen, and *could react with these groupings by themselves*. From the point of view of the chemist, this is probably the greatest single step forward ever taken in the study of immunology, since it advanced the science at once from the stage at which it was thought that antibodies could be produced only in response to an unknown, special constitution, peculiar to proteins, to the stage at which the chemical composition of the groups determining antibody production could be studied.

Study of synthetic artificial antigens has shown that antibodies produced by them may be of several sorts. In the first place, especially if the chemical treatment has not been too drastic, the serum of an animal immunized with such a conjugated protein may contain antibodies directed towards the protein substrate, having no relation to the new specificity. It may contain antibodies directed chiefly towards the introduced groups, or these groups and the parts of the protein molecule with which they combine. Also, antibodies may occasionally be found whose combining group is directed simultaneously towards the original protein and the introduced group (77,85,170).

Since antisera prepared by injecting such conjugated protein antigens often contain, in addition to the antibodies against the introduced chemical group in which we are interested, antibodies against the protein carrier, we cannot test for the first sort of antibodies by use of the same antigen which was injected, for we could not easily distinguish between a reaction with the introduced groups and one with the unchanged protein parts of the molecule. Therefore it is necessary to perform the test with an antigen prepared, by the same chemical treatment, from an unrelated protein. The primary reaction (see Chapter 6) will then be relatively independent of the protein.* For most purposes it will not matter if the injected antigen, and even the test antigen, consist of mixtures of proteins instead of

* There is reason to think that actually at least some of the antibodies are directed not solely against the hapten but partly against certain adjacent parts of the protein molecule (81,100).

being each a chemical entity, as the essential reaction does not concern the protein part. Landsteiner used horse serum for the preparation of the antigen for injection, and chicken serum for the test antigen. Purified proteins for the preparation of the antigen for injection have been found suitable, although sometimes not quite so potent (102). It has been found that purified hemocyanins and serum globulins are quite good. If it is desired to use purified proteins throughout, a hemocyanin can be used in the preparation of the antigen for injection, and a protein such as casein (which has the advantage of being more resistant to chemical treatment than, for example, egg albumin) for the preparation of the test antigen.

Landsteiner and Lampl (132) coupled, among others, the two aromatic amines shown on the left of Table 3-3 to the proteins of horse serum, by

TABLE 3-3

Example of the Specificity Observed in Antisera to Artificial Antigens Obtained by Coupling Proteins with Simple Aromatic Amines

Antisera made with	Tested against antigens made with					
	$C_6H_5NH_2$ (aniline)	NH_2-benzene-COOH	NH_2-benzene-COOH (with COOH)	NH_2-benzene(Cl)-COOH	NH_2-benzene(CH_3)-COOH	NH_2-benzene-SO_3H
NH_2-benzene-COOH	0	$+++$	0	$++++$	$+++$	$+$
NH_2-benzene-SO_3H	0	0	0	0		$++++$

$0 =$ no reaction, $+ =$ positive reaction, $++++ =$ very strong reaction.

diazotizing them with nitrous acid and allowing them to react with horse serum made strongly alkaline. Immune sera produced by injecting rabbits with these preparations reacted as shown in the table with antigens, made by diazotizing the amines shown at the top and coupling them with the proteins of chicken serum. The degree of reaction in the different cases shows quite clearly the influence of chemical constitution on serological specificity.

This experiment shows, for example, that the antibody-forming mechanism can distinguish clearly between a benzene ring bearing an acid group and one without such a group. Two different acid groups are distinguished (carboxylic and sulfonic). Furthermore, we see that the antibodies formed are specific, not only for the kind of acidic group, but also for its position, as we note that the antibodies to the compound having the carboxyl meta to the amino group (which serves as the point of attachment to the protein in the conjugated antigen) do not react to proteins coupled with the isomeric compound in which the carboxyl is in the para position. Other observations, such as a certain degree of cross reaction between carboxyl and sulfonic acid, and the relatively slight influence of groups such as chloride and methyl, could be made.

Pauling and Pressman (203) studied the inhibition by haptens of the precipitation with antisera homologous to o-, m-, and p-azophenylarsonic groups, and concluded from the degrees of cross reaction observed that the combining site on the antibody was adapted to conform spatially to the homologous hapten, although it could, presumably by slight stretching (about 1 A.) accommodate also the isomeric haptens. They also found good agreement between calculated van der Waals attraction energies and free energy changes $RT \ln K'_0$.

By use of such methods it has been possible to establish the limits of resolution possible by means of serological specificity. Working with various benzene ring derivatives, Landsteiner made a very large number of tests. A summary of the results will be found in (128).

Although in some cases the specificity seemed complete, *i.e.*, the immune serum reacted only with the homologous antigen, more frequently cross reactions were found, although the reaction with the homologous antigen was most intense. In other words, the immunological mechanism was not able to distinguish absolutely between some of these closely related compounds. We may suppose that the antibodies, although they reflect in some way the characteristic electronic pattern of the antigen or hapten, do not reflect every detail perfectly. There will be some blurring of outlines. Or we might change the metaphor and say the antibody is a lock fitted by the hapten as a key. The lock, however, is of somewhat simpler construction than the key, so that keys for other locks may also open it, though perhaps not so readily. The cross reactions showed definite regularities, which possibly furnish valuable information on immunological specificity, and which are best given in Landsteiner's own words (126).

"1. First of all, the nature of the acid groups is of decisive influence. Sulfonic acid immune sera reacted markedly with several sulfonic acids, but little, if any, with carboxylic acid antigens, and immune sera to the latter only exceptionally gave distinct reactions with azoproteins containing sulfonic acid groups. The determining influence of the arsenic acid radicals was still more pronounced, as is indicated by the fact that arsanilic acid serum precipitated all of the six substances tested which contain the group AsO_3H_2, and none of the other antigens.

"2. In contrast to the acid groups, substitution of the aromatic nucleus by methyl, halogen, methoxyl and nitro groups is of less influence on the specificity. Thus in the tests presented in Table 3-4 the immune sera act

TABLE 3-4

Reactions of Artificial Antigens Made with "Neutral" Haptens (126)

Antigens from	Immune sera for				
	Aniline	o-Chloro-aniline	p-Toluidine	p-Nitro-aniline	p-Chloro-aniline
Aniline	++±	++	+±	+	+
o-Toluidine	++	++±	+±	±	±
o-Anisidine	+	++	±	0	0
o-Nitroaniline	+	+	±	±	0
o-Chloroaniline	+±	++±	+	±	±
m-Toluidine	++	++	+±	+	+
m-Nitroaniline	+	+	+	+±	±
m-Chloroaniline	++	+±	+±	+	+
m-Bromoaniline	++	++	+±	+	+
p-Toluidine	+±	+	++	+	++
p-Anisidine	++	+	++±	+	+±
p-Nitroaniline	+	±	+±	++	++
p-Chloroaniline	++±	+	++	+±	++
p-Bromoaniline	++	+±	++	+±	++
p-Iodoaniline	+±	+	++	+±	++
3-Nitro-4-methylaniline	++	+±	++	+±	+
4-Nitro-2-methylaniline	+	±	+	+±	±
as-m-Xylidine	+±	++	++	+	+±
p-Xylidine	+±	++	+	+	±
Acetyl-p-phenylenediamine	0	0	0	0	0
p-Aminoacetophenone	±	0	+	+	0
Monomethyl-p-phenylenediamine	+±			+±	

Concentration of antigens 0.01%.

± = trace.   Increasing amounts of precipitate indicated by ±, +, +±, etc.

with varying intensity on almost all of the antigens possessing mono- or di-substituted benzene nuclei. The groups NO_2 and OCH_3 appear to change the specificity to a somewhat greater extent than halogen and CH_3. The radicals containing a carbonyl group constitute an exception, for the antigens prepared from acetyl-p-phenylenediamine and p-aminoaceto-phenone did not give any, or but weak precipitation." Hopkins and

Wormall (104,105) also found that introduction of bromine into phenyl groups did not alter the specificity significantly.

Haurowitz (78) showed that strongly basic groups are probably just as effective as acid groups in directing specificity.

Evidently because of the strong influence of polar groups, sera to proteins coupled with phenylazo ($-N:NC_6H_5$) do not precipitate antigens containing acid groups, and conversely antisera to azoproteins containing acid groups do not react, or react weakly, with such "neutral" antigens.

Landsteiner and van der Scheer (134) found that an azoprotein prepared from the methyl ester of *p*-aminobenzoic acid reacted as a "neutral para-antigen," reacting with antisera to aniline and *p*-toluidine, and only very faintly with an antiserum for *p*-aminobenzoic acid. But, if the azoprotein was gently treated with sodium hydroxide so as to hydrolyze off the methyl group, the protein gradually lost its precipitability by immune anti-"neutral" sera, while at the same time it began to react strongly with *p*-aminobenzoic acid serum. Similarly, immune sera prepared with proteins containing the ester reacted with other proteins so treated, but not with proteins containing the plain *p*-aminobenzoic acid.

Landsteiner (126) pointed out that the pronounced effect of esterification of terminal carboxyl groups suggests that the terminal portions of the molecule have a particularly significant influence on the specificity. He went on to say: "If one visualizes the protein molecule not as a straight chain but, with Svedberg, as spherical or elliptical in shape, which according to Sørensen results from the coiling up of peptide chains, this would be in agreement with the assumption that the groupings at the periphery of the molecule, oriented towards the solvent, play a prominent part in the reactions." (Compare Marrack's view, mentioned on p. 375.)

Another important influence of acid groups is that their presence seems to define more sharply the specificity of the nucleus in which they are found, so that other substituted groups in the ring exert more influence on the specificity than they do in neutral antigens.

Lansteiner continued:

"3. Another regularity, as seen from the very specific reactions of the three isomeric aminobenzoic acids and aminocinnamic acids, is that the relative position of the acid radical to the azo-group* determined the specificity and the appearance of cross reactions."

Having studied the specificity of introduced aromatic nuclei, Landsteiner next proceeded to investigate the specificity of aliphatic chains. It was necessary to fasten these to a benzene ring in order to have a method of attaching the compound to the protein "carrier," but this

---

* The point of attachment to the protein.

TABLE 3-5

Conjugated Antigens with Aliphatic Side Chains (126)

Antigens from	Immune sera						
	p-Amino-oxanilic acid	p-Amino-succinanilic acid	p-Amino-adipanilic acid	p-Amino-suberanilic acid	p-Amino-phenyl-acetic acid	p-Amino-phenyl-butyric acid	p-Amino-phenyl-caproic acid
p-Aminooxanilic acid	++	0	0	0	0	0	0
p-Aminomalonanilic acid, $n = 1$	0	0	0	0	0	0	0
p-Aminosuccinanilic acid, $n = 2$	0	++++	±	±	0	0	±
p-Aminoglutaranilic acid, $n = 3$	0	+	+	+±	0	±	+
p-Aminoadipanilic acid, $n = 4$	0	0	+++	+++	0	±	+
p-Aminopimelanilic acid, $n = 5$	0	0	+±	++++	±	+	+
p-Aminosuberanilic acid, $n = 6$	0	0	+±	++++	0	0	0
p-Aminobenzoic acid	0	0	0	±	+±	±	±
p-Aminophenylacetic acid	0	0	±	+	+±	+±	+
p-Aminophenylbutyric acid	0	0	±	++	0	+	+
p-Aminophenylcaproic acid	0	0	±	++	0	+	+±

Concentration of antigens 0.01%. Symbols as in Table 3-4.

General formula of aminoanilic acids: $NH_2C_6H_4HNCO(CH_2)_nCOOH$.

feature remained the same in any series of experiments, so that the effects of varying the aliphatic portion could be studied. Table 3-5 shows some of these results.

The compounds used were made from the dibasic fatty acids, in each case by forming a link between one of the carboxyl groups and an aromatic amino group, in which another (*p*-amino) group was developed for purposes of coupling. The part that varied was the aliphatic part, *i.e.*, the dibasic acid. It will be seen that the immune sera against the lower acids (oxalic and succinic) were quite specific, so that lengthening or shortening the chain by only one carbon atom produced a marked difference, whereas the antisera to the higher acids (adipic and suberic) showed much stronger overlapping reactions with the neighboring members of the series.

Therefore we find, just as in organic chemistry, that, as the carbon chain becomes longer, shortening or lengthening it by one carbon makes a smaller difference. It would also seem, since the specificity of the antisera for these compounds is after all rather high, that the polar group, CONH, common to all of them, has an influence somewhat like that of the acid groups.

It was of the greatest interest to investigate the specificity of peptides (compounds of amino acids), since proteins are made up of peptide chains. Landsteiner and van der Scheer (126) carried out this investigation in analogous fashion. The peptides were combined with nitrobenzoyl chloride, and the nitro group was reduced to an amino group for coupling with proteins. It was found that the antisera to these compounds were quite specific, so that strong cross reactions were obtained only with closely related amino acids, glycine and alanine, valine and leucine, and aspartic and glutamic acid. Nevertheless these related amino acids could be differentiated without difficulty.

Antisera to dipeptides precipitated most strongly the homologous antigen (Table 3-6) and gave overlapping reactions with other antigens where the terminal amino acid was the same as in the immunizing antigen. This is probably again due to the prominent influence of the acid groups referred to above; it might also be thought that the terminal group would appear more prominent, so to speak, to the antibody-forming mechanism, as is suggested by other experiments of a somewhat different sort. Landsteiner pointed out that the specificity observed here is in many ways similar to that of the enzymic splitting of dipeptides by dipeptidase.

When Landsteiner tested antibodies to larger peptides, he still found that cross-reactions occurred with peptides having the same terminal amino acids, but such cross-sections did not always occur, and some

TABLE 3-6

Reactions of Peptide Azoproteins (139,140).

Immune sera	Antigens from			
	Glycylglycine	Glycyl-leucine	Leucylglycine	Leucyl-leucine
Glycylglycine	++±	0	0	0
Glycyl-leucine I	0	++±	0	±
Glycyl-leucine II	+	+++	0	+
Leucyglycine I	+	0	+++	0
Leucylglycine II	++	0	+++	±
Leucyl-leucine	0	+	0	++

Concentration of antigens 0.01%. Symbols as in Table 3-4.

cross-reactions were found to be due to common amino acids in other positions. The cross-reactions were definitely related to similarities of constitution (Table 3-7). For instance, an antibody for the pentapeptide

TABLE 3-7

Cross-Reactions of Glycine and Leucine Haptens[a]

Antibody for	Antigen containing[b]									
	G	L	GG	GL	LG	GGG	GGL	GGGG	GGGL	GGGGG
GGGGG	0	0	±	0	0	+±	0	+±	0	+±
GGGGL	0	+	0	+±	0	0	++	0	++	0

[a] Landsteiner (128).
[b] G = glycine, L = leucine.

GGGGG, where G stands for glycine, precipitated —GG but not —LG antigen, where L stands for leucine, and precipitated much less —LGG than —GGG. The amount of precipitate produced by an anti-GGGGL antiserum with various peptide-containing antigens increased in the order —L, —GL, —GGL, —GGGL, —GGGGL (Table 3-8).

TABLE 3-8

Increase in Strength of Cross-Reactions with Increase in Length of Hapten[a]

Antibody for	Antigen containing[b]				
	L	GL	GGL	GGGL	GGGGL
GGGGL	+±	++±	+++	+++±	++++

[a] Landsteiner (128).
[b] G = glycine, L = leucine.

Fig. 3-5. Amide of *p*-aminobenzoylglycylglycine.

The strongest reactions were not always obtained with haptens having the terminal portions identical with those of the immunizing hapten. For instance, when Landsteiner prepared antisera against polypeptides in which the terminal carboxyl group had been converted to the amide (Fig. 3-5) he found that an antiserum for GGLGGAm reacted with −GGLAm and −GGGGLAm but not with −LGGAm (Table 3-9), in

TABLE 3-9

Cross-Reactions of Glycine–Leucine–Amino Polypeptides[a]

Antibody for	Antigen containing[b]			
	GGLGGAm	GGLAm	GGGGLAm	LGGA
GGLGGAm	++±	+±	+±	0

[a] Landsteiner (128).
[b] G = glycine, L = leucine.

spite of the fact that the terminal three units of this last hapten are identical with the terminal three units of the immunizing hapten. Landsteiner attributed this to a failure of the amide groups to have as strong an effect on serological specificity as the free carboxyl groups have.

Landsteiner obtained evidence that the antibodies to such complex peptide haptens were at least partly directed toward the whole peptide and not merely to the component amino acids. For one thing, varying the order of the amino acids in the peptide made a marked change, so that −GGL, −GLG, and −LGG were serologically different, as were −GGGGL, −GGGLGG, and −LGGGG.

Other evidence that antibody is directed toward the whole peptide was obtained by "absorbing" an antiserum, *i.e.*, by reacting the antiserum with heterologous antigens until no further precipitate formed, and then reacting the absorbed antiserum with hapten. Suitable absorption of an antiserum for GGLGG left antibodies which reacted with the homologous hapten but not with related haptens, except for a slight reaction with −LGG. Tests made for comparison with diluted antiserum showed that this change in reactivity was not due merely to diminution in total antibody content.

A third line of evidence came from inhibition experiments. Landsteiner found that antibodies to a given peptide were generally better inhibited by homologous than by heterologous haptens, even when they reacted with a heterologous antigen (Table 3-10).

TABLE 3-10

Inhibition of Heterologous Reaction by Homologous Hapten[a]

		Reaction in presence of hapten[b]		
Antibody for	Antigen containing	GGG	GGGGG	GGLGG
GGG	GGG	±	±	+±
GGGGG	GGG	+	±	++
GGLGG	GGG	±	±	0

[a] Landsteiner (128).
[b] G = glycine, L = leucine.

From the evidence that antibodies can be directed toward the whole of a peptide containing as many as five amino acids we may conclude that the antigenic determinants in natural proteins may be as large as this. Nevertheless, there seems to be a limit to the size of the antigenic determinant to which the combining group of a single antibody molecule can be directed, for Landsteiner and van der Scheer (140a) found that when

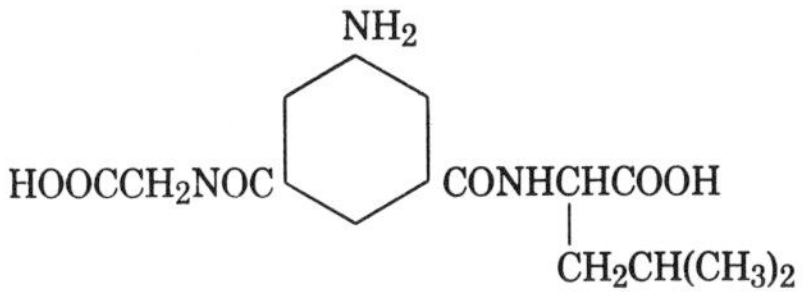

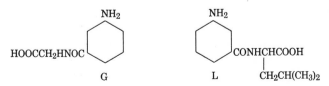

Fig. 3-6. Aminoisophthalyl glycyl-leucine (GIL).

they used symmetrical aminoisophthalyl glycyl-leucine (Fig. 3-6), which they referred to as GIL, as hapten they obtained two distinct antibodies. One reacted with m-aminobenzoyl glycine (G) and the other with m-aminobenzoyl leucine (L) (Fig. 3-7). The anti-G of such a serum was not

Fig. 3-7. M-aminobenzoyl glycine (G) and m-aminobenzoyl leucine (L).

removable with antigen containing only L, and the anti-L was not removable with antigen containing only G. Evidently the two amino acid residues in GIL were too far apart to be spanned simultaneously by a typical antibody determinant, although there was some evidence for the presence in the antiserum of a slight amount of a special antibody which might have been directed toward the whole hapten GIL. At the same time, evidence was obtained that the anti-G and anti-L of the antiserum produced by injecting the GIL antigen were not quite identical with those produced by injecting G- and L-coupled antigens.

Kreiter and Pressman (123), repeating Landsteiner's work, found evidence that the anti-G and anti-L were both directed partly towards other features of GIL. The addition of the second amino acid increased the binding energy from 6.9 kcal to 7.3 in the case of anti-G and from 6.5 to 7.4 in the case of anti-L.

These experiments indicated that a large number of serologically different compounds could be made up from amino acids, in conformity with the large numbers of specificities found in natural proteins. They also indicate that the antibody-forming mechanism can recognize as a unit a fairly large chemical compound. Just how large a group can be responded to as a whole is not known; the maximum must be smaller than the surface of the smallest protein molecules. See p. 128

Nevertheless, it will be seen below that the immunological mechanism may on occasion single out parts even of chemical compounds of moderate size, so that the specificity in some cases is chiefly or solely directed towards one part of the molecule.

9. Influence of Optical Activity

The differences observed in antibodies to aromatic compounds containing the same substituents, but in different positions, indicate that the spatial arrangement of groups, as well as their chemical nature, is of importance in immunology. This is in line with what was already known of other aspects of biological chemistry, where spatial arrangement has been found important. Thus enzymes have frequently been found to be specific for one of the stereoisomers (spatial isomers of a substance), different isomers of optically active dyes have been found to have different staining effects, optical isomers of some of the amino acids have different tastes, and optical isomers of drugs usually exhibit different potencies.

Landsteiner and van der Scheer (126) differentiated serologically between d- and l-p-aminobenzoylphenylaminoacetic acids:

$$H_2N-\bigcirc-CONH\underset{\underset{COOH}{|}}{\overset{\overset{H}{|}}{C}}-\bigcirc \quad \text{and} \quad H_2N-\bigcirc-CONH\underset{\underset{H}{|}}{\overset{\overset{COOH}{|}}{C}}\bigcirc$$

For a second experiment tartaric acid, which exists in three forms, dextro, levo, and meso, was used. It was coupled through one carboxyl group to an aromatic amino group, which as usual was then linked to the protein through an amino group. Table 3-11 shows that the antisera distinguished all three of these isomers. These antisera to tartaric acid also reacted with antigens prepared with malic acid; the d-serum chiefly with the d-, the l- with the l-. It is known that the malic and tartaric acids are configurationally thus related; it has proved possible to establish previously unknown spatial configurations by serological methods.

Later, by application of the inhibition technic (see p. 160), it was possible to differentiate the isomers in a typical case of cis–trans isomerism (maleic and fumaric acids).

Studies by Goebel and Avery (69) carried the differentiation of steric isomers still further. They showed that antibodies could be made against antigens containing sugar molecules linked (through the benzeneazo group) to proteins, and the anti-sugar molecules would react with the sugars alone. They found that such antibodies clearly differentiated glucose and galactose, which differ only in the spatial arrangement of the H and OH on the fourth carbon (Fig. 3-8). In later work (9), they showed that such antibodies would even distinguish between the alpha and beta forms of glucose, where the difference (Fig. 3-9) is so slight that the free

TABLE 3-11
Specificity of Stereoisomeric Compounds (136)

	Antigens from					
	l-Tartaric acid COOH $\mid$ HOCH $\mid$ HCOH $\mid$ COOH		d-Tartaric acid COOH $\mid$ HCOH $\mid$ HOCH $\mid$ COOH		m-Tartaric acid COOH $\mid$ HCOH $\mid$ HCOH $\mid$ COOH	
Immune sera						
l-Tartaric acid	+++	++±	±	0	+	±
d-Tartaric acid	0	0	+++	++±	+	±
m-Tartaric acid	±	±	0	0	+++	+++

Concentration of antigens 0.05% (first column), 0.01% (second column).
Symbols as in Table 3-4.

Fig. 3-8. Glucose and galactose.

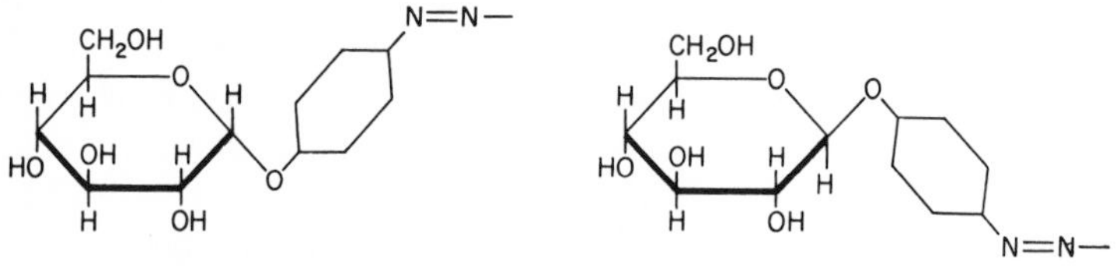

Fig. 3-9. Alpha- and beta-glucosides.

alpha and beta forms of glucose spontaneously convert into the other form until an equilibrium is set up. The distinction was not made quite as sharply, however, as was that between glucose and galactose, for the antisera also precipitated the heterologous antigens somewhat.

As might have been predicted, it was found that substitution of an acetyl group for the hydrogen on the sixth carbon atom modified the specificity of a hexose, so that an antigen prepared with the acetyl-beta-glucoside formed no precipitate with antisera to the alpha glucoside, and even with the plain glucoside antigen precipitated less than with the fully homologous acetylated beta-glucoside antigen.

Goebel, Avery, and Babers (70) then proceeded to study antibodies to disaccharides, including in their work maltose, lactose, cellobiose, and gentiobiose. Here the features determining specificity were found to be the molecular pattern of the disaccharide as a whole, the spatial and chemical configuration of the terminal hexose, and the position of the linkage between the two monosaccharides (Fig. 3-10).

Goebel (66) found that antisera to coupled glucose and glucoronic acid antigens were entirely distinct, showing no serological crossing. These compounds differ in that the sixth carbon atom of one is alcoholic and of the other acidic (Fig. 3-11). This again illustrates how the acid groups can strongly influence specificity, exerting, in this case, much more effect than an acetyl group (see above). It was also found that glucuronic and galacturonic acid did not cross-react serologically, similarly to the behavior of glucose and galactose.

The specific capsular polysaccharides of pneumococci of types II, III, and VIII are constituted from molecules of glucose and glucuronic acid (66). In view of the prominent effect of acid groups, we might expect the specificity of antibodies to these polysaccharides to be directed chiefly towards the glucuronic acid. This seems to be the case, since antigens prepared from glucuronic acid are precipitated even in high dilutions by antipneumococcus horse sera of these types, while the corresponding glucose compounds exhibit little or no activity (66). It is known that type I pneumococcus polysaccharide contains galacturonic acid (86), so that we might expect type I antipneumococcus sera to precipitate antigens prepared from galacturonic acid; this also proved to be the case (71). A low degree of cross precipitation between the less closely related types III and VIII was not considered seriously to weaken the argument, as various data suggsted that this cross reaction was entirely nonspecific.

The reactions with the glucuronic and galacturonic acids are thought by Goebel and Hotchkiss (71) possibly to be simply reactions between the acidic groups of the antigen and the basic groups of the antibody protein molecule. In experiments based on this assumption, they showed that antipneumococcus horse serum of type III would precipitate antigens containing other organic acid radicals (p-aminocarboxylic and p-amino-sulfonic acids) quite unrelated to the uronic acids. Since the reactions occurred only with immune serum, not with normal, nor with immune serum from which antibody had been removed, we are justified in considering them as real antibody–antigen reactions.

In later work with cellobiuronic acid (a disaccharide composed of one molecule of glucuronic acid and one of glucose), which seems to be the structural unit of type III pneumococcal polysaccharide, Goebel (67) obtained antisera that would precipitate type III polysaccharide when this was combined with a heterologous protein. Antigens containing cellobiuronic acid reacted vigorously with antipneumococcus sera of types II, III, and VIII. Furthermore, the antiserum to antigen containing the cellobiuronic acid conferred on mice passive protection to infection with virulent pneumococci of types II, III, and VIII (68). This was apparently the first instance of the production of effective immunity to an actual disease by the injection of an artificial antigen containing a purely synthetic hapten. Thus the problem of specificity in the case of these organisms seems to be approaching a solution.

Residual Native Specificity. When coupled proteins are injected some antibodies specific for the untreated protein are generally formed. Even the antibodies directed towards the introduced group react better with that group when it is coupled to tyrosine. Hooker and Boyd (100), using

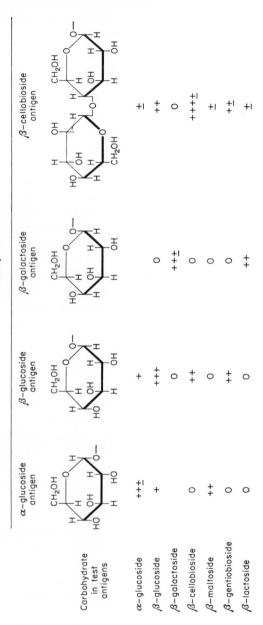

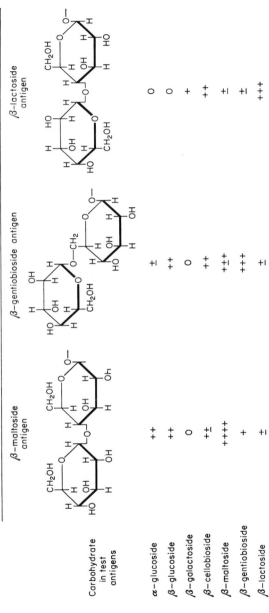

Carbohydrate in test antigens	β−maltoside antigen	β−gentiobioside antigen	β−lactoside antigen
α−glucoside	++	±	0
β−glucoside	++	++	0
β−galactoside	0	0	+
β−cellobioside	+±	++	++
β−maltoside	++++	++±	±1
β−gentiobioside	+	+++	±1
β−lactoside	±1	±1	+++

Fig. 3-10. Serological reactions of disaccharides.

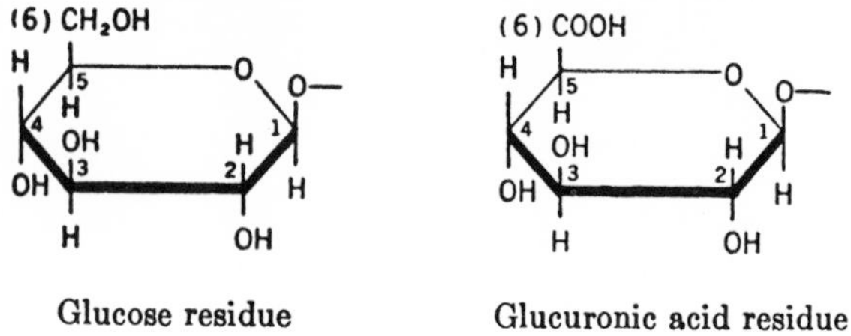

Glucose residue   Glucuronic acid residue

Fig. 3-11. Glucose and glucuronic acid.

antibodies for horse serum proteins coupled with arsanilic acid and casein-arsanilic acid as the test antigen, found that the specific inhibitory activity per mole of compound tested increased rapidly in the order, arsanilic acid, phenol-azo-arsanilic acid (or imidazol-azo-arsanilic acid), gelatin-azo-arsanilic acid. Since we assume that the inhibitory power of a hapten is greater, the greater its resemblance to the actual determinant in the antigen that is responsible for the production of the antibody, this indicated that the "antiarsanilic" antibodies were directed not solely towards the introduced arsonic acid group but also towards the tyrosine (and histidine)-azo-arsanilic residues, and that they showed some influence of other (presumably adjacent) parts of the intact protein molecule (Fig. 3-12). Landsteiner (128), using antibodies to methylated, acylated, halogenated, and nitrated proteins, where antibodies to the native protein are not always produced, observed that if the tests were carried out with diminishing quantities of antibody, the reactions were stronger with the exactly homologous antigen, showing that the specificity depends to some extent upon the specific protein background.

In considering work with such altered or conjugated proteins, it should be kept in mind that they probably consist of mixtures which are modified to various degrees from the native protein, the abundance of the various molecular species possibly following a distribution function such as the Gaussian curve (p. 697).

10. Inhibition Reaction

Although antisera against conjugated antigens containing simple chemical compounds were often found to be quite specific for the particular hapten used, and readily precipitated antigens containing the hapten coupled to another protein, nevertheless Landsteiner observed that no precipitation or other visible reaction occurred if the antisera were simply mixed directly with the hapten alone, instead of with the hapten-protein compound. This did not at the time seem surprising, since it was then

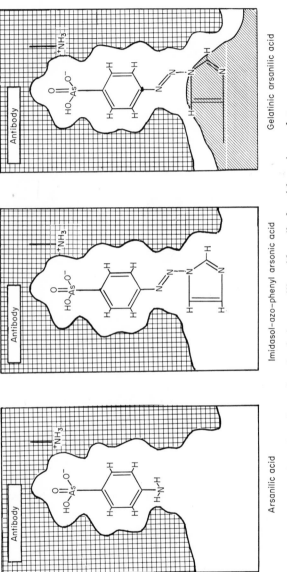

Fig. 3-12. Reactions of anti-gelatin-arsanilic acid antibody with various substances.

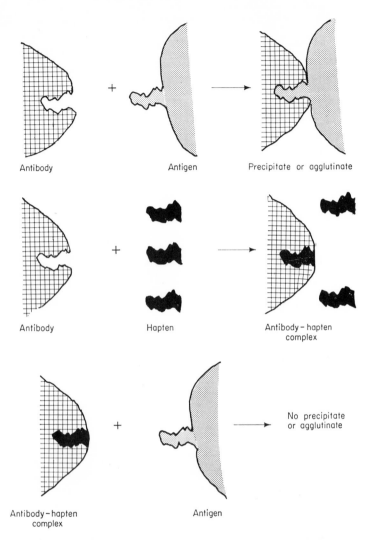

Fig. 3-13. Principle of inhibition of serological reactions by a hapten.

believed that only substances of high molecular weight, which give colloidal solutions, could take part in the precipitin reaction.

Landsteiner, reasoning that nevertheless some sort of reaction must occur, since the point of union in the case of the artificial antigens was obviously the hapten, took account of the fact that precipitation by immune sera is prevented or diminished when an excess of antigen is present, and deduced that the addition of an excess of the hapten might prevent the precipitation by antibody of the artificial antigen containing the hapten. Experiments proved that this actually happened, and specific inhibition of the precipitin reaction was obtained by the addition of the simple chemical compound towards which the antibody was directed, or of related compounds. The chief new result was to show that antibodies could react, not only with protein or parts of protein, but—unexpectedly— even with very simple chemical compounds, such as benzoic acid or tartaric acid.

The inhibition technic simplified the chemistry of these studies, since it made it possible to make tests on compounds without actually combining them with a protein, and in certain cases the specificity was more sharply demonstrated.

The inhibition reaction results from a union of the haptenic substance with the antibody, as was expected, and as was proved by experiments of Landsteiner (125), Marrack and Smith (160), and others (see 126). See Fig. 3-13.

The results of the inhibition reactions are in general agreement with those of precipitin reactions with artificial antigens, but the inhibition reaction has furnished new information because of the ease with which it is possible to investigate numerous compounds, and because of the appearance of additional group reactions.

The reaction was seen by Landsteiner to provide a possibility of determining the nature of the specifically reacting groups in antigens of unknown composition. This possibility was realized by Wormall (255), who showed that the reactions of immune sera for iodized proteins with other iodoproteins were not inhibited by halogen compounds chosen at random, but only, of those tested, by 3,5-dihalogenated tyrosine, the effect diminishing in the order iodine, bromine, chlorine. This was taken to prove that diiodotyrosine was the active group. The possibility that iodo- or diiodoimidazole may also be active does not seem to have been considered.

The inhibition reaction was utilized by Hooker and Boyd (100) to study the relative affinity for antibody of simple compounds more or less closely related to the antigenic determinant in conjugated proteins, and by Pauling and collaborators (221,222,203) for similar purposes and to study the intermolecular forces involved. A quantitative theory was proposed by Pauling et al. (204).

The quantitative inhibitior test is discussed in Chapters 16 and 17.

11. Specificity of Native Proteins

The natural proteins occur in plant and animal tissues, in the cells of bacteria and parasites, in viruses, and among the soluble products secreted into the culture medium by certain bacteria. Even now, not a great deal is known about the chemical basis of the specificity of such proteins, and our ideas are mostly the result of deduction and extrapolation from experiments of the sort already discussed. We may pause to define two terms which are often used in discussing natural proteins, "functional specificity" and "species specificity."

Functional Specificity

Proteins from the same species which have different functions in the body, and thus by inference (or in some instances demonstrably) differences in structure, usually differ widely in specificity, so that as a rule no serological cross reaction whatever is observed between pure preparations. Thus blood hemoglobin is a different protein serologically from the proteins of kidney tissue, and the serum globulins are different from the serum albumin. There is evidence that most organs possess special proteins or carbohydrates peculiar to them, and organ-specific antisera have been obtained. It seems to be a rule that proteins which are structurally different are also serologically different.

On the other hand, serum albumins of related species, all evidently fulfilling roughly the same function, are chemically similar, and at one time during World War II it was hoped that bovine serum albumin could replace human serum albumin as a blood substitute. Serum albumins of different mammalian species are evidently antigenically similar, but not absolutely identical.

Crystalline insulin from a variety of species at first appeared to be identical in chemical structure, although later some differences in amino acid composition were found (219). It is therefore not surprising that insulin is a poor antigen—a fortunate thing for those diabetics who must administer species-foreign insulin parenterally to themselves every day of their lives.

Although insulin is a poor antigen, nevertheless some patients do become sensitized to it. One such patient even gave allergic manifestations to human insulin (152). Even in this case, however, human insulin, unlike the commercial insulin to which the patient had become resistant, produced a fall in blood sugar, showing an immunological difference.

Species Specificity

The second general regularity we observe in the serological behavior of natural proteins is that the specificity is usually different when the proteins are from different species, even if the proteins are functionally analogous. The more closely related any two species are, apparently, the greater the serological likeness of their corresponding proteins.

There can be no doubt that these serological similarities and differences in proteins from different species are due to chemical similarities and differences develop, and proteins fulfilling a given function in two differ-diverge in the course of evolution, chemical as well as morphological differences develop, and proteins fulfilling a given function in two different species no longer have quite the same chemical composition. This difference is reflected in their immunological characteristics.

The first extensive investigation of species specificity was the classic work of Nuttall (187), who studied the serum proteins of a very large number of species, testing them with antisera from rabbits. Nuttall was one of the first to attempt to estimate quantitatively the differences in strength of precipitin reactions, which he did by measuring the volume of the precipitate formed. Today there are many objections which could be brought against Nuttall's work; notably his use of whole serum (a complex mixture of proteins) as antigen, instead of some one purified protein, and his lack of attention to the proportion in which antiserum and antigen are mixed, which influences the amount of precipitate. Neverthe-

TABLE 3-13

Relative Amounts of Precipitate with Three Different Antihuman Rabbit Sera and Equal Amounts of Blood Serum of Various Species (188)[a]

	Immune serum		
Species	1	2	3
Man	100	100	100
Chimpanzee	—	—	130[b]
Gorilla	—	—	64
Orangutan	47	80	42
Mandrill (*Cynocephalus mormon*)	30	50	42
Cercopithecus petaurista	30	50	—
Ateles vellerosus	22	25	—
Cat (*Felis domesticus*)	11	—	3
Dog (*Canis familiaris*)	11	—	3

[a] Amount of precipitate obtained with human blood taken arbitrarily as 100.

[b] Loose precipitate.

less his work demonstrated the power of the serological method in comparative zoology, and his results have been quoted ever since in textbooks on evolution. Some of his data obtained with three antisera to human blood serum are shown in Table 3-13.

It will be seen that the intensity of the precipitation diminished in the order, anthropoid apes, Old World monkeys, New World monkeys. The variability in the results with the different antisera is also apparent.

A number of authors have studied the species specificity of the egg white proteins of various birds (250). In this system, as in many others, immunologists have found the precipitation reaction in gels, as developed by Oudin (191) and especially by Ouchterlony (190), a powerful method of distinguishing mixtures of antigens from pure antigens (117,115).

Individual Specificity

Even individuals of the same species are not always antigenically exactly alike. The best known examples of this variation are of course the human blood groups (see Chapter 5). The blood groups of animals, analogous to those in man but in some ways even more complicated, have been omitted from consideration in this book. The subject has been discussed in a review (50).

The human blood group antigens in the ABO system are mucopolysaccharides (Chapter 5). As the investigation of human variability continues, an increasing number of hereditary individual biochemical differences are being discovered. A good example of this is provided by human hemoglobin.

At least ten genetically distinct conditions that may be characterized by differences in the composition of the hemoglobin of the erythrocytes have been found, and at least five different kinds of human hemoglobin exist (184,107,20). These hemoglobins can often be distinguished by their electrophoretic mobilities. Fetal hemoglobin (hemoglobin F) is the predominant form during prenatal life. In the majority of healthy adults it is no longer detectable, but it may persist in certain chronic anemias, in varying amounts along with normal hemoglobin (hemoglobin A). In sickle-cell anemia and sickle-cell trait, where the deoxygenated erythrocytes change shape and become multipointed or sickle-shaped, another hemoglobin (hemoglobin S) is present. A fourth type (hemoglobin C) is produced by the thalassemia gene (230).

The existence of many other hereditary antigenic differences is shown by the behavior of skin grafts and organ transplants. See Chapter 12.

12. Serological Study of Zoological and Botanical Relationships

It is clear that Nuttall's and similar results have an important bearing on the question of animal (and plant) relationships. A rather large number of workers have attempted to make more precise use of serological methods in this problem. The work of Boyden (28) and his pupils is of particular interest.

Not all workers, perhaps, have taken account of the many possible sources of error in this kind of work, and this fact, coupled with the specialized terminology employed, has tended to discourage zoologists from making full use of the results of serological investigations. One important limitation has been that practically only one species, the rabbit, is commonly used as the producer of the antiserum. This has led to what Landsteiner (126) called "faulty perspective," because the tissues of an animal tend to distinguish, among antigens coming in contact with them, finer differences in the antigens of species that are closely related to the injected animal itself. The reason for this, which on reflection does not seem surprising, seems to be that in the injected animal (the rabbit, for instance), structural features of foreign proteins which are duplicated in some of the rabbit's own proteins do not call forth the production of antibodies; instead, the antibodies are directed towards features of the foreign antigens which are different from rabbit proteins, although structurally these differences may be relatively minor. In responding to antigens from species that are taxonomically distant, on the other hand, the rabbit produces antibodies concerned chiefly with main structural features, while it tends to ignore the minor characteristics in which these distant species differ from each other. Thus we find that antisera prepared by injecting the rabbit with the serum proteins of other rodents may readily distinguish relatively small taxonomic differences, whereas rabbit antisera prepared by injecting bird proteins seem to indicate a much greater serological similarity between the various species. Therefore it would be desirable, whenever possible, to use as the antibody-producing animal a species not too distantly related to the group whose relationships we wish to study, instead of using rabbits for all such experiments.

Another difficulty is due to the individual variation in antibodies produced by different animals of the same species. Apparently, not only do different species recognize different parts of antigens as the most significant, but different individuals may vary in this respect, so that antibodies of different specificity are obtained in different animals. It has also been found (101,254,164) that the specificity of the antibodies produced by an individual animal tends to diminish with prolonged immunization, so that variation also results from differences in length of the course of immunization, and probably also in the amount of antigen injected.

The various ways of estimating serological relationships quantitatively may not measure the same thing. Also, the apparent degree of relationship of two species may differ when different proteins are used in the experiment. Thus we find considerable differences among the blood proteins of various species, whereas the proteins of the lens of the eye seem to be practically identical. It is not entirely clear which observation ought to be given the most weight taxonomically. Nevertheless, in spite of the elements of arbitrariness which derive from individual variation in antibody production, and in spite of the fact that reciprocal tests (using the animals in reverse order as antigen source and antibody producer) often fail to indicate identical degrees of relationship, relationships based on the results of serological tests must have a certain reality and may serve as contributing evidence in appropriate cases. The problem was well discussed by Boyden (28).

Other proteins besides the serum proteins exhibit species specificity. Though rather poor antigens, the hemologlobins are an example. Muscle proteins, fibrinogen (149), egg proteins, and milk proteins also show more or less species specificity. The globulins of the various organs probably should be included, and keratins (211) also seem to show some species specificity. Enzymes (*e.g.*, pepsin, pepsinogen, and trypsin), though often very similar chemically, are serologically different in different species (128,219). Wells and Osborne (see 248) made an extensive study of the specificity of plant proteins and found that these also exhibited marked species specificity.

13. Medicolegal Tests

The species specificity of proteins makes possible the application of serological tests to forensic medicine. Striking results have been obtained (90,187,243). The subject has been reviewed by Dodd (47).

We are usually interested in the differentiation of human and animal blood, but similar methods have been applied to the determination of the species origin of flesh and other parts of lower animals. The antisera are easily prepared by injecting blood serum into rabbits. Antihuman sera may react only with blood proteins of man and the higher anthropoids (see Table 3-13), but in many cases there may be weak cross reactions with proteins of other mammals. Such a serum can be rendered specific by "absorption." By such methods it is quite easy to differentiate human blood, even when dried, from that of other species. This may make it possible to prove, for example, that an accused murderer's story, that the stains found on his clothing were pig blood, is false, thus suggesting that he *may* be guilty of the crime attributed to him.

14. Organ Specificity

The term "organ specificity" is used in two different senses. In the first, it signifies that various organs of the body can be differentiated serologically. This is not surprising, since it would be expected that the functional differentiation of organs would be based on chemical, and therefore serological, differences in the substances therein contained. Table 3-14 shows results of tests carried out by Landsteiner *et al.* demonstrating organ specificity in cattle (135).

TABLE 3-14

Complement Fixation Titers with Antisera from Rabbits to Various Organs of Cattle (135).

Antigen (from cattle)	Rabbit serum vs.			
	Trachea	Thymus	Kidney	Sperm
Trachea	80	<10	<10	0
Thymus	20	40	0	<10
Kidney	<10	0	80	<10
Sperm	0	0	0	40

Morphologically different parts of a cell can also sometimes be differentiated serologically, for example, the heads and tails of spermatozoa (94). See Chapter 4.

In its second usage, the term "organ-specific" implies that antibodies to an organ of one species will react with the substances from the corresponding organ of certain other species. In related species this is not surprising, but in some cases the cross reaction may extend rather farther taxonomically than would have been anticipated, the lens protein of fish, for example, reacting with antisera to mammalian lens (91). Somewhat similar experiments with casein have already been referred to. Antisera have also been obtained that react with substances contained in alcoholic extracts of the brain of various species (see 253). Such antisera also react with testicle extracts (144). These reactions seem to depend on lipides extracted from the organs.

The specificity of a number of organs and secretions has been studied, including brain, kidney, suprarenal, placenta, hypophysis, stomach, in-

testine, lens, leukocytes, tumors, glioma, milk, and saliva.   For references
to the literature see (126).

Some of the organ-specific antigens seem to be large molecules and can
be separated by sedimentation at about 25,000 r.p.m.   In this class of
molecule Henle and co-workers (92,93) described characteristic antigens
of brain, liver, kidney, lung, testicle, and heart muscle of cow and mouse.
References to other work will be found in (228,48).

Pressman and collaborators (223,121) carried out extensive investigations
on antibodies to organs such as kidney, lung, liver, and spleen, and have
studied with the aid of radioactive tracers the zone of localization of these
antibodies when they are introduced into an animal of the species which
furnished the antigen.   There was considerable localization in the organ
used for the antigen, particularly in the vascular bed of the organ, although there was some cross reaction with other organs.

Antiorgan sera may specifically damage the target organ *in vivo* (cytotoxic effect) (135,185,228,48).   The injurious action of antikidney serum
was observed many years ago (148), but was given little attention until
Masugi (162) demonstrated toxicity of the antikidney serum for the
kidney in the rat.   It has proved possible to produce nephritis by antikidney sera in rats, rabbits, dogs, and guinea pigs.

The damage done by such antiorgan sera brings up the possibility that
diseases such as nephritis and encephalitis in man may sometimes be the
result of damage by autoantibodies produced by the patient.   Discussion
of this subject will be postponed until Chapter 13.

Tumor Immunity

Mention of the cytotoxic effect of some antiorgan sera brings to mind
an old dream of the immunologist, namely, the production of an antiserum which will react specifically with, and destroy, the cells of malignant growths (128).   Or, if antibodies are produced to tumor tissue by
the host, such antibodies might be of great value in the diagnosis of early
cases.   There seems something specifically different about a tumor, after
all, so why should antitumor antibodies not be produced?

There have been two main theories of carcinogenesis, the mutation
theory and the virus theory (247).   According to the former, cancers
result from the imperfect duplication of one of the genes in the nucleus
of a body cell, a mutation which somehow alters the growth characteristics, presumably through change in one or more of the enzyme systems.
According to the other theory, cancer is a virus disease (not necessarily
due to a single virus, of course) , and cells become cancerous when chronic

irritation renders them susceptible to the virus already present in them. Some of the evidence for the virus theory was summarized by Dmochowski (45). Martin *et al.* have presented evidence that viruses can be carriers of chemical carcinogens (161).

If the mutation theory of carcinogenesis is correct, it might be supposed that antibodies against tumor tissue would develop with difficulty and might be relatively ineffective, because the characteristic enzymes, although proteins, and presumably antigenic, might be present in very small amount, and confined to the interior of the tumor cell, so that they exerted very little antigenic stimulus on the host. These enzymes might or might not cause the production of proteins that were antigenically distinct from normal proteins of the cell, and against these new antigens antibodies would be formed.

The virus theory *might* lead one to expect the role of immunological factors to be important, yet it would not have to be so. Viruses are intracellular and consequently not easily reached by antibodies, and we know that some virus infections (*e.g.*, herpes) can coexist with circulating antibody. The amount of virus present in each tumor cell might be too small to provoke much antibody formation.

Antibodies have been repeatedly produced by injecting human tumor tissue into animals (128,48), but they have in general exhibited imperfect specificity and have given overlapping reactions with normal tissues.

Kosyakov and Korosteleva (122) were not able to find any antigen common to all malignant tumors in man. No anti-tumor antibodies have exhibited any definite curative effect, nor have they proven to be of any diagnostic value. Serological reactions (complement fixation) have been obtained with tumor extracts and the sera of patients suffering from malignant disease, but the sera of many other patients (pregnancy, syphilis, etc.) also give such reactions.

Nevertheless some hopeful results have been obtained. With the sera of rabbits bearing transplantable tumors, Kidd (128,48) was able to obtain complement fixation tests which would sharply differentiate two agents (Brown-Pearce sarcoma and V2 sarcoma) for each other and from normal tissue. Antibodies which neutralize the causative filterable agents of fowl tumors can be produced in rabbits, and have been found in the sera of some birds. These sera did not exert any marked curative effect, however.

In spite of the inconclusive results of this early work, there is considerable evidence that an immunological mechanism is involved in resistance to tumor growth (237). Mitchison (174) has presented data showing how a tumor (a lymphosarcoma), which regressed with a median survival time of 9.9 ± 0.8 days in untreated mice, had a median survival time of only 2.1 ± 0.3 days in mice which had been immunized by previous transplants. This immunity could not be transferred to susceptible mice by injection of serum, suggesting that a possible difficulty with the previous work is that circulating antibodies are not produced. Belief in the existence of a real immunological mechanism for the resistance is supported by the observation that immunity could be transferred by lymph node grafts.

The immunological aspects of cancer are discussed by Woodruff (254a).

15. Toxins

In the early days of bacteriology the word toxin meant an antigenic substance of high molecular weight produced by bacteria. Two groups were distinguished: exotoxins, secreted by the organisms into the medium in which they were growing, and endotoxins, which formed part of the body of the organism, and which were liberated only when destruction of the cell occurred. The exotoxins were heat-labile, highly antigenic, and easily converted to toxoid by treatment with formaldehyde.

More recently the distinction between the two classes of toxins has grown less sharp, since substances having the properties of exotoxins can be obtained in high concentration by allowing certain bacteria to autolyze or by extracting with certain solvents. It has also been found that the toxic activities of a bacterial filtrate are sometimes due to a number of different substances. Because of these increases in our knowledge, Oakley (188) suggested that the word toxin should be replaced by "soluble bacterial antigen," although he admitted that the word "toxin" is so thoroughly embedded in the literature that is not likely to be given up.

In addition to the toxins produced by bacteria, it is customary to include in this class snake and bee venoms, spider poisons, and certain antigenic vegetable poisons such as ricin.

The toxins which have been investigated all seem to be proteins, since they are (1) inactivated by treatments which denature proteins, (2) non-dialyzable, (3) precipitated by the usual protein precipitants, (4) insoluble in organic solvents, (5) destroyed by proteolytic enzymes, and (6) antigenic.

A few toxins have been prepared in a state pure enough to conform to the usual criteria of homogeneity in proteins, but the greater number of toxins have not yet been isolated. To obtain a general idea of the properties of toxins it may be useful to inspect some of the results obtained with the purified preparations. These are shown in Table 3-15, from van Heyningen (97).

It will be seen that these purified toxins have typical protein properties, aside from their extreme toxicity. Their toxicity is shown by the fact that

TABLE 3-15

Properties of Purified Toxins (Modified from 97)

	Diphtheria	Botulinus type A	Tetanus	Shiga	Ricin	Rattlesnake	Cobra
Lethal dose per kg. animal, μg.	290 (mouse) 0.29 (guinea pig)	0.0016 (mouse) 0.00083 (guinea pig)	0.005 (mouse) 0.00083 (guinea pig)	0.0013 (mouse) 0.00083 (rabbit)	78 (mouse) 0.100 (rabbit)	360 (mouse)	7200 (pigeon)
Isoelectric point	4.1	5.5	5.1	ca. 4	5.4–5.5	4.71	8.55–8.66
Diffusion constant (cm.^{2}/sec.) ($\times 10)^7$	6.0	2.14	—	5.7	6.0	8.59	9.9
Sedimentation constant	4.6	17.3	4.5	4.8	4.8	3.13	—
Frictional coefficient, f/f_0	1.22	1.76	—	1.26	1.2	1.2	—
Molecular weight ($\times 10^{-3}$)	72	900–1130	67	82	77	30	33

the lethal dose of the most poisonous nonprotein compounds is less, except for the most toxic; aconitine, 120 μg. per kilogram rabbit, and sodium fluoroacetate ("1080"), 50 μg. per kilogram dog. With the exception of botulinus toxin, all toxins have molecular weights in the "albumin" class.

Toxins, being proteins, and antigenic, will produce antibodies if injected into an animal, unless the animal is too highly susceptible to the toxic action. There is no particular reason to think that the toxic groups in a toxin are necessarily identical with those which act as determinants when it functions as an antigen. The antibodies to toxin will neutralize toxin, and hence are called antitoxins, but their action might be due to a blocking of the toxic groups, *i.e.*, the latter might simply be covered up by the antitoxin molecules although these were attached to other groups.

Neutralizing antibodies have been successfully produced for toxins from the following bacteria: *Corynebacterium diphtheriae, Clostridium tetani, Cl. chauvoei, Pseudomonas aeruginosa, Cl. botulinum, Cl. perfringens, Cl. septicum, Cl. novyi, Cl. bifermentans, Shigella dysenteriae, Streptococcus pyogenes, Staphylococcus aureus,* and for various animal toxins such as snake venoms, spider poisons, and scorpion venom, and for various plant toxins, such as ricin (from the castor bean) and abrin (from the seed of the Indian licorice, *Abrus precatorius*) (258).

Patients can be passively immunized by injecting serum of horses or other animals immunized against toxins, and such sera are useful therapeutically if given early enough. It is the antitoxin in such sera which is effective. It is better to stimulate the patient (in advance) to manufacture his own antitoxin by active immunization. Antisera to snake venoms and to scorpion venom have also been found effective.

In those toxins that have been studied, the toxicity seems to be an integral part of the molecule, not dependent on any prosthetic group. In several cases it has been found that the toxicity can be destroyed, without violent alteration of the molecule otherwise, by the action of formaldehyde (see below) and other agents.

Some toxic proteins are enzymes and their toxicity is due to their enzyme activity. For instance, the α-toxin of *Clostridium welchii (perfringens)* and the toxin of the rattlesnake *Crotalus terrificus* are phosphatidases, and the κ-toxin of *Cl. welchii* and the coagulant toxins of many snake venoms are proteolytic enzymes. However, it should not be concluded that all toxins are enzymes, for the mode of action is in most cases not understood. It is thought that at least one toxin, diphtheria toxin, acts by inhibition of the synthesis of a cytochrome.

Van Heyningen (97) classified toxins as follows: (*1*) competitive inhibitors, *i.e.*, diphtheria toxin, (2) neutrotoxins, (3) dehydrogenase inhibitors, (4) blood coagulants, (5) anticoagulants, (6) shock-producing substances, (7) spreading factors, *i.e.*, hyaluronidases, (8) polymolecular toxins (phospholipide–polysaccharide–protein complexes). Some organisms produce more than one sort of toxin.

Bacterial Toxins

Bacterial toxins are found in the cells of the organisms or in the culture medium in which they have grown. The toxins of the Gram-positive organisms are often extracellular and actively secreted during growth. Some are secreted into the medium as inactive precursors which are activated by proteolytic enzymes (97). The toxins of Gram-negative organisms are intracellular, but may appear in the medium of autolyzed cultures. The toxins of the enteric group of Gram-negative bacteria are structural components of the cells, identical with the dominant O antigens (see Chapter 4).

We give here a list, modified from van Heyningen (97), of the toxins produced by the principal pathogenic microorganisms which are toxin producers. The term histotoxic is used to mean that when the toxin is injected into the skin it produces an area of skin damage or necrosis. The toxicity of some of the substances listed here (*e.g.*, the deoxyribonucleases) is either unknown or comparatively low, but it is thought they assist in the spread *in vivo* of the bacteria and their products.

Corynebacterium diphtheriae: A lethal, histotoxic toxin.

Staphylococcus aureus (Micrococcus pyogenes var. *aureus):* (1) α-toxin (lethal, hemolytic); (2) β-toxin(lethal, hemolytic); (3) γ-toxin (lethal, hemolytic); (4) ε-toxin (hemolytic); (5) hyaluronidase; (6) staphylocoagulase (coagulant); (7) staphylokinase (fibrolytic).

Streptococcus pyogenes: (1) Dick toxin (lethal, erythrogenic); (2) streptolysin-O (lethal, cardiotoxic, hemolytic); (3) streptolysin-S (lethal, hemolytic); (4) hyaluronidase; (5) streptokinase (fibrolytic); (6) streptodornase (deoxyribonuclease).

Clostridium botulinium: (1–6) Six type-specific neurotoxins; (7) a hemagglutinin.

Clostridium oedematiens: (1) α-toxin (lethal, histotoxic); (2) β-toxin (phosphatidase C) (lethal, hemolytic); (3) γ-toxin (phosphatidase C) (lethal, hemolytic); (4) δ-toxin (hemolytic); (5) ε-toxin (lipase) (lethal, hemolytic); (6) ζ-toxin (hemolytic).

Clostridium septicum: (1) α-toxin (lethal, hemolytic); (2) β-toxin, deoxyribonuclease.

Clostridium tetani: (*1*) tetanospasmin (neurotoxic); (*2*) tetanolysin (cardiotoxic, hemolytic).

Clostridium welchii: (*1*) α-toxin (phosphatidase C) (lethal, histotoxic, hemolytic); (*2*) β-toxin (lethal); (*3*) γ-toxin (lethal); (*4*) δ-toxin (lethal); (*5*) ε-toxin (lethal, histotoxic); (*6*) η-toxin (lethal?); (*7*) ι-toxin (lethal, histotoxic); (*8*) θ-toxin (lethal, cardiotoxic, hemolytic); (*9*) κ-toxin (collagenase) (lethal, proteolytic); (*10*) λ-toxin (proteolytic); (*11*) μ-toxin (hyaluronidase); (*12*) deoxyribonuclease.

Diphtheria toxin was prepared in fairly pure form by Eaton (51), Pappenheimer (192), and Lepow and Pillemer (143). Pope and Stevens (215) obtained a crystalline preparation which, however, they did not positively identify as pure toxin of *C. diphtheriae,* but refered to as "another step towards the isolation of the specific toxin." The characteristics of Pappenheimer's toxin are given in Table 3-16. Petermann and Pappenheimer

TABLE 3-16

Chemical Composition and Properties of Purified Diphtheria Toxin

Composition, %		Properties	
C	51.47	Specific rotation	$-39°$
H	6.75	Isoelectric point	4.1
N[a]	16.00	Molecular weight	72,000
S	0.75	Dissymmetry coefficient (f/f_0)	1.22
P	<0.05	Ratio of major to minor axes	4.7
Ash	1.4	Per cent N specifically precipitable	95–98
Amino nitrogen	0.98		
Tyrosine	9.5	MLD per mg.	14,000
Arginine	3.8	Mg. N per L_f unit	0.00045
Lysine	5.3		

[a] Corrected for ash.

found that purified diphtheria toxin has a pH stability range of 5.6 to 10.1 in buffers 0.172M in sodium chloride.

It has been suggested that Pappenheimer's toxin (Table 3-16) was not pure. When tested by the Oudin technic, crude toxin showed 24 lines, indicating at least as many antigen components, and Pappenheimer's toxin showed 14 lines. However, Pappenheimer believes that most of these lines represent trace antigens. Pappenheimer's toxin had 2170 L_f/mg. N, but both Pope *et al.* (214) and Lepow and Pillemer (143) obtained toxins with higher values than this. The former authors report a value of 3200 L_f/mg. N for one of their preparations, which they still do not consider necessarily pure. Bowen (15) believes that the actual amount of contaminants in Pappenheimer's preparations may not have been large. Relyveld (231) obtained crystalline diphtheria toxin with about 3000 L_f/mg. N. Pope and Stevens (216) and Katsura *et al.* (118) obtained crystalline toxin with 3200–3300 L_f/mg. N, but Pope and Stevens nevertheless found that their material was a mixture of antigens with distinct immunological properties.

Pappenheimer (194,195,196) proposed a persuasive theory of the origin and mode of action of diphtheria toxin. It is based on the observation that toxin production by *Corynebacterium diphtheriae* is at its maximum when the amount of iron in the medium is just the minimum needed to support adequate growth (about 100 μg. Fe per liter), and that for every four atoms of iron added above this level one molecule fewer of toxin, and four molecules of porphyrin (coproporphyrin III) are produced. At the minimum level of iron the organisms oxidize succinic acid at a much reduced rate, for which oxidation the enzyme cytochrome b_1 is required. Cytochrome b_1 is made up of a moiety of protein coupled with four molecules of a porphyrin (protoporphyrin IX) and four atoms of iron. The diphtheria bacillus, unable to manufacture cytochrome b_1, nevertheless continues to make the protein moiety, or a related protein, and a porphyrin (coproporphyrin III), but discharges them into the medium as waste products. The protein produced may be similar to, but not identical with, the protein moiety of mammalian cytochrome b_1, and might exert its toxic effects by inhibiting the synthesis of this vital respiratory enzyme in the tissues of the host.

Pappenheimer and Williams (198) obtained support for this theory from a study of the action of diphtheria toxin on various stages of the developing silkworm (*Cecropia*).

Botulinus toxin was crystallized by Lamanna, McElroy, and Eklund 124) and by Abrams, Kegeles, and Hottle (2). It contains 16.29 per cent nitrogen. The crystalline preparation was found to be electrophoretically homogeneous at pH 4.38 in 0.1M sodium acetate buffer with a mobility of 2.75 $\times$ 10^{-5}.

Buehler, Schantz, and Lamanna (31) found 19 amino acids in crystalline botulinus toxin which accounted for all of the molecule. Aspartic acid, tyrosine, and theonine are present in greater amounts than generally found in proteins, even in tetanus toxin.

Crystalline botulinus toxin type A does not satisfy all the criteria for purity of proteins. Solubility experiments indicated the possible presence of more than one component.

Tetanus neurotoxin, also called tetanospasmin, is responsible for the fatal outcome of infection with *Cl. tetani*. It was isolated in homogeneous crystalline form by Pillemer *et al.* (209), and its physical properties are shown in Table 3-15. It contains the following amino acid residues per molecule: 13 Arg, 76 Asp, 47 Glu, 30 Gly, 5 His, 43 Leu, 48 i-Leu, 46 Lys, 8 Met, 20 Phe, 29 Thr, 3 Try, 31 Val.

. Tetanus toxin, like botulinus toxin, affects the parasympathetic cholinergic nerve endings (97), but its main effect is on the central nervous system, reaching the anterior horn cells after being absorbed by the motor nerves and transported along the nerve trunks. Glycogen synthesis in tetanized muscle is impaired and anaerobic glycolysis reduced, apparently at a stage between the breakdown of glucose 6-phosphate and the formation of pyruvic acid. Wensinck (249) suggested that tetanic contracture may be due to a resulting decrease in the formation of high-energy phosphate bonds. The receptor with which tetanus toxin combines seems to be a ganglioside (98).

Crystalline tetanus toxin in a 1 per cent solution is pale yellow. It is very stable in the presence of dipolar ions between pH 5.0 and 6.0. It is electrophoretically homogeneous with a mobility of 2.8×10^{-5} in veronal buffer of ionic strength 0.1 and pH 8.6. The optical rotation is $-63°$. Freshly prepared tetanus toxin behaves in constant solubility studies like a one component system. Tetanus toxin is easily detoxified by formaldehyde; the product is antigenic and can be used for immunization (212).

The chemistry of tuberculin is discussed in Chapter 4.

Boivin antigens are discussed below.

Enzymes

Enzymes are proteins and thus antigenic in animals from which they do not derive. The immunochemistry of enzymes has practically become a specialty in itself. A summary will be found in (39).

Animal Venoms

A wide range of animals possess the ability to produce venomous secretions (97). There are about 600 species of venomous snakes in the world, but of these only 150 are dangerous to man. Reviews of the chemistry of venoms will be found in references (217) and (197). The toxic action of snake venoms is due to proteolytic enzymes, phosphatidases, and neurotoxins. Different families of snakes are to some extent characterized by the effects produced by their venoms. Elapine (cobra, asp) venoms are mainly neurotoxic and hemolytic and only slightly hemorrhagic and cytolytic. Some of the Australian elapine venoms are powerfully coagulant. Crotaline (copperhead, rattlesnake, bushmaster, fer de lance) venoms are hemolytic, coagulant, powerfully hemorrhagic, and cytolytic, and only slightly neurotoxic. Viperine venoms resemble crotaline venoms in their action.

Bee venom is neurotoxic, hemorrhagic, cytolytic, hemolytic, and coagulant (97). It can be separated into an acidic component of low molecular weight and a basic protein. Toxic polypeptides have been isolated. Bee venom contains a hemolytic phosphatidase A and is stated by van Heyningen to be the richest known source of a dehydrogenase inhibitor.

Cases of violent or fatal reactions to bee stings are probably due to anaphylaxis.

Plant Toxins

There are many poisonous plants and four toxic plant proteins are known, abrin from *Abrus precatorius,* crotin from *Croton tiglium,* ricin from *Ricinus communis,* curcin from *Jatropha curcas,* and robin from *Robinia pseudoaccacia.* Other plants contain hemolytic agglutinating proteins (18), and one, *Vicia faba,* sometimes produces a hemolytic disease in certain persons of Italian descent (153), but these hemagglutinins are not toxic when ingested by the average person. The mushroom *Amanita phalloides* contains toxic polypeptides, amanitine and phalloidin (97).

Ricin, from the castor bean, has been prepared in rather pure form, and its physical properties are shown in Table 3-15. However, even four-times crystallized ricin did not seem to be homogeneous. The immunological characteristics of ricin have been reported by Kabat *et al.* (112).

Ricin, although a protein, is toxic when ingested, apparently because it is very resistant to proteolytic enzymes. The mechanism of its toxic action is not known.

Abrin and crotin have properties similar to those of ricin.

The chemistry of toxins has been reviewed by Pillemer and Robbins (212), van Heyningen (96,97), Burrows (33), and Oakley (188).

16. Toxoids

It was early observed that on storage toxins might lose part of their toxicity while retaining their power to neutralize antitoxin. Treatment with certain chemicals had a similar effect. Ramon (229) found it possible to destroy the toxic properties completely, without appreciable loss of antigenic qualities, by incubating toxin with formaldehyde. Ramon called his product "anatoxine," but the name toxoid is more common in the English language literature.

There is no appreciable change in the amount of nitrogen in one flocculating unit when toxin is converted to toxoid. There have been some experiments indicating that the *in vivo* combining power has been somewhat affected.

Formaldehyde apparently acts directly on the toxic groups without affecting other parts of the toxin molecule which are concerned with antigenicity and combining activity. It is natural to suppose that the effect is due to combination with the free amino groups of the toxin, but Hewitt (95) pointed out that the reaction between toxin and formaldehyde to form toxoid is slow and irreversible, while that between formaldehyde and the free amino groups of proteins, polypeptides, and amino acids is rapid and reversible. The amount of formaldehyde required for toxoid formation is also less.

Goldie (72) and Pappenheimer (193) found that, although the reaction is irreversible and consequently, as mentioned above, not due merely to the formation of methylene linkages with the amino nitrogen, nevertheless toxicity was abolished by combination of other groups with the amino groups, as by treatment with ketene gas.

Toxoid is a more stable product than toxin. It does not appear to lose its antigenic value with aging, and it is more resistant to heat than toxin. Eaton (52) pointed out that the fact that toxin and toxoid have the same optical rotation suggests that the optically active atoms adjacent to the peptide linkages may not have been affected.

Diphtheria toxin can also be converted to toxoid in other ways. For example, Agner (4) showed that the toxicity was destroyed by peroxidative oxidation (oxidation by hydrogen peroxide, peroxidase, and an oxidizable, dialyzable cofactor). The flocculation titer remained unchanged. It was suggested that the conversion of crude diphtheria toxin to toxoid which occurs on storage may be due to a slow peroxidative process.

17. Specificity of Carbohydrates

Dochez and Avery (46) found in cultures of pneumococci a soluble substance that precipitated specifically with antiserum of corresponding type. Zinsser and Parker (259) obtained similar precipitable products which were free from protein. Avery and Heidelberger demonstrated that these nonprotein precipitable substances were polysaccharides (see the review by Heidelberger (82). This discovery powerfully stimulated the chemical investigation of antigens.

It has been found that some carbohydrates can be antigenic, and that quite a number may react specifically with antisera obtained by injecting either whole organisms or various mixtures of substances. The species specificity of carbohydrates seems often to be somewhat less than that of proteins, possibly because of the smaller number of different compounds possible in the carbohydrate series. Consequently, cross reactions with distantly related species are more common. Thus, by chemical accident

(49) a rabbit antiserum for the encapsulated type B Friedländer bacillus precipitates the capsular carbohydrate of type II pneumococcus (and vice versa) and antisera for type XIV pneumococcus react with human erythrocytes, especially of blood group A (see Chapter 4).

The structure of five polysaccharides has been studied sufficiently to relate it to their immunological behavior (see 126,157). These are: the specific carbohydrates of pneumococci of types III and VIII, the polysaccharide of Friedländer's bacillus (type A), the purified polysaccharide of gum acacia, and the gum of *Penicillium luteum*.

The structure of polysaccharide S3 is probably the best worked out. It is built up of aldobionic acid molecules united by a glucoside link. These aldobionic acid molecules are composed of one molecule of glucoronic acid and one of glucose, united by a glucoside link involving the reducing group (aldehyde) of the glucuronic acid and carbon 4 of the glucose, giving cellobiuronic acid (106). See Fig. 3-14. These aldobionic acid molecules

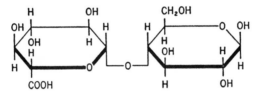

Fig. 3-14. Cellobiuronic acid.

are joined together by a glucoside link involving the reducing group of the glucose, and leaving the carboxyl group of the glucuronic acid free (see p. 206).

The polysaccharide of type VIII pneumococcus also contains cellobiuronic acid, but in addition contains glucose in some other form. Marrack and Carpenter (159) found that an antiserum against type II pneumococcus would react with a number of natural vegetable gums, even when these were diluted 1:10,000 or more. They tested cherry gum, acacia gum, plum gum, apricot gum, gum ghatti, mesquite gum, gum tragacanth, and flax mucilage. With all the gums except the last, the precipitate formation was inhibited by salts of glucuronic acid and glucuronides. These reactions serve well to illustrate the more limited species specificity found with carbohydrates. They raise the interesting question of the possible effect on bacterial infection of ingestion of similar carbohydrates in the diet.

Heidelberger and Wolfram (89) found that horse antipneumococcus XIV serum strongly reacted with the galactan isolated from cow lung and a polysaccharide from tamarind seed. The common characteristic of the two polysaccharides, an unsubstituted galactose linked to galactose, xylose, or glucose, enabled these authors to predict that one of the three galactose molecules in type XIV pneumococcus polysaccharide will be found to be an unsubstituted unit attached to another of the galactose units or to the N-acetylglucosamine. The quantitative data point to the former alternative.

It has been shown that immunization of human beings by the intracutaneous injection of small amounts (0.03 to 0.06 mg.) of specific pneumococcal polysaccharides, or mixtures of several common types, exerts a strong protective effect against the homologous type of pneumonia (53).

The chemical properties of a number of specific carbohydrates and vegetable gums are given in Tables 4-4 and 4-5 (pages 223 and 207) in the next chapter.

Almost all types of bacteria contain serologically active carbohydrates; the following is a partial list; references to the literature will be found in (126,32) (see also Chapter 4): streptococci, staphylococci, gonococci, meningococci, members of the *Phytomonas* and *Pasteurella* groups, *Hemophilus influenzae, Salmonella* bacilli, dysentery bacilli, bacilli of the *Brucella* group, *Proteus vulgaris, Hemophilus, Mycobacteria, Bacillus anthracis,* various spirochetes, yeasts and fungi, *Klebsiellae, Escherichiae, Aerobacter, Proteus, Rickettsiae,* and *Monilia.*

Specific polysaccharides will be discussed more in detail in the following chapter.

Reactive carbohydrates have also been found in other organisms. For example, Campbell (35) isolated from *Ascaris lumbricoides* (from hog) a nitrogen-free polysaccaride, apparently free from protein, which is antigenic.

Pyrogen

A major source of trouble in the manufacture of biological and other therapeutic products intended for intravenous injection are the heat-stable substances called pyrogens which cause undesirable febrile reactions. It has been found that distilled water stored in clean sterile vessels does not develop this pyrogenic property, which is water-soluble, filtrable, and produced by bacterial action (Sabin, 233). A number of molds and bacteria, including such common aerial contaminants as *Proteus vulgaris* and *B. subtilis,* have been incriminated. Even today, workers engaged in experiments involving parenteral injection, such as drug testing, do not always allow for the possibility that their diluent may contain pyrogens.

Purified pyrogen from *Salmonella typhosa* has been found to be a gummy polysaccharide containing one glucosamine molecule per five or six hexose units. The results of chemical analyses have been summarized by Burger (32).

18. Lipide Antigens

The question of the possible antigenicity of lipides has been long debated. It has not been demonstrated that any pure lipide is by itself capable of inciting antibody formation, but antibodies have been obtained by injecting lipides mixed with protein. In particular lecithin (even synthetic) and cholesterol have been found antigenic in this sense by some workers, but others have reported failure when purified lecithin preparations were used.

The work of Tal and Olitsky (245) and Waksman *et al.* (246) suggested that a new class of compounds must be considered to have a demonstrated antigenicity, at least of a rather special kind. These are the proteolipides, protein–lipide combinations with the physical properties of lipides. The conclusion is based upon the loss of antigenic activity when the lipide is split off from the protein by repeated drying from organic solvents in the presence of water.

Heidelberger believed (83) that the lack of clearly defined antigenicity in the lipides may be explained by the lack of repetition of structural units in the molecule, so that no definite pattern is present to serve as antigenic determinant.

The *Forssman antigen* is discussed in Chapter 4.

19. Deoxyribonucleic Acids

It does not seem certain even today whether DNA can function as an antigen. It does seem to be established that it can function as a hapten when injected in the form of nucleoprotein (44).

20. Boivin Antigens (Carbohydrate–Lipide–Protein Complexes)

Boivin and Mesrobeanu (13,14) discovered a new type of antigen. By extracting *Salmonella typhimurium* and a number of other Gram-negative bacteria with trichloroacetic acid in the cold, they obtained a complex which consists of nonantigenic polysaccharides (Ps) and nonantigenic phospholipide (Pl). This substance was nondialyzable, gave opalescent solutions, and was specific, toxic, and antigenic. It was not found in rough variants of these organisms or in any Gram-positive organisms. The lethal dose was 5 to 10 mg. per kilogram of mouse, and this substance accounted for the whole of the toxicity of the bacteria. The substance seemed to be identical with the O-antigen (Chapter 4).

Morgan (175,177–179,199) showed that the complex also contained protein (Pr). With diethylene glycol, toxic Pl-Ps-Pr complex was extracted which represented 5 to 7 per cent of the dry weight of smooth strains of *Sh. shigae* and *Salmonella typhi.* Treatment with formamide split off the lipide, leaving Ps-Pr which retained all the antigenicity, specificity, and toxicity of the original. Treatment with acid dissociated Ps-Pr into a degraded polysaccharide and an acidic conjugated protein. These conjugated proteins could easily recombine with the undegraded polysaccharides, or with other polysaccharides such as the blood group antigens (176,200), to yield antigens whose specificity was determined by the polysaccharide portion.

Boivin antigens will be discussed in more detail in the following chapter.

21. Haptens

The term hapten (without any final "e") was introduced by Landsteiner (126), who described them as ". . . specific protein-free substances [which], although reactive in vitro, induced no, or only slight antibody response. For serologically active substances of this sort, in contradistinction to the protein antigens which possess both properties, the term hapten has been proposed. . . ."

It will be seen that this definition includes most of the carbohydrates, the Forssman "antigen," and the large numbers of simple substances which have been found to react specifically with appropriate antisera. By use of the term hapten much of the confusion resulting from the two senses of the word antigen can be avoided.

Although the haptens, by definition, have little if any antigenic power, it has been found that certain simple substances, which can also serve as haptens, possess the power of producing specific skin sensitization (see Chapter 9).

The reaction of the separate hapten may or may not be a visible one. In the case of the specific polysaccharides the reaction is usually a precipitation, but if the polysaccharide is hydrolyzed to smaller units, the precipitability eventually disappears, although the fragments may still possess specific reactive power, as shown by "inhibition tests" (prevention of precipitation with conjugated protein antigen). The technic of this reaction is described in Chapter 16. With simple chemical substances, it is generally necessary to use the inhibition reaction to demonstrate the specific reactivity, although it has been found (17,137,138,202) that some azo dyes will precipitate specifically. Some of these substances were also found to elicit anaphylactic shock, even when only a fraction of a milligram was injected. Thus at least two serological reactions once thought to be restricted to proteins have been found to be possible also with simple substances of known chemical constitution.

References

1. Abel, J., and W. W. Ford, *J. Biol. Chem.*, **2**, 1273 (1907).
2. Abrams, A., G. Kegeles, and G. A. Hottle, *J. Biol. Chem.*, **164**, 63 (1946).
3. Adler, F. L., *J. Immunol.*, **78**, 201 (1957).
4. Agner, K., *J. Exptl. Med.*, **92**, 337 (1950).
4a. Allen, S. L., *Cancer Res.*, **15**, 315 (1955).
4b. Ammann, P., G. von Muralt, and A. Hässig, *Schweitz. Med. Wochenschr.*, **93**, 818 (1963).
5. Asimov, I., *J. Chem. Educ.*, **31**, 125 (1954).
6. Astbury, W. T., S. Dickenson, and Bailey, *Biochem. J. (London)*, **29**, 2351 (1935).
7. Avery, O. T., and W. F. Goebel, *J. Exptl. Med.*, **54**, 437 (1931).
8. Avery, O. T., and W. F. Goebel, *J. Exptl. Med.*, **58**, 731 (1933).
9. Avery, O. T., W. F. Goebel, and F. H. Babers, *J. Exptl. Med.*, **55**, 769 (1932).
10. Berenblum, I., and A. Wormall, *Biochem. J. (London)*, **33**, 75 (1939).
11. Bjørneboe, M., *Z. Immunitätsforsch.*, **99**, 245 (1941).
12. Blumenthal, D., *J. Biol. Chem.*, **113**, 433 (1936).
13. Boivin, A., and I. Mesrobeanu, *Rev. immunol.*, **1**, 553 (1935).
14. Boivin, A., I. Mesrobeanu, and L. Mesrobeanu, *Compt. rend. soc. biol.*, **113**, 490 (1933); **114**, 307 (1933).
15. Bowen, H. E., *J. Immunol.*, **68**, 429 (1952).
16. Boyd, W. C., unpublished data.
17. Boyd, W. C., *J. Exptl. Med.*, **75**, 407 (1942).
18. Boyd, W. C., *J. Immunol.*, **65**, 281 (1950).
19. Boyd, W. C., unpublished experiments, 1952.
20. Boyd, W. C., "The proteins of immune reactions," in *The Proteins*, H. Neurath and K. Bailey, eds., Vol. 2, Part B, Academic Press, New York, 1954.
21. Boyd, W. C., and S. B. Hooker, *J. Gen. Physiol.*, **17**, 341 (1934).
22. Boyd, W. C., and S. B. Hooker, *J. Biol. Chem.*, **104**, 329 (1934).
23. Boyd, W. C., and S. B. Hooker, *J. Gen. Physiol.*, **22**, 281 (1939).
24. Boyd, W. C., and S. Malkiel, *J. Bacteriol.*, **39**, 32 (1940).
25. Boyd, W. C., and S. Malkiel, *J. Infect. Diseases*, **75**, 262 (1944).
26. Boyd, W. C., and P. Mover, *J. Biol. Chem.*, **110**, 457 (1935).
27. Boyd, W. C., and E. R. Warshaver, *J. Immunol.*, **52**, 97 (1945).
28. Boyden, A., *Systematic Zoology*, **2**, 19 (1953).
29. Brown, R. K., J. Duricux, R. Delaney, E. Leikhin, and B. J. Clark, *Ann. N. Y. Acad. Sci.*, **81**, 524 (1959).
30. Buckley, E. E., and N. Porges, Am. Assoc. Adv. Sci., Washington, D. C. (1956).
31. Buehler, H. J., E. J. Schantz, and C. Lamanna, *J. Biol. Chem.*, **169**, 295 (1947).
32. Burger, M., *Bacterial Polysaccharides*, Charles C Thomas, Springfield, Illinois, 1950.
33. Burrows, W., *Ann. Rev. Microbiol.*, **5**, 181 (1951).

34. Butement, F. D. S., *Nature*, **161**, 731 (1948).
35. Campbell, D. H., *J. Infect. Diseases*, **59**, 266 (1936).
36. Campbell, D. H., and N. Bulman, *Fortschr. Chem. org. Naturstoffe*, **9**, 443 (1952).
37. Cebra, J. J., *J. Immunol.*, **86**, 190, 197, 205 (1961).
38. Chambers, L. A., *J. Immunol.*, **36**, 543 (1939).
39. Cinader, B., *Ann. N. Y. Acad. Sci.*, **103**, 495–548 (1963).
40. Clutton, R. F., C. R. Harington, and T. H. Mead, *Biochem. J. (London)*, **31**, 764 (1937).
41. Clutton, R. F., C. R. Harington, and M. E. Yuill, *Biochem. J. (London)*, **32**, 1111 (1938).
42. Coons, A. H., *J. Immunol.*, **87**, 499–503 (1961).
43. Dakin, H. D., and H. W. Dudley, *J. Biol. Chem.*, **15**, 271 (1913).
44. Davies, D. A. L., *Mod. Trends Immunol.*, **1**, 1–24 (1963).
45. Dmochowski, L., *Science*, **133**, 551–561 (1961).
46. Dochez, A. R., and O. T. Avery, *J. Exptl. Med.*, **26**, 477 (1917).
47. Dodd, B., *Clinical Aspects of Immunology*, F. A. Davis, Philadelphia, 1963.
48. Doerr, R., *Die Immunitätsforschung*, Vol. 3, Springer-Verlag, Vienna, 1948, p. 50.
49. Dubos, R. J., *The Bacterial Cell in Its Relation to Problems of Virulence, Immunity and Chemotherapy*, Harvard University Press, Cambridge, 1945.
50. Dujarric de la Rivière, M. S.-P., and A. Eyquem, *Les Groupes Sanguins chez les Animaux*, Editions Méd. Flammarion, Paris, 1953.
51. Eaton, M. D., *J. Bacteriol.*, **31**, 367 (1936).
52. Eaton, M. D., *Bacteriol. Rev.*, **2**, 3 (1938).
53. Edsall, G., *New Engl. J. Med.*, **241**, 18, 60, 99 (1949).
54. Edsall, G., in *The Nature and Significance of Antibody Response*, A. M. Pappenheimer, ed., Columbia University Press, New York, 1953.
55. Ehrlich, P., *Deut. med. Wochschr.*, **17**, 976 (1891).
56. v. Eisler, M., and E. Löwenstein, *Centr. Bacteriol. Parasitenk.*, **I**, **63**, 261 (1912).
57. French, D., and J. T. Edsall. *Adv. Protein Chem.*, **2**, 277 (1954).
58. Freund, J., *Ann. Rev. Microbiol.*, **1**, 291 (1947).
59. Freund, J., *Am. J. Clin. Pathol.*, **21**, 645 (1951).
60. Freund, J., in *The Nature and Significance of Antibody Response*, A. M. Pappenheimer, ed., Columbia University Press, New York, 1953.
61. Freund, J., *et. al.*, *Science*, **102**, 202 (1945).
62. Fuchs, S., R. Aron, and M. Sela, *Bull. Res. Council Israel*, **11A**, 58 (1962).
63. Fujio, O., *J. Biochem. (Japan)*, **33**, 241 (1941).
64. Furth, J., *J. Immunol.*, **10**, 777 (1925).
65. Gaunt, W. E., and A. Wormall, *Biochem. J. (London)*, **33**, 908 (1939).
66. Goebel, W. F., *J. Exptl. Med.*, **64**, 29 (1936).
67. Goebel, W. F., *J. Exptl. Med.*, **68**, 469 (1938).
68. Goebel, W. F., *J. Exptl. Med.*, **72**, 33 (1940).
69. Goebel, W. F., and O. T. Avery, *J. Exptl. Med.*, **50**, 521, 533 (1929).
70. Goebel, W. F., O. T. Avery, and F. H. Babers, *J. Exptl. Med.*, **60**, 599 (1934).
71. Goebel, W. F., and R. D. Hotchkiss, *J. Exptl. Med.*, **66**, 191 (1937).
72. Goldie, H., *Compt. rend. soc. biol.*, **126**, 974, 977 (1937).
73. Gonzalez, P., and M. Armangue, *Compt. rend. soc. biol.*, **106**, 1006 (1931).
74. Gostev, V. S., *Khimiya Spetsificheskovo Immuniteta*, Medgiz, Moscow, 1959 (Russian).
75. Grabar, P., and M. Kaminski, *Bull. soc. chim. biol.*, **32**, 620 (1950).
76. Harris, T., and H. Eagle, *J. Gen. Physiol.*, **19**, 383 (1935).

77. Haurowitz, F., Z. physiol. Chem., 245, 23 (1936).
78. Haurowitz, F., J. Immunol., 43, 331 (1942).
79. Haurowitz, F., Chemistry and Biology of Proteins, Academic Press, New York, 1950.
80. Haurowitz, F., Biol. Rev. Cambridge Phil. Soc., 27, 247 (1952).
81. Haurowitz, F., K. Sarafian, and P. Schwerin, J. Immunol., 40, 391 (1941).
82. Heidelberger, M., Physiol. Rev., 7, 107 (1927).
83. Heidelberger, M., J. Mt. Sinai Hosp., 9, 893 (1943).
84. Heidelberger, M., A. C. Aisenberg, and W. Z. Hassid, J. Exptl. Med., 99, 343 (1954).
85. Heidelberger, M., and F. E. Kendall, J. Exptl. Med., 59, 519 (1934).
86. Heidelberger, M., F. E. Kendall, and H. W. Scherp, J. Exptl. Med., 64, 559 (1936).
87. Heidelberger, M., C. M. MacLeod, and M. M. Lapi, J. Immunol., 66, 145 (1951).
88. Heidelberger, M., et. al., J. Immunol., 53, 113 (1946).
89. Heidelberger, M., and M. L. Wolfram, Federation Proc., 13, 496 (1954).
90. Hektoen, L., J. Am. Med. Assoc., 70, 1273 (1918).
91. Hektoen, L., and K. Schulhof, J. Infect. Diseases, 34, 433 (1924).
92. Henle, W., and L. A. Chambers, Science, 92, 313 (1940).
93. Henle, W., L. A. Chambers, and V. Groupé, J. Exptl. Med., 74, 495 (1941).
94. Henle, W., G. Henle, and L. A. Chambers, J. Exptl. Med., 68, 335 (1938).
95. Hewitt, L. F., Biochem. J. (London), 24, 983 (1930).
96. van Heyningen, W. E., Bacterial Toxins, Charles C Thomas, Springfield, Illinois, 1950.
97. van Heyningen, W. E., "Toxic Proteins," in The Proteins, H. Neurath and K. Bailey, eds., Vol. 2, Part A, Academic Press, New York, 1954.
98. van Heyningen, W. E., J. Gen. Microbiol., 20, 310–320 (1959).
99. Hooker, S. B., and W. C. Boyd, J. Immunol., 23, 465 (1932).
99a. Hooker, S. B., and W. C. Boyd, J. Immunol., 24, 141 (1933).
100. Hooker, S. B., and W. C. Boyd, J. Immunol., 25, 61 (1933).
101. Hooker, S. B., and W. C. Boyd, J. Immunol., 26, 469 (1934).
102. Hooker, S. B., and W. C. Boyd, J. Immunol., 38, 479 (1940).
103. Hooker, S. B., and W. C. Boyd, J. Immunol., 45, 127 (1942).
104. Hopkins, S. J., and A. Wormall, Biochem. J. (London), 27, 740, 1706 (1933).
105. Hopkins, S. J., and A. Wormall, Biochem. J. (London), 28, 228 (1934).
106. Hotchkiss, R. D., and W. F. Goebel, J. Biol. Chem., 121, 195 (1937).
107. Itano, H. A., Science, 117, 89 (1953).
108. Jerne, N. K., Ann. Rev. Microbiol., 14, 341–358 (1960).
109. Johnson, L. R., and A. Wormall, Biochem. J. (London), 26, 1202 (1932).
110. Kabat, E. A., J. Cellular Comp. Physiol., 50, Suppl. 1, 79 (1957).
111. Kabat, E. A., Federation Proc., 21, 694–701 (1962).
112. Kabat, E. A., et. al., J. Biol. Chem., 168, 629 (1947).
113. Kabat, E. A., and O. Berg, J. Immunol., 70, 514 (1953).
114. Kabat, E. A., and M. Heidelberger, J. Exptl. Med., 66, 229 (1937).
115. Kaminski, M., Bull. soc. chim. biol., 36, 79 (1954).
116. Kaminski, M., and P. Grabar, Bull. soc. chim. biol., 31, 684 (1949).
117. Kaminski, M., and O. Ouchterlony, Bull. soc. chim. biol., 33, 758 (1951).
118. Katsura, T., and I. Kato, Japan. J. Microbiol., 1, 213 (1957).
119. Kleczkowski, A., Brit. J. Exptl. Pathol., 21, 98 (1940).
120. Kleczkowski, A., Brit. J. Exptl. Pathol., 26, 41 (1945).
121. Korngold, L., and D. Pressman, J. Immunol., 71, 1 (1953).
122. Kosyakov, P. N., and V. S. Korosteleva, Methods of specific absorption in the analysis

of the structure of tumors and normal tissues of man, Trydy Nauchnoi Konferentsii, Moscow, 1959 (Russian).

123. Kreiter, V. P., and D. Pressman, *Immunochemistry,* 1, 151–163 (1964).
124. Lamanna, C. H., W. Eklund, and O. E. McElroy, *J. Bacteriol.,* 52, 1 (1946).
125. Landsteiner, K., *Kgl. Acad. Wet. Amsterdam,* 31, 54 (1922); ref. to in 126.
126. Landsteiner, K., *The Specificity of Serological Reactions,* Charles C Thomas, Springfield, Illinois, 1936.
127. Landsteiner, K., *J. Exptl. Med.,* 75, 269 (1942).
128. Landsteiner, K., *The Specificity of Serological Reactions,* 2nd rev. ed., Harvard University Press, Cambridge, 1945.
129. Landsteiner, K., and C. Barron, *Z. Immunitätsforsch.,* 26, 142 (1917).
130. Landsteiner, K., and J. Jacobs, *Proc. Soc. Exptl. Biol. Med.,* 30, 1055 (1933).
131. Landsteiner, K., and H. Lampl, *Z. Immunitätsforsch.,* 26, 133 (1917).
132. Landsteiner, K., and H. Lampl, *Biochem. Z.,* 86, 343 (1918).
133. Landsteiner, K., and E. Prasek, *Z. Immunitätsforsch.,* 20, 211 (1913).
134. Landsteiner, K., and J. v. d. Scheer, *J. Exptl. Med.,* 45, 1045 (1927).
135. Landsteiner, K., and J. v. d. Scheer, *Proc. Soc. Exptl. Biol. Med.,* 25, 140 (1927).
136. Landsteiner, K., and J. v. d. Scheer, *J. Exptl. Med.,* 50, 407 (1929).
137. Landsteiner, K., and J. v. d. Scheer, *Proc. Soc. Exptl. Biol. Med.,* 29, 747 (1932).
138. Landsteiner, K., and J. v. d. Scheer, *J. Exptl. Med.,* 56, 399 (1932).
139. Landsteiner, K., and J. v. d. Scheer, *J. Exptl. Med.,* 55, 781 (1932).
140. Landsteiner, K., and J. v. d. Scheer, *J. Exptl. Med.,* 59, 769 (1934).
140a. Landsteiner, K., and J. v. d. Scheer, *J. Exptl. Med.,* 67, 709 (1938).
141. Landsteiner, K., and J. v. d. Scheer, *J. Exptl. Med.,* 71, 445 (1940).
142. Lapresle, C., and T. Webb, *Bull. soc. chim. biol. (Paris),* 46, 1701–1710 (1964).
143. Lepow, I. H., and L. Pillemer, *J. Immunol.,* 69, 1 (1952).
144. Lewis, J. H., *J. Immunol.,* 27, 473 (1934).
145. Lewis, J. H., *J. Infect. Diseases,* 55, 203 (1934).
146. Lewis, J. H., *J. Immunol.,* 41, 397 (1941).
147. Lin, K.-H., H. Wu, and T.-T. Chen, *Chinese J. Physiol.,* 2, 131 (1928).
148. Lindemann, W., *Ann. inst. Pasteur,* 14, 49 (1900).
149. Lorand, L., and W. R. Middlebrook, *Science,* 118, 515 (1953).
150. Low, B. W., "The Structure and configuration of amino acids, peptides and proteins," in *The Proteins,* H. Neurath and K. Bailey, eds., Vol. 1, Part A, Academic Press, New York, 1953.
151. Lowell, F. C., *J. Clin. Invest.,* 23, 225, 233 (1944).
152. Lowell, F. C., in *The Nature and Significance of Antibody Response,* A. M. Pappenheimer, ed., Columbia University Press, New York, 1953.
153. Luisada, A., *Medicine,* 20, 229 (1941).
154. Malkiel, S., *J. Immunol.,* 57, 51 (1947).
155. Malkiel, S., *Atti Congr. Intern. Microbiol.,* 6, Rome, 2, 265 (1953).
156. Markin, L., and P. Kyes, *J. Infect. Diseases,* 65, 156 (1939).
157. Marrack, J. R., *Med. Res. Council Brit. Spec. Rept. Ser.,* No. 230 (1938).
158. Marrack, J. R., "Immunity reactions in relation to the structure of proteins," in *Immunochemistry,* R. T. Williams, ed., Cambridge University Press, Oxford, 1953.
159. Marrack, J., and B. R. Carpenter, *Brit. J. Exptl. Pathol.,* 19, 53 (1938).
160. Marrack, J., and F. C. Smith, *Brit. J. Exptl. Pathol.,* 13, 394 (1932).
161. Martin, C. M., S. Magunsson, P. J. Goscienski, and G. F. Hausen, *Science,* 134, 1985–1986 (1961).

162. Masugi, M., *Beitr. pathol. Anat. u. allgem. Pathol.*, **92,** 429 (1934).
162a. Matsubara, S., and W. C. Boyd, *J. Immunol.* **91,** 641 (1963).
163. Maurer, P. H., *Proc. Soc. Exptl. Biol. Med.*, **83,** 879 (1953).
164. Maurer, P. H., *J. Immunol.*, **72,** 119 (1954).
165. Maurer, P. H., and T. Cashman, *J. Immunol.*, **90,** 393–398 (1963).
166. Maurer, P. H., and M. Heidelberger, *J. Am. Chem. Soc.*, **73,** 2070 (1951).
167. Maurer, P. H., and M. Heidelberger, *J. Am. Chem. Soc.*, **73,** 2076 (1951).
168. Maurer, P. H., M. Heidelberger, and D. H. Moore, *J. Am. Chem. Soc.*, **73,** 2072 (1951).
169. Medveczky, A., and A. Uhrovits, *Z. Immunitätsforsch.*, **72,** 256 (1931).
170. Meyer, K., *Compt. rend. soc. biol.*, **124,** 430 (1937).
171. Miller, B. F., *J. Exptl. Med.*, **58,** 625 (1933).
172. Miller, J. J., J. B. Humber, and J. O. Dowrie, *J. Pediat.*, **24,** 281 (1944).
173. Mirsky, A. E., and L. Pauling, *Proc. Natl. Acad. Sci. U. S.*, **22,** 439 (1936).
174. Mitchison, N. A., *Proc. Roy. Soc. (London)*, **B142,** 72 (1954).
175. Morgan, W. T. J., *Biochem. J. (London)*, **31,** 2003 (1937).
176. Morgan, W. T. J., *Chem. Ind. (London)*, **60,** 722 (1941).
177. Morgan, W. T. J., and S. M. Partridge, *Biochem. J. (London)*, **34,** 169 (1940).
178. Morgan, W. T. J., and S. M. Partridge, *Biochem. J. (London)*, **35,** 1140 (1941).
179. Morgan, W. T. J., and S. M. Partridge, *Brit. J. Exptl. Pathol.*, **23,** 151 (1942).
180. Mudd, S., and M. Wiener, *J. Immunol.*, **45,** 21 (1942).
181. Mutsaars, W., *Compt. rend. soc. biol.*, **129,** 510, 511 (1938).
182. Mutsaars, W., *Ann. inst. Pasteur*, **62,** 81 (1939).
183. Nairn, R. C., ed., *Fluorescent Protein Tracing*, E. and S. Livingstone, Edinburgh, 1962.
184. Neel, J. V., *Science*, **118,** 116 (1953).
185. Nettleship, A., *Am. J. Pathol.*, **18,** 689 (1942).
186. Neurath, H., *J. Am. Chem. Soc.*, **65,** 2039 (1943).
187. Nuttall, G. H. F., *Blood Immunity and Blood Relationship*, Cambridge University press, Oxford 1904.
188. Oakley, C. L., *Ann. Rev. Microbiol.*, **8,** 411 (1954).
189. Obermayer, F., and E. P. Pick, *Wien. Klin. Woschenschr.*, **17,** 265 (1904).
190. Ouchterlony, O., Paper presented at the VI International Congress for Microbiology, Rome, September 1953.
191. Oudin, J., *Methods in Medical Research*, Vol. 5, A. C. Corcoran, ed., Year Book Publishers, Chicago, 1952.
192. Pappenheimer, A. M., *J. Biol. Chem.*, **120,** 543 (1937).
193. Pappenheimer, A. M., *J. Biol. Chem.*, **125,** 201 (1938).
194. Pappenheimer, A. M., *J. Biol. Chem.*, **167,** 251 (1947).
195. Pappenheimer, A. M., and E. D. Hendee, *J. Biol. Chem.*, **171,** 701 (1947).
196. Pappenheimer, A. M., and E. D. Hendee, *J. Biol. Chem.*, **180,** 597 (1949).
197. Pappenheimer, A. M., H. P. Lundgren, and J. W. Williams, *J. Exptl. Med.*, **71,** 247 (1940).
198. Pappenheimer, A. M., and C. W. Williams, *J. Gen. Physiol.*, **35,** 727 (1952).
199. Partridge, S. M., and W. T. J. Morgan, *Brit. J. Exptl. Pathol.*, **21,** 180 (1940).
200. Partridge, S. M., and W. T. J. Morgan, *Brit. J. Exptl. Pathol.*, **23,** 84 (1942).
201. Pasteur, L., and G. Jonvert, *Compt. rend. acad. sci.*, **85,** 107 (1877).
202. Pauling, L., D. H. Campbell, and D. Pressman, *Proc. Natl. Acad. Sci. U. S.*, **27,** 125 (1941).

203. Pauling, L., and D. Pressman, *J. Am. Chem. Soc.*, **67**, 1003 (1945).
204. Pauling, L., D. Pressman, and A. L. Grossberg, *J. Am. Chem. Soc.*, **66**, 784 (1944).
205. Pauly, H., *Z. physiol. Chem.*, **42**, 508 (1904).
206. Pauly, H., *Z. physiol. Chem.*, **44**, 159 (1905).
207. Pauly, H., *Z. physiol. Chem.*, **94**, 284 (1915).
208. Philpot, J. St. L., and P. A. Small, *Biochem. J. (London)*, **32**, 542 (1938).
209. Pillemer, L., *Science*, **103**, 615 (1946).
210. Pillemer, L., E. E. Ecker, and E. W. Martiensen, *J. Exptl. Med.*, **70**, 387 (1939).
211. Pillemer, L., E. E. Ecker, and J. R. Wells, *J. Exptl. Med.*, **69**, 191 (1939).
212. Pillemer, L., and K. C. Robbins, *Ann. Rev. Microbiol.*, **3**, 265 (1949).
213. Plaut, F., and H. Rudy, *Z. Immunitätsforsch.*, **81**, 87 (1833).
214. Pope, C. G., *et. al.*, *Brit. J. Exptl. Pathol.*, **32**, 246 (1951).
215. Pope, C. G., and M. F. Stevens, *Lancet*, **II**, 1190 (1953).
216. Pope, C. G., and M. F. Stevens, *Brit. J. Exptl. Biol.*, **39**, 139–149 (1958).
217. Porges, N., *Science*, **117**, 47 (1953).
218. Porter, R. R., *Biochem. J. (London)*, **46**, 473 (1950).
219. Porter, R. R., "The relation of chemical structures to the biological activity of the proteins," in *The Proteins*, H. Neurath and K. Bailey, eds., Vol. 1, Part B., Academic Press, New York, 1953.
220. Portier, P., and C. Richet, *Compt. rend. soc. biol.*, **54**, 170 (1902).
221. Pressman, D., D. H. Brown, and L. Pauling, *J. Am. Chem. Soc.*, **64**, 3025 (1942).
222. Pressman, D., J. H. Bryden, and L. Pauling, *J. Am. Chem. Soc.*, **67**, 1219 (1945).
223. Pressman, D., and B. Sherman, *J. Immunol.*, **67**, 1 (1951).
224. Pressman, D., and L. A. Sternberger, *J. Am. Chem. Soc.*, **72**, 2226 (1950).
225. Pressman, D., and L. Sternberger, *J. Immunol.*, **66**, 609 (1951).
226. Prudhomme, R. O., and P. Grabar, *Bull. soc. chim. biol.*, **29**, 122 (1947).
227. Putnam, F. W., "The chemical modification of proteins," in *The Proteins*, H. Neurath and K. Bailey, eds., Vol. 1, Part B, Academic Press, New York, 1953, p. 894.
228. Raffel, S., *Immunity*, Appleton-Century-Crofts, New York, 1961.
229. Ramon, G., *Compt. rend. soc. biol.*, **89**, 2 (1923); **177**, 1338 (1923).
230. Ranney, H. M., *J. Clin. Invest.*, **33**, 1634 (1954).
231. Relyveld, E. H., *Toxine et antitoxine diphtériques*, Hermann, Paris, 1959.
232. Rothen, A., and K. Landsteiner, *Science*, **90**, 65 (1939).
233. Sabin, F. R., *J. Exptl. Med.*, **53**, 339–362 (1931).
234. Salk, J. E., *Proc. Soc. Exptl. Biol. Med.*, **46**, 709 (1941); *Science*, **101**, 122 (1945).
235. Sela, M., Paper contributed to a symposium on poly-alpha-amino acids; University of Wisconsin Press, 1962.
235a. Sela, M., and S. Fuchs, *Biochem. Biophys. Acta.*, **74**, 796–798 (1963).
236. Snapper, I., and A. Grunbaum, *Brit. J. Exptl. Pathol.*, **17**, 361 (1936).
237. Spencer, R. J., *J. Natl. Cancer Inst.*, **2**, 317 (1942).
238. Spiegel-Adolf, M., *Biochem. Z.*, **170**, 126 (1926).
239. Stahmann, M., *et. al.*, *Compt. rend. Acad. Sci.*, **241**, 1528–1529 (1955).
240. Ten Broeck, C., *J. Biol. Chem.*, **17**, 369 (1914).
241. Tuft, L., *Clinical Allergy*, Saunders, Philadelphia, 1949.
242. Uhlenhuth, P., and E. Remy, *Z. Immunitätsforsch.*, **92**, 171 (1938).
243. Uhlenhuth, P., and W. Seiffert, *Handbuch path. Mikr.*, **3**, 365 (1930).
244. Uwazumi, S., *Arb. med. Fak. Okayama*, **4**, 53 (1934).
245. Tal, C., and P. K. Olitsky, *Science*, **116**, 420 (1952).
246. Waksman, B. H., *et. al.*, *J. Exptl. Med.*, **100**, 451 (1955).

247. Walker, B. S., W. C. Boyd, and I. Asimov, *Biochemistry and Human Metabolism,* 3rd ed., Williams and Wilkins, Baltimore, 1957.
248. Wells, H. G., *The Chemical Aspects of Immunity,* Chem. Catalog Co., New York, 1929.
249. Wensinck, F., *Biochem. Biophys. Acta,* **10,** 184 (1953).
250. Wetter, L. R., M. Cohn, and H. F. Deutsch, *J. Immunol.,* **70,** 507 (1953).
251. Wetter, L. R., and H. F. Deutsch, *Arch. Biochem.,* **28,** 122 (1950).
252. Wetter, L. R., and H. F. Deutsch, *Arch. Biochem.,* **28,** 399 (1950).
253. Witebsky, E., and H. O. Behrens, *Z. Immunitätsforsch.,* **73,** 415 (1932).
253a. Wofsy, H. Metzger, and S. J. Singer, *Biochemistry,* **1,** 1031 (1962).
254. Wolfe, H. R., *J. Immunol.,* **29,** 1 (1935); **31,** 103 (1936).
254a. Woodruff, M. F. A., *Lancet,* **2,** 265–270 (1964).
255. Wormall, A., *J. Exptl. Med.,* **51,** 295 (1930).
256. Wu, H., *Chinese J. Physiol.,* **5,** 321 (1931).
257. Wu, H., C. Ten Broeck, and C. P. Li, *Chinese J. Physiol.,* **1,** 277 (1927).
258. Zinsser, H., J. F. Enders, and L. D. Fothergill, *Immunity: Principles and Application in Medicine and Public Health,* Macmillan, New York, 1939.
259. Zinsser, H., and J. T. Parker, *J. Exptl. Med.,* **37,** 275 (1923).

CHAPTER 4

Cell Antigens

In theoretical immunochemistry we are interested mainly in antibodies to individual antigenic substances. In clinical medicine, however, what interests us is usually resistance to the living agent of a disease, which is often a microorganism having a chemically complex structure. And even theoretical studies are often based on antibodies to complex cells such as erythrocytes. Human isoagglutinins, natural and immune, for the red cells of human blood are of the greatest importance in transfusion (see Chapter 5), and lysins for erythrocytes have been very useful in laboratory work because of the ease with which hemolysis is observed, and the ease of preparing homogeneous cell suspensions. Bacterial agglutinins have found wide application because they aid in the identification of bacteria when known immune serum is allowed to act on the bacteria, and aid in identifying the disease by detecting agglutinins which result from infection, as in the Gruber-Widal test for typhoid. They have made possible the subdivision of various bacterial species into serological strains (see below).

Antibodies to cells are not directed towards the cell as a unit. The cell is a complex mosaic of proteins, lipides, and carbohydrates, and it is conceivable that any of these, after being taken up by the reticuloendothelial system, might function as an antigen, for although it was formerly assumed that of the constituents of the cell only the proteins were antigenically active, it is now known that in addition the carbohydrates are important, lipides play some role, and protein–carbohydrate–lipide complexes may be good antigens (Chapter 3). The antigenicity of the cell as a whole often seems to be greater than that of any of its components, at least after the rather drastic chemical treatment these have usually undergone during the process of isolation.

Cell antigens possess certain distinguishing characteristics which justify us in treating them in a separate chapter. For example, cells of closely related species, and even of individuals of the same species, may differ strikingly in antigenic constitution (blood groups), and substances reacting similarly may occur in distantly related animals, and even plants (heterogenetic antigens). Landsteiner (91) suggested that these features, together with observations on the chemical nature of the antigens, indicate that two systems of species specificity exist in the animal kingdom, the specificity of proteins and that of haptens.

1. Differentiation of Closely Related Species

Agglutinating sera prepared by injecting blood corpuscles of one species will also react with the corpuscles of related species. We have already presented some of the results of Nuttall with precipitins for human and primate blood; in Table 4-1 will be found analogous reactions of immune

TABLE 4-1

Limiting Titers Obtained When Three Different Immune Agglutinating Sera Were Tested against Blood Corpuscles of Four Species (95)

	Immune serum against		
Blood corpuscles of	Human blood	Chimpanzee blood	Rhesus blood
Man	400	160	60
Chimpanzee	200	640	40
Baboon	80	40	800
Macacus rhesus	80	40	800

agglutinating sera prepared with human and monkey blood. The numbers represent the highest active dilutions of the serum (limiting titers).

A better differentiation between blood cells of closely allied species can be achieved by absorption experiments, that is, by treating the serum with enough of the heterologous antigen to remove all activity for it; more specific antibodies for the homologous antigen will then remain (96). This method also finds application in experiments on bacteria. A typical (hypothetical) example of this method is shown in Table 4-2, which

TABLE 4-2

Ideal Example of Differentiation of Bacterial Species by Agglutinin Absorption
(Castellani Experiment) (30)

Immune serum for	Absorbed with	Titer when tested against		
		"A"	"B"	"C"
Bacillus "A"	(Unabsorbed)	4000	2000	2000
	A	0	0	0
	B	2000	0	2000
	C	2000	2000	0
Bacillus "B"	(Unabsorbed)	2000	4000	2000
	A	0	2000	2000
	B	0	0	0
	C	2000	2000	0
Bacillus "C"	(Unabsorbed)	2000	2000	4000
	A	0	2000	2000
	B	2000	0	2000
	C	0	0	0

illustrates how three closely related species could be differentiated by the
absorption technic.

Not only different species but different individuals of the same species
can sometimes be differentiated by such agglutination reactions (blood
groups)—something which has never been certainly accomplished with
precipitins. These blood differences found within the same species will be
discussed in Chapter 5.

2. Heterogenetic Antigens

The Forssman Hapten. The recognition of the presence of serologically
related substances in the cells of animals which are widely separated in
the zoological system is due to Forssman (52), who found that injection of
ground-up guinea pig organs into rabbits produced lysins of high titer for
sheep erythrocytes. The Forssman hapten is found widely distributed in
the animal, and even the plant, kingdom, but, as will be seen in Table 4-3,
its distribution is not wholly random. It is possible that more extensive
investigations would reveal still more order in its taxonomic distribution.

The Forssman "antigen" is probably not a definite chemical entity, but a
serological conception, a collective term covering substances which, injected into rabbits, produce sheep hemolysins. The original Forssman
antigen was a somewhat more narrow concept; the "heterogenetic" (or
"heterophile") antisera produced by it had certain properties, *i.e.,* they

TABLE 4-3

Occurrence of Forssman Antigens in Various Groups of Animals and Plants (19,140,153)

Present	Absent	Present	Absent
PLANTS		*Cetacea*	
Spinach (?)	Oats	Whales	
Corn (one variety)	Beans	*Perissodactyla*	
	Rice	Horse	
	Mushrooms	*Artiodactyla*	Cattle
MICROORGANISMS		Camel	Deer
		Goat	Pig
		Sheep	Roe
Pasteurella cuniculi-	*Vibrio comma*	*Rodentia*	
cica,[a] certain sal-	*Escherichia coli*	Guinea pig	Rabbit
monella	*Salmonella typhosa*	Hamster	Rat
Shigella dysenteriae[c]	*Salmonella enteriditis*	Mouse (?)	
Pneumococcus	*Mycobacterium tu-*	*Procyonidae*	
Bacillus anthracis	*berculosis*	*Cercoleptes*	
	Staphylococcus	*caudivovulus*	
	Yeast	*Procyon lotor*	
		(Raccoon)	
	Shigella dysenteriae[d]	*Canidae*	
		Dog	
		Fox	
		Lycaon pictus	
		Wolf	
ANIMALS		*Felidae*	
		Cat	
Worms		Lion	
		Ocelot	
Trichinella spiralis	Meal worm	Puma	
	Tapeworm	Tiger	
Crustacea		*Primates*	
Lobster (?)		Lemurs (1	*Cebus* (2 species)
Orthoptera		species)	
	Cockroach	*Nyctipithecus*	*Cercocebus albigens*
Mollusca		*trivirgatus*	
Fish	Various shell fish	Man (group A	*Cercocebus fulginosis*
Carp[b]	Codfish	and AB)[e]	Chimpanzee
Eel[b]	Herring		Gibbon
Pike[b]			*Hapala jacchus*
Tench[b]			*Macacus rhesus*
Amphibia			Man
Toad	Frog		*Papio hamadryas*
Reptiles			*Presbytis maurus*
Turtle			*Pygathrix cristata*
Birds			
Chicken	Cuckoo		
Ostrich	Crossbill		

TABLE 4-3 (*Continued*)

Present	Absent	Present	Absent
Turkey buzzard	Goose		
	Owl		
	Pigeon		
	Sparrow hawk		
	Wagtail		

[a] Certain strains
[b] Germ cells only.
[c] R type.
[d] S cultures.
[e] Using the term "Forssman antigen" in the broader sense.

contained no lysin for cow cells and no, or almost no agglutinin for sheep red cells, and their antibodies were absorbable by tissues containing the Forssman antigen (horse and guinea pig kidney).

Almost every rabbit will respond promptly to these original Forssman antigens (F antigens). They are resistant to boiling and are alcohol-soluble. They were studied chemically by Landsteiner and Levene (93,94) and by Brunius (25). They usually occur in the organs and not in the erythrocytes, but in some cases occur only in the erythrocytes (sheep and goat) and may occur in both (chicken).

Several authors have used the term F antigen for all types of substances that produce sheep hemolysins, except material from sheep or closely related species. The antibodies obtained are not identical *inter se* as the original F antibodies were supposed to be. Some data on the F antigen are based not on immunization experiments but on absorption tests. In certain cases it might be doubted if the antibody observed was a real immune F antibody.

Landsteiner and Levene found the purified Forssman substance to be soluble in water, dilute alkali, or pyridine, but not soluble, or barely so, in most organic solvents. Analyses gave: carbon, 55 to 58 per cent, hydrogen, about 9 per cent, and nitrogen, 2 to 3 per cent. Reducing sugar was obtained on hydrolysis. Brunius found carbon, 59.5 to 63.8 per cent and nitrogen, 2.0 to 2.3 per cent. On hydrolysis hexosamine was found. Chase and Landsteiner (31) stated that another carbohydrate, probably a hexose, is also present. Heterophile antigens have been reviewed by Jenkin (75).

Other Antigens. The Forssman antigen, as usually isolated, is not a "complete" antigen, because when injected alone it does not produce antibodies. To obtain these it is necessary to mix the substance with something else. It is customary to use pig serum for this purpose, though other proteins, even serum from the animal species being immunized, will do. It has also been found that the Forssman antigen, if it has not been purified too much, will produce antibodies when injected adsorbed on kaolin or charcoal (see Chapter 2). The protein used in such experiments is called a "Schlepper"; Landsteiner supposed that its efficacy is due to a loose combination with the Forssman antigen (hapten) (92).

Paul-Bunnell Antigen. In the serum of patients suffering from the disease infectious mononucleosis, Paul and Bunnell (125) discovered strong agglutinins for sheep erythrocytes. These were originally thought to be Forssman antibodies, but later studies (12,154) showed that the antigen is a component of sheep cell stroma which is also found in the erythrocytes of cattle, a Forssman-negative species (Table 4-3). This discovery provided a diagnostic test for infectious mononucleosis. The various antibodies are differentiated by absorption; if the sheep cell agglutinins are removed by a suspension of guinea pig tissue, they are considered to be of the Forssman type, whereas if guinea pig tissue fails to remove them, while bovine erythrocytes do so, they are considered to be of the infectious mononucleosis type (98). However, it is generally believed that in patients who have developed serum sickness as a result of the administration of horse serum, agglutinins for sheep erythrocytes may be found which are neither Forssman nor directed against the infectious mononucleosis antigen.

In addition to the serological cross reactions between distantly related species due to the Forssman antigen, there are a number of other cross reactions thought to be due to a common antigen, or some structure possessed in common by carbohydrates and proteins of certain species (19). The Rh blood groups in man were so named because antibodies to erythrocytes of the rhesus monkey were found to agglutinate erythrocytes of certain human beings.

A common antigenic component occurs in the rickettsiae of typhus and certain typhus-like fevers, and in the O antigen of certain strains of *Proteus vulgaris.* This forms the basis of a diagnostic reaction, the Weil-Felix test, for rickettsial infections.

3. Localization of Cell Antigens

Serological methods have been applied to the study of the localization of different antigens in the cell. When antibody directed against a particular chemical constituent of a microorganism agglutinates suspensions of these organisms, it is evidently necessary to suppose that this particular antigen is located, at least in part, on or near the surface. Some of the best examples will be found in studies on bacteria, some of which are about to be discussed, but an interesting example is also provided by the experiments of Henle *et al.* (67) on mammalian spermatozoa. These workers found one antigen (heat-stable) common to the heads of the spermatozoa and to the tails. This antigen was species-specific. In addition, both heads and tails contained (heat-labile) antigens peculiar to themselves. By use of the different antisera two different types of agglutination, head-head and tail-tail, could be demonstrated, so these antigens are evidently on the surface. In the heads, an interior antigen was demonstrated by breaking up the spermatozoa before injection. A similar distinction between tail and head antigen was reported by Lanni and Lanni (98) for coliphage T2.

4. Bacterial Types

Bacteria as a group are probably a heterogeneous collection of more or less unrelated forms (42), classified together because of their being roughly the same size. The antigens contained in them vary widely.

There are two staining reactions of bacteria which, although they were developed as empirical procedures, and their mechanisms are still obscure, detect fundamental differences in the cellular structure. They are the Gram stain and the acid-fast stain.

In the Gram stain technic the bacteria are stained with a basic triphenylmethane dye such as gentian violet, mordanted with iodine, washed with a neutral organic solvent such as alcohol, and then counterstained with a dye of contrasting color such as safranin. The bacterial species that are decolorized by the alcohol treatment and take up the counterstain are referred to as Gram-negative, whereas those that retain the original stain are called Gram-positive.

In using the acid-fast stain the usual steps involve staining with a mixture of a basic dye (fuchsin) and phenol, usually with heating, washing with acidified alcohol, and counterstaining.

It is possible (43) to classify all bacterial species into three broad groups: Gram-positive, Gram-negative, and acid-fast, although there are intermediate forms with poorly defined staining reaction. These classes differ in a number of important chemical reactions.

The Gram-positive organisms have a marked preponderance of acid over basic groups, with isoelectric points ranging from pH 2.5 to 4.0. They are in general much more susceptible to the inhibiting effects on their growth of basic dyes, anionic detergents, penicillin, bacitracin, etc.

The isoelectric points of the Gram-negative bacteria are between pH 4.5 and 5.5. Extraction of such bacteria with trichloracetic acid, diethylene glycol, etc., yields the phospholipide–polysaccharide–protein complexes known as O antigens or endotoxins. Complexes with similar antigenic and toxic properties have not been recovered from Gram-positive bacteria. Gram-negative bacteria are usually much more susceptible to the bactericidal effect of immune serum and complement.

The acid-fast bacteria are characterized by very high concentrations of a variety of lipides, amounting to as much as 30 per cent of the total weight of the cell in pathogenic species. This high lipide concentration accounts for the hydrophobic character of the cell surface of mycobacteria, and the lipides elicit characteristic types of response in the host (Chapter 9). The acid-fast bacteria are resistant to many ordinary antiseptics, but susceptible to others which are relatively inactive against ordinary bacteria. Tubercle bacilli are strikingly resistant to strong acids and alkalis.

Antigenic Analysis. If serological methods are applied to the differentiation of various bacteria, it is found that, while in general the results parallel the accepted classification of these organisms, species which on the basis of morphological and cultural characteristics are classified together may exhibit sharp differences in serological behavior, and the species may thus be subdivided into types. Such differences have been found in many sorts of bacteria, and in some cases the number of types is quite large. They may or may not be correlated with some detectable difference in cultural or pathogenic behavior.

If we inject the antigenically most complete (*e.g.*, smooth, flagellated) form of a microorganism, we may obtain an antiserum which may contain antibodies to all the antigens of this species. Such a serum will agglutinate a suspension of the organism, but it will not be clear which of the possible antibodies are acting. Suppose, however, there exist some strains of the organism which contain only one of the two somatic antigens, which we may call I and II. One of these strains will be antigenically I, the other II, and the antigenically complete strain I, II. If we now absorb the serum obtained by injecting I, II with strain I, we obtain a serum which agglutinates strain II and the complete organism I, II. If we absorb with strain II, we get agglutinins for antigen I and the complete organism. The fact that our "complete" strain is agglutinated by both absorbed sera tells us it contains both antigens I and II. Similar methods can be applied when the antigens are more numerous, and when the flagella have antigens distinct from the body of the cell, if we have both flagellated and nonflagellated forms to work with. In actual practice the antigen–antibody relationship may not be as clear-cut as we have just supposed, and a spectrum of antibodies of somewhat different activities may be obtained.

It should be recognized, of course, that the serological distinction between antigens I and II does not necessarily prove that they are distinct chemical molecules. It is quite possible for them to be different aspects of the same complex molecule.

Another way of recognizing the presence of antibodies to different antigens depends upon the method of optimal proportions (Chapter 6). The presence of several zones of precipitation, in the case of bacterial suspensions, shows the presence of distinct antigens and antibodies. This method was applied to the antigenic analysis of bacteria by Miles.

A more accurate quantitative method is that of Heidelberger and Kendall (p. 686) for the determination of antibody by nitrogen analysis. A calibration curve can be prepared showing the amount of antibody-nitrogen precipitated from a serum by varying amounts of a given antigen, and this serum can then be used to estimate the amount of this antigen in an unknown mixture.

The specific affinity of bacteriophages for bacteria can also be utilized in antigenic analysis. In some cases it has been established that certain strains of phage attach themselves to certain antigens in the bacterial surface, preparatory to lysis. Tests of a bacterial strain with various strains of phage may reveal that it has one or several of the antigens for which the phage varieties are specific.

Antigenic Variation. Bacteria of a given species may vary considerably in regard to virulence, immunizing power, and chemical constitution. There are two main types of such variation: loss or gain variations, and substitutive variations.

Loss or gain variations in turn consist of two main types. The $S{\rightarrow}R$ *variation,* or dissociation, is exemplified classically by the change of certain *Salmonella* and *Shigella* from forms which gave smooth colonies on agar and suspended evenly in saline, into forms which gave rough colonies and tended to agglutinate spontaneously in saline. It proved that these "rough" variants had lost important antigenic factors (the O or Boivin antigens p. 183), and the term "rough" came to be applied to all such antigenic loss, even when the resulting colonies were "smooth." Topley and Wilson (159) suggested retaining merely the letters R and S for the variants. Pneumococci may go from S to R, losing their capsules (and virulence).

The cause of the $S{\rightarrow}R$ variation is often simply cultivation on a laboratory medium. The reverse transformation, $R{\rightarrow}S$, can occur, but is much less frequent.

Another variation, $H{\rightarrow}O$ *variation,* also involves the loss of antigens, but involves at the same time the loss of the organ (the flagella) which contained these antigens. [The significance of the terms H and O is explained below (p. 216).] The H→O transformation is less common than the S→R change, and harder to induce experimentally.

In *substitutive variations* one set of antigens is lost but is replaced by another set. It is this sort of variation which accounts for the "phase" variation in the flagellar antigens of the *Salmonella* (p. 217).

There is considerable evidence that bacterial variations have a genetic basis, just as do hereditary changes in higher organisms. The student will find a good elementary introduction to bacterial genetics in the book by Braun (23).

Since spontaneous mutations are constantly occurring in bacteria as in other organisms, whenever the environmental conditions favor a variant the mutant type will tend to replace the original type. Thus it has been found (23) that accumulation of alanine *in vitro* is responsible for the selective establishment of nonsmooth mutants of *Brucella,* and inoculation of a relatively nonvirulent strain into guinea pigs may lead to the development *in vivo* of a virulent S strain, because the virulent variant survives and grows better in the living host.

The S→R change in pneumococci can be reversed experimentally, and a study of this transformation is instructive in regard to bacterial genetics and genetic mechanisms in general. The first observations were those of Griffith (59), who found that if mice were injected with living R (non-encapsulated avirulent) forms dissociated from type II pneumococci, together with dead type III pneumococci, the mice were infected and died, and cultures from these animals showed living type III pneumococci. It was evident that the R organism had somehow acquired the capsule characteristic of the dead type III pneumococci. However, the isolated type III polysaccharide, of which the capsule consists, would not bring about the transformation.

The explanation was found by Avery and his associates (10), who showed that the agent responsible for the transformation was a highly polymerized deoxyribonucleic acid (DNA). This substance, active in a dilution of 1:6000,000,000, was specific for the transformation to type III S forms. Similar substances with the power of transforming to types II and IV have since been isolated, and similar transformations have been accomplished with other bacteria, as in *Escherichia coli, Hemophilus influenzae,* and *Shigella paradysenteriae.*

Capsule Formation. The capsule of bacteria is not the analog of the continuous capsular membrane or sheath which encloses the cysts of various protozoan parasites or surrounds the seeds of many plants. It is a layer of highly polymerized, viscous material, usually but not always polysaccharide in nature, which is produced by the cells and tends to stick to the cell surface, although some diffuses into the medium.

The surface component of Gram-negative bacteria, on the other hand, is a phospholipide–carbohydrate–protein complex (somatic or O antigen) which is toxic and antigenic, with a specificity determined by the carbohydrate portion of the complex.

a. Gram-Positive Bacteria

Recent improvements in the techniques of immunochemical dissection have made it possible to localize some bacterial antigens in discrete elements of the microbial structure. Antigens fixed in the bacterial cell were formerly all called "somatic" antigens, but many of them have now been related to definite locations such as the cytoplasm, the cytoplasmic membrane, or the cell wall. The improvement in our knowledge has been greatest in the last category, and this subject has recently been reviewed by McCarty and Morse (109).

Pneumococcus Types. The existence of *pneumococcus* types was definitely established by Neufeld and Händel (122), who found that immune sera protecting mice against certain strains of pneumococci were not effective against other strains, and these differences were correlated with differences in agglutination reactions. The study of pneumococci has resulted in their classification into a large number of serological types (83,163). These types differ because of serological differences in the polysaccharides of the capsule. Many of these polysaccharides have been studied and found to be chemically different (references in 24,74,106). Some of these results, together with figures for other serologically reactive polysaccharides, are shown in Tables 4-4 and 4-5, taken mainly from (106) and (24).

It has already been mentioned that capsular polysaccharides of pneumococci of types I, II, III, and VIII are made up of molecules of glucose and glucuronic acid (55). The structures of the polysaccharides of types III and VIII have been discussed in Chapter 3. We may recall that the type III polysaccharide has been shown to be made up of units consisting of cellobiuronic acid (68). The linkage between these units in the intact carbohydrate has now been shown to be through the reducing groups of one to the third carbon atom of the glucuronic acid residue of the other (130). If we assume that this linkage has the β-configuration, as there is reason to believe (130), the constitution of the structural unit of this important cell antigen becomes completely known, and according to Reeves and Goebel (130), it is that shown in Figure 4-1.

The minimal molecular weights of the capsular polysaccharides of types III and VIII have been calculated to be 62,000 and 140,000, respectively (63).

TABLE 4-4

Chemical Composition of Some Pneumococcus Capsular Polysaccharides

Source of material	$[\alpha]_D$	Acid equivalent	Per cent of						Components identified
			C	H	N	P	Reducing sugar	Acetyl	
Pn I	+265- +277	576	42.55	6.58	4.85	0-0.25	32	7.1-10	Galacturonic acid, amino sugar
Pn I	+255.6							6.83	
Pn II	+54- +58	970 (600)	(45.8)	(6.4)	0.14- 0.73	0.1- 3.70	86- 95	0.4-3.8	Glucose, aldobionic acid, uronic anhydride
Pn II	+56.8				0.26	0.06		1.52	
Pn III	-36.0	330-350	(42.6)	(5.6)	0.08	0-0.01	84	0.5-0.9	Glucose, glucuronic acid
Pn (species-specific)	+42	1050			6.1			Present	Amino sugar, H_3PO_4

Pn = pneumococcus.   For reference to the literature, see (19,24,74,106).   Parentheses indicate values which are somewhat uncertain.

TABLE 4-5

Chemical Composition of Some Other Serologically Active Polysaccharides

Source of material	[α]D	Acid equivalent	Per cent of						Components identified
			C	H	N	P	Reducing sugar	Acetyl	
Fr. A.	−100	430	43.95	6.0	0		65		Glucose, aldobionic acid, disaccharide
Fr. B	+100	680	44.6	6.1	0		70		Glucose, aldobionic acid
Fr. C	+100	680			0		70		Glucos, aldobionic acid
Anthrax bacillus	+62				4.1		59	Present	Glucose, glucosamine
Gum acacia	−10.7	800			0.8		68		Galactose, glucuronic acid
T. B. Fraction C	+84–95	ca. 7000			0.1	0.2	87		D-Arabinose, D-mannose
T. B. Fraction B	+10–41	ca. 2000			0.6–0.8	0.2–1.0	61		D-Arabinose
B.C.G.	+77.4	1244			0.8	0.9	77		D-Mannose, D-arabinose, inositol
B. dys. (Shiga)	+98	9000	41.9	6.35	1.61		97	Present	Hexosamine
Blood Group A substance									
(human saliva)	−8 to −21				4.7–6.1		56–61	9–10	L-Fucose
A substance (human stomach)	−2.5 to −5				5.3–6.8		47–51		
A substance (hog stomach)	+16?				5.9–6.6		55–61	9–11	L-Fucose, D-galactose, D-glucosamine, D-chondrosamine[a]

Fr. = Friedländer bacillus, B. dys. = Shiga bacillus, T.B. = tubercle bacillus, B.C.G. = modified tubercle bacillus (B.C.G.). A substance = blood-group-specific A substance; the A substances contained from 0.08–1.96% sulfur. For references to the literature, see (19,24,74,106,77,78).

[a] And small amounts of a number of amino acids.

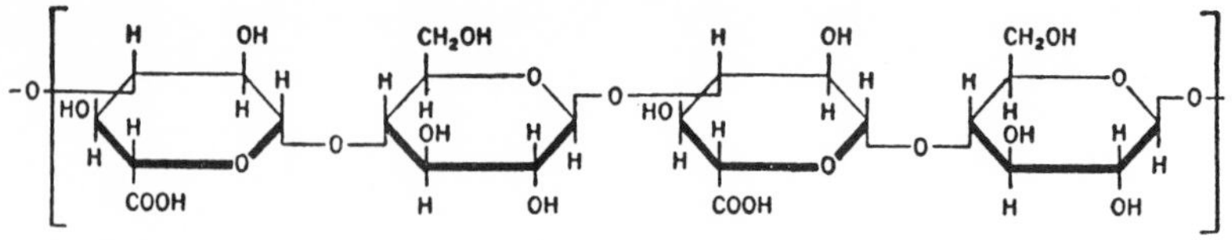

Fig. 4-1. The structural unit of the type III pneumococcus polysaccharide.

The specific carbohydrate of type I pneumococcus differs from SII and SIII in containing about 5 per cent nitrogen as a part of the molecule. Half of this nitrogen can be liberated by treatment with nitrous acid, and is probably present in the form of an amino sugar. The basic unit of the molecule seems to be a trisaccharide containing two molecules of uronic acid (possibly both galacturonic acid) and two atoms of nitrogen.

As the polysaccharide SI was first isolated, it contained no acetyl groups, and would not remove all protective antibodies from type I antiserum. It was later found that, if it were prepared without the use of alkali, it contained 5.9 to 6.9 per cent acetyl, was antigenic, and did remove all the protective antibodies. Treatment of this product with alkali split off acetyl groups and gave a carbohydrate identical with that originally isolated.

The molecular weights of these carbohydrates proved hard to establish. Those first isolated probably had molecular weights somewhere in the range 1000 to 10,000. But Heidelberger, Kendall, and Scherp (64) found that specific polysaccharides SI, SII, and SIII prepared by milder methods, which avoided high temperatures, strong acid, or alkali, were much more viscous, and probably therefore of higher molecular weight. The new preparations also gave more precipitate with specific rabbit antisera than did the old.

In addition to the type-specific capsular polysaccharides, pneumococci contain a species-specific polysaccharide, and a series of type-specific M proteins which closely resemble the M proteins of streptococcus, but which vary independently of the capsular polysaccharides (9).

An antigenic relationship which has been observed between the capsular polysaccharides of pneumococcus type XIV and human erythrocytes is of theoretical and practical interest. Horse pneumococcus type XIV antisera contain agglutinins for human erythrocytes of all four major blood groups in high titers (50). Antipneumococcal horse sera of other types do not exhibit this phenomenon. These agglutinins are evidently antibodies directed against the capsular polysaccharides of the organism, for they can be removed by treating the serum with type XIV polysaccharide (166) as well as with the whole organism (50). They evidently cause the agglutination of human erythrocytes by combining with antigens contained in these cells. Beeson and Goebel (15) succeeded in removing most, but not all, of the type XIV antibody and of the hemagglutinins by treatment with the purified group A substance, which has been shown to be similar chemically to the type XIV polysaccharide (57). It is now believed that these hemagglutinins were responsible for some of the fatal reactions which sometimes followed the use of this serum (50). Rabbit antipneumococcus sera of type XIV (but also of other types) often, but not always, contain agglutinins for human erythrocytes of groups A and AB. In these animals, evidently, the antibodies produced show an even clearer relationship to the A substance, but the relationship is not restricted to type XIV pneumococcus, as it is with the horse. In the horse, as a matter of fact, the relationship is closer to bloods of group O (and subgroup A_2) than to group A (Subgroup A_1) (100).

The presence of galactose in the specific polysaccharide of type XIV pneumococcus suggested to Heidelberger and Wolfram (66) that there might possibly be a cross reaction with the galactan isolated from cow lung. It was found in fact that there is a strong cross reaction, and a quantitative study of the reaction was made. The galactan contains galactose as alternate substituted and unsubstituted members of a chain linked 1→6, with galactose as substituent in position 3 of the alternate chain members. It was also found that a polysaccharide isolated from the seed of the tamarind would precipitate with type XIV antiserum. The single form of galactose in this polysaccharide is linked in unsubstituted units to xylose or glucose. This type of linkage is thus the common factor in these two polysaccharides which cross-react with antipneumococcus type XIV serum. From this fact Heidelberger and Wolfram predicted that one of the three galactose molecules in the type XIV polysaccharide would be found to be an unsubstituted unit attached to another of the galactose units or to the N-acetylglucosamine. They believed that the quantitative data point to the latter alternative.

Ketha gum, an exudate from the tree *Feronia elephantum*, precipitates with anti-pneumococcus sera of types I and II. Heidelberger, Tyler and Mukherjee (65) concluded from this that ketha gum would, like type I pneumococcus polysaccharide, contain D-galacturonic acid, and chemical investigation confirmed this.

Chemical similarity produces antigenic similarity in cell antigens as in other cases. As Dubos (42) pointed out, it is simply a chemical accident that antisera to the encapsulated type B Friedländer bacillus precipitate the capsular polysaccharide of type II pneumococcus, and vice versa. The two organisms, one a Gram-positive coccus, the other a Gram-negative bacillus, are phylogenetically entirely unrelated. The capsular polysaccharides simply happened to be chemically similar.

It has been observed (61) that glycogens from various animal and plant sources precipitate with antipneumococcal horse sera of types II, VII, IX, XII, XX, and XXII, especially the last four, and Heidelberger *et al.* (61) suggested that it will be found that the polysaccharides of these four types are related closely to glycogen, which is a highly branched polymer of glucose.

An antigenic relationship has been observed between type VI pneumococcus and *Hemophilus influenzae* of type B (121,174).

The capsule of the pneumococcus is highly important for virulence. R strains are nearly, but not quite, avirulent for mice (lethal dose 100,000,-000 to 2,000,000,000 living organisms as opposed to 1 to 5 organisms of the S strain). Virulence is also related to the kind and quantity of capsular polysaccharide formed. For instance, strains of type II that produce small amounts of SSS II (SSS = soluble specific substance) are less virulent for mice than strains that produce larger amounts. (The quantity of SSS synthesized by a strain is under genetic control.) The influence of the kind of polysaccharide produced is shown by the fact that type XIV is avirulent for mice, but when R strains derived from them are transformed into type II they become highly virulent, whereas R strains derived from type II when transformed into type XIV are avirulent.

Somatic factors also influence the virulence of pneumococci, however, as shown by the existence of two strains of type III, with identical capsular polysaccharides, one of which, SV-III, is highly virulent for rabbits, whereas the other, A 66, is nearly avirulent (43).

Immunologically reactive polysaccharides have been found in many other bacteria, but their chemical nature is not so well understood, and their value in classification has not always proved so great as it was in the pneumococcus. A partial list of bacterial and other specific polysaccharides will be found in (92) and (26). It includes, in addition to the microorganisms specifically treated at some length in later sections of this chapter, *Vibrio cholerae, Meningococcus, Bacterium proteus, B. lactis, Bacterium aerogenes, Klebsiella, Bacillus anthracis,* the *Phytomonas* and *Pasteurella* groups, *H. influenzae, Malleomyces mallei, Fusobacterium, Corynebacterium diphtheriae, Clostridium welchii,* spirochetes, *Asterococcus, Rickettsiae,* yeasts and fungi, and helminths and other worms. Typical methods are given in (26).

Streptococci. The antigenic analysis of the streptococci has been carried on mainly by studying the precipitin reaction of substances extracted from the cell (84,85). On the basis of antigenic carbohydrates, collectively

TABLE 4-6

Streptococci Which Produce Group-Specific Carbohydrates (43)

Group	Common name	Usual habitat	Usual pathogenicity	Number of types	Type-Specific antigen
A	Human *Str. pyogenes*	Man	Many human diseases	40+	Protein M
B	*Str. agalactiae* (*Str. mastitidis*)	Cattle	Mastitis	6 (main) 15+ subtypes	Polysacch.
	St. equi	Horse	Strangles	1	
	Animal *Str. pyogenes*	Many animals	Many animal diseases	2+	Prob. prot.
	Human C	Man & animals	Resp. & other infections	8±	
	Str. dysgalactiae	Cattle	Mastitis	?	
E	Group E	Normal milk	None	?	
F	Group F (minute)	Man	Slight; upper resp. tract	4	Prob. polysacch.
G	Group G (minute)	Man	Upper resp. tract	1	Prob. polysacch.
	Group G (large colony)	Man	Many areas	Several	
		Dogs	Genital & resp. tracts		
H	Group H	Man	Doubtful; resp. tract	?	
K	Group K	Man	" "	?	
L	Group L	Dogs	Genital tract	?	
M	Group M	Dogs	Resp. Tract	?	
O	Group O	Man	Doubtful; upper resp. tract	?	
D	Enterococci *Str. fecalis* *Str. liquefaciens* *Str. zymogenes* *Str. durans*	Intestinal contents Man, many animals, & dairy products	Genitourinary tract, gastrointestinal tract, abscesses, heart valves, wounds, food poisoning	Several	Prob. polysacch.
N	*Str. lactis*	Milk	None	?	
	Str. cremoris	Cream	None	?	

Modified from table in *Bacterial and Mycotic Infections of Man*, edited by R. J. Dubos. Courtesy of Dr. Dubos, J. B. Lippincott Co., publishers, and the National Foundation for Infantile Paralysis.

called carbohydrate C, streptococci have been classified into 13 groups, as shown in Table 4-6, slightly modified from Dubos (43). Many streptococci, however, have not been shown to produce such polysaccharides, and have not been classified into serological groups.

Several of the groups can be further classified into clearly distinct types. In group A, which contains the more important members of the beta hemolytic streptococci responsible for human infections, the type-specific antigens are proteins, and this is probably true also for group C. In groups B, D, E, F, and G, however, the type antigens are probably polysaccharides.

Group A has been the most thoroughly studied. Most of the group produce, in addition to the C carbohydrate which is the same for all members of the group, two distinct antigenic components, designated M and T. Both of these may be specific for the type.

The M antigens are closely associated with the virulence of the group A streptococci (87), and antibodies to them are closely related to the type-specific protective action of immune sera. M occurs chiefly in those variants which form mucoid or matt colonies. Glossy colony avirulent variants produce little or no M substance, but not all M-producers are virulent for any particular animal. After repeated passage through artificial media, or even while living in carriers, virulent streptococci tend to deteriorate from matt to glossy and lose their virulence and their capacity to produce M substance. Such variants can be made virulent again by repeated animal passage, after which they are observed to grow in matt colonies and produce M substance (132).

The second antigen, which is closely connected with the agglutination reactions of group A streptococci, and is therefore important, is the T substance, which is also a protein. It is more tightly bound to the cell structure than is the M substance. The T substances are much more powerful antigens than the C or M substances, but antibodies to them have no known protective action.

In some types both the M and T antigens are specific for that particular type, but in other types the M substance is type-specific, while the T substance is closely related to that produced by some other type or types. This accounts for numerous cross-agglutinations which were originally found confusing.

The C substance from group A streptococci has been extracted with formamide and by pepsin digestion. It is a polysaccharide with a molecular weight of about 8000, and is composed chiefly of rhamnose and glucosamine in the approximate ratio of 5 to 2. The M antigens are alcohol-soluble proteins, heat-stable, and are rapidly digested by proteolytic enzymes (86). The T antigens are also proteins, but are not alcohol-soluble, resist digestion, and are heat-labile at acid pH but more resistant to heating in alkaline solution. The isoelectric point of the M proteins is about 5.3, that of the T proteins is close to 4.5 (88,89).

From type 28 group A streptococci Lancefield and Perlmann (90) isolated an R antigen, similar to the T antigens, but differing from them in being susceptible to peptic digestion and being easily removed from the cells by heating at an alkaline pH. It is type-specific for type 28, but occurs in some other strains. It seems to have no relation to virulence. The R substance is quite antigenic for rabbits, but it is not known whether anti-R antibodies are produced in man as a result of infection with R-containing streptococci.

Nucleoproteins have also been isolated from the streptococci, but those from group A do not seem to contain much type-specific antigen and are not homogeneous. They probably make up a large part of the cell. Many strains of streptococci produce streptokinase, a substance which activates the proteolytic action on clots of the plasminogen which occurs in all human sera. Streptokinase has not been proved to injure human tissue but has on the contrary been shown to have valuable therapeutic properties. Antibodies which neutralize streptokinase are found in the serum of patients with a history of streptococcal infections, and to some extent in all human serum.

Practically all group A and B streptococci produce the enzyme deoxyribonuclease (streptodornase), which has the power of depolymerizing deoxyribonucleoprotein and deoxyribonucleic acid. Antibodies to this enzyme are found in patients who have had group A streptococcal infections, and can be produced by injecting animals (107).

Mixtures of streptokinase and streptodornase have been found to be valuable in treating hemothorax, pleurisy with effusion, empyema, infected burns, chronic osteomyelitis, and other conditions (157).

Some streptococci produce hemolysins, which dissolve erythrocytes and are also toxic for other cells. Group A streptococci elaborate two different streptolysins, O and S. Streptolysin S is formed only by group A strains, but O is formed by most members of group A and large colony forms of group G. Streptolysin O is an antigen and antibodies will neutralize its hemolytic action; there is no good evidence that streptolysin S is antigenic. Both are very toxic. These toxins do not seem to have pathogenic significance, but the O toxin has proved useful in epidemiological surveys, the finding of antibodies to it being interpreted as a sign of recent infection.

Streptolysin O is one member of a class of immunologically related, easily oxidized hemolysins, all very similar. The class includes pneumolysin, tetanolysin, and the theta toxin of *Clostridium welchii* (108).

Some of the differences between these two lysins are shown in Table 4-7.

TABLE 4-7

Contrast between Streptolysins O and S [Modified from McCarty (108)]

Property	Streptolysin O	Streptolysin S
Activation by SH compounds	Activated	Not activated
Antigenicity	Antigenic	Apparently not antigenic
Neutralization by specific antibody	Neutralized	Not neutralized by any known antibody
Influence of serum or polyribonucleotide on formation	Not marked	Formation greatly enhanced
Action of trypsin	Destroyed	Not destroyed
Action of cholesterol in minute amounts	Inhibits	Does not inhibit
Action of lecithin in very low concentration	Does not inhibit	Inhibits
Relation of rate of lysis to concentration of lysin	Related but not directly proportional	Directly proportional
Induction period preceding hemolysis	Relatively short	Relatively long
Critical thermal increment (20° to 30°C.)	21,400	14,600

Modified from a table in *Streptococcal Infections*, edited by M. McCarty.   Courtesy of Dr. McCarty, and Columbia University Press.

Many streptococci produce a soluble erythrogenic toxin. In contrast to diphtheria toxin, this toxin resists heating to 60°C. but is destroyed by boiling. Different strains produce qualitatively different toxins. At least five different toxins have been recognized, but about 80 per cent of the strains studied by Coffey (34) produced a toxin which was neutralized by serum from animals immunized with the N.Y. 5 strain. This multiplicity of toxins apparently explains why patients can, rarely, have repeated attacks of scarlet fever. Immunity, natural or artificial, seems to be antitoxic and not antibacterial.

Most strains of streptococci produce hyaluronidase. This has been considered a factor which enhances virulence, but the evidence is not conclusive. Most patients infected with group A streptococci eventually have antihyaluronidase in their sera, which suggests that hyaluronidase is a strong antigen.

Most group A streptococci produce a proteinase which resembles papain in certain respects. It is produced as an inactive precursor which is converted to the active enzyme by an autocatalytic reaction. Both forms have been crystallized (108). They are distinguishable by antibodies obtained by injecting them into rabbits.

Staphylococci. Staphylococci produce cellular polysaccharides and can be separated into groups on the basis of differences among these polysaccharides. In addition to the differences these substances exhibit in their precipitin reactions with immune serum, they show differences in the products they yield on hydrolysis, and in optical rotation.

On the basis of the precipitin reaction two large groups have been distinguished: Type A (pathogenic) and Type B (nonpathogenic) (76). The antisera used are obtained by injecting the whole organism, as the polysaccharides alone do not seem to be antigenic. Types A and B contain in addition constituents in common, among them an antigenic protein.

Two groups of workers (156,35) distinguished an additional "Type C" group, but the two "C" groups are not equivalent. Verwey (162) found specific proteins in Types A and B and the Type C of Thompson.

By the use of agglutinin absorption technics, Cowan (35) and Christie and Keogh (32) demonstrated the existence of nine subtypes among the pathogenic staphylococci, and more may exist.

Types of staphylococci have also been demonstrated by bacteriophage typing (43).

The staphylococci produce various toxins and enzymes which are partly responsible for their ability to produce infection (16). An antigenic exotoxin which causes tissue necrosis is found. It can be converted to a toxoid by treatment with formalin.

Four staphylococcal hemolysins have been described: α-hemolysin, β-hemolysin, γ-hemolysin, and δ-hemolysin (43). They differ in the ease with which they hemolyze erythrocytes of different species. The α-hemolysin, which particularly affects rabbit erythrocytes, is generally thought to be identical with the exotoxin just mentioned.

Staphylococci produce a toxic substance, leukocidin, which destroys leukocytes (161). It is distinct from the exotoxin.

Certain strains of staphylococci produce a nonantigenic "enterotoxin" which is responsible for the acute gastrointestinal symptoms of certain types of food poisoning (37). This is unfortunately relatively thermostable, resisting boiling for 30 minutes.

Staphylococci produce a substance which has the power of clotting blood plasma. This substance, coagulase, reacts with an "activator" or "coagulase-reacting factor" which is normally present in the blood of man and certain animals. Coagulase is formed only by the pathogenic strains. This fact has been utilized in a simple laboratory test to distinguish the two types. It has been thought that coagulase may prevent phagocytosis (142). It seems to be antigenic.

An enzyme, fibrinolysin, which can dissolve fibrin clots is formed by certain strains (nearly all pathogenic) of staphylococci. It acts much more slowly than the lysin produced by β-hemolytic streptococci.

As do some other pathogenic bacteria, staphylococci produce a spreading factor (44), which is probably a hyaluronidase. By increasing the permeability of the connective tissue, it aids in establishing the local lesion.

Diphtheria Bacilli. The toxin of *Corynebacterium diphtheriae* was discussed in Chapter 3. A potent toxin-producing strain isolated by Park and Williams in 1898 is generally used for routine toxin production. Three types, *mitis* (mild), *intermedius,* and *gravis* (severe) of this bacillus (and the disease it produces) are recognized, although McLeod (110) found a few strains which could not be classified satisfactorily into any of these types. All three types can be subdivided into a number of different serological types, although little is known about the antigens responsible for these serological reactions (160).

Anthrax Bacillus. The specific substance of the body of the *Anthrax bacillus* has been found to be a colloidal polysaccharide constructed of *d*-glucosamine, galactose, and acetic acid (74,162). The acetic acid is at least partly in the form of *N*-acetyl. Thus the constituents of this carbohydrate are the same as those of type XIV pneumococcus and correspond in part to those of the human blood group A substance. Ivánovics (74) found that horse antianthrax sera agglutinated type XIV pneumococcus, although rabbit antisera did not. Pneumococcus type XIV would not absorb all precipitins for the anthrax polysaccharide from horse antisera, however. Horse antianthrax sera did not react with group A substance, nor did they agglutinate human group A cells specifically.

The specific substance of the capsule of anthrax, unlike those of many other microorganisms, is not a polysaccharide, but a protein-like substance (74), a polypeptide composed apparently of the single amino acid, D(−)-glutamic acid, which is thus in the "unnatural" form (the natural form being L(+)-glutamic acid, where L indicates configuration, and the (+) the actual rotation. It is possible, however, that some elements of the cell-wall polysaccharide reach to the surface of the capsule (160). It is possible that the unnatural form of the amino acid in this substance, which might make it resistant to the natural enzymes, may be connected with the virulence of the organisms (74).

The main somatic polysaccharide, on hydrolysis, yields N-acetyl-D-glucosamine and galactose in equimolecular quantities. Ketose, pentose, and uronic acid were absent, and acetyl groups were present. The per cent of nitrogen was about 4.1; reducing sugars (calculated as glucose) amounted to nearly 60 per cent. The substance had a high positive optical rotation (26).

Agglutination and precipitin tests are of little diagnostic value for anthrax bacilli, but Ascoli (8) discovered a heat-stable precipitinogen which could be extracted even from infected tissues, which reacted specifically with antisera to anthrax. Tomcsik and his associates (26) showed that this precipitinogen was identical with the capsular "P" substance and the somatic specific polysaccharide of the anthrax bacillus. Since it made possible the recognition of infected tissues, such as skins, destined for commercial use, this test has had extensive applications, especially in Europe.

b. Gram-Negative Bacteria

Gram-negative bacteria are characterized by the fact that, when they are dyed with a basic triphenylmethane dye such as gentian violet, the color can be removed by washing with alcohol. Gram-negative bacteria have a number of other features in common. One of the most interesting of these features to the immunologist is their content of *endotoxins*. These characteristic substances, not released to any great extent into the culture medium as the organism grows (in contrast to *exotoxins* such as diphtheria toxin), can be obtained by lysing the bacteria or by extracting them with trichloracetic acid, diethylene glycol, etc. They are toxic in animals in very small amounts (of the order of 0.001 microgram per kilogram of body weight), producing fever, leukopenia, etc.

The first important step in the study of endotoxins was the development by Boivin (17) of a method of extracting them with trichloracetic acid. Boivin reported that the endotoxins of a number of Gram-negative bacteria consisted mainly of polysaccharide and lipid.

Knowledge of the chemistry of endotoxins derives mainly from the work of Morgan (117,119,120,120a) and Goebel (56), who showed that endotoxins are complexes containing phosphorylated polysaccharide and protein. Further work by these and other workers on the degradation products of the endotoxins revealed that they have the makeup shown in Table 4-8 (169).

It appears that the lipid A component is responsible for many of the toxic effects of these complex substances (136,168). All the preparations of this component examined from various enterobacteria seem to be similar or perhaps identical (168), containing about 20 per cent D-glucosamine, 7-8 per cent phosphoric ester, 50 per cent long-chain fatty acid (including hydroxy-fatty acids), and a peptide side chain containing serine and dicarboxy amino acids.

Although the lipid A component of the endotoxins of the gram-negative bacteria is essential for many of the endotoxic manifestations and can act

TABLE 4-8
The Endotoxin Complex of the Cell Wall of Gram-Negative Bacteria[a]

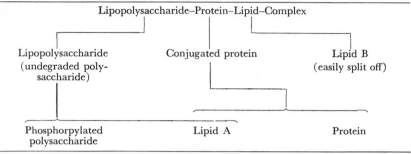

Lipopolysaccharide–Protein–Lipid–Complex		
Lipopolysaccharide (undegraded poly- saccharide)	Conjugated protein	Lipid B (easily split off)
Phosphorpylated polysaccharide	Lipid A	Protein

[a] Westphal and Lüderitz (169).

as a potent adjuvant in the production of antibodies (168), the portion which determines the specificity of protective antibodies is the polysaccharide component. Such antipolysaccharide antibodies do not protect the organism producing them against the pyrogenic effects of endotoxin if it is experimentally injected, but they do account for the species-specific immunity which generally follows recovery from an infection with one of the microorganisms. Consequently it is the anti-polysaccharide antibodies which are of greatest interest to immunologists. Considerable progress has recently been made in the study of the chemical basis for the immunological differences which are observed, especially in the group of Gram-negative bacteria known as the Salmonella. Before we can discuss them we must pause to recall a few salient facts about this important group of microorganisms.

The Salmonella

The Salmonella are Gram-negative, non-spore-forming, motile bacteria which are generally pathogenic for both man and animal. *S. typhosa,* causative agent of typhoid fever, *S. paratyphi A,* and possibly *S. sendai,* cause disease only in man.

The Salmonella are mostly flagellated. The flagella as well as the body of the organism contain antigens. The flagellar antigens are called H antigens, the somatic antigens O antigens. The letters originated with German writers who observed that colonies of the motile (*i.e.,* flagellated) Salmonella on agar medium were surrounded by a "Hauch" (breath or emanation), while colonies of the nonmotile organisms were "Ohne Hauch" (without emanation).

The H antigens are of two kinds: those shared by a number of species or types, and those peculiar to a particular species or type, or shared by only a few species or types. Many of the species or types are *diphasic;* that is, at one stage of a culture the specific flagellar antigens may occur (specific phase), whereas at another the group antigens may be present (group phase). Any given culture of such an organism may consist entirely of one or the other of the phases or may contain both. A bacillus in one phase usually keeps the same phase for a number of generations, but is always capable of giving rise to the other phase. As a matter of fact, the antigens of either phase may occur in various types, although the specific antigens are generally restricted to a smaller number of types (42). These complicated antigenic properties of the *Salmonella* can be a source of confusion unless they are understood.

It was formerly the practice to designate the somatic (O) antigens by Roman numerals, as shown in Table 4-9, but following a decision made in

TABLE 4-9

Somatic and Flagellar Antigens in Certain Common Salmonella[a]

Group	Species	O Antigens[b]	Phase 1 (specific)	Phase 2 (group)
A	S. paratyphosa	(I), II, XII	a	—
B	S. schottmuelleri	(I), IV, (V), XII	b	1,2
	S. typhimurium	(I), IV, (V), XII	i	1,2
C₁	S. hirschfeldii	VI, VII,	c	1,5
	S. choleraesuis	VI, VII	c	1,5
	S. oranienburg	VI, VII	m,t	—
	S. montevideo	VI, VII	g,m,s	—
C₂	S. newport	VI, VIII	e,h	1,2
D	S. typhosa	IX, XII,	d	—
	S. enteritidis	(I), IX, XII	g,m	—
	S. gallinarum	I, IX, XII	—	—
	S. pullorum	I, IX, XII	—	—
E	S. anatum	III, X	e,h	1,6

Header: H Antigens spans Phase 1 and Phase 2.

[a] Modified from a table in *Bacterial and Mycotic Infections of Man*, edited by R. J. Dubos, 1952. Courtesy of Dr. Dubos, Dr. H. R. Morgan, J. B. Lippincott Co., and the National Foundation for Infantile Paralysis (43).
[b] Parentheses indicate that the antigen is not invariably present.

1953 at the Sixth International Congress of Bacteriology in Rome, the workers who have contributed so much to our knowledge of the chemical structure of these antigens, employ Arabic numerals. I shall follow this usage. It was former practice to denote the species flagellar antigens by small Roman letters, and the group flagellar antigens by Arabic numerals. Thus *Salmonella newport* possesses O antigens VI and VIII, species H antigens e and h, and group H antigens 1 and 2. From here on, however, we shall be speaking of *S. newport* as possessing O antigens 6 and 8. The flagellar antigens will not come into the picture, because I do not intend to discuss them further.

The antigenic structure of the Salmonella has been studied in great detail by Kauffmann (80) and White (172); the classification of these authors, based on the somatic and flagellar antigens, is in common use. In general, the species of Salmonella are divided into groups on the basis of similarity with respect to the O antigens, and the species within a group are often differentiated according to differences between their H antigens (81,82). The species have been arranged in groups designated A, B, C, etc., according to similarities in the content of O antigens.

Chemistry of the Polysaccharide Component of Salmonella Antigens

On hydrolysis, the Salmonella polysaccharides split into monosaccharides and phosphoric acid. Chromatographic study of the sugars shows that they represent a fairly complicated mixture; a single polysaccharide

TABLE 4-10

Naturally Occurring 3,6-Dideoxyhexoses[a]

Name	First found in	References
Abequose	Endotoxin of *S. abortus equi*	Westphal, Lüderitz, Fromme, and Joseph (170).
Tyvelose	Endotoxin of *S. typhosa*	Pon and Staub (129), Westphal, Fromme, and Joseph (170).
Ascarylose	Glycolipid of eggs of *Parascaris equorum*	Fouquey, Polonsky, and Lederer (53).
Paratose	Endotoxin of *S. paratyphi*	Davies, Fromme, Lüderitz, Staub, and Westphal (40).
Colitose	Endotoxin of *Eschenchia coli* O 111	Lüderitz, Staub, Stirm, and Westphal (101).

[a] Westphal (168).

may consist of six to seven different sugars, including hexosamines (glucosamine and galactosamine), heptoses, hexoses, pentoses, and deoxy sugars (38,113,39). The dideoxy sugars move faster on chromatographic paper than the other sugars do, and their discovery, based on this property, by Staub (147) and Westphal (167) was a new fact of great immunochemical interest. They play a very important role in the structure of the Salmonella antigens because:

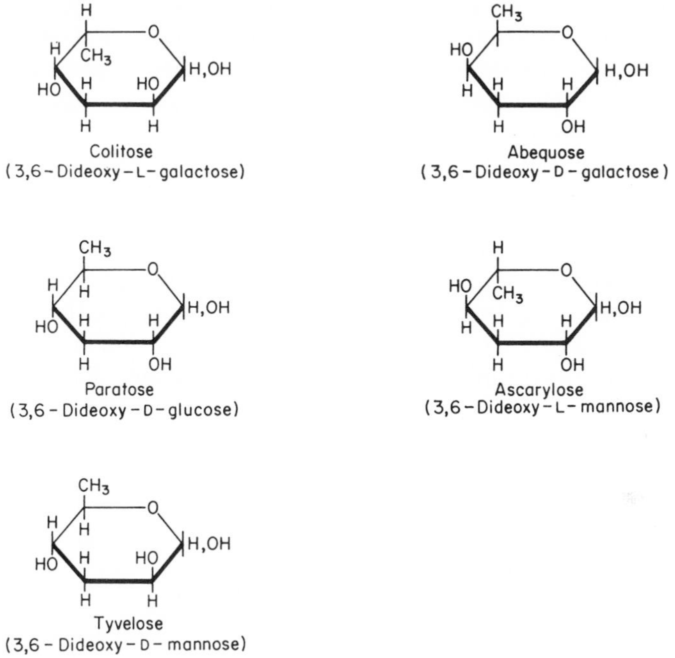

Colitose
(3,6-Dideoxy-L-galactose)

Abequose
(3,6-Dideoxy-D-galactose)

Paratose
(3,6-Dideoxy-D-glucose)

Ascarylose
(3,6-Dideoxy-L-mannose)

Tyvelose
(3,6-Dideoxy-D-mannose)

Fig. 4-2. Five naturally occurring 3,6-dideoxyhexoses.

(a) Brief acid hydrolysis of the Salmonella lipoidpolysaccharides always splits off these dideoxy sugars before significant amounts of other sugars are released. This shows that the deoxy sugars are *terminal* and acid labile in the branched polysaccharide structure. It is known (see above, p. 148) that the terminal groups play a predominant role in hapten specificity.

(b) When pathogenic "smooth" Salmonella forms change to the nonpathogenic "rough" forms, the fast chromatographic sugar components in hydrolysates of the antigens are missing, although the endotoxic lipoid A component is still present.

These dideoxy sugars are all 3,6-dideoxyhexoses, and five have so far been identified in natural antigens (Table 4-10).

The structures of these dideoxyhexoses are shown in Fig. 4-2. It will be noted that two of them, colitose and ascarylose, have the configuration of the "unnatural" L-series of hexoses, which are suspected of playing a role in the structure of the human Rh antigens (see Chapter 5). This does not necessarily mean that any serological similarities between the Salmonella antigens and the Rh blood group antigens are to be expected, although this is a point which so far as I know has not been tested. But it does tend to confirm our suspicion that the "unnatural" sugars are more widely distributed in nature than was expected. What their relative abundance will turn out to be is another question.

Relation of Structure of Salmonella Antigens to Specificity

Comparison of the results of chromatographic analyses of Salmonella antigens with their position in the Kauffmann-White classification (149, 147,171) showed that the terminal dideoxy sugars did play an important antigenic role, as expected. Each Salmonella species produces only one such sugar, and this sugar is characteristic of the group, A, B, etc., into which the species falls in the Kauffmann-White scheme. Paratose is characteristic of species in group A, for example, and colitose of group O (Table 4-11).

TABLE 4-11

Carbohydrate Structural Units of Specific O Antigens (Endotoxins) of *Salmonella* Groups A, B, D, and O[a]

(Heptoses and aminosugars not included)

Group species	Kauffmann-White antigens	Hexoses		6-Deoxyhexoses			3,6-Dideoxyhexoses		
		Galactose	Glucose	Mannose	Rhamnose	Abequose	Colitose	Paratose	Tyvelose
A *S. paratyphi*	1,2,12	+	+	+	+			+	
B *S. schottmuelleri*	1,4,5,12	+	+	+	+	+			
B *S. typhimurium*	1,4,5,12	+	+	+	+	+			
B *S. abortus equi*	4,12	+	+	+	+	+			
B *S. budapest*	1,4,12	+	+	+	+	+			
B *S. stanley*	4,5,12	+	+	+	+	+			
B *S. salinatus*	4,12	+	+	+	+	+			
D *S. typhosa*	9,12	+	+	+	+				+
D *S. enteritidis*	1,9,12	+	+	+	+				±
D *S. gallinarum*	1,9,12	+	+	+	+				+
D *S. dar-es-salaam*	1,9,12	+	+	+	+				+
O *S. adelaide*	35	+	+				+		
O *S. monschaui*	35	+	+				+		

[a] Westphal (168).

It has been further shown (149) that different dideoxyhexoses function as terminal groups of various antigenic factors of the Kauffmann-White scheme, abequose being the terminal unit of antigen 4 of group B, tyvelose of antigen 9 of group D, and colitose of antigen 35 of group O.

There seems to be no evidence that more than one of the 3,6-dideoxy-hexoses occurs in the endotoxin of any one species of Salmonella. When a 3,6-dideoxyhexose does occur it always occupies the terminal position in a side chain of the antigenic determinant of the carbohydrate antigen. This does not mean that other sugars cannot be terminal, for glucose and rhamnose can occur in this position.

Staub, Westphal, and colleagues (148,149) took advantage of the fact that degree of inhibition can be measured quantitatively if the reaction inhibited is the precipitation of a soluble antigen by a precipitatng anti-body, see above, p. 219; they made use of soluble antigens obtained by acetic acid lysis of the microorganisms and purification by Freeman's method (54) of the product (Table 4-12).

TABLE 4-12

Specific Inhibition of Precipitation of Salmonella Antigens by
Anti-*S. typhosa* Antiserum[a]

| Inhibitor | Horse anti-typhoid serum reacted with | | Rabbit anti-typhoid serum reacted with | | |
	$PsTy^b$ $(12,9)_2$	$PsTy_{ox}{}^c$ (9)	$PsTyB^d$ (12)	$PsTy^b$ (12,9)	$PsPtB^d$ (12)
Glucose	3	2	3	58	73
Galactose	5	0	3	25	26
Mannose	4	10	0	19	25
Rhamnose	23	2	85	11	10
Tyvelose	27	66	0	7	0

[a] Staub *et al*. Numbers indicate per cent inhibition. (149).

[b] Polysaccharide extracted from *S. typhosa*.

[c] PsTy oxidized with periodic acid.

[c] Polysaccharide from *S. schottmuelleri* (formerly paratyphoid B) = *S. paratyphi B*.

[d] Somatic antigens 9 and 12 of the Kauffman-White scheme. The italic number indicates the antigen which characterizes group D, the group that includes *S. typhosa*.

In this table PsTy stands for the polysaccharide extracted from *S. typhosa*, PsTyB for the polysaccharide from *S. schottmuelleri* (formerly paratyphoid B), and $PsTy_{ox}$ for the carbohydrate of *S. typhosa* after treatment with periodic acid. The reason for including such oxidized antigens in the studies is that periodic acid destroys substances possessing two adjacent hydroxyl groups, such as terminal glucose or galactose. Terminal 3,6-dideoxyhexoses, however, do not possess such a combination of hydroxyls and are not attacked.

From the results obtained with the horse anti-typhoid serum shown in

Table 4-12, Staub *et al.* (149) concluded that tyvelose is the terminal sugar of antigen 9 and rhamnose that of antigen 12.

It will be seen from Table 4-12 that the results obtained with the rabbit serum were quite different from those of the horse serum. The precipitation of the polysaccharide of *S. typhosa* (PsTy) by horse anti-typhoid was inhibited significantly only by rhamnose and tyvelose, whereas these sugars inhibited precipitation of the same antigen by rabbit anti-typhoid very poorly. Glucose was much more active with rabbit serum. The difference in inhibition of precipitation of the polyoside of *S. schottmuelleri* (PsPtB) was even greater. It was therefore concluded that antigen 12, common to *S. typhosa* and *S. schottmuelleri,* contains a side chain terminating in glucose as well as one terminating in rhamnose.

Similar studies carried out by Staub *et al.* on antisera to *S. schottmuelleri* (containing antigens 4, 5, and 12) showed that abequose inhibited the precipitation of PsPtB and especially of PsPtB$_{OX}$. This showed that abequose is the terminal unit of either antigen 4 or 5. Since abequose and antigen 4 are found in all Salmonella of group B, but antigen 5 is lacking in some members of this group, Staub *et al.* concluded that abequose plays no role in antigen 5. This was confirmed by the observation that the precipitation of an extract of *S. typhimurium,* which contains no 5 antigen, is inhibited by abequose and by the finding that when all the antibody precipitable by an extract of this *S. typhimurium* was removed from the anti-PsPtB serum, the action of the serum on PsPtB was not inhibited by the abequose.

Staub *et al.* (149) suggested that the dideoxyhexoses may play an especially important role in the specificity of the Salmonella antigens, not only because they are always terminal, but because the two hydrophobic CH$_2$-groups they contain are able to approach much closer to the corresponding surface of the antibody than the hydrophilic CHOH-groups, thus strengthening the van der Waals forces between the antigenic determinants and the antibody (see Chapter 6).

Cross-Reactions

As a result of extensive studies similar to those just outlined, Staub et al. concluded that although distinct Salmonella antigens generally have different terminal sugars, this is not always the case. For instance, abequose occurs at the extremity of both antigens 4 and 8, and glucose at the extremity of antigens 1 and 12. It seems reasonable to conclude that in such cases the next-to-terminal sugar is different, or attached in a different way. In order to test this idea, the authors carried out quantitative cross-

TABLE 4-13

Cross-Reactions of Horse Serums for S. schottmuelleri and S. typhosa
with Certain Polysaccharides[a]

Polysaccharide	Antibody remaining for antigens	Precipitating serum absorbed with:				
		— (4,5,12)	PsPtB —	PsPtB$_{ox}$ (12)	PsTy (4,5)	PsTm[b] (5)
1. Anti-S. schottmuelleri serum						
Galactomannan of						
Gum ghatti		270	19	40	—	—
Lucerne		255	28	—	243	2
Clover		200	25	—	—	—
Dextran		67	—	—	33	
2. Anti-S. typhosa						
	Antibody remaining for antigens	9,12	9			
Dextran		108	7			

[a] Staub et al., (149) Numbers indicate micrograms of precipitate nitrogen.
[b] Polysaccharide from S. typhimurium. Other antigens abbreviated as in Table 4-12.

reactions with a number of polysaccharides. Some of their results are shown in Table 4-13.

From the precipitation observed with the galactomannans of gum ghatti, lucerne, and clover, Staub concluded that the Salmonella antigen 4 has structural similarities with these polysaccharides; for, whenever the antibodies to antigen 4 were removed, precipitation of the galactomannans was reduced virtually to zero. Antibody to antigen 12, on the other hand, seems not to cross-react with these galactomannans, as is shown by the fact that removal of anti-12 by absorption with polysaccharide of S. typhosa does not much affect the precipitation of the serum with lucerne.

The antibodies precipitable by dextran are seen to be, at least in part, anti-12 antibodies, since removal of anti-12 by treatment with PsTy considerably reduces the amount of precipitation with dextran. This is shown even more clearly by the fact that removal of the anti-12 from the anti-S. typhosa serum eliminates, for all practical purposes, precipitation with dextran.

From these results Staub and her co-workers concluded that antigen 12 contains glucose units linked as they are in dextran. They felt they could not decide whether these glucoses were in the side chain which terminates in rhamnose or part of a chain terminating in glucose. They further concluded that antigen 4 contains groupings similar to those present in the galactomannans. These polysaccharides contain long chains of mannose linked 1→4, with occasional side chains consisting of galactose linked 1→6, as shown in the following scheme:

It is evident that the precipitability of anti-4 antibodies by these galactomannans is due to their specificity for a terminal galactose, a galactose–mannose group, or a chain of mannose linked 1→4. The last possibility is eliminated by the fact that oxidized paratyphoid polysaccharide still precipitates this antibody, for mannose linked 1→4 would be destroyed by periodic acid oxidation. The probability that the cross-reaction is due to a terminal galactose was diminished by the failure of Heidelberger and Cordoba (62) to obtain cross-reactions with other polysaccharides containing terminal galactoses. Also, periodic acid oxidation would destroy a terminal galactose, yet the oxidized polysaccharide is still able to absorb out the anti-4 antibodies. One is, therefore, led to conclude that the grouping common to antigen 4 and the galactomannans is the galactose-mannose grouping. But, since antigen 4 terminates in a non-oxidizable sugar and the only such sugar present is abequose, the terminal portion of antigen 4 may be:

abequose—galactose—mannose

Staub et al. (149) were able to detect a weak cross-reaction between S. schottmuelleri and S. newport owing to the terminal abequose which forms part of antigen 4 in the former and part of antigen 8 in the latter. This cross-reaction took place with horse serum only, which suggested that the horse produces antibodies specific for the terminal sugar more rapidly than the rabbit does.

In later work Staub et al. established the terminal sequence of sugars in antigens 1 and 12 as:

α-glucose—galactose—mannose—rhamnose

The linkages between the glucose and galactose are different in the two antigens, probably 1→6 in antigen 1 and 1→4 in antigen 12 (147,151,158).

A summary of the conclusions of Westphal, Staub, et al. about the antigenic structure of several Salmonella species in terms of chemical structure of the Kauffmann-White classification is shown in Fig. 4-3. To anybody familiar with the (largely unavoidable) vagueness of serological methods of classifying bacteria, the concreteness of the new results will seem like a

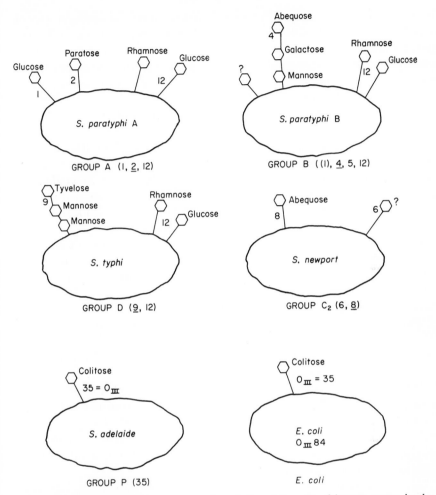

Fig. 4-3. Scheme showing our present knowledge of the role of known sugars in the specificity of some Kauffmann-White antigens (149). Ellipses indicate bacteria, projecting chains O antigens.

ray of light in a dark room. We may confidently anticipate that this ray will grow brighter until the whole intricate structure is illuminated.

The Vi Antigen. Felix and Pitt (49) found that different smooth strains of typhoid bacilli differed in their agglutinability by O antiserum, and that the more virulent were the less agglutinable. This was later shown to be due to the presence in the virulent strains of a special, very labile antigen, which Felix called the Vi antigen (48). Only strains which possess maximal amounts of O and Vi have the highest degree of pathogenicity of which the typhoid bacillus is capable. The Vi antigen is so labile that tests for it were originally carried out only with living suspensions. Peluffo (126), however, reported results which suggested that the stability of the Vi antigen to other destructive agents is greater than previously supposed, and he believes that when dehydrated it resists heat fairly well. Felix reported being able to prepare vaccines killed with alcohol which are still antigenic for Vi.

A Vi antigen apparently identical with that of *S. typhosa* has also been recognized in other *Salmonella, e.g., S. hirschfeldii* and *Paracolobactrum ballerup.* It also seems to occur in *E. coli.* Certain other *Salmonella,* such as *S. schottmuelleri,* possess different Vi antigens. Webster, Landy, and Freeman (165) found the Vi antigen to be a fairly strong acid, yet not to contain uronic, sulfuric, or phosphoric acid residues. Acetyl groups and nitrogen are present, but apparently not in the usual form of *N*-acetyl-hexosamine. Webster, Clark, and Freeman (164) isolated an amino hexuronic acid from the hydrolysis products of the Vi antigen from *Escherichia coli,* and suggest that the antigen is a polymer of *N*-acetylaminohexuronic acid units.

Purification and characterization of Vi antigens from three species of *Enterobacteriaceae* was described by Baker *et al.* (14). Chemically they seemed to be quite similar, being composed mainly (33) of a polymer of *N*-acetylaminohexuronic acid.

The classification of the *Salmonella* was sharpened by the discovery of Craigie and Yen (36) of bacteriophages that are active specifically against cultures of typhoid bacillus which contained the Vi antigen. These bacteriophages show a high degree of specificity for a particular strain of *S. typhosa.* Strain-specific bacteriophages have also been found of use in identifying strains of *S. schottmuelleri* (43).

Meningococcus (Neisseria meningitidis). On the basis of agglutination reactions and agglutinin absorptions, meningococci have been classified into four types. Two such classifications were those of Gordon and Murray (58) and Nicolle, Debains and Jouan (123). A sub-committee of the Nomenclature Committee of the International Association of Microbiologists recommended a new classification based on capital Roman letters (see 21):

New designation	Gordon and Murray type	Nicole, Debains, and Jouan type
A	I and III	A
B	II	B
C	—	C
D	IV	B

Judging by the results of agglutination and agglutinin absorption, group A is fairly homogeneous, group C less so, and group B relatively complex (22).

A carbohydrate or "C" substance, common to all meningococci and to some other microorganisms (pneumococci and some strains of Freidländer bacilli), has been obtained. There is also found a protein or "P" substance, also found in gonococci and type III pneumococcus. The sodium salt of a polysaccharide acid is responsible for the specificity of the group A strains. The specificity of the group C strains is also due to a soluble specific polysaccharide, but the specificity of the group B strains has been claimed to be determined by a protein substance (160).

Gonococcus. The antigenic classification of the *gonococcus* has proved exceedingly difficult. Each of eight strains studied by Stokinger *et al.* (152) contained one or more antigens not present in other strains, and no classification into types or groups could be made.

Carbohydrates of a greater or less degree of specificity have been isolated from gonococci (26), but the state of our knowledge concerning them is unsatisfactory.

Influenza Bacillus. The influenza bacillus (*Hemophilus influenzae*) is not the cause of influenza, which is a virus disease, but may possibly have played an important role as a secondary invader in the great 1918 pandemic.

The antigenic structure of "smooth" (encapsulated) pathogenic varieties of *H. influenzae* seems to be surprisingly like that of the pneumococci (128). Types a, b, c, d, e, and f have been defined on the basis of specific soluble substances produced by the organism and concentrated in the capsule.

As with pneumococci, the type may be established by observing the capsular swelling which takes place when the organisms are suspended in the appropriate serum.

The antigenic similarity to pneumococci extends even further, for three of the types, a, b, and c, cross react with certain types of pneumococci (1).

There are also somatic antigens in *H. influenzae,* but less is known about them. Two proteins, a "P" substance, and an "M" substance, have been found, and Dubos (41) obtained from one strain a toxic antigen, believed to be an endotoxin.

Whooping Cough Bacillus. All recently isolated strains of the whooping cough bacillus (*Bordetella pertussis*) seem to be in the smooth state and to belong to the same antigenic type.

Antigenic variation is found in *B. pertussis;* however, some of it is connected with changes of the S→R type when the organism is grown in cultures (99).

Somatic and capsular antigens are present (160). One of these is an "agglutinogen," which seems to be the antigen stimulating the production of an active immunity to pertussis. In addition there is present a hemagglutinin, at least one toxin, protective antigens, and a "histamine-sensitizing" factor. This latter increases the ordinarily low sensitivity of mice to histamine 50 to 100 times (124). *B. pertussis* vaccines also sensitize rats to histamine (104), but make rabbits and guinea pigs slightly less sensitive.

Plague Bacillus (Pasteurella pestis). It has long been known that immunogenic, toxic extracts of plague bacilli may be prepared (13). Rowland found a soluble, toxic antigen capable of producing immunity in rats, and a water-insoluble portion which was not immunogenic in rats. Schutze demonstrated, by serological test, an antigen soluble at 56°C. and destroyed by boiling, which he termed the "envelope" antigen, and another antigen soluble and stable at 100°C., which he termed the "somatic" antigen.

Jawetz and Meyer (13), after a study of avirulent *Pasteurella pestis* strains, proposed that an antigenically complete strain contains an envelope antigen, a somatic antigen, a virulence factor (vi) and an antigen responsible for the immunogenic efficiency of certain strains. They suggested that the only difference among all types of plague bacilli lies in quantitative differences in these hypothetical antigens.

Baker *et al.* (13) isolated and purified some of these antigens. They isolated two proteins from the water-soluble fraction of *P. pestis*. These two proteins were nontoxic and had a high immunogenic potency in mice and rats but a relatively low potency in guinea pigs. One of the proteins, Fraction IA, contained a carbohydrate moiety and was viscous in solution, whereas the other, Fraction IB, contained no carbohydrates and was relatively nonviscous. It could be crystallized from ammonium sulfate solution. These two fractions were homogeneous electrophoretically. They gave virtually identical absorption spectra. It was thought that the protein moieties of the two fractions might be identical.

Baker *et al.* surmised that these two antigens were on the surface of the bacillus, because antisera prepared against them agglutinated whole bacilli.

In addition to fractions IA and IB, the water-soluble portion of *P. pestis* contains a toxic substance which was separated and concentrated, but neither purified nor characterized.

The water-insoluble residue contains antigenic substances effective in the guinea pig. It was not studied in detail, but Baker *et al.* felt that some fraction of it was undoubtedly the "somatic" antigen of Schütze.

Brucella. It was postulated by Wilson and Miles (173) that *Brucella* organisms contained two antigens, A and M. The supposed antigenic constitution of *Br. suis* and *Br. melitensis* is shown in Fig. 4-4. The observations of Miles (114) on rates of agglutination of these bacteria are consistent with this picture.

Substances corresponding to the hypothetical A and M antigens have not been isolated. Pennell and Huddleson (127) and Miles and Pirie (115) have isolated complex endoantigens from *Brucella,* amounting to about 25 per cent of the bacterial cell. These contained lipoids and phospholipides, protein-like material, a substance designated as AP, similar to the

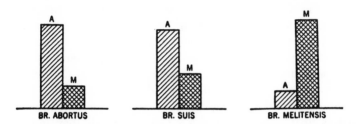

Fig. 4-4. Hypothetical antigenic composition of three species of *Brucella.*

Boivin antigens, and the polymerized formyl derivative of an amino compound. Both the A and M antigens seemed to be present in the AP substance.

More recent investigations revealed the existence of an antigen, called the L antigen, which resembles serologically the Vi antigen of *S. typhi* (174).

The toxic antigenic complex of *Brucella* organisms seems (42,115) to consist of a compound of a phospholipide and an arginine-containing protein. There is reason to believe this complex is on the surface of the cell.

Antigenic and toxic materials have been extracted from *Brucella* by trichloracetic acid, using Boivin's method. They consisted of phospholipide–polysaccharide–protein complexes. Pennell and Huddleson (127) studied the quantitative reactions of these antigens isolated from *Br. melitensis, Br. abortus,* and *Br. suis,* with both homologous and heterologous goat sera. The quantitative course of the cross reactions differed markedly from that of the homologous reactions. From *suis* antiserum, *abortus* antigen (BA) would remove about two-thirds of the total antibody, as would *suis* antigen (BS) from *abortus* antiserum. But from *melitensis* antiserum all the antibody could be removed with BS. In fact it took less

BS to precipitate all the antibody than it did homologous BM.   This was explained by assuming that BM contains a grouping which occurs much more abundantly in BS, making it possible for the latter to combine with more antibody per unit weight.

In the BA-anti-*suis* system there was found practically no inhibition in the region of antigen excess.   Kabat and Mayer (79) suggested that this is because BA can enter into fewer combinations with *suis* antibody than can the homologous BS.   It was in fact observed that the ratio of antibody to antigen was lower in the BA-anti-*suis* system than in the BA-anti-*abortus* system.

These quantitative studies suggest that the hypothesis of Wilson and Miles, that the strains of *Brucella* contain varying amounts of the same two antigens, is an oversimplification.

Dysentery Bacilli.   The antigenic behavior of the *dysentery bacilli* (*Shigella*) is complex, but has been explained as being due to the presence of various amounts of a number of different antigens (7).   The work of Morgan on the antigenic complex isolated from the Shiga bacillus has already been referred to (Chapter 3).   Morgan and Partridge (119) considered this to be a homogeneous substance, which they represented as ABC, where A stands for a phospholipide, B a polysaccharide, and C a "polypeptide-like" substance now claimed to be a conjugated protein. Injection of ABC gives rise to antibodies similar to those produced by the intact organisms, together with a little precipitin for C.   Morgan and Partridge (119) succeeded in removing the phospholipide from this complex, leaving a complex of polysaccharide and polypeptide-like material which is strongly antigenic and gives rise to the Shiga heterogenetic antibodies (see p. 195) as well as the Shiga agglutinins and preciptins. By the use of alkali, or preferably phenol-alcohol methods, the carbohydrate was isolated (120).   A alone and AB were not antigenic.   Injection of C into rabbits gave rive to antibodies which precipitated C or BC.   An antigenic complex BC could be regenerated from isolated B and C.   Since attempts to produce antibodies by injecting the polysaccharide absorbed on nonspecific substances were unsuccessful, it was concluded that the polysaccharide determined the specificity, and the "polypeptide-like" component made the complex antigenic.   Later work suggested that C is really composed of a simple protein and a prosthetic group containing phosphorus, and that the special antigenic property is due to the prosthetic group (150).

Wilson and Miles (160) state that the *Shigella* group is generally considered to consist of four main subgroups.

Subgroup A members are related antigenically to Shiga's bacillus (138).

The group is often referred to as the Large-Sachs group (160).

Subgroup B is serologically related to *Sh. flexneri* (51).

Subgroup C was described by Boyd (18).

Subgroup D contains only one member, *Sh. sonnei* (143).

Serological tests indicate that subgroup A contains ten distinct sero-types, each antigenically distinct, but most of them related to members of the *Escherichia* group. For example, the O antigen of Shiga's bacillus is related to that of the *E. coli* group 1 (160).

In subgroup B, the antigenic structure of Flexner's bacillus has been represented as consisting of four main antigenic components, the proportions of these components varying in the various strains (7). Boyd, however (18), suggested a different picture, in which at least six different antigenic components could be present, but some strains could lack one or more of these.

The antigenic structure of subgroup C is simpler. Nearly all serotypes are distinct. Nearly every *Sh. boydii* O antigen is more or less related to an *Escherichia* group antigen.

Sonne's bacillus, subgroup D, is antigenically homogeneous, but does exhibit phase variation (160).

Different bacteriophages (155) distinguish subtypes of Flexner's bacillus that correspond closely to the recognized serotypes, and similar results have been obtained with other subgroups of the *Shigella* (160).

Sonne and Boyd bacilli frequently produce antibiotic substances active against enterobacteria (45). According to the activity of these *colicines,* the bacilli producing them can be classified into a variety of types (160).

A Source of Error. A source of error in investigations on bacterial poly-saccharides was pointed out by Sordelli and Mayer (144) and Morgan (116). It consists in the fact that a constituent of the medium on which bacteria are often grown is agar, itself a carbohydrate, and capable of producing antibodies when injected adsorbed on bacteria, particularly with Gram-negative bacilli, or with conjugated protein extracted from them. The reactions of such antibodies have probably misled certain workers into reporting false cross reactions of some bacterial carbohydrates (92).

c. Acid-Fast Bacteria

The *acid-fast bacteria* (*mycobacteria*) cannot at present be differentiated on the basis of cell antigens as well as by culturing methods. It has, however, been found possible to distinguish four main serological types by ag-glutination, absorption of agglutinins, and complement fixation (see 159).

These types are: mammalian, avian, cold-blooded, and saprophytic. The human and bovine types are not distinguishable by this means. The pathogenicity of these three types for various species is different. The bovine type seems to be the most uniformly infective.

The acid-fast property of these bacteria seems to be due to the presence of an unsaponifiable wax (3). Anderson and his colleagues (2–6) studied the chemical structure of the acid-fast bacilli in great detail (see 160). An antigenic lipo-polysaccharide obtained from tubercle bacilli contains (9), in addition to mycolic acids and polysaccharide, diaminopimelic acid, which has so far been found only in certain strains of mycobacteria and corynebacteria. It appears that larger amounts of this complex can be extracted from virulent than from avirulent strains of the tubercle bacillus. The phosphatide was found by Sabin and her colleagues (133) to be capable, on repeated intraabdominal injection into rabbits, of giving rise to massive tuberculous tissue. One of the active constituents appeared to be a fatty acid, phthioic acid, the structure of which is not yet fully known.

The acid-fast bacteria contain a large proportion of ether-soluble constituents so firmly bound to the cellular structure that they cannot be removed by extraction with neutral solvents. They are called the "firmly bound lipoids"; they represent about 12 per cent of the human tubercle bacillus. On saponification these lipoids give fatty acids, which are almost wholly optically active hydroxy acids of high molecular weight, and specific polysaccharides. The hydroxy acid is different in each type of bacillus.

Old Tuberculin (OT) is a concentrated filtrate from cultures of the tubercle bacillus, essentially an autolytic heated aqueous extract of *Mycobacterium tuberculosis*. Seibert (137) isolated an active principle that was a protein (actually a mixture of several different antigens) (60), which she called PPD (purified protein derivative). It has been found that there is a carbohydrate in filtrates of cultures of the tubercle bacillus that also has immunological reactivity (11).

By reaction with antibodies in gels, Gussoni (60) showed that Old Tuberculin contains six thermostable antigenic components. The tubercle bacteria themselves were found to contain at least four more antigenic components that are not released into the culture medium.

5. Virus Antigens

The word "virus" was originally used to mean a poison, such as snake venom. It was later used to mean any infectious disease-producing entity, irrespective of its nature, and lost this significance only as the bacterial causes of certain diseases became clear. Its use persisted in those diseases where the causative agent remained mysterious, and as the virus diseases remained longest in this class, we finally have the meaning restricted to this class of agents. For a discussion of the nature of viruses, see Burnet and Stanley (29). The simplest appear to consist of protein and nucleic acid, and the most complex, of a number of materials, indistinguishable chemically from those found in bacteria.

Some viruses contain RNA, a few contain DNA, and a few seem to contain both (29).

In the viruses that contain RNA this nucleic acid is enclosed in a tightly fitting protein shell or *capsid* (131) (Fig. 4-5). This proten comprises the majority of the mass of the virus (95 per cent in the case of tobacco mosaic virus and 75 per cent in the case of poliovirus), but it is the nucleic acid

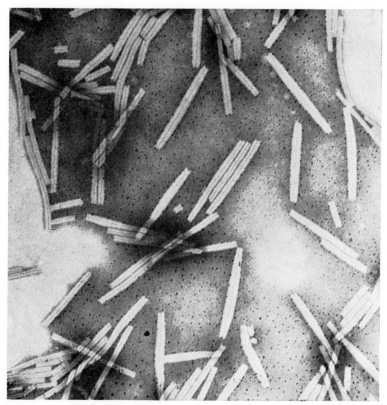

Fig. 4-5. Electron micrograph of tobacco mosaic virus, showing hollow core (where infective RNA resides). Ca. 72,000 ×. Courtesy P. Schuyler Miller, Fisher Scientific Co., Electron Optics Div.

portion that is infective.   The protein molecules are arranged in quite symmetrical fashion, and many, perhaps most, viruses seem to be regular geometrical solids (Richter 131; Caspar 67a).

Viruses are essentially foreign genetic determinants (102).   That is, their DNA (or RNA) contains instructions for the preparation of more virus, and is able to force the synthetic mechanisms of the infected cell to undertake this job instead of their normal function.   Luria (102) calls virus infection a form of *infective heredity.*

However, in spite of the similarity to genes, the nucleoprotein of viruses is not very similar to that of normal cells (131).

Originally viruses were characterized by their ability to go through pores which hold back bacteria (and therefore referred to as "filterable viruses"), and by the facts that they could not be seen under the microscope and that they grew only in the presence of living cells.   It is now known that they vary in size very much.

Plant Viruses.   The first big steps forward in the chemical study of viruses were taken in the field of plant viruses.   However, since in this book we do not treat plant diseases or the subject of plant immunity, we shall restrict ourselves to some remarks about tobacco mosaic virus, the first to be thoroughly studied and still one of the best understood.

Tobacco mosaic virus (Fig. 4-6) appears to be composed only of protein and nucleic acid.   In 1935 Stanley (145) isolated this virus in crystalline form.   The particles of virus which compose such crystals have a diameter of about 150 A., with a length of about 2800 A. (molecular weight about 40×10^6).

Data on the amino acid composition and on the nucleic acid present in tobacco mosaic and other plant viruses may be found in (29).

Animal Viruses.   Vaccinia virus is a giant among viruses; it can be seen under suitable conditions with a good laboratory microscope, and can be sedimented by ordinary laboratory centrifuges.   The particles average some 250 mμ in diameter.   The electron microscope shows them to be roughly brickshaped, with a well-defined central "nucleus" (Fig. 4-7). As might have been suspected from its size, vaccinia virus is much more complex than many viruses, resembling in this respect bacteria more than plant viruses.   The elementary composition is N, 15.3 per cent, P, 0.57 per cent, and C, 33.7 per cent.   The virus contains 5.7 per cent of total fat, of which 2.2 per cent is in the form of phospholipide and 1.4 per cent is cholesterol.

A nucleoprotein of the deoxyribose type was isolated from the virus, in

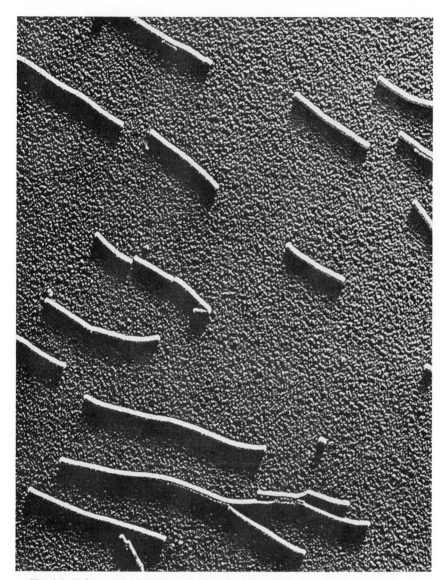

Fig. 4-6. Tobacco mosaic virus. Shadowed electron micrograph, about 97,000 ×.
Courtesy P. Schuyler Miller, Fisher Scientific Co., Electron Optics Div.

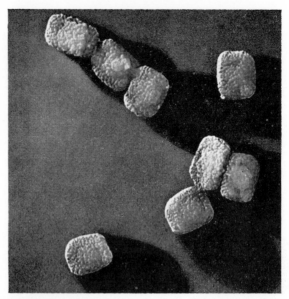

Fig. 4-7. Electron micrograph of vaccinia virus (*ca.* 57,500×). (Courtesy Dr. I. M. Dawson and A. S. McFarlane.)

the amount of about 5.6 per cent. It has not been certainly established that there is no nucleic acid of the ribose type (105). Copper is found to the extent of 0.05 per cent, as well as flavin adenine dinucleotide and a number of enzymes which, however, have probably merely been adsorbed onto the virus particles.

Influenza virus probably comes next as regards our knowledge of its chemistry, because material became available for chemical study in connection with the large-scale production of virus for vaccines.

There are a number of strains of influenza virus. It can never be known what virus caused the great pandemic of 1918, but Burnet (27,28) inclined to think it was related to the A viruses. He mentions that there is some evidence that human beings were not the only victims in this case, for large numbers of baboons died in South Africa, and their deaths were popularly ascribed to the "flu." But more substantial than this is the evidence that the hogs of the U.S.A. were also attacked, giving rise to a new swine disease which has persisted. The hog disease is a complex infection due to the association of a virus and a bacillus. The virus is certainly closely related to influenza A. Strain A has tended to be more important in causing human epidemics than strain B, and most of our knowledge of the influenza viruses is derived from work done on strain A.

Influenza virus is also larger than the average, though smaller than the vaccinia virus. The electron microscope shows it to consist of relatively uniform spherical particles with a diameter of about 80 mμ (29). It contains some lipide, and some polysaccharide, as does the B virus, but it is possible that all or a large part of these are derived from the tissues of the chicken embryo. Markham and Smith (105) pointed out that if all of these derive from the host, the amount of host material in the particles must be about 60 per cent, instead of the 20 to 30 per cent estimated by immunological tests.

An observation of practical and of theoretical importance is the agglutination of erythrocytes by influenza and certain other animal viruses. In the case of the myxoviruses, the virus particle itself is the hemagglutinating agent, but there is also present an enzyme (neuraminidase) which destroys the receptors in the red cells and allows the virus to be eluted. Some viruses, including one member of the poliovirus group, agglutinate but seem to possess no eluting enzyme and do not destroy the red cell receptors. Other viruses, including some of the poxvirus group and some strains of psittacosis, produce a separate hemagglutinin during their growth in suitable cells (29).

It seems likely that this power of some viruses to attach themselves to the erythrocyte surface provides us with a model of the first stage of cell infection, and that the erythrocyte receptors with which the viruses combine are similar to, or identical with, those on the surface of the susceptible cells.

This agglutination of red cells by virus can be utilized to titrate amounts of virus in unknown mixtures, and (by observing inhibition of agglutination) can be used also to titrate antibody to virus. Burnet also thinks that it is the power of attaching itself to cells of the respiratory tract, and enter them, which enables it to initiate an attack of influenza.

Poliomyelitis virus. Through the cooperative efforts of several laboratories operating under the Typing Committee of the National Foundation for Infantile Paralysis, it has been determined, by tests with monkeys, that the majority, if not all, of the poliomyelitis virus strains encountered can be assigned to one of three antigenic types, designated at I (Brünnhilde),* II (Lansing), and III (Leon). A strain of type II has been adapted to cotton rats and mice. The successful growth of the poliomyelitis virus in tissue cultures by Enders and co-workers (46,47) revolutionized methods of typing strains of poliomyelitis virus, and made possible the production of inactivated and attenuated vaccines in practical amounts. Dead polio

---

* The name of this strain apparently derives, not from the heroine of "Die Walküre," but from a female chimpanzee of the same name in which this strain was first recognized. Perhaps for this reason the name of the strain is generally spelled Brunhilde, and the pronunciation correspondingly Americanized.

virus has been used by Salk to immunize and Sabin used a live attenuated form.

The poliomyelitis virus was obtained in crystalline form by Schaffer and Schwerdt (135). It seems to have a molecular weight of about 6.7×10^6 (29). It is classed as one of the enteroviruses, and contains only protein and RNA.

Rabbit Papilloma virus. This virus causes warts on the cottontail rabbit in the United States. It is of interest because when it is used to produce benign papillomatous growths in the domestic rabbit, these growths sometimes become malignant. It is not possible to demonstrate the virus in such malignant growths, but it seems to be present, since the rabbit continues to produce antibodies against it (139) In view of the possibility that human cancer may be caused by a virus or viruses, this makes the papilloma virus of some interest.

Preparations of the virus show a measurable size distribution and a definite internal organization (105).

The techniques of column chromatography, with cellulose ion exchangers, have been applied by Hoyer *et al.* (69) to the purification and recovery of mammalian viruses and rickettsiae.

The bacteriophages form part of the subject matter of bacteriology rather than immunology, and we can hardly do more than mention them here. They seem clearly to be a type, or rather types, of virus which attack bacteria. They are of great importance in bacteriology because of the high degree of specificity shown by many of them, which makes possible their use in the study of bacterial genetics (105,23,103).

Many of the bacteriophages which have been examined under the electron microscope present a similar and unusual morphology. They consist of a spherical or short rod-shaped head, around 50 to 100 mμ in diameter, attached to which is a tail some 100 to 200 mμ long. Those which have been purified and analyzed consist almost entirely of protein and deoxyribonucleic acid, the latter amounting sometimes to about 40 to 50 per cent of the dry weight.

6. Antigens of Parasites

Parasites also contain antigenic proteins (111) and polysaccharides. These probably play, in parasitic infection, roles analogous to those of the corresponding antigens of bacteria. For instance, Melcher and Campbell (112) isolated in "a reasonably pure chemical condition," a polysaccharide from *Trichinella spiralis,* which gave immunologically specific reactions when tested on *Trichinella*-infested rabbits.

The most widely distributed polysaccharide of parasites is glycogen. It has been found in parasitic protozoa, mesozoa, helminths, and arthropods. The glycogen of *Ascaris lumbricoides* has been studied intensively (20). It has about the same unit chain length (12 to 13 glucose units) as mammalian glycogen but apparently has a somewhat lower molecular weight.

Parasites of course contain proteins, but the chemistry of these proteins is very imperfectly known (20). Proteins from tapeworms, when isolated, were combined with glycogen and cerebrosides.

Some parasites, such as tapeworms, seem to be harmless to their hosts, but others, such as flatworms, produce toxic substances, and others, such as *Cysticercus fasciolaris,* seem to produce some carcinogenic substance.

Rupture of a hydatid cyst caused by *Echinococcus granulosus* may cause death, but the reaction seems not to be a direct intoxication by products of the parasite, but an anaphylactic reaction to antigens to which the host has been gradually sensitized.

7. Antigens of Animal Cells

The cells of the higher animals contain quite a variety of proteins, carbohydrates, and carbohydrate–lipide complexes, and many of these are antigenic. Nevertheless they do not directly concern us in our study of mechanisms of resistance to disease, and consequently relatively little will be said about them here. The questions of organ specificity, tumor immunity, and individual antigenic differences within a species are discussed in Chapter 3; the antigenic differences found within the erythrocytes of different individuals of the same species (blood groups) are discussed in Chapter 5.

8. Structure of Cell Antigens

Bacterial and animal cells consist of a "mosaic" of antigens. In view of the known complexity of these cells, this view has an inherent plausibility, and it will be noted that in many cases it has been supported by the isolation of one or more of the hypothetical antigenic "factors." However, in other cases (for example, *Brucella,* Shiga) it has not proved possible to separate out chemically distinct substances corresponding to the hypothetical antigens, and from other work (see p. 153) we know that one chemical complex can give rise to more than one distinct antibody. A number of workers (Boivin, Raistrick, Morgan) emphasized that there is a certain risk in separating a cell arbitrarily into proteins, carbohydrates, lipides, etc., when it is likely that the living cell substance is essentially a complex, labile combination of all these elements simultaneously. The particular compound which is obtained by breaking down the cell might depend on which constituents happen to emerge in combination with each other in the final product. This would account for the variety of compounds which can be isolated by different procedures.

Thus Morgan (118) thinks it is probable that bacterial antigen as it exists in a bacterial cell is not a simple compound of rigid chemical constitution, but consists of a labile molecular aggregate, possessing some essential component—such as polysaccharide—of definite chemical structure and fixed composition, which determines the strict specificity of the antigen, together with other loosely bound constituents which endow the essential component with antigenic properties.

When an antiserum to the cells of one species is tested against those of a related organism, and a cross reaction is obtained, it is natural to assume that this is because the cells of the second species possess a chemical substance in common with the homologous cells. If the serum is absorbed with the heterologous cells, and, as is usually the case, antibody is left which still reacts with the homologous cells, it is again natural to assume that the antiserum contained antibodies to two (or more) chemical components in the homologous cells, only one (or a few) of which was common to the two sorts of cells. This has probably been the prevailing view among immunologists, and it is illustrated by the following scheme, taken from Landsteiner (91), which is meant to indicate the antigenic composition of several individuals. Columns 1 and 2 represent the antigenic components of two individuals of the same species, column 3 those of a related, and column 4 of an unrelated, species.

A	A	B	D'
B	B	C'	L
C	C	F	M
D	D	G	N
E	F	H	O
.	.	.	.
.	.	.	.

The reader may have noticed in the above pages, however, how often this sort of explanation has been invoked by the various workers to explain the antigenic variation in different bacteria. As Landsteiner (91) pointed out, it is not likely that the assumption of different distinct chemical structures to explain the observed reactions is invariably correct. We have seen that an antibody may react with several different substances of related constitution, and different immune sera may react with the same substance. Therefore, as Landsteiner (91) said: ". . . it is not requisite that an antigen which reacts with several antibodies has an equivalent number of binding substances or distinctive, specific groups. Neither is the fractionation of antisera by partial exhaustion with heterologous antigens by itself unfailing proof for this conclusion, and an alternative explanation is to be considered, namely, the formation of divers antibodies in response to a single determinant group."

So in some cases we should suppose, not that the related cells contain one or more chemical compounds in common with the homologous cells, but rather that they contain similar, but not identical, chemical structures. This might well be the explanation, for instance, of the observations on *Brucella* and the Shiga bacillus, mentioned above. It probably explains some of the peculiar observations made in the study of the Forssman hapten (see above). Landsteiner (91) said: "The incomplete absorption of sheep hemolysins by human blood A (Schiff and Adelsberger) and of lysins in group-specific anti-A sera by sheep blood can be explained if one assumes that antibodies of different reaction range are formed through the action of single determination structures similar but not identical, in each of the two antigens, less specific antibodies being responsible for the cross reactions."

References

1. Alexander, H. E., G. Leidy, and C. MacPherson, *J. Immunol.*, **54**, 207 (1946).
2. Anderson, R. J., *J. Biol. Chem.*, **71**, 407 (1926); **74**, 525, 537 (1927).
3. Anderson, R. J., *Physiol. Rev.*, **12**, 166 (1932).
4. Anderson, R. J., *Proc. Intern. Congr. Microbiol. 3rd, New York*, **1940**, 221.
5. Anderson, R. J., F. P. Nabenhauer, and R. L. Shriner, *J. Biol. Chem.*, **71**, 401 (1926).
6. Anderson, R. J., and R. L. Shriner, *J. Biol. Chem.*, **71**, 401 (1926).
7. Andrewes, F. W., and A. C. Inman, *Med. Res. Council Brit. Spec. Rept. Ser.*, No. 42 (1919).
8. Ascoli, A., *Die Thermopräzipitinreaktion*, Verlag von Josef Šafář, Vienna and Leipzig, 1922.
9. Austrian, R., and C. M. MacLeod, *J. Exptl. Med.*, **89**, 439 (1949).
10. Avery, O. T., C. M. MacLeod, and M. McCarty, *J. Exptl. Med.*, **79**, 137 (1944).
11. Baer, H., and S. D. Chaparas, *Science*, **146**, 245–247 (1964).
12. Bailey, G. H., and S. Raffel, *J. Clin. Invest.*, **14**, 228 (1935).
13. Baker, E. E., *J. Immunol.*, **68**, 131 (1952).
14. Baker, E. E., R. E. Whiteside, R. Basch, and M. A. Derow, *J. Immunol.*, **83**, 680–686 (1959).
15. Beeson, P. B., and W. F. Goebel, *J. Exptl. Med.*, **70**, 239 (1939).
16. Blair, J. E., *Bacteriol. Rev.*, **3**, 97 (1939).
17. Boivin, A., and L. Mesrobeanu, *Compt. rend. soc. biol.*, **112**, 76, 611, 1009; **113**, 490; **114**, 307 ff. (1933).
18. Boyd, J. S. K., *J. R. Army Med. Cps.*, **57**, 161; **59**, 241, 331; **66**, 1; *J. Hyg. Camb.*, **38**, 477; *Trans. R. Soc. Trop. Med. Hyg.*, **33**, 553; *Proc. 4th. Int. Cong. Trop. Med. Malaria, Wash., D. C.*, p. 290 (1931, 1932, 1936, 1938, 1940).
19. Boyd, W. C., *Tabulae Biologicae*, **17**, 113 (1939).

20. von Brand, T., *Chemical Physiology of Endoparasitic Animals*, Academic Press, New York, 1952.
21. Branham, S. E., *Bacteriol. Rev.*, **17**, 175 (1953).
22. Branham, S. E., *Int. Bull. Bacteriol. Nomencl.*, **8**, 1 (1958).
23. Braun, W., *Bacterial Genetics*, Saunders, Philadelphia, 1953.
24. Brown, R., *J. Immunol.*, **37**, 445 (1939).
25. Brunius, F. E., *Chemical Studies on the True Forssman Hapten, the Corresponding Antibody and Their Interaction*, Aktiebolaget Fahlcrantz Boktryckeri, Stockholm, 1936.
26. Burger, M., *Bacteriological Polysaccharides*, Charles C Thomas, Springfield, Illinois, 1950.
27. Burnet, F. M., *Viruses and Man*, Penguin Books, Melborne, 1953.
28. Burnet, F. M., *Natural History of Infectious Disease*, Cambridge University Press, Cambridge, 1953.
29. Burnet, F. M., and W. M. Stanley, *The Viruses*, Academic Press, New York-London, 1959.
30. Castellani, A., *Z. Hyg. Infektionskrankh.*, **40**, 1 (1902).
31. Chase, M. W., and Landsteiner, *Ann. Rev. Biochem.*, **8**, 579 (1939).
32. Christie, R., and E. V. Keogh, *J. Pathol. Bacteriol.*, **51**, 189 (1940).
33. Clark, W. R., J. McLaughlin, and M. E. Webster, *J. Biol. Chem.*, **230**, 81 (1958).
34. Coffey, J. M., *J. Immunol.*, **35**, 121 (1938).
35. Cowan, S. T., *J. Pathol. Bacteriol.*, **46**, 31 (1938).
36. Craigie, J., and C. H. Yen, *Can. J. Pub. Health*, **29**, 448, 484 (1938).
37. Dack, G. M., *Food Poisoning*, University of Chicago Press, Chicago, 1943.
38. Davies, D. A. L., *Biochem. J.*, **59**, 696 (1955).
39. Davies, D. A. L., *Adv. Carbohydrate Chem.*, **15**, 271 (1960).
40. Davies, D. A. L., I. Fromme, O. Lüderitz, A. M. Staub, and O. Westphal, *Nature*, **181**, 822 (1958).
41. Dubos, R. J., *J. Bacteriol.*, **43**, 77 (1941).
42. Dubos, R. J., *The Bacterial Cell in Its Relation to Problems of Virulence, Immunity and Chemotherapy*, Harvard University Press, Cambridge, 1945.
43. Dubos, R. J., and J. G. Hirsch, eds., *Bacterial and Mycotic Infections in Man*, Lippincott, Philadelphia, 1965.
44. Duran-Reynals, F., *Bacteriol. Rev.*, **6**, 197 (1942).
45. D'yakov, S. I., *J. Microbiol. Epidem.*, **28**, 1296 (1957).
46. Enders, J. F., *Hartford Hosp. Bull.*, **9**, 4 (1954).
47. Enders, J. F., *Ann. Rev. Microbiol.*, **8**, 473 (1954).
48. Felix, A., *Proc. Intern. Congr. Microbiol., 3rd New York*, **1940**, 798.
49. Felix, A., and R. M. Pitt, *J. Pathol. Bacteriol.*, **38**, 409 (1934).
50. Finland, M., and E. C. Curnen, *J. Immunol.*, **38**, 457 (1940).
51. Flexner, S., *Zbl. Bakt.*, **28**, 625 (1900).
52. Forssman, J., *Biochem. Z.*, **37**, 78 (1911).
53. Fouquey, C., J. Polonsky, and E. Lederer, *Bull. soc. chim. biol.*, **39**, 101 (1957).
54. Freeman, G. G., *Biochem. J.*, **36**, 340 (1942).
55. Goebel, W. F., *J. Exptl. Med.*, **64**, 29 (1936).
56. Goebel, W. F., *J. Exptl. Med.*, **81**, 315 (1945).
57. Goebel, W. F., P. B. Beeson, and C. L. Hoagland, *J. Biol. Chem.*, **129**, 455 (1939).
58. Gordon, M. H., and E. G. Murray, *J. R. Army Med. Cps.*, **25**, 411 (1915).
59. Griffith, F., *J. Hyg.*, **27**, 113 (1928).

60. Gussoni, C., *Am. Rev. Resp. Dis.*, **85**, 248–257 (1962).
61. Heidelberger, M., A. C. Aisenberg, and W. Z. Hassid, *J. Exptl. Med.*, **99**, 343 (1954).
62. Heidelberger, M., and F. Cordoba, *J. Exptl. Med.*, **104**, 375 (1956).
63. Heidelberger, M., E. A. Kabat, and M. Mayer, *J. Exptl. Med.*, **75**, 35 (1942).
64. Heidelberger, M., F. E. Kendall, and H. W. Scherp, *J. Exptl. Med.*, **64**, 559 (1936).
65. Heidelberger, M., J. M. Tyler, and S. Mukherjee, *Immunology*, **5**, 666–672 (1962).
66. Heidelberger, M., M. L. Wolfram, *Federation Proc.*, **13**, 496 (1954).
67. Henle, W., G. Henle, and L. A. Chambers, *J. Exptl. Med.*, **68**, 335 (1938).
67a. Horsfall, F. L., and I. Tamm, eds., *Viral and Rickettsial Diseases of Man*, J. B. Lippincott, Philadelphia, 1965.
68. Hotchkiss, R. D., and W. F. Goebel, *J. Biol. Chem.*, **121**, 195 (1937).
69. Hoyer, B. H., E. T. Bolton, R. A. Ormsbee, G. Le Bouvier, D. B. Ritter, and C. L. Larson, *Science*, **127**, 859–863 (1958).
70. Hoyle, L., *J. Hyg.*, **42**, 416 (1942).
71. Irwin, M. R., *J. Genet.*, **35**, 351 (1938).
72. Irwin, M. R., *Genetics*, **24**, 709 (1939).
73. Irwin, M. R., *Am. Naturalist*, **74**, 222 (1940).
74. Ivánovics, G., *Z. Immunitätsforsch.*, **97**, 402 (1940).
75. Jenkin, C. R., *Adv. Immunol.*, **3**, 351–376 (1963).
76. Julianelle, L. A., and C. W. Wieghard, *J. Exptl. Med.*, **62**, 11, 23, 31 (1935).
77. Kabat, E. A., *J. Exptl. Med.*, **85**, 685 (1947).
78. Kabat, E. A., *Blood Group Substances, Their Chemistry and Immunochemistry*, Academic Press, New York, 1956.
79. Kabat, E. A., and M. M. Mayer, *Experimental Immunochemistry*, Charles C Thomas, Springfield, Illinois, 1948.
80. Kauffmann, F., *Z. Hyg. Infektionskrankh.*, **120**, 177 (1937).
81. Kauffmann, F., *The Diagnosis of Salmonella Types*, Charles C Thomas, Springfield, Illinois, 1950.
82. Kauffmann, F., *Enterobacteriaceae*, Ejnar Munksgaard, Copenhagen, 1951.
83. Kauffmann, F., E. Mørch, and K. Schmith, *J. Immunol.*, **39**, 397 (1940).
84. Lancefield, R. C., *J. Exptl. Med.*, **47**, 91, 469, 481, 843, 857, (1928).
85. Lancefield, R. C., *J. Exptl. Med.*, **57**, 571 (1933).
86. Lancefield, R. C., "Cellular constituents of group A streptococci concerned in antigenicity and virulence," in *Streptococcal Infections*, M. McCarty, ed., Columbia University Press, New York, 1954.
87. Lancefield, R. C., *J. Immunol.*, **89**, 307–313 (1962).
88. Lancefield, R. C., and V. P. Dole, *J. Exptl. Med.*, **84**, 449 (1946).
89. Lancefield, R. C., and G. E. Perlmann, *J. Exptl. Med.*, **96**, 71 (1952).
90. Lancefield, R. C., and F. E. Perlmann, *J. Exptl. Med.*, **96**, 83 (1952).
91. Landsteiner, K., *The Specificity of Serological Reactions*, Charles C Thomas, Springfield, Illinois, 1936.
92. Landsteiner, K., *The Specificity of Serological Reactions*, 2nd rev. ed., Harvard University Press, Cambridge, 1945.
93. Landsteiner, K., and P. A. Levene, *J. Immunol.*, **10**, 731 (1925).
94. Landsteiner, K., and P. A. Levene, *J. Immunol.*, **14**, 81 (1927).
95. Landsteiner, K., and C. P. Miller, *J. Exptl. Med.*, **42**, 841 (1925).
96. Landsteiner, K., and J. v. d. Scheer, *J. Immunol.*, **9**, 213 (1924).
97. Landy, M., and R. Ceppellini, *Nature*, **176**, 1266 (1955).
98. Lanni, E., and Y. T. Lanni, *Federation Proc.*, **12**, 450 (1953).

99. Lawson, G. M., *Am. J. Hyg.*, **29**, 119 (1939).
100. Levine, P., J. G. M. Bullova, and E. M. Katzin, *Proc. Soc. Exptl. Biol. Med.*, **41**, 617 (1939).
101. Lüderitz, O., A. M. Staub, S. Stirm, and O. Westphal, *Biochem. Z.*, **330**, 193 (1958).
102. Luria, S. E., *The Viruses*, F. M. Burnet and W. M. Stanley, eds., Academic Press, New York, 1959.
103. Luria, S. E., *Ann. Rev. Microbiol.*, **16**, 205–240 (1962).
104. Malkiel, S., and B. J. Hargis, *Proc. Soc. Exptl. Biol.*, **81**, 689 (1957).
105. Markham, R., and J. D. Smith, *The Proteins*, H. Neurath and K. Bailey, eds., Academic Press, New York, 1954, Ch. 2.
106. Marrack, J. R., *The Chemistry of Antigens and Antibodies*, Med. Research Council Brit. Spec. Rept. Ser., No. 230 (1938).
107. McCarty, M., *J. Exptl. Med.*, **88**, 242 (1949).
108. McCarty, M., ed., *Streptococcal Infections*, Columbia University Press, New York, 1954.
109. McCarty, M., and S. I. Morse, *Adv. Immunol.*, **4**, 249–286 (1964).
110. McLeod, J. W., *Bacteriol. Rev.*, **7**, 1 (1943).
111. Melcher, L. R., *J. Infect. Diseases*, **73**, 31 (1943).
112. Melcher, L. R., and D. H. Campbell, *Science*, **96**, 431 (1942).
113. Mikulaszek, E., *et al.*, *Ann. inst. Pasteur*, **91**, 40 (1956).
114. Miles, A. A., *Brit. J. Exptl. Pathol.*, **20**, 63 (1939).
115. Miles, A. A., and N. W. Pirie, *Brit. J. Exptl. Pathol.*, **20**, 83, 109, 278 (1939).
116. Morgan, W. T. J., *Biochem. J. (London)*, **30**, 909 (1936).
117. Morgan, W. T. J., *Biochem. J.*, **31**, 2003 (1937).
118. Morgan, W. T. J., *Nature*, **152**, 82 (1943).
119. Morgan, W. T. J., and S. M. Partridge, *Biochem. J. (London)*, **34**, 169 (1940).
120. Morgan, W. T. J., and S. M. Partridge, *Biochem. J. (London)*, **35**, 1140 (1941).
120a. Morgan, W. T. J., and S. M. Partridge, *Brit. J. Exptl. Pathol.*, **23**, 151 (1942).
121. Neter, E., *Proc. Soc. Exptl. Biol. Med.*, **52**, 289 (1943).
122. Neufeld, F., and Händel, *Z. Immunitätsforsch.*, **3**, 159 (1909).
123. Nicolle, N., E. Debains, and C. Jouan, *Ann. inst. Pasteur*, **32**, 150 (1918).
124. Parfentjev, I. A., and M. A. Goodline, *J. Pharmacol.*, **92**, 411 (1948).
125. Paul, J. R., and W. W. Bunnell, *Am. J. Med. Sci.*, **183**, 90 (1932).
126. Peluffo, C. A., *Proc. Soc. Exptl. Biol. Med.*, **48**, 340 (1941).
127. Pennell, R. B., and I. F. Huddleson, *J. Exptl. Med.*, **68**, 73 (1938).
128. Pittman, M., *J. Exptl. Med.*, **53**, 471 (1931).
129. Pon, G., and A. M. Staub, *Bull. soc. chim. biol.*, **34**, 1132 (1952).
130. Reeves, R. E., and W. F. Goebel, *J. Biol. Chem.*, **139**, 511 (1941).
131. Richter, A., *Ann. Rev. Microbiol.*, **17**, 415–428 (1963).
132. Rothbard, S., and R. F. Watson, *J. Exptl. Med.*, **87**, 521 (1948).
133. Sabin, F. R., C. A. Doan, and C. E. Forknel, *J. Exptl. Med.*, **52**, Suppl. 3 (1930).
134. Seal, S. C., *Proc. Soc. Exptl. Biol. Med.*, **77**, 675 (1951).
135. Schaffer, F. L., and C. L. Schwerdt, *Proc. Natl. Acad. Sci.*, **41**, 1020 (1955).
136. Schmidt, G., E. Eichenberger, and O. Westphal, *Experientia*, **14**, 289 (1958).
137. Seibert, F. B., *Ann. Rev. Microbiol.*, **4**, 35 (1950).
138. Shiga. K., *Zbl. Bakt.*, **23**, 599 (1898).
139. Shrigley, E. W., *Ann. Rev. Microbiol.*, **5**, 241 (1951).
140. Sievers, O., *Acta Pathol. Microbiol. Scand.*, *Suppl.*, **37**, 458 (1938); **16**, 44 (1939).
141. Smadel, J. E., and T. Shedlovsky, *Ann. N. Y. Acad. Sci.*, **43**, 35 (1942).

142. Smith, W., J. H. Hale, and M. M. Smith, *Brit. J. Exptl. Pathol.*, **28,** 57 (1947).
143. Sonne, C., *Zbl. Bakt.*, **75,** 408 (1915).
144. Sordelli, A., and E. Mayer, *Compt. rend. soc. biol.*, **107,** 736 (1931).
145. Stanley, W. M., *Science,* **81,** 644 (1935); *Physiol. Rev.*, **19,** 524 (1939).
147. Staub, A. M., *Ann. inst. Pasteur,* **98,** 814 (1960).
148. Staub, A. M., and R. Tinelli, *Bull. soc. chim. biol.*, **39,** Suppl. 3, 65 (1957).
149. Staub, A. M., R. Tinelli, O. Lüderitz, and O. Westphal, *Ann. inst. Pasteur,* **96, 303** (1959).
150. Steabben, D., *J. Hyg.*, **43,** 83 (1943).
151. Stocker, B., A. M. Staub, R. Tinelli, and B. Kopacka, *Ann. inst. Pasteur,* **98,** 505 (1960).
152. Stokinger, H. E., C. M. Carpenter, and J. Plack, *J. Bacteiol.*, **47,** 149 (1944).
153. Streng, K. O., *Acta Pathol. Microbiol. Scand., Suppl.*, **37,** 493 (1938).
154. Stuart, C. A., *et al.*, *Proc. Soc. Exptl. Biol. Med.*, **34,** 209 (1936).
155. Thomen, L. F., and M. Frobisher, *Am. J. Hyg.*, **42,** 225 (1945).
156. Thompson, R., and D. Khorazo, *J. Bacteriol.*, **34,** 69 (1937).
157. Tillet, W. S., *Harvey Lectures Ser.*, **45,** 149 (1952).
158. Tinelli, R., and A. M. Staub, *Bull. soc. chim. biol.*, **42,** 583, 601 (1960).
159. Topley, W. W. C., and G. S. Wilson, *The Principles of Bacteriology and Immunity*, 5th ed., by G. S. Wilson and A. A. Miles, Wm. Wood, Baltimore, 1964.
160. Topley, W. W. C., and G. S. Wilson, *The Principles of Bacteriology and Immunity*, by G. S. Wilson, and A. A. Miles, 5th ed., Williams and Wilkins, Baltimore, 1964.
161. Van de Velde, H., *La Cellule,* **10,** 403 (1894).
162. Verwey, W. F., *J. Exptl. Med.*, **71,** 635 (1940).
163. Walter, A. W., *et al.*, *J. Immunol.*, **41,** 279 (1941).
164. Webster, M. E., W. R. Clark, and M. E. Freeman, *Arch. Biochem. Biophys.*, **50,** 223 (1954).
165. Webster, M. E., M. Landy, and M. E. Freeman, *J. Immunol.*, **69,** 135 (1952).
166. Weil, A. J., and E. Sherman, *J. Immunol.*, **36,** 139 (1939).
167. Westphal, O., *Angew. Chem.*, **64,** 314 (1952).
168. Westphal, O., *Angew. Chem.*, **72** (Dec.) (1960).
169. Westphal, O., and O. Lüderitz, *Angew. Chem.*, **66,** 407 (1954).
170. Westphal, O., O. Lüderitz, I. Fromme, and N. Joseph, *Angew. Chem.*, **65,** 555 (1953).
171. Westphal, O., O. Lüderitz, A. M. Staub, and R. Tinelli, *Zentr. Bakteriol. I. Orig.*, **174,** 307 ff. (1959).
172. White, P. B., *Further Studies of the Salmonella Group*, Great Britain Med. Res. Council Special Rep. Series, No. **103,** 1951.
173. Wilson, G. S., and A. A. Miles, *Brit. J. Exptl. Pathol.*, **13,** 1 (1932).
174. Wolff, H., and J. E. Dinger, *J. Pathol. Bacteriol.*, **63,** 163 (1951).
175. Zepp, H. D., and H. L. Hodes, *Proc. Soc. Exptl. Biol. Med.*, **52,** 315 (1943).

Бывало, писывала кровью
Она в альбомы нежных дев

—Pushkin, *Eugene Oniegin*, Part 2, XXXIII

CHAPTER 5

Blood Groups

Since we have seen that the more closely related two species are, the more similar are their proteins and other antigens, and the more difficult it is to distinguish them serologically, it might perhaps have been supposed that serological reactions which would enable two individuals of the same species to be distinguished would be still weaker or would not take place at all. The actual facts are otherwise; it is often possible serologically to distinguish individuals of the same species, and the reactions which do so are quite likely to be strong and well marked. This is because in nearly every species of higher animal we have tested, well-marked inherited antigenic factors, present in some but not all individuals of the species, exist. This is probably because natural selection, which has produced the species of plants and animals in the world, favors, not complete genetical uniformity, but a certain reserve of variabilty, and consequently most species are "polymorphic" for a number of characteristics.

A. ABO BLOOD GROUPS

1. Group Substances

The four main groups into which human blood can be divided are well known because of their importance for blood transfusion. These groups, discovered by Landsteiner (90), depend on the presence or absence in the red blood cells of the individual of two chemical structures, called A and B.

Although numerous attempts have been made to isolate these substances from erythrocytes (46,49,48), none of the products thus obtained are very pure or very active serologically. The best preparations have been

247

made from human saliva (85), gastric juice (183), stomach (85), and cyst fluid (2), and from the stomach of hogs, cows, and horses (6,84,120,48). Judged by their reactivity with anti-A precipitins, some of these preparations are nearly 100 per cent pure. The chemical properties of some of these preparations of blood group substance are given in Table 5-1, based on Kabat (83).

Aminoff, Morgan, and Watkins (2) found their preparation of blood group A substance from human cyst fluid to be essentially homogeneous electrophoretically and to have a molecular weight of 260,000, with a frictional ratio of 3.2 (highly asymmetrical). Their preparation was dextrorotary to polarized light, whereas the preparations of Kabat *et al.* from human saliva and stomach were levorotatory. The significance of this difference is not understood, nor is that of the larger levorotation found by Kabat *et al.* for A substance from the salivas of A_2 (see below) individuals. It is evident from the table that the blood group substances studied by the above workers are mucopolysaccharides. They contain amino acids also (2,6), in amounts which account for about 38 per cent of the total nitrogen, but they are usually contaminated with some free amino acids (103), and most of the constituent amino acids are not split off by mild hydrolysis which destroys the blood group activity, so the role of the amino acids in the specificity of the substances is doubtful.

The group A substances from animals are chemically and serologically quite similar to those from human sources, but show some differences detectable by hemagglutination inhibition and by quantitative precipitin determinations (84). Hog A substance in particular is very similar to human, and many of the differences found are at the limits of error of our present methods. However, in one case human A substance precipitated significantly less antibody from an antihog serum than did the homologous substance, and human individuals who fail to respond by antibody production to injections of human A substance may respond to hog A.

Blood group A, B, and "O" (=H) substances, from any given species, constitute a family of similar substances, varying chiefly in their fucose content. Their sharply different specificities are evidently due to internal structural differences, for their general analyses are very similar, and all react with type XIV antipneumococcus serum. A and B substances seem in certain respects more similar to each other than either is to H substance, as shown by their reactivity with agglutinins (lectins) from certain plants (42).

We might be tempted to consider the O characteristic of human blood

TABLE 5-1

Properties of Blood Group A, B, and "O'(=H) Substances [after Kabat (83)]

Material	Human A			Hog A	Horse A	Bovine A	Human B	Hog "O"
Source	Saliva	Stomach	Cyst fluid	Gastric mucosa	Gastric mucosa	Abomasus	Saliva	Gastric mucosa
No. samples[a]	5	4	1	7	6	9	5	3
Nitrogen, per cent	4.7–6.1	5.3–6.8	5.7	5.9–6.6	6.1–7.4	5.0–6.1	4.2–5.3	5.7–6.1
Reducing sugar, per cent	54–61	47–51	54–58	55–61	46–54	51–60	59–61	56–59
Hexosamine, per cent	26–32	25–28	34–37	32–34	21–29	23–34	26–30	32–34
Acetyl, per cent	8.6–10.3	—	8.8–9.1	9.3–11.3	8.4–11	—	13	9.4–9.9
Fucose, per cent	15–16	—	18	6.7–9.6	2.6–6.9	1.5–5.2	11–15	6.5–12.7
Optical rotation	−8—21	−2.5—5	+12–15	+10	—	—	−13—45	−5
Relative viscosity	1.13–1.37	1.11–1.13	1.14	1.39–1.71	—	—	—	1.47–1.63
Electrophoretic mobility[b]	—	—	—	-1.4×10^{-5}	—	—	—	-1.3×10^{-1}
Constituents identified[b]	L-Fucose D-Galactose D-Glucosamine D-Chondrosamine	L-Fucose D-Galactose D-Glucosamine D-Chondrosamine	L-Fucose D-Galactose D-Glucosamine D-Chondrosamine?	—	L-Fucose	L-Fucose	—	L-Fucose D-Glucosamine D-Galactose

[a] Some of the samples were not analyzed for all the constituents listed.

[b] In addition to the sugars listed, the human A substance from cyst fluid contained lysine, arginine, aspartic acid, glutamic acid, glycine, serine, alanine, threonine, proline, valine, leucine, and isoleucine. The hog A substance contained glycine, valine, isoleucine, proline, phenylalanine, tryptophane, histidine, lysine, aspartic acid, glutamic acid, serine, and tyrosine. However, six of these amino acids have been found free as contaminants in hog A substance, namely, aspartic acid, glutamic acid, lysine, serine, threonine, and glycine (103).

as merely the absence of A and B, but it is possible to obtain sera which react specifically with O (and A_2) bloods, although these sera seldom give as strong reactions with O cells as anti-A and anti-B do with A and B cells. Such sera may be obtained by absorbing the blood of certain cattle, or certain eels, with A_1 or A_1B blood, and agglutinins having this specificity have been found in a number of plants, such as *Ulex europeus* and *Cytisus* (144,21,52). All these agglutinins are inhibited by the saliva of secreting individuals of group O. Precipitins which react with O saliva have also been obtained (45).

It seems evident that a blood group substance is present in the erythrocytes of individuals of group O and in the saliva of secreting individuals of group O. It was formerly customary to call this "O" substance, but this is not a very logical name for an antigen produced by the action of either the O or the A_2 gene, and Morgan and Watkins (122) suggested calling it the H substance.

Analytical Studies

The results of chemical analyses of the ABH and Le^a blood group antigens* have been disappointing: they have not revealed any chemical differences that can be correlated with differences in blood group activity. At a glance, the four antigens seem very much alike. They each contain the same two sugar components, L-fucose and D-galactose, and the same amino sugar components, D-glucosamine and D-galactosamine. They also contain the same eleven amino acids (83,123). The role of the amino acids is not clear, for the specificity of the antigens seems to be determined mainly by the carbohydrate portions. Morgan believes, however, that the blood group antigens are not merely a loose combination of a macromolecular polysaccharide with protein but consist of carbohydrate chains and peptide units bound together by primary chemical bonds.

Of all the sugars present in the H blood group substance, for example, only L-fucose (Fig. 5-1) specifically inhibits the agglutinating action of an anti-H from eel serum. Similar results were obtained with an anti-H of plant origin, of the seeds of *Lotus tetragonolobus*. It was also found that anti-H from either of these two sources was inhibited more strongly by α-methyl-L-fucopyranoside than by the β-furanoside or by fucose alone. These results suggested that L-fucose is an important part of the H substance molecule; by analogy with Landsteiner's findings with composite haptens (p. 148), L-fucose is probably the terminal group of the specific

---

* Le^a is an antigen of the Lewis system (see 141).

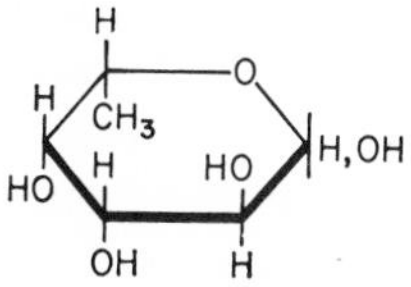

Fig. 5-1. L-Fucose.

part. The fact that the α-methylfucopyranoside inhibited better than the β-methylpyranoside suggested that the fucose was connected by an alpha linkage to the next residue of the reactive portion of the H molecule.

The first information concerning the role of a particular sugar in the specificity of the A substance was obtained by tests on anti-A rea-

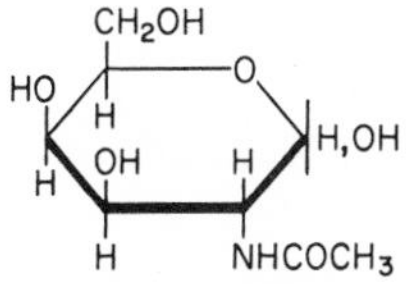

Fig. 5-2. N-Acetyl-D-galactosamine.

gents of plant origin (124). Anti-A lectins were specifically inhibited by N-acetylgalactosamine (Fig. 5-2). Most of the human anti-A reagents tested were not inhibited by this amino sugar but were inhibited by the disaccharide O-α-N-acetyl-D-galactosylaminoyl-(1→3)-D-galactose (Fig. 5-3). This suggests that this disaccharide must be very similar to, or possibly identical with, the terminal disaccharide portion of the specific part of the human A substance (124).

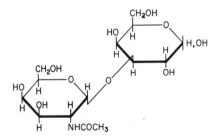

Fig. 5-3. O-α-N-Aceyl-D-galactosaminoyl-(1→3)-D-galactose.

Kabat and co-workers (83), also using the inhibition technique, found evidence bearing on the structure of the specific part of the B antigen. Of the monosaccharides present in the molecule, D-galactose was the best inhibitor of anti-B antibodies, but the galactose-containing disaccharide melibiose, the trisaccharide raffinose, and the tetrasaccharide stachyose (Fig. 5-4) inhibited even better than galactose alone (Fig. 5-5). This would

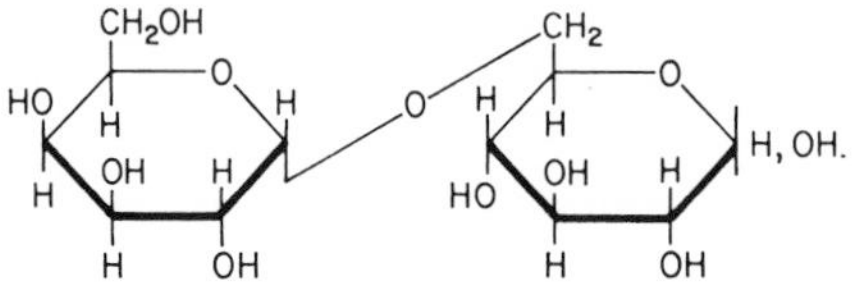

Melibiose

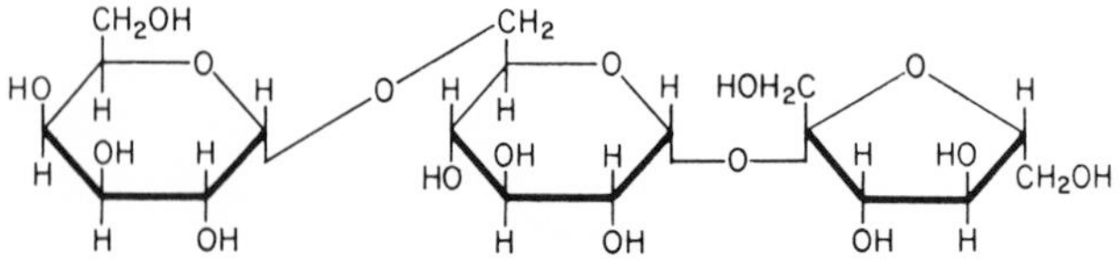

Raffinose

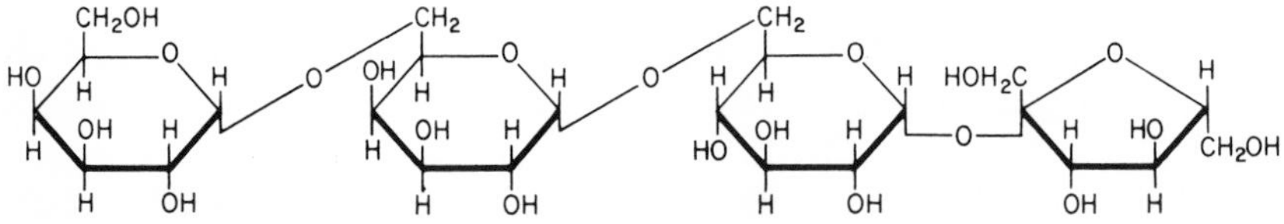

Stachyose

Fig. 5-4. Melibiose, raffinose, and stachyose.

have been expected if the specific part of the B antigen consisted of a terminal nonreducing galactose unit joined by an alpha linkage to another sugar unit. That the linkage is alpha is pretty well shown by the fact that α-methylgalactoside inhibits better than galactose, but the β-galactoside inhibits not as well (Fig. 5-5).

Kabat was also able to draw some conclusions about the sugar residue next to galactose in the specific side chain of the B antigen. It could not be glucose, for glucose is not a part of the B molecule. It was not likely to be another galactose, for, if it were, stachyose, which contains a terminal galactose bound by a 1→6 alpha linkage to another galactose, would be a better inhibitor than melibiose or raffinose, where the sugar next to galactose is glucose. But stachyose is no better an inhibitor than melibiose or raffinose. According to Kabat, N-acetylglucosamine is the only remaining possibility for the next-to-terminal sugar in the specific side chain of B antigen.

Some of this information may eventually see practical application, for Kabat suggests that the introduction of a number of melibiosyl residues into a polysaccharide would endow it with substantial blood group B activity.

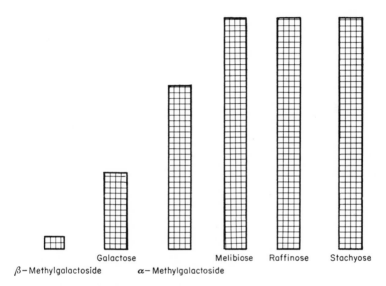

Fig. 5-5. Relative inhibiting power for anti-B of various sugars and glycosides [redrawn from Kabat (83)].

How many other sugars are present in the active side chains of the A and B molecules is not known, but on the basis of his determinations of the size of the reactive group of dextran, Kabat belives that the total is of the order of six. This would mean that in the light of our present knowledge the specific portions of the A and B molecules would resemble the structures shown in Fig. 5-6, where x stands for a number of the order of four.

Additional and independent evidence for the part played by L-fucose, N-acetylgalactosamine, and D-galactose in H, A, and B specificity, respectively, was obtained by Watkins and Morgan (170) from the results of enzyme inhibition by these sugars. It is known that an enzyme can be inhibited by an excess of one of the products of its action on its substrate. An enzyme preparation was available from *Trichomonas foetus* which destroyed the substrates consisting of A, B, and H substances. As expected, the destructive action of the enzyme preparation of A substance was inhibited by *N*-acetylgalactosamine, the action on B substance by galactose, and the action on H substance by fucose.

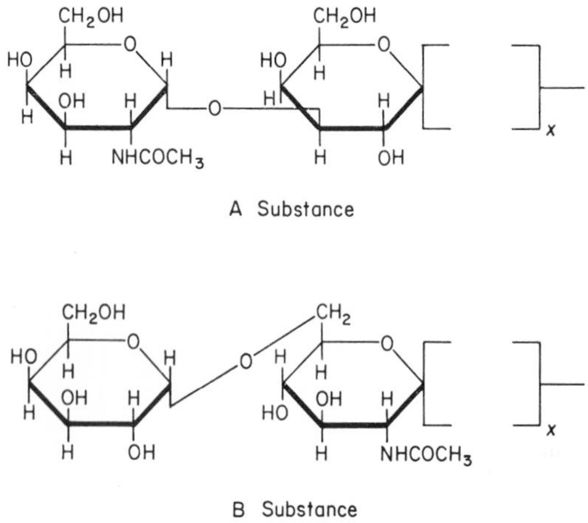

A Substance

B Substance

x = approx. 4

Fig. 5-6. Suggested structures of reactive groups of blood group A and B substances.

There is at present no clue to the identity of the monosaccharide unit next to fucose in the specific part of the H substance. Our best picture of its structure is shown in Fig. 5-7, where x stands for a number of the order of five.

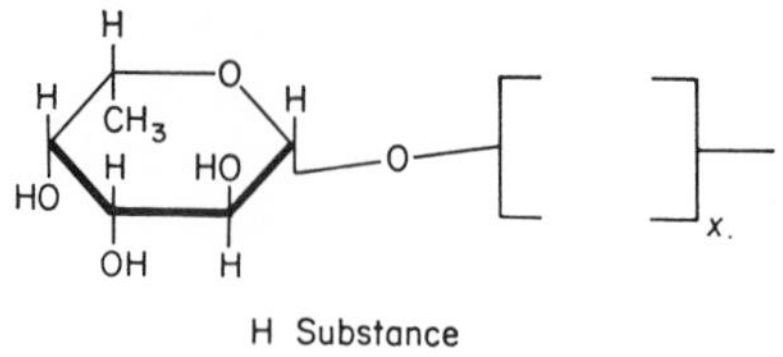

H Substance

x = approx. 5

Fig. 5-7. Suggested structure of blood group H substance.

2. Action of Genes

The way in which the ABO, secretor,* and Lewis genes cooperate to produce the various blood group substances found in the body fluids of persons of different genotypes is still to be worked out. Watkins and Morgan (124) have proposed the following scheme as a first approximation. Three independent gene systems, L′ and l′, S′ and s′, and the ABO genes, are supposedly involved. In various ways they act to modify the precursor substance, a mucopolysaccharide which is believed to be identical with the material found in the secretions of the individuals who secrete neither A, B, or H nor Le^a or Le^b substances. The L′ gene acts to add α-fucosyl units to this precursor substance, and the S′ gene adds still more. The B gene adds α-galactosyl units, and the A gene adds α-galactosaminoyl units (see Table 5-2).

TABLE 5-2

Possible Genetic Pathways for the Production of Blood Group Substances[a]

Sequence and products of gene action			Secretor type
Precursor substance	l′ gene (inactive) →	Precursor substance (not acted on by S′, A, or B genes)	Nonsecretor ABH Nonsecretor Le^a
↓ L′ gene (+ α-fucosyl units)			
Le^a substance	s′ gene (inactive) →	Le^a substance (not acted on by A or B genes)	Nonsecretor ABH Secretor Le^a
↓ S′ gene (+ α-fucosyl units)		O gene (inactive) →	H substance + Unconverted Le^a + Le^b
H substance + Unconverted Le^a −		B gene (+ α-galactosyl units) →	B substance + Unconverted H and Le^a + Le^b
		A gene (+ α-N-acetyl galactosaminoyl units) →	A substance − Unconverted H and Le^a + Le^b

The last three rows are bracketed as: ABH secretor

[a] Watkins and Morgan (124).

The scheme of Table 5-2 is inadequate in some respects, and Watkins and Morgan suggest replacing it by the more complicated system shown in Table 5-3.

These group substances are antigens. Alcohol extracts of human

* See p. 268.

erythrocytes of groups A and B, especially if mixed with proteins, will produce specific antibodies in rabbits, and will give flocculation and other *in vitro* reactions. The purified substances are not such good antigens: Morgan and van Heyningen (121) failed to obtain a response in rabbits to A substance purified from cyst fluid, although the same substance when conjugated into an "artificial antigen" (see p. 141) was strongly antigenic in rabbits. However, Kabat, Baer, Day, and Knaub (84) did obtain antibody response in a human individual of group B by injecting purified A substance from saliva, and the A substance from hog gastric mucin has been found to give a response in about half of the individuals of group O or B who were injected (184,84,16,39).

The A substance has been found to be related to the Forssman hapten (153). Some rabbit sera against sheep cells will agglutinate human cells containing A, and antisera against human A cells will even more frequently lyse sheep cells (see Chapter 4).

TABLE 5-3

Possible Genetic Pathways for the Production of Blood Group Substances [a]

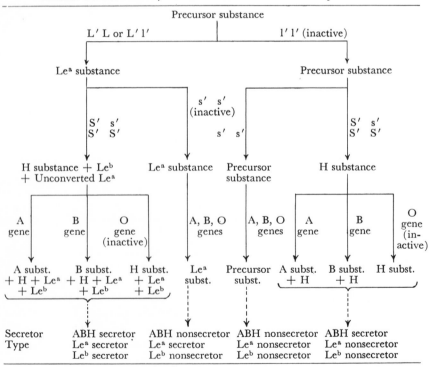

[a] After Watkins and Morgan (124).

3. Basis of the Four Classical Groups

The group-specific substances A and B may be present in the erythrocytes of an individual either singly or both together, or both may be absent. This makes four combinations, determining the blood groups, as is illustrated in Table 5-4.

TABLE 5-4

The Landsteiner Blood Groups

International nomenclature	Substance in cells	Agglutinin in serum
O	—[a]	Anti-A + anti-B
A	A	Anti-B (β)
B	B	Anti-A (α)
AB	A + B	—

[a] For simplicity blood group substance H is omitted from this chart.

4. Agglutinins

It has been shown (80,91) that the substances A and B, as they occur in the cell, are antigens, and immune agglutinins and hemolysins can be prepared for them by injecting rabbits with human erythrocytes of groups A and B and absorbing out undesired antibodies directed towards other features of the cell. Since the substances A and B can give rise to agglutinins, we may refer to them as agglutinogens. These immune agglutinins have certain advantages for theoretical, and possibly for practical, investigation (12). Morgan (119) also showed that artificial complexes of (hog) A substance with the conjugated proteins from the Shiga bacillus would produce, in rabbits, powerful and specific anti-A sera. By use of such agglutinins, the presence or absence of A and B can be ascertained, and the blood group determined.

However, it is not necessary to rely solely on these artificially produced agglutinins, for as may be seen from Table 5-4, agglutinins are present in normal human serum. The distribution of these agglutinins exhibts a regularity known as Landsteiner's rule, which has been stated by Landsteiner (92) as follows: ". . . the serum regularly contains the agglutinins active for the absent agglutinogens . . . corresponding agglutinins and agglutinogens do not coexist in one blood . . ."

Antibodies in the serum of an individual for antigens of other individuals of the same species are called isoantibodies; these agglutinins evidently belong in this class.

For grouping unknown bloods it is sufficient to use human sera of groups A and B only, as will be seen from Table 5-5. Groups can also be determined, if both serum and cells are available, by using serum and cells of group A or group B. The reader can easily work out the method of doing this for himself (see 154).

TABLE 5-5

Determination of Blood Group of Unknown Cells

Serum	Agglutination			
Cells + anti-A (= normal human B serum)	−	+	−	+
Cells + anti-B (= normal human A serum)	−	−	+	+
Group	O	A	B	AB

The exact mode of origin of the normal isoagglutinins is still not settled. Some workers, such as Wiener (176), believe they are immune antibodies produced in response to antigens, related to the A and B of man, occuring in bacteria and animal parasites. Others, such as Furuhata (73) and the Wurmsers (65), believe that they are formed as a direct result of gene action (see p. 332). It has been shown that the human A and B antigens will produce immune agglutinins in human beings, if blood containing one agglutinogen is transfused into individuals without it (179). Animal A and B substances are also antigenic in man (see above). Normal hemolytic antibodies (isohemolysins) are found in many bloods, especially if the tests are made with erythrocytes which have been stored for a time. Their possible occurrence depends on the blood group in the same way as does that of the isoagglutinins.

Springer *et al.* (160) found that germ free chicks did not develop the anti-B for human erythrocytes that is normally found in chicken blood, or developed it much later than did chicks reared under non-aseptic conditions. From this he concluded that the normal birds probably develop the anti-B in response to B-like antigens in bacteria with which they come in contact.

The naturally occuring isoagglutinins seem to be composed of 19S globulins (86). Keckwick and Mollison (86) thought immune agglutinins might be partly 7S and 19S.

5. Importance in Transfusion

From a scheme such as that of Table 5-4 it is easy to see why it is essential to determine the blood groups before performing a blood transfusion. Since all human sera, except group AB, contain agglutinins for

A or B or both, introduction of a blood containing agglutinogens that are capable of reacting with an isoantibody in the donor's plasma is likely to lead to agglutination, hemolysis, and renal shut-down, with resulting disaster. It is generally believed that the effect of the agglutinins of the recipient on the cells of the donor is most to be considered, as the agglutinins of the donor are diluted, and may also combine with soluble group substances in the serum of the recipient, and thus usually fail to exert harmful effect. For this reason the practice grew up of using for a donor any person whose cells could not be agglutinated by the serum of the recipient. This gave the transfusion possibilities shown below, where the arrows indicate the direction of transfusion.

```
              O
              ↓
         ┌─── O ───┐
         │         ↓
A→A      │       B←B
 │       ↓         │
 └──→AB←──┘
         ↑
         AB
```

It will be noted that group O could give, in theory, to each of the other three groups, and thus the popular but somewhat misleading term "universal donor" arose. In actual practice it has been found best to use for a donor a person of the same blood group as the recipient, and the so-called "universal donor" is now used only in emergencies, or after neutralization of the agglutinins present by the addition of A and B substances (184). Large amounts of group O blood were, however, flown to the fighting fronts during World War II.

It has been found necessary also to test the cells of the donor against the serum of the recipient, and if possible, vice versa, in order to guard against reactions of incompatibility which sometimes occur, even when the groups seem to be identical. In some cases, these unexpected incompatibilities may be due to a weakly developed isoantibody, which may lead to errors in grouping or cross-matching, but they are more likely to be due to incompatibility in respect to other blood factors such as Rh (see below).

6. Inheritance

Geneticists have shown that the hereditary characters of animals and plants are determined by units localized in submicroscopic structures called "genes." These are localized in small but microscopically visible rodlike bodies that occur in the nuclei of the cells of which plant and animal bodies are built up and by which they are propagated. These rods are called "chromosomes" and are observed to occur in pairs. A chromosome may carry a number of genes but only one of a kind. One member of each pair of chromosomes carries at each point of its structure a gene corresponding to the one at that same point in the other member of the pair.

During the formation of the cells concerned in reproduction (sperm and ova), these pairs of chromosomes separate, and each sperm or ovum contains only one of each kind of chromosome, and forms an exception to the general rule that each cell contains a pair of each kind. Figure 5-8 may assist in making this clear.

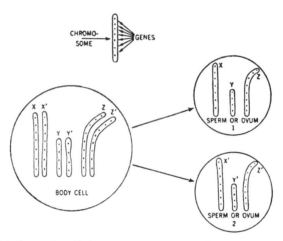

Fig. 5-8. Separation of chromosome pairs in the formation of gametes.

In the very numerous experiments on many varieties of living things propagated by sexual reproduction, it has been observed that hereditary characters occur in the individual in pairs, whose relationship is shown by breeding experiments, just as this chromosomal theory would demand (7). The classical human blood groups are inherited by such a mechanism. They are predetermined by the presence or absence in the chromosomes of genes called "*A*" and "*B*" and "*O*." Although the O gene causes the production of O (or H) substances in the cells, we may treat it, for the purposes of a discussion of heredity, as merely meaning no A or B. Since each body cell has a pair of chromosomes, each of which carries or fails to carry one of these factors, an individual's genetic constitution may be represented by *AB, AA, AO, BB, BO,* or *OO.* From this it is easy to see that the individual whose genetic formula (genotype) is *AB* will exhibit both of these agglutinogens in his blood (and other) cells, while the *AA* individual will have only the A characteristic, and the *OO* will have neither A nor B. The thing that is tested for in the blood cells is not the gene itself, but the substances A and B produced under the specific influence of the inherited genes. The fact that the *AO* individual has only one dose, so to speak, of the A gene seems to make no practical difference, and his blood is routinely indistinguishable, by direct test, from that of the *AA* individual. This means that we have but four groups of blood (phenotypes), O, A, B, and AB, routinely distinguishable from each other by direct laboratory tests. These types or groups are given in Table 5-6.

TABLE 5-6

Designation of the Blood Groups and Their Genetic Formulas

Name (phenotype)	Genetic constitution (genotype)	Approximate percentage in U.S.A. (11)
O	*OO*	45
A	*AA* or *AO*	41
B	*BB* or *BO*	10
AB	*AB*	4

Knowing the way in which mature reproductive cells ("gametes") of each sex emerge with only one chromosome of a pair, and consequently only one gene of a pair, we can predict mathematically the way in which the blood groups will be inherited. When sperm and ovum merge it is clear that the resulting cell contains its set of pairs of chromosomes; each parent has contributed one member of each pair.

A man of group AB produces two kinds of sperm, one containing the gene *A* and one containing the gene *B*. These are produced, on the average, in equal numbers. A woman of group AB will produce two types of ovum, one containing *A* and one containing *B*. If such a man and woman mate, it will be a matter of even chances whether an *A* sperm fertilizes a *B* or an *A* ovum, and whether a *B* sperm fertilizes a *B* or an *A* ovum, so that three types of offspring could be produced, *AB, AA, BB, BA*. (The *AB* and *BA* offspring will be just alike, since each will have both substances in his blood.) So the percentage of offspring of the various groups, if we observe a statistically large enough number of such matings (or of children of one such mating), will be, A, 25 per cent; B, 25 per cent; and AB, 50 per cent. It is conventional in genetic literature to illustrate such a process of reasoning about the results of a mating by the checkerboard diagrams shown in Table 5-7. (Either factor shown on the left may combine with either of the two at the top of each diagram.)

When we come to a mating involving an individual ("phenotype") of group A or B we must remember that there are really two genotypes in each group; *e.g.*, one whose genetic constitution is *AA* (homozygous),

TABLE 5-7

Diagrammatic Examples of the Hereditary Transmission of the Factors That Determine Certain Blood Groups

(I) Mating $AA \times AA$		(II) $AA \times AO$		(III) $AO \times BO$		(IV) $OO \times AB$	
A	A	A	O	B	O	A	B
A	AA	AA	A	AA	AO	A	AB	AO	O	AO	BO
A	AA	AA	A	AA	AO	O	BO	OO	O	AO	BO
100% A		100% A		*Progeny* 25% O 25% A 25% B 25% AB		50% A 50% B	

On the top of each diagram are designated the factors possessed (and transmissable) by one parent; on the left, those of the other; the letters under the horizontal lines show the possible results in progeny. Diagrams of all the 21 possible types of mating are tabulated in (182).

and another whose constitution is *AO* (heterozygous). The first will produce only one kind of gamete (or sexual cell), all containing A, while the other will produce two types of gamete, 50 per cent containing A and 50 per cent not containing A.

Four of the twenty-one possible kinds of mating are shown in Table 5-7. The third shows how a child's group may differ from that of either parent; the fourth shows that an O parent cannot have an AB child, that an O child cannot descend from a AB parent, and that an AB child cannot descend from an O parent. The reader will be able to work out readily the other 17 possible types of mating for himself, and thus verify Table 5-8.

Blood group studies on thousands of families have given results in perfect agreement with the predictions of this theory save for occasional children who were doubtless illegitimate (154,173).

Gene Symbols

Plausible suggestions have been made by various authors that instead

TABLE 5-8

Blood Groups of Offspring Possible or Impossible from any Mating Combination

Alleged father	Known mother	Possible children from their mating	Children not possible from their mating. Decisive for nonpaternity	Impossible from this mother in any mating
O	O	O	A, B, (AB)	AB
O	A	O, A	B, AB	
O	B	O, B	A, AB	
O	AB	A, B	(O) AB	O
A	O	O, A	B, (AB)	AB
A	A	O, A	B, AB	
A	B	O, A, B, AB		
A	AB	A, B, AB	(O)	O
B	O	O, B	A, (AB)	AB
B	A	O, A, B, AB		
B	B	O, B	A, AB	
B	AB	B, A, AB	(O)	O
AB	O	A, B	O, (AB)	AB
AB	A	A, B, AB	O	
AB	B	A, B, AB	O	
AB	AB	A, B, AB	(O)	O

The letters designate the blood types of the respective individuals (see Table 5-4). Those in parentheses, in column 4, could not be children of the corresponding mothers (column 2) in any mating (see complete listing of genotypic matings (182,173,140)). Therefore no such child could exist to raise a problem of proof, and these instances are omitted from Table 5-9, which summarizes the net indications of nonpaternity deducible from these blood groupings.

TABLE 5-9

Combinations Allowing a Man to Establish Nonpaternity, Omitting Instances of Impossible Mother–Child Combination

Putative father	Known mother	Known child
O	O	A, B
O	A	B, AB
O	B	A, AB
O	AB	AB
A	O	B
A	A	B, AB
B	O	A
B	B	A, AB
AB	O	O
AB	A	O
AB	B	O

of calling the Landsteiner blood group genes A, B, and O, we ought, following current genetical practice, to call them something like I^O, I^A, and I^B. I have not adopted this notation here, and indeed I am not in sympathy with it. Such symbols are fine for a reader who does not know what locus, or perhaps even what animal, is being referred to. But the reader of blood group literature does know what system, and what animal, is under discussion, and he does not need the clumsy carrying symbol I.

Subgroups

It was early found that there were two kinds of individuals of group A. The cells of one reacted strongly with anti-A agglutinin; those of the other (the less common) reacted more weakly with anti-A (94). These have been designated as A_1 and A_2, respectively. The corresponding difference is observed in group AB, so that these two groups are subdivided into subgroups as follows:

$$A = A_1 \text{ and } A_2$$
$$AB = A_1B \text{ and } A_2B$$

The routine determination of the subgroups of A and AB is today carried out with lectins from *Dolichos biflorus* and *Ulex europeus,* as suggested by Boyd and Shapleigh (44). See Table 5-10.

The qualitative and quantitative differences in reactive power of the two kinds of A may not always be striking, but it can usually be demonstrated by absorbing a serum of group B (containing anti-A) with cells of subgroup A_2 until the serum no longer acts on these cells. It will then generally be found that the absorbed serum will agglutinate only cells of group A_1 and A_1B. However, cells of group A_2 are not completely devoid

TABLE 5-10
Determination of Subgroups of A and AB with Lectins[a]

Subgroup	Reaction with extract of	
	Dolichos biflorus	*Ulex europeus*
A_1	++++	0
A_2	0	+++
A_1B	+++	0
A_2B	0	+++

[a] Boyd and Shapleigh (44).

of absorbing action on the anti-A_1 agglutinins (which are not as specific or avid as anti-A or anti-B) in the B serum. If larger amounts are used, the agglutinating power of the serum for A_1 cells may be reduced. The difference between the two types of cells is probably not purely a matter of *quantity* of A substance, however, as indicated by certain observations of Landsteiner and Witt (100) and Wiener (179).

It has also been found that A_2 cells react more strongly than do A_1 cells with certain sera agglutinating cells of group O (such as certain absorbed cow sera and goat anti-Shiga sera and anti-H lectins), and with certain weak agglutinins occasionally found in the serum of group A_1B or A_1. There have been a number of hypotheses (11) to account for the difference between these two forms of A.

The subgroups of A and AB seem to be inherited (94), although considerable variation in reactivity of the cells of various individuals belonging to the same subgroup has been observed (14). A hypothetical mechanism of inheritance, which is a simple extension of the Bernstein theory for A and B, has been offered by Thomsen, Friedenreich, and Worsaae. The families thus far studied conform to this theory on the whole, but there have been a few exceptions.

7. Applications to Legal Medicine

Disputed Paternity

From the above it should be clear how we may apply our knowledge of the inheritance of the blood groups in testing cases of disputed paternity. If a man is accused of being the father of an illegitimate child, we may determine whether the group of the child is such that, according to Table 5-8, the man could not be the father. In Table 5-9 are collected all the combinations which make this possible.

Naturally, if the groups are such that the man *could* have been the father, in the majority of cases we cannot state that he was, for there is always the possibility that some other man of the same group (or some other compatible group) is the father. Only in unusual circumstances of isolation would it be possible thus affirmatively to fix paternity on a man. Blood grouping evidence is admitted by law in a number of states in the U.S.A., but not yet in England, although in that country, as well as in the states here that have not yet passed legislation making it possible for the courts to order blood tests, such evidence is often accepted. In our states that have such laws it is provided that blood grouping evidence shall not be introduced unless the paternity of the man is *excluded*.

Disputed Maternity

It is rare that any uncertainty arises over the maternity of a woman and her presumed child. From Table 5-8, it will be seen that in certain cases nonmaternity could be established. Cases have actually been observed in which the woman tried to introduce into a legitimacy case a child not her own.

Interchange of Infants

In case of suspected interchange of infants, if all four parents and the children are available for testing, it can often be shown, if any interchange has really occurred, that the blood groups indicate that the allocation of the infants is incorrect. This can easily be seen from the tables, and the method has had practical application.

The legal aspects of the medicolegal use of blood groups are discussed by Wigmore (182), Schatkin (152), and Lombard (111). See also (176).

Determination of Blood Group of Blood Stains

In a number of forensic cases the question of the identity of a blood stain comes up. Let us suppose, for instance, that a suspect is arrested for murder. The crime was one which involved the spilling of blood and in the possession of the suspect a blood-stained handkerchief is found. The police believe that the stain resulted from wiping hands or a weapon on the cloth at the scene of the crime, but the accused says it is his own blood, from a nosebleed. It is clearly desirable to check his story.

If we determine the blood group of the suspect, the group of the blood on the handkerchief, and (if possible) the group of the victim, we may possibly find that the group of the blood on the handkerchief is different from that of the suspect, in which case his story is false, and the case against him becomes stronger than ever. It has been found possible to determine the group of dried blood, even when it is quite old, by means of its absorptive power for the agglutinins anti-A and anti-B. A summary and description of technic was given by Schiff and Boyd (154) and in (33).

Determination of the M,N type (p. 269) of dried blood stains has proved much less certain than determination of the A,B groups, although the methods for M are probably reliable enough to be recommended for forensic work. Since M and N do not seem to occur outside the erythrocytes, it is not possible to determine the M,N types from other dried material.

Material Other than Blood

It is possible, in fact often even easier than with blood, to determine the blood groups from dried material other than blood, because of the presence of the antigens A and B in other tissues and fluids of the body, often in higher concentration than in the blood (see below). This determination has been made with saliva, sperm, etc. The forensic application of both the precipitin test and blood grouping tests, and the qualifications of an expert in these technics, have been discussed elsewhere at some length by the present author (13,15) and by Wiener (176).

8. Occurrence of A and B in the Human Body Outside of the Erythrocytes

The antigens A and B are not restricted to the red cells of the blood. They seem to occur in all cells and tissue fluids, except the cerebrospinal fluid, testicle, lens, chorin frondosum of the placenta, hair, compact bone,

TABLE 5-11

Amounts of Group Substances in Organs and Fluids (77,150)

I. Relative amounts of water-soluble group substances in organs and feces of secretors (inhibiting doses per gram)

Organ	Moist weight	Dry weight	Organ	Moist weight	Dry weight
Brain	2–4	26	Lungs	9–22	111
Spleen	4	—	Kidney	20	86
Feces	5	100	Heart	34	107
Aorta	10	24	Oesophagus	200	—
Muscle	10–20	36	Pancreas	180–310	1390
Liver	16	48	Duodenum	400	—
Fat	16	—	Stomach	2000	—
Kidney	16	—			

II. Relative amounts of group substances in excretions and secretions, compared with erythrocytes (dilutions which inhibit isohemagglutination) (139)

Material	Dilution	Material	Dilution
Saliva	128–1024	Tears	2–8
Sperm	128–1024	Urine	2–4
Amniotic fluid	64–256	Cerebrospinal	0
Erythrocytes	8–32	fluid	

cartilage, epithelial cells of the skin, and the nails. Table 5-11, taken from Boyd (11), shows the relative amounts in the parts of the body which have been studied quantitatively.

Szulman (166), using the fluorescent antibody technique, found A and B blood group substances in the endothelia of blood vessels, in stratified epithelia, mucous-secreting apparatus, and the pancreas and sweat glands. The secretor status of the individual seemed to govern mainly the presence of the antigens in tissues associated with mucous secretions, in most, but not all locations.

9. Blood Group Enzyme

The group substances are largely destroyed in descending the digestive tract. This is not due to the ordinary digestive enzymes, such as pepsin or trypsin. Sterile filtrates of stool suspensions (human and animal) have this action; they lose it after being heated. The "O" (H) characteristic seems to be destroyed in the same way. Saliva itself has some destructive power, but the activity is bound to the cellular debris if autolysis is prevented by cooling immediately after collecting the saliva.

10. Secreting and Nonsecreting Types

Antigens A and B are not invariably present in the saliva even when present in the blood. Their presence or absence in the saliva is determined by a pair of Mendelian genes, designated by S (secretor) and s (nonsecretor) (155). The secreting type is more common; the relative frequencies of secretors and nonsecretors seem to vary in different races. There is a close relationship between the secreting genes and the Lewis blood groups (see below), secretors (SS and Ss) being Le(a−) and most nonsecretors (ss) being Le(a+) (140). There is evidence that the group substance found in the saliva is actually manufactured in the salivary glands (69).

In the organs of nonsecretors little or no water-soluble group substance is found, but active substances can be extracted with alcohol, and the group specificity of the organs can also be demonstrated by absorption experiments.

Secretors are ordinarily detected by the inhibiting action of their saliva on agglutinating sera of appropriate type (anti-A for persons of group A, anti-B for group B, either anti-A or anti-B or both for AB, anti-H for group O). It has been shown that a single reagent (anti-H from *Ulex europeus*) will serve in all cases (43).

B. THE MNS BLOOD GROUPS

1. Discovery of M and N

In 1927 Landsteiner and Levine (95) discovered three additional anti-gens in human erythrocytes which they called M, N, and P. These factors had escaped detection because of the absence of agglutinins for them in normal human serum and because of their negligible bearing on transfusion problems. They have proved to have considerable forensic and anthropological importance, however.

2. Differences from the ABO Blood Groups

The M and N factors differ in a number of important respects from the A and B antigens. In the first place, as already mentioned, iso-agglutinins for M and N are rarely found in normal human serum. This means that M and N must be detected by the use of immune agglutinins from animals (a usable anti-N agglutinin has been found in the seeds of *Vicia graminea* (132)).

Not too much is known about the chemical nature of the M and N antigens. One of the leading workers has been Kosyakov (87). Baranow-ski *et al.* (5) found the M and N substances to be mucoids, comprised of about 40 per cent carbohydrate (hexoses, hexosamines, fucose, sialic acids) and amino acids and water (10–15 per cent). The substances were quite acid, which might be correlated with the roughly 20 per cent sialic acid content.

Springer (81,161) found that N substance isolated by phenol extraction contained 24 per cent sialic acid, 9 per cent hexosamine, 1 per cent nitro-gen, 17 per cent reducing sugar (calculated as glucose), and methyl pen-tose *ca.* 1 per cent. The sedimentation constant of the main component was 16.4. It was interesting that RDE (an enzyme from *Vibrio comma*) destroyed the N activity of the substance as measured by the reaction with human and rabbit anti-N, but caused no change in the reactivity with the anti-N of *Vicia graminea*.

Influenza viruses and RDE inactivate or remove both the M and N receptors from human erythrocytes, though they do not seem to affect other agglutinogens (159). Romanowska reports (146) that the group-specific M or N activity of the cell disappears when the virus has liberated about 50 per cent of the N-acetylneuraminic acid.

3. Inheritance of M and N

The M, N types are inherited as a simple Mendelian pair, without dominance. No person is found without M or N, or both, in his blood, so no MN type corresponding to Group O occurs.

Thus we have the genetic formulas MM, NN, and MN, giving the blood types M, N, and MN. The inheritance will be readily understood on the basis of the same considerations applying to the ABO groups (above), and the results in Table 5-12 can be verified by the reader.

TABLE 5-12

Inheritance of the M, N Types

Mating	Per cent of children of types		
	M	MN	N
M × M	100	0	0
N × N	0	0	100
M × N	0	100	0
M × MN	50	50	0
N × MN	0	50	50
MN × MN	25	50	25

4. Application to Forensic Medicine

Since the laws of inheritance of M and N are known, it is possible to make use of these factors in forensic cases involving relationship, including disputed paternity, disputed maternity, and interchange of infants. From Table 5-13 the combinations which will enable a falsely accused man to establish his innocence can easily be seen.

N_2 and M_2

More weakly agglutinable forms of the agglutinogen N when combined with the M factor to form the heterozygote MN have been reported [see (68)]. They are of rare occurrence. One case of an M factor reacting more

TABLE 5-13

Combination Allowing a Falsely Accused Man to Establish Nonpaternity by M, N Types

Accused	Mother	Child
M	M	MN
M	MN	N
M	N	N
N	M	M
N	MN	M
N	N	MN

weakly with about half the anti-M sera, but more strongly with about one-fourth of them, has been reported (70).

5. The S Factor

In 1947 Walsh and Montgomery (169) sent a sample of human serum to Race and Sanger. This serum was known to contain an anti-Rh antibody, but in addition a new antibody was present, which Sanger and Race (150) found to be associated with M and N; they called it anti-S. It is important not to confuse this S with the gene for the secreting factor (p. 268). Race and Sanger (140) suggested that either there are really four alleles at the MN locus, namely, Ms, MS, Ns, and NS; or S and s constitute a separate gene pair, at a locus which is so close to the MN locus that the two pairs are closely linked in inheritance. They suggested that if an anti-s antibody were found, "as we confidently anticipate," the second interpretation would seem the more probable. This additional

TABLE 5-14

Arrangement of MNS Genotypes into Phenotypes, Depending on Sera Available for Testing

Phenotype	Genotypes
1. Two sera available (anti-M and anti-N)	
M	MsMs + MSMS + MSMs
MN	MsNs + MSNS + MSNs + MsNS
N	NsNs + NSNS + NSNs
2. Three sera (anti-M, anti-N, and anti-S)	
M	MsMs
MS	MSMS + MSMs
MN	MsNs
MNS	MSNS + MSNs + MsNS
N	NsNs
NS	NSNS + NSNs
3. Four sera (anti-M, anti-N, anti-S, and anti-s)	
Ms	MsMs
MS	MSMS
MSs	MSMs
MNs	MsNs
MNS	MSNS
MNSs	MSNs + MsNS
Ns	NsNs
NS	NSNS
NSs	NSNs

antibody in fact was found by Levine *et al.* (107). Since the linkage is obviously very close in this case, the two hypotheses do not differ in their genetic predictions. S, for example, will remain attached to M, if it is found in that combination in the parents, either because it is part of the product of a single gene, or the product of a gene at an adjacent locus on the same chromosome so close that crossing over either never occurs or is extremely rare. The addition of the anti-S serum enables the three M,N groups of Landsteiner and Levine to be split up into six groups, and the addition of the (at present very rare) anti-s serum enables nine phenotypes to be distinguished. Table 5-14 shows the way the ten different genotypes fall into three, six, and nine phenotypes, depending on the number of antisera available for testing. It will be noted that when all four sera are used only two of the genotypes remain undistinguishable.

6. Inheritance of MNS

The subdivisions of the MN groups defined by S greatly increase the number of distinguishable matings, but the reader should have no trouble working out the children possible and impossible from each possible mating, using the principles explained above. Tables will be found in Race and Sanger (140) and Wiener (176). The number of different matings of individuals belonging to p distinguishable blood groups is $p(p + 1)/2$. Therefore when only three phenotypes are distinguished the number of different matings is $(3 \times 4)/2 = 6$ (see Table 5-12). When six phenotypes are distinguished the number is 21, and when nine phenotypes are distinguished the number is 45. In a study by Race *et al.* (142), using three sera on 123 English families, all but 2 of the 21 types of mating were found, and no exceptions to the theory of inheritance were observed (*cf.* 140).

The MNS blood groups can therefore be applied to medicolegal problems such as disputed paternity, and the addition of the anti-S serum somewhat increases the usefulness of M and N in this field. The anti-s, if routinely available, would make a still bigger improvement (see below).

C. THE RH BLOOD GROUPS

1. Discovery of Rh

The Rh groups were discovered in 1940 by Landsteiner and Wiener (98), with whose work must be associated the work of Levine and Stetson in 1939 (110). Landsteiner and Wiener made their discovery with the serum of a rabbit which had been injected with the blood of a rhesus monkey, and they designated the new blood factor, which they found to be independent of the ABO or MN groups, as Rh, from the first two letters of rhesus.

This discovery might have had no important consequences, however, had not Wiener and Peters (180) showed that certain transfusion imcompatibilities in which the recipient had received repeated transfusions were due to the Rh factor, and especially had not Levine et al. (104) demonstrated that Rh incompatibility between mother and child could be the cause of *erythroblastosis fetalis,* or hemolytic disease of the newborn. It was later demonstrated that an earlier case of Levine and Stetson had involved Rh.

2. Rh and Transfusion Reactions

A natural outgrowth of the new knowledge of blood incompatibility was the concept that transfusions of blood containing a factor not present in the recipient's serum, even though no natural isogglutinin was present at the outset, might result in the formation of an immune isoagglutinin or produce some other form of sensitization, so that later transfusions of blood containing this factor would eventually be harmful. This was specifically suggested in the case of the M,N series by Lattes (101), and the warning was reiterated by numerous others. Actually, the M and N factors, though antigenic for rabbits, seem seldom to be isoantigenic in man, so the difficulty which was feared did not immediately arise. In all the bloods that have been examined, only relatively few cases of human anti-M or anti-N (133, 178, 176) agglutinins have been described.

Nevertheless, accidents and untoward results (58,114) did continue to occur in transfusion much more frequently than was desirable, or than many clinicians were willing to admit. Some of them, but probably only a few, may have been attributable to the use of a "dangerous universal donor" (4, 57, 108, 129, 179), whose anti-A and anti-B agglutinins were unusually potent and, when transfused, caused destruction of the recipient's erythrocytes or other undesirable effects.

Wiener and Peters (180) reported three cases in which repeated transfusions of blood of the proper group gave rise to hemolytic reactions. Two of these reactions resulted in the death of the patient. In two of these cases the appearance in the blood of the Rh-negative patient of anti-Rh agglutinins was demonstrated. There could be little doubt that the patients had been stimulated by the transfused Rh-positive blood to produce anti-Rh antibodies, and the combination of the antibodies with the cells introduced during the last transfusion had been the cause of the hemolytic reaction. Since this time, numerous other cases of the same sort have been reported (176). The discovery of Rh has thus elucidated the cause of a large number of the hitherto unexplained transfusion reactions when donor and recipient were apparently of the same blood group. When repeated transfusions are required, especially at considerable intervals, it is necessary to cross match the bloods of donor and recipient carefully each time, and preferably to do a complete Rh typing and to accept only Rh-compatible donors.

3. Rh and Erythroblastosis Fetalis

When Diamontl, Blackfan, and Baty (60) suggested in 1932 that universal edema of the fetus, *icterus gravis neonatorum,* and anemia of the newborn were all manifestations of the same disease and could conveniently be grouped together and known as *erythroblastosis fetalis,* no thought of a possible serological origin of the condition, apparently, was in their minds.

Following up the suggestion of Levine and Stetson (110), Levine *et al.* (104) considered more fully the role of isoimmunization in the pathogenesis of *erythroblastosis fetalis.* The latter authors concluded that isoimmunization of an Rh-negative mother to the Rh antigen contained in her Rh-positive fetus, with subsequent passage of the immune anti-Rh agglutinin back across the placenta, was the cause of erythroblastosis in the great majority of cases. As statistical evidence they pointed out that whereas only 15 per cent of the random population was Rh-negative, of the 153 mothers whose infants were affected with erythroblastosis fetalis, 141 (92 per cent) were Rh-negative. Also, of 76 infants and 89 husbands tested in this group, *all* were Rh-positive. In 70 cases the mother's serum was tested for agglutinins within two months of delivery; anti-Rh antibodies were found in 33 of these. Confirmatory observations have been published (9,172).

It was clear from the start that the combination Rh-negative mother and Rh-positive fetus, which occurs in about 9.5 per cent of all pregnancies in England and North America, does not automatically cause erythroblastosis, for the highest estimate of the incidence of this disease is only about 1 in 200 or 1 in 400 births (82). As Mollison (118) points out, therefore, only about once in 40 times does the potentially dangerous combination actually lead to morbidity. Evidently certain other conditions must also be fulfilled. We do not know what they all are, but one essential seems to be the passage of Rh-containing fetal cells (or possibly just Rh antigen?) through the placenta into the maternal circulation,

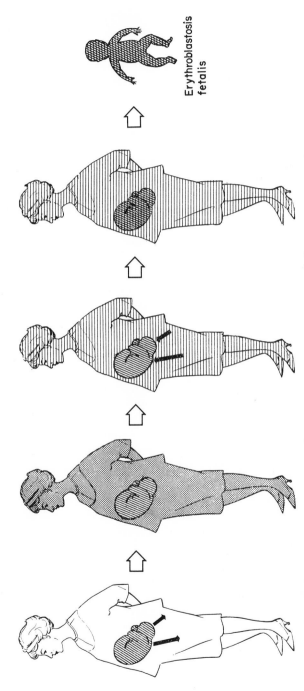

RH positive blood

RH antigen

Anti-RH antibody

Erythroblastosis fetalis

Fig. 5-9. Diagramatic representation of mechanism of production of hemolytic disease of the newborn by mother–fetus incompatibility. Rh+ cells and/or antigen (diagonal cross hatching) passes the placental barrier into the mother's circulation (uniform shading). The mother may respond by producing anti-Rh antibody (horizontal cross hatching). Such antibody diffuses back across the placental barrier and reacts with Rh+ cells of the fetus, causing *erythroblastosis fetalis* (double cross hatching).

with resulting immunization (unless this has already happened in a previous pregnancy). See Fig. 5-9.

The Rh factor is genetically and antigenically complex, so the simple scheme just outlined does not explain all the instances of erythroblastosis which occur. Therefore we need a summary idea of the laws of inheritance of these groups.

4. Inheritance of Rh Blood Groups

There are two notations for the Rh types, agglutinogens, and their genetic basis, that of Wiener, and that of the British workers. The British system is based on a suggestion of R. A. Fisher (140); Wiener's notation is the result of successive modification by him of his first published notation. Wiener's system has priority. However, the British system has certain features which render it attractive to most of the workers in the field, and both systems are in current use. Therefore no student can hope to understand the literature on this important subject without being able to read papers written in either notation. There are indications that this situation will persist for some time; in fact Race and Sanger (140) state that in their opinion *three* different notations are needed: (*1*) the simple distinction between Rh-positive and Rh-negative already mentioned, (*2*) the British notation, and (*3*) a "shorthand" version of Wiener's notation.

A committee appointed by the U.S.A. National Institutes of Health (51) recommended that Rh blood grouping sera be labeled with both the Wiener and the British notation, and this is perforce done in the case of all sera offered for sale in interstate commerce.

In spite of the great difference in appearance of the British and Wiener notations, and the differences in basic genetic and serological philosophy which underlie them, it should be emphasized at the outset that the predictions which they make about inheritance are *exactly the same,* and that at present no way of deciding which is right and which is wrong exists. In fact it is doubtful if any discovery could be made which would be agreed by either party to the controversy to provide conclusive disproof of their point of view. Which notation we prefer will therefore be partly a matter of personal feeling, and will be influenced by our particular experiences. The present author has found it convenient in teaching medical students to begin with the British system (18).

The British notation was based on these assumptions: (*1*) there exist 3 adjacent and therefore closely linked loci on the chromosome which

TABLE 5-15

Possible Chromosome Types and Reactions with Anti-Rhesus Sera, According to the British Nomenclature

Chromo-some	Reaction with serum[a]					
	Anti-C	Anti-D	Anti-E	Anti-c	Anti-d	Anti-e
cde	−	−	−	+	+	+
Cde	+	−	−	−	+	+
cdE	−	−	+	+	+	−
CdE	+	−	+	−	+	−
cDe	−	+	−	+	−	+
CDe	+	+	−	−	−	+
cDE	−	+	+	+	−	−
CDE	+	+	+	−	−	−

[a] The symbol + indicates a positive reaction (agglutination); − indicates a negative reaction.

carries the Rh genes; (2) each of these genes determines the production of one of the Rh antigens. It was proposed that 3 pairs of genes would account for the situation. These pairs were designated C,c; D,d; E,e. Thus 6 different antigens should be produced and it was postulated that 6 different antisera would be found to react with them. At the time the prediction was made 2 of the antisera were still unknown; since then one of them has certainly been found, and the discovery of the other has been claimed. Since each individual chromosome will possess 3 of the possible 6 Rh antigens, the possible chromosome combinations are 8 in number, as shown in Table 5-15.

The basic problem of symbolizing the results of the reaction of a number of different antibodies with a number of different antigens has been subjected to a penetrating analysis by Hirschfeld (78).

If three different gene loci were involved in the inheritance of the Rh groups, crossing-over would be possible between them, as Wiener (175), Rife (145), and others have pointed out, and the eight different chromosomes shown in Table 5-15 should be in cross-over equilibrium* in any given population. This is, in general, not true, however, and consequently it would seem either that the three-locus theory is incorrect or that the loci are so close together that crossing-over is extremely rare.

According to Wiener (175), the Rh blood groups are inherited not by a series of linked loci but by a series of at least eight allelomorphic genes

* That is, the various types of chromosomes should be equally frequent, allowing for differences in the population in the frequencies of the various Rh genes.

all capable of occupying the same locus. According to Wiener's notation, these genes, in the order shown in Table 5-15, are r, r', r'', r^y, $R^{0'}$, $R^{0''}$, R^z. The gene $R^{0'}$ produces two antigens (C and D) designated by Wiener as rh' and Rh$_0$, and is thus a "double acting" gene. Wiener designates it R^1 for short. Similarly $R^{0''}$ (cDE) is designated as R^2 The rare combinations CDE and CdE were not encountered by Wiener in his earlier studies, but were identified later by other workers and by him. Adopting the suggestions of the British workers, Wiener now represents them by R^z and r^y.

Originally only antisera reacting with genes which Wiener calls "Rh genes" were observed, but soon Levine (109) and co-workers found a serum which systematically reacted with all the Rh-negative bloods. He called this an anti-Hr serum, obtaining the symbol by inverting the letters Rh. However, it was found that (1) more than one anti-Hr serum (see below) was possible and (2) such sera did not react solely with the Rh-negative bloods. The English workers do not use the symbol Hr, but Wiener and certain other American workers continue to do so.

Rh-Hr genes and their reactions with the various antisera according to Wiener's nomenclature are shown in Table 5-16.

According to Wiener's nomenclature, the antisera designated by the British as anti-C, anti-D, and anti-E (Table 5-15) are designated anti-rh', anti-Rh$_0$, and anti-rh," respectively, and the sera called by the British anti-c, anti-d, and anti-e are designated as anti-hr', anti-Hr$_0$, and anti-hr". The only blood which is correctly called completely Rh-negative would react with none of the three anti-Rh sera, anti-C, anti-D,

TABLE 5-16

Rh Genes and Their Reactions with Anti-Rh and Anti-Hr Antisera, According to Wiener's Nomenclature

Gene	Reaction with serum					
	Anti-rh'	Anti-Rh$_0$	Anti-rh''	Anti-hr'	Anti-Hr$_0$	Anti-hr''
r	−	−	−	+	+	+
r'	+	−	−	−	+	+
r''	−	−	+	+	+	−
r$_y$	+	−	+	−	+	−
R$_y$	−	+	−	+	−	+
R^1	+	+	−	−	−	+
R^2	−	+	+	+	−	−
R^z	+	+	+	−	−	−

or anti-E, and, as can be seen from Tables 5-15 and 5-16, would react with all of the anti-hr sera. If we consider all six of the sera, then, there is no blood which would not react with at least three of them.

In the Rh series we have, in effect, 8 allelic genes, not counting more recently established alleles (see below). This means that different genotypes* are possible, and they are shown together with their reactions with the 6 antisera, in Table 5-17.

It will be noted that many genotypes can react with both of two alternative sera, such as anti-C and anti-c.

Table 5-17 is expressed in the British nomenclature, but the reader who has followed the above exposition should have no difficulty in translating it into Wiener's nomenclature, if he cares to.

It will be seen from Table 5-17, or from the table of Wiener, that not all of the 36 possible genotypes are distinguishable, for some give identical reactions with all antisera. We may easily calculate the number of distinguishable genotypes. Considering each pair of antisera, such as anti-C and anti-c, we have three possibilities: $++$, $+-$, and $-+$ (since C and c are considered as alleles, and thus one or the other must be present, the possibility $--$ does not arise). Thus we have $3 \times 3 \times 3 = 27$ possible different reactions with the 6 antisera, and 27 different phenotypes can be distinguished serologically. Thus certain of the 36 genotypes are serologically indistinguishable, even if all 6 sera were available.

The situation is actually much more complicated than we have indicated thus far. At each of three loci, C, D, and E, additional alleles have been found. At the C locus, for example, alleles designated as C^w, C^v, C^u, and C^x have been reported. Most anti-C sera are in fact mixtures of anti-C and anti-C^w. By use of all the known sera 28 phenotypes, corresponding to 55 genotypes, can be distinguished. Details will be found in the books by Wiener (176) and Race and Sanger (140).

None but a very few workers have available more sera than anti-C, anti-c, anti-D, and anti-E, so that with each of the latter two sera only two possibilities arise, namely, $+$ and $-$. Therefore the use of these four sera enables only $3 \times 2 \times 2 = 12$ different genotypes to be distinguished routinely. These are: CDe/C, CDe/c, CDE/C, CDE/c, cDE, cDe, Cde/C, Cde/c, CdE/C, CdE/c, cdE, and cde. Since we do not have an anti-d serum available, the phenotype CDe/C includes CDe/

---

* If n genes are available to occupy a chromosome locus, the number of different genotypes equals $n(n + 1)/2$.

TABLE 5-17

The 36 Possible Rh Genotypes, Showing the Reaction of Each
with Each of the 6 Antisera[a]

Genotype	Reaction with serum					
	Anti-C	Anti-D	Anti-E	Anti-c	Anti-d	Anti-e
cde/cde	−	−	−	+	+	+
cde/Cde	+	−	−	+	+	+
cde/cdE	−	−	+	+	+	+
cde/CdE	+	−	+	+	+	+
cde/cDe	−	+	−	+	+	+
cde/CDe	+	+	−	+	+	+
cde/cDE	−	+	+	+	+	+
cde/CDE	+	+	+	+	+	+
Cde/Cde	+	−	−	−	+	+
Cde/cdE	+	−	+	+	+	+
Cde/CdE	+	−	+	−	+	+
Cde/cDe	+	+	−	+	+	+
Cde/CDe	+	+	−	−	+	+
Cde/cDE	+	+	+	+	+	+
Cde/CDE	+	+	+	−	+	+
cdE/cdE	−	−	+	+	+	−
cdE/CdE	+	−	+	+	+	−
cdE/cDe	−	+	+	+	+	+
cdE/CDe	+	+	+	+	+	+
cdE/cDE	−	+	+	+	+	−
cdE/CDE	+	+	+	+	+	−
CdE/CdE	+	−	+	−	+	−
CdE/cDe	+	+	+	+	+	+
CdE/CDe	+	+	+	−	+	+
CdE/cDE	+	+	+	+	+	−
CdE/CDE	+	+	+	−	+	−
cDe/cDe	−	+	−	+	−	+
cDe/CDe	+	+	−	+	−	+
cDe/cDE	−	+	+	+	−	+
cDe/CDE	+	+	+	+	−	+
CDe/CDe	+	+	−	−	−	+
CDe/cDE	+	+	+	+	−	+
CDe/CDE	+	+	+	−	−	+
cDE/cDE	−	+	+	+	−	−
cDE/CDE	+	+	+	+	−	−
CDE/CDE	+	+	+	−	−	−

[a] The symbols C, D, E, etc., are explained in the text. The symbol / is used to separate the two chromosome formulas (Fisher) = genes (Wiener). Note that genotypes CDE/cde, CDe/cdE, Cde/cDE, and CdE/cDe give identical serological reactions. Similarly, CDE/Cde and CDe/CdE react the same, as do CDE/cDe and CDe/cDE. Cde/cdE and CdE/cde react the same, as do cDE/cde and cdE/cDe.

CDe and CDe/Cde and the phenotype CDe/c includes CDe/cde, CDe/cDe, and Cde/cDe.* And so on.

The anti-Rh antibody first discovered by Landsteiner and Wiener was anti-D (anti-Rh_0), and this is still the antibody most frequently encountered. Landsteiner and Wiener (99) studied the inheritance of this Rh factor in 60 families, and found no exception to the rule that Rh positive (D) behaved as a dominant to Rh negative (d). Later studies by Wiener and Sonn (181), Race *et al.* (143) and Broman (47) also agreed well with this hypothesis. However, Race and Sanger (140) point out that if anti-d had been discovered first, the factor d would have been described as dominant and D as recessive. In most blood grouping work it is simply a matter of the availability of a reagent for the agglutinogen produced by a gene to decide whether or not we describe the gene as dominant (the Lewis groups seem to be an exception to this).

The simplest way of studying the inheritance of the Rh blood groups, therefore, is to consider separately the inheritance of the pairs, C,c; D,d; and E,e. Each pair of factors gives three combinations, just as in the MN system. For instance the C,c pair gives the types CC, Cc, and cc, and with anti-C and anti-c sera available all three can be distinguished. The rules of inheritance are the same as with M and N (see above).

Since anti-d serum is not available, in this case we cannot distinguish DD from Dd, so that the rules of inheritance reduce to those for D+ and D− matings, as in the earliest days of Rh testing. The only mating decisive for nonpaternity is D− × D−, which cannot give a D+ child.

Race and Sanger (140) summarized the results of tests with anti-C and anti-c on 800 families, in which they found only one exception, a cc child in a CC × Cc family. Presumably this child is illegitimate. In studies of 209 families with anti-E and anti-e, one exception, known to be an extramarital child, was found.

Wiener (177) summarized the results of his studies on the inheritance of Rh in 1346 families (some of them included in the above figures), and finds only two exceptions, apparently illegitimate, to the rules of inheritance. The Rh blood groups may therefore be used in questions of disputed parentage, interchange of infants, etc.

The above description does not by any means exhaust the complexity of the inheritance of the Rh blood groups. It is impossible to sum-

* Some workers always write the "most probable genotype" for any given set of reactions. Thus some would write CDe/cDE (or R_1R_2) for the blood which gave positive serological reactions with anti-C, anti-D, anti-E, and anti-c. It is obvious that this involves some guesswork, and that such genotypes cannot always be correct. Thus the e antigen written in this case, might actually be missing, and the genotype might be CDE/cDE (Rh_zRh_2). It still seems better to the present author to write only what is actually found.

marize these complexities here. The book by Race and Sanger (141) offers a clear and readable account.

The Rh series of genes, like the MNS series, are carried on a different
pair of chromosomes from the ABO series, and consequently no genetic
linkage between them is observed.

5. Forensic Applications of Rh

The Rh blood groups can also be used in forensic medicine. Let
us consider the exclusion of paternity of a falsely-accused man. As in
the ABO and MNS systems, there are certain combinations of accused
man, mother, and child that show the accused man is not in fact the
father of the child. Such combinations can be compactly summarized
(25) in a table such as Table 5-18.

The numbers indicate phenotypes of children which if born to a mother
of the type indicated to the left, exclude the paternity of a man of Rh
type indicated at the top.

This table assumes that the tests are done with the usual four antisera,
anti-C (anti-rh'), anti-D (anti-Rh_0), anti-E (anti-rh''), and anti-c (anti-
rh'). Only a few laboratories are equipped to make more elaborate tests
than these, and they will not need the assistance of a table in deciding
whether the results exclude paternity. It is also assumed in constructing
this table that the Ry gene is absent in the population concerned. It is
in fact probably present in most European populations, but at such a
low frequency that it would contribute very little to the chances of excluding paternity. Consequently the phenotype CdE/C (R_yR'), which
is number 10 in a complete listing of the 12 phenotypes distinguishable
with 4 sera, is omitted in Table 5-18. No *exclusions* depending on an assumed absence of Ry are included, however.

Finally, phenotypes of children which, on these assumptions, could
not be born to mothers of a given phenotype are not included in the table.

The numbers given the phenotypes, which are here expressed in both
systems of notation, along the left hand side of the table and at the top,
are the key to the phenotypes which these numbers designate in the body
of the table (see Table 5-18).

6. Possibilities of Isoimmunization in Rh Series

Although the first cases of erythroblastosis to be elucidated were due
to the production by the mother of anti-D due to stimulus from a D-
positive fetus, and the cases of transfusion reaction explained on the
basis of Rh were due to the same antibody, it is nevertheless possible, in

TABLE 5-18

Phenotypes of Children Establishing Non-Paternity in Various Combinations of Mothers and Alleged Fathers (25)

Phenotype of mother	Phenotype of alleged father									
	1 rh cde	2 Rh" cdE	3 Rh_0 cDe	4 Rh_2 cDE	5 Rh'rh Cde/c	6 Rh'Rh" CdE/c	7 Rh_1rh CDe/c	9 Rh'Rh' Cde/C	11 Rh_1Rh_1 CDe/C	12 Rh_1Rh_2 CDE/C
1. rh cde	2,3,4,5,7,8	3,4,5,7,8	2,4,5,7,8	5,7,8	2,3,4,7,8	3,4,7,8	2,4,8	1,2,3,4,7,8	1,2,3,4,8	1,2,3,4
2. Rh" cdE	3,4,5,6,7,8	3,4,5,6,7,8	5,6,7,8	5,6,7,8	3,4,7,8	3,4,7,8	—	1,2,3,4,7,8	1,2,3,4	1,2,3,4
3. Rh_0 cDe	2,4,5,7,8	5,7,8	2,4,5,7,8	5,7,8	2,4,8	—	2,4,8	1,2,3,4,8	1,2,3,4,8	1,2,3,4
4. Rh_2 cDE	5,6,7,8	5,6,7,8	5,6,7,8	5,6,7,8	—	—	—	1,2,3,4	1,2,3,4	1,2,3,4
5. Rh'rh Cde/c	2,3,4,6,7,8,9,11,12	3,4,7,8,9,11,12	2,4,6,8,9,11,12	9,11,12	2,3,4,6,7,8,11,12	3,4,7,8,11,12	2,4,6,8,12	1,2,3,4,6,7,8,11,12	1,2,3,4,6,8,12	1,2,3,4
6. Rh'Rh" CdE/c	4,7,8,9,11,12	4,7,8,9,11,12	9,11,12	9,11,12	4,7,8,11,12	4,7,8,11,12	—	2,4,7,8,11,12	2,4	2,4
7. Rh_1rh CDe/c	2,4,6,8,9,11,12	9,11,12	2,4,6,8,9,11,12	9,11,12	2,4,6,8,12	—	2,4,6,8,12	1,2,3,4,6,8,12	1,2,3,4,6,8,12	1,2,3,4
8. Rh_1Rh_2 CDE/c	9,11,12	9,11,12	9,11,12	9,11,12	—	—	—	1,2,3,4	1,2,3,4	1,2,3,4
9. Rh'Rh' Cde/C	6,7,8,9,11,12	7,8,9,11,12	6,8,9,11,12	9,11,12	6,7,8,11,12	7,8,11,12	6,8,12	5,6,7,8,11,12	5,6,7,8,12	5,6,7,8
11. Rh_1Rh_1 CDe/C	6,8,9,11,12	9,11,12	6,8,9,11,12	9,11,12	6,8,12	—	6,8,12	5,6,7,8,12	5,6,7,8,12	5,6,7,8
12. Rh_1Rh_2 CDE/C	9,11,12	9,11,12	9,11,12	9,11,12	—	—	—	5,6,7,8	5,6,7,8	5,6,7,8

some cases, for an individual who does not possess one of the other Rh factors to be immunized to it, and to produce anti-Rh antibodies. It will therefore be understood that incompatibility in regard to any one of the Rh factors, even in regard to one of the "Rh-negative" factors, c, d, or e, may result in sensitization and possible transfusion reaction and/or erythroblastois. However, sensitization to the other Rh factors is even less common than to D, and even there, it will be remembered, it is the exception rather than the rule. This may be because of lower antigenicity of the other Rh antigens, which seem to decrease in effectiveness in sensitization in the order D, C, E, c, e, d. It is for this reason that antisera to some of these factors are not routinely available, and although anti-d was reported by Haberman *et al.* (75), Wiener and others (140) doubt its existence. Some of the variants of the Rh factors, which we shall not discuss here, are also evidently better antigens than d.

For descriptions of cases of transfusion reaction and erythroblastosis due to Rh factors, the reader should consult some of the specialized literature cited in the references to this chapter.

7. Rh Antigens

The chemical nature of the Rh antigens is still largely unknown. Studies by the inhibition technique (Chapter 3) have suggested a variety of rather confusing ideas (76,148,53,40,135,162).

8. Anti-Rh Antibodies

The anti-Rh antibody first found in human serum was an agglutinin, active, like other agglutinins, against erythrocytes suspended in saline, but unlike most other blood group antibodies more active at 37°C. than at lower temperatures. It can be absorbed by red cells and eluted from them, and apart from the complicated specificities involved does not differ particularly from other antibodies.

In addition to the saline agglutinin, there is a kind of antibody which does not agglutinate cells suspended in saline, but which does combine with cells containing the proper receptor, and which, when it has combined with cells, renders them insusceptible to agglutination by the ordinary saline agglutinin. It is therefore called blocking antibody (176). Some workers, believing that this antibody acts as it does because it has only one combining group instead of the more usual two, call it "incomplete" antibody (140). The name blocking antibody, which is descriptive of its action and does not assume any unproven theory as to its nature, is preferable (see Chapter 2).

Diamond and Abelson (59) found that the blocking antibody could be induced to agglutinate if it were tested on a slide against a thick suspension of red cells, and Wiener (176) deduced from this that the agglutination was made possible by the residual serum adhering to the red cells. He proposed a form of the test carried out in test tubes. Diamond and Denton (61) showed that agglutination was produced with blocking antibodies if the cells were in bovine serum albumin. Wiener proposed the name "conglutination test" for these procedures, but this has been criticized by British workers in that it involves a change in the original meaning of conglutination (p. 49).

Another approach to the detection of blocking antibodies was the antiglobulin test of Coombs, Mourant, and Race (56). Red cells treated with blocking antibody and washed free of serum proteins were agglutinated by exposure to the serum of a rabbit immunized against human serum globulin. This technic has proven to be more delicate in some cases than the use of cells suspended in albumin.

Morton and Pickles (125) found that if Rh-positive cells were treated with trypsin, they became agglutinable by blocking antibodies. There is now a large literature on the action of enzymes on the agglutinability of erythrocytes. The mechanism is still not fully understood. It has been shown that the enzyme combines with the cells, and the effect is one on the cells and not on the antibody, although peptides that might be liberated by the proteolytic enzymes used have not been demonstrated (137,138,136,117). The subject has been reviewed by Springer (158).

D. OTHER BLOOD GROUP SYSTEMS

In addition to the three blood group systems just described, a number of others are now known. Blood grouping has become a specialty in itself, and it does not seem wise to attempt to give all the newer knowledge here. A good summary of the information up to about 1962 will be found in the book by Race and Sanger (141). Instead of trying to summarize the facts about the blood group systems discovered since 1940, I shall content myself with a brief account of Xg, which is interesting because it is the first example of a sex-linked blood group system. In other words, the locus at which the genes determining these hemagglutinogens occurs is on the X chromosome.

It was discovered in 1962 (115) that an antibody discovered in crossmatching tests on a patient in Grand Rapids defined a new antigen whose occurrence, unlike that of all the other blood group antigens so far discovered, was not independent of sex. This antigen was named Xg^a, the antibody anti-Xg^a, the phenotypes designated as Xg(a+) and Xg(a—): and the gene responsible for the antigen Xg^a was designated as Xg^a, and the one responsible for the thus far silent allele as Xg.

The results of the tests on the original 342 random-sample ("Caucasian") bloods were:

	Male	Female
Xg(a+)	95	167
Xg(a—)	59	21

It does not take a knowledge of statistics to see that the difference in the incidence of positives in the two sexes is significant. From the nomogram in Chapter 17, we find that the probability of such a distribution arising from random sampling is about 10^{-8}, or one in one hundred million.

The inheritance of a sex-linked blood group gene follows certain rules, unfamiliar to most blood group workers, but familiar to geneticists. From the mating positive × positive there can be no negative daughters; from the mating positive male × negative female, all sons have to be negative and all daughters positive; from the mating negative male × positive female, all sorts of children are possible. All of these predictions were found to be fulfilled by the data that Race and Sanger (141) proceeded to acquire.

Being on the X chromosome, the Xg gene should be linked in inheritance with the other sex-linked conditions known in man, such as hemophilia and color blindness, and this has been found to be so.

The principal value seen for the Xg blood group system so far is that it will facilitate the mapping (determining the order in the chromosome of the various loci) of the X chromosome of man.

E. GENERAL CONSIDERATIONS

1. Number of Blood Group Specific Receptors (Epitopes) per Erythrocyte

It is still not exactly known how many specific combining sites of any particular specificity are present on an erythrocyte. Before we discuss the evidence, however, a few remarks are in order. The erythrocyte is often thought of as a bag of hemoglobin enclosed by a thin membrane (stroma) which contains all the blood group (and other) antigens. Actually, the cell would be better visualized as a sponge (the stroma), filled with hemoglobin. To be sure the sponge diminishes in density towards the center of the cell, and to be sure the cell has the osmotic functions associated with a cell membrane. But there is probably no point in the interior of the erythrocyte where membrane abruptly leaves off and cell contents begin.

There is no reason to think that all the blood group antigens are on the "surface" of the cell; it seems more likely that they are rather uniformly distributed throughout the stroma. It is probable, of course, that those in the interior are less accessible to antibodies. Boyd, Bhatia, Diamond, and Matsubara (30) found evidence that when the chemical potential of an antibody is increased enough, the interior antigenic sites become accessible, though with corresponding difficulty.

Boursnell, Coombs, and Rizk (10), using a serum marked by the introduction of I^{131} into its proteins, found a value of 5.5×10^3 for the number of Rh (D) sites on an Rh positive erythrocyte, and about 5×10^5 Paul-Bunnel (see p. 198) sites. Masouredis (117), in a series of beautiful investigations, has found similar values. Filitti-Wurmser et al., (65), by observing the number of erythrocytes agglutinated by sera containing known amounts of anti-B agglutinin, as determined by the antibody nitrogen fixed to B stroma, calculated that there are 5×10^5 B-combining groups on a group B erythrocyte. Kabat (83) criticised these values as being impossibly high, showing, by certain calculations, that they would imply that the red cell contains an impossibly high content of blood group substance. Kabat's calculations, however, seem to have been based on a confusion between the number of *molecules* of group substance, and the number of *combining groups*. The latter can of course be much greater than the former, since the combining group, by Kabat's own showing, probably consists merely of six or so monosaccharide units.

Boyd, Bhatia, Diamond, and Matsubara (30), using I^{131} labeled anti-A lectin, found evidence that as many as 10×10^6 molecules of anti-A could combine with a single erythrocyte, and did not succeed in finding an upper limit to the number. Greenbury, Moore and Nunn (74), using I^{131} labeled antibody, estimated the number of A sites on an A_1 erythrocyte as of the order of 10^6. Until disproved experimentally, these high values will have to stand.

2. Ontogenetic Development of Group-Specific Factors

Agglutinogens A, B, M, and N are detectable in newborn infants, and, after the first few months, in the fetus. The A and B factors, at any rate, seem to increase in strength after birth, and may again become weaker in old age, but they seem always to be strong enough in newborn infants to allow the blood groups to be determined without error if strong sera are used, immune sera being valuable here as a check. Moureau has done the MN grouping without difficulty on fetuses of various ages, the youngest being nine weeks. The Rh antigens have been found well developed in fetuses (140). Others of the blood groups have been found to be readily demonstrable in cord blood. On the whole, consequently, there seems to be no reason not to undertake the blood grouping of infants of any age.

Only about one-half of newborn infants have demonstrable isoagglutinins. The agglutinins in newborn infants are apparently those of the mother; at least the infant never has an agglutinin capable of acting on the mother's cell. These agglutinins disappear shortly after birth and are later replaced by the infant's own agglutinins, so that the group becomes complete in this sense also between the third and twelfth month after birth.

3. Forensic Applications of Blood Groups: General

Our knowledge of the exact mode of inheritance of the blood groups gives them considerable importance in the solution of such problems as disputed parentage, interchanged infants, and the diagnosis of twins. The individualization of human blood which they made possible also enables them to be applied to problems of identity and criminological investigations involving blood stains. A brief suggestion of these applications has been given above. For further details the reader should consult references such as (154,173,176,140,147).

It is of interest to know the chances that a wrongly accused man will be able to establish nonpaternity by blood grouping tests, and such calculations were made by a number of workers, including the present writer, in the early days of the subject (11,154,173). The discovery of the newer blood group systems has considerably increased the chances then calculated, as is shown by Table 5-19 (24,25).

The calculations are based partly on English gene frequencies, which, however, are sufficiently close to those in the United States for our purposes. The figures under the heading "first level" are calculated on the assumption that the tests are done without all the sometimes hard-to-obtain sera being available. In the case of the ABO system this assumes anti-A and anti-B are available (in this case the second level tests are not different); in the case of MNS, first level testing means merely anti-M and anti-N; for Rh, merely anti-D; and for each of the other systems merely one of the two possible sera (in the case of the secretor phenome-

TABLE 5-19

Chances in Per Cent of an Accused Man's Being Exonerated of a False Charge of Paternity

Blood group system	Exclusion by each system (first level)	Combined exclusion (first level)	Exclusion by each system (second level)	Combined exclusion (second level)
1. ABO	16.5	16.5	16.5	16.5
2. MNS	18.7	32.1	23.9	36.5
3. Rh	1.8	33.3	25.6	52.7
4. Kell	4.2	36.1	4.7	55.0
5. Lutheran	3.3	38.2	3.3	56.4
6. Secretion	1.9	39.4	1.9	57.3
7. Duffy	5.0	42.4	18.3	65.1
8. Kidd	2.8	44.1	18.7	71.6

non it means assuming the secreting gene is a dominant). For the second level tests it is assumed that for the MNS tests an anti-S serum is also available, for Rh also anti-C, anti-E, and anti-c, for Kell also anti-k, for Duffy also anti-Fy^b, and for Kidd also anti-Jk^b. Distinguishing the subgroups of A and AB would increase the chances slightly in the ABO system (see, however, p. 265); addition of an anti-s in the MNS system would increase the chances to about 31.5 per cent; and addition of anti-c would increase the chances in the Rh system by about 0.7 per cent.

Obviously, the more complete testing greatly increases the chances of exclusion. The MNS system is the most useful, with Rh next, followed by the Kidd, Duffy, and ABO systems in that order. The combined chances are now over 70 per cent. No matter how many systems are added, of course, the chances will never equal 100 per cent. Even if the ABO, MNS, and Rh tests alone are done, however, the chances are well over 50 per cent.

Similar calculations relating to the exclusion of maternity, detection of interchange of infants, and diagnosis of monozygotic ("identical") twins, will be found in the references cited.

4. Blood Groups and Race

Thus far no serological property of the blood has been found which is regularly present in one race and absent from all others.* In view of

---

* This statement is still essentially true, but it should be noted that there has been discovered a gene in the Duffy series, tentatively designated merely as Fy, which is very common in Negroes and extremely rare in white Americans and English (151), and that the "Diego" antigen is fairly common in some American Indian tribes and has not yet been found in unmixed whites (106).

the enormous amount of mixture which went into making the present human "races," it is not likely that any such character will ever be found. It was shown by Hirszfeld and Hirszfeld (79), however, that the proportion of a population belonging to one or another blood group may vary in different ethnic groups. By following up this lead, serologists and anthropologists have been able to refine and correct the ideas of race previously held, and the subject has become a specialty of its own, with a large literature. The present author (11) published a summary, nearly complete, of the blood group studies on different populations published up to June, 1938; large amounts of material have accumulated since then, particularly in regard to the newer blood groups. Most of this material is summarized in the book by Mourant (126), who has also discussed the anthropological implications. The present author has written a book which will serve as an introduction to the subject and which contains tables of selected data (19). From the references the interested reader will be able to obtain a key to the literature.*

It would be out of place here to make any attempt to summarize this already large subject. We may merely mention that on the basis of studies of blood groups and other genetic traits a division of mankind into the following basic races has been proposed (174,19): (1) Early Europeans, (2) Europeans, (3) Africans, (4) Asians, (5) Americans (the aboriginal inhabitants), (6) Australians (the aborigines). Further refinements permit subdivision of these categories: a subdivision intermediate beween European and Asian which is to include the populations of Pakistan and India has since been proposed (34).

5. Gene Frequencies

In applications of blood groups to anthropology, in the calculations of the expected proportion of different types of offspring in various matings, and in calculating the probable usefulness of blood groups in cases of disputed parentage, it is necessary to know, not only the frequency of the various phenotypes in the population, but the frequency of the various genes which go to make up these phenotypes, These frequencies can usually be estimated by more or less simple methods.

Consider the simplest case, a gene D which is dominant over d. We then have in the population two phenotypes; D+, which consists of genotypes DD and Dd, and D—, which consists merely of the genotype dd. If the individuals of the population mate at random (in so far as these genotypes are concerned), it is easy to show that the frequencies

---

* For a popular discussion, see *Races and People,* by W. C. Boyd and I. Asimov (29).

of the two phenotypes are $D^2 + 2Dd$ and d^2, where D and d represent the frequencies of the genes D and d, respectively. From this we see that the frequency of the gene $d = \sqrt{(D-)}$, and since the sum of the two frequencies must equal 1, the frequency of $D = 1 - d$. This result is exact if the population is in genetic equilibrium and our sample is large enough to be representative. It can be in error if our sample of D− individuals happens to be atypical. It can be shown mathematically that $d = \sqrt{(D-)}$ is the best estimate of the frequency of d under the circumstances.

If D is not dominant, or to put it in serological terms, if we have both an anti-D and an anti-d serum, the situation is different. Now we can classify the population into three phenotypes, D, Dd, and d (just as in the case of M and N, each phenotype corresponds to just one genotype) and the frequencies of these types, in terms of the gene frequencies D and d, are

$$D = D^2$$
$$Dd = 2Dd$$
$$d = d^2$$

We can estimate the gene frequencies by the square-root method as before and obtain $D = \sqrt{(D)}$, $d = \sqrt{(d)}$, but we may find that these two frequencies do not add up to one, showing that our sample was not representative, or that the population is not in genetic equilibrium. It can be shown that these estimates are not in this case the best possible, and it is better to note instead that each individual of type Dd has one gene for D and one for d, and each individual of type D has two D genes, and each d individual two d genes, so we can write

$$D = D + Dd/2, \, d = d + Dd/2$$

These estimates are just the result of counting up the genes, and are consequently the best possible, as can be shown mathematically. They are used for estimating the frequency of the M,N genes, and the frequency of other genes in cases where three phenotypes corresponding to three genotypes are distinguished, as in the MN system.

In the case of the ABO blood groups, we have three allelic genes defining six genotypes but only four phenotypes. Hence the direct gene-counting method does not work, and we have to make an estimate analogous to that of the simple square-root method described above. If we let the frequencies of the A, B, and O genes be represented by p, q, and r, as is customary, we can put (see following page)

$$p = 1 - \sqrt{(B + O)}$$
$$q = 1 - \sqrt{(A + O)}$$
$$r = \sqrt{(O)}$$

These estimates are also not the best possible, and it is better to correct them by applying formulas due to Bernstein (8)

$$p' = p(1 + D/2)$$
$$q' = q(1 + D/2)$$
$$r' = (r + D/2)(1 + D/2)$$

where $D = 1 - (p + q + r)$. These corrected frequencies are nearly the best, but can be improved slightly by Fisher's method of maximum likelihood (163).

In the MNS and Rh systems, and all systems where more than three alleles are involved, the problem of estimation of gene frequencies becomes more complicated. Square-root formulas analogous to those for the ABO groups can be obtained, but they do not give the best estimates, and using them in preference to mathematically better estimates is often equivalent, in so far as precision of estimate is concerned, to throwing away 20 or 30 per cent of the determinations. Modern blood grouping is sufficiently complicated and difficult so that few workers would care to do this. This means that for exact work the gene frequency estimates must be made by the method of maximum likelihood, but this method is too complicated to be presented here. It was applied to the Rh system by Fisher in two fundamental papers (66,67), and the present author has presented a somewhat simplified application of it to the MNS system (22) and to the Rh system (23).

6. Related Factors in Animals

Antigens similar to the A and B in man occur in some animals (72) (see Table 5-1). Such antigens are found, for example, in the saliva of the horse. In this animal A and B, together, alone, or neither, may occur, thus establishing four groups, probably hereditary, similar to those in man; but the antigens are not present also in the blood, as they are in man (71). In other animals the erythrocytes contain similar, but distinct, antigens. Certain workers have separated A and B into various hypothetical fractions (see 11) by comparing them with such related antigens. To this hypothetical fractionation the same objection is possible as in the case of related bacterial antigens (see Chapter 4), although in some cases the fractions may correspond to something real.

The greatest interest for students of human evolution attaches, of course, to the question of blood group factors in the apes and monkeys, and considerable work has been done on this line (for instance, 96). It has been found that in the higher primates substances indistinguishable from the A and B of man may be found; in the gorilla (50) and the monkeys a substance reacting with the anti-B agglutinin, but somewhat different from B, is found. See Fig. 5-10.

From this it is evident that properties related to A and B are by no means restricted to mankind, but are widely distributed through the animal kingdom. There is a striking analogy with the Forssman hapten and with the specific carbohydrates of certain bacteria. Since there is reason to think (see Chapter 3) that the possible chemical variety in the carbohydrate series (to which these antigens all belong, at least in part) is less than in the protein series, this may account for the more

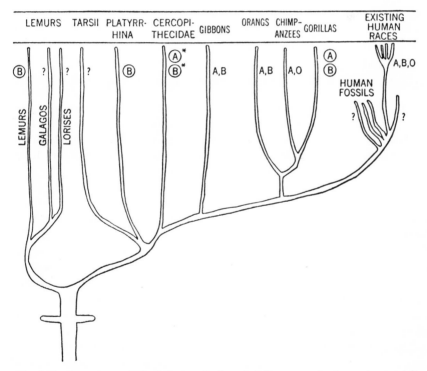

Fig. 5-10. Occurrence of blood factors O, A, and B in man and other primates (after Landsteiner). Encircled A and B indicate A-like and B-like antigens reacting with human anti-A and anti-B agglutinins. Encircled A and B with asterisk indicate A-like and B-like antigens found in the tissues and secretions.

marked inter-species reactions observed also in the present instance. The probability of two carbohydrates taken at random being serologically similar would be greater in general than that for two unrelated proteins (93). A carbohydrate which is capable of reacting with either anti-A or anti-B has been isolated from *Ascaris* (130) and other helminths (131).

It has been found that the higher primates also possess blood structures capable of reacting with antisera for M, but the degree of reaction is often quite different with blood from the same animal when different anti-M sera are used. It does not seem that the M factor is ever lacking in any individuals of a primate species in which it is found, indicating a difference in the genetic mechanism from that operating in man (97,171). (See however (105).) It is of interest to recall that it was in the course of the study of the M antigen in primates that Landsteiner and Wiener discovered Rh (176).

Many animals other than man have blood groups of their own, and there is now a large literature on this subject. The topic has been reviewed by Dujarric de la Rivière and Eyquem (63) and by Stone and Irwin (164).

7. Function of the Group Substances: Blood Groups and Disease

All persons produce and secrete mucin, and these secretions are probably essential for the normal working of the body and for the life of the individual. As yet, however, we have little idea of their exact physiological function. However, some recent work on the connection of blood groups and disease has provided some very suggestive leads.

A search for possible connections between blood groups and certain diseases began very early (11), but until recently there existed no adequate body of data to show that individuals of any particular blood group were more susceptible than other persons to any particular disease. Difficulties of examining enough patients to amass numbers that would be statistically significant, difficulties in finding sufficiently homogeneous populations to test, difficulty in finding suitable controls, and the swamping of significant data by large masses of nonsignificant data, were among the causes of this situation. Some authors even went so far as to state there was no connection between blood groups and disease.

The situation has been radically changed in recent years (1,133,102). Aird *et al.* (1) have demonstrated that if an individual belongs to blood group O, he has about a 35 per cent better chance of developing peptic ulceration (requiring treatment in a hospital) than individuals of any other blood group, and individuals of blood group A have a definitely greater chance of developing gastric carcinoma. No similar relation was found between blood groups and carcinoma of the colon, rectum, breast, and lung. Pike and Dickins (134) demonstrated that toxemia of pregnancy was significantly more frequent in women of blood group O. Struthers (165) found a significant excess of group A in children dying of bronchopneumonia.

The present writer (38,55) found correlations between disease and the Rh blood groups.

The relation of the Rh blood groups to hemolytic disease of the newborn has already been discussed. In this case it is not solely the blood group of the individual which predisposes him to a certain disease, but his blood group taken together with the blood group of his mother.

Evidently blood groups do have a definite connection with susceptibility to certain diseases, and there are probably therefore forces of natural selection acting to affect the various blood group frequencies. Aird *et al.* (1) point out that it is, however, possible that the selective forces may be acting to stabilize the existing blood group frequencies in cases where the heterozygotes for a gene have an advantage, while the homozygotes are at a disadvantage, as in the case of peptic ulcer and group O. In fact, students of human evolution are beginning to believe that this advantage of the heterozygotes, predicted long ago by Fisher and Ford, plays an important role in stabilizing the frequencies of many genes, not only genes which are only slightly disadvantageous like O, but definitely disadvantageous genes like the one for sickle-cell anemia (20).

It is not too easy to devise a hypothetical explanation for these new facts. Aird *et al.* suggest that the simplest explanation of the excess of group A in gastric carcinoma might be that the group A substance is primarily slightly carcinogenic. It is a fact that large amounts of group substances occur in the stomach (Table 5-8). Or it might be that the other group substances are more protective against carcinoma than is group A substance. The excess of group A in bronchopneumonia might have quite a different explanation; in earlier editions of this book it was pointed out that the serological relationship of group A substance to some bacterial polysaccharides (in particular to type XIV pneumococcus) might mean that individuals of group A would have more difficulty than others in manufacturing antibodies to such bacteria. The author (Dr. A. E. Mourant) of an unsigned leading article (102) in the *British Medical Journal* suggests that it should be investigated whether the chemical and serological similarity between gonadotropic hormone and blood group A substance has any bearing on the hormonal changes which occur in toxemia.

It seems to the present writer that the simplest explanation of the observed correlations would be based on the fact that most (perhaps all) genes are pleiomorphic (affect more than one characteristic of an organism). Thus the gene A, which produces the antigen-A in the red cells, might have as one of its other effects a lowering of the resistance of the individual, or of his stomach at least, to the virus or viruses that cause gastric carcinoma.

8. Blood Groups of Ancient Human Remains

Antigens A and B are much more stable than most (protein) antigens. It is comparatively easy to demonstrate A and B in dried tissue, boiled erythrocytes, or tissues which have been preserved in formaldehyde. These facts led Boyd and Boyd (31,32) to attempt to demonstrate A and B in mummified human remains. The attempt seemed to be successful. These workers tested more than 300 specimens, mostly from Egypt in the Old World and from Mexico and Peru in the New World. The technique, though exacting and at times even exasperating, was simple in theory; pulverized dried tissue (usually muscle) was mixed with carefully titrated anti-A and anti-B agglutinins and the mixture tested after a suitable interval for evidence of removal of one or more of the agglutinins. Removal of anti-B was considered to indicate the presence in the tissue of the B antigen, removal of anti-A the presence of A. Removal of neither suggested either that the specimen came from an individual of group O or that any antigens originally present had deteriorated. Removal of both anti-A and anti-B suggested group AB or nonspecific destruction or removal of agglutinins or antibodies in general.

The results obtained were on the whole in line with the present distribution of the A and B antigens in human races, confirming the antiquity of the ABO blood group system. (Some authors had suggested, amazingly, that the A and B genes were of recent origin.) The B antigen was apparently found in pre-Columbian specimens from Mexico (167), a finding which, if ever confirmed, might support the suggestion, made on other grounds, that the B gene was eliminated in the aboriginal inhabitants of America by natural selection (26). This subject has been reviewed by Smith (157).

9. Obtaining Sera for Blood Grouping

Originally it was customary to use serum from any individual of group B as an anti-A reagent, and serum from any A as an anti-B. This practice led to many errors, however, as the agglutinin in the serum of many individuals is not strong enough for reliable routine use, and in particular the serum of some group B individuals reacts very weakly or not at all with bloods of subgroups A_2 and A_2B. The best reagents are prepared by stimulating donors of groups B and A, preferably with purified A and B substances, as recommended by Witebsky, Klendshoj, and McNeil (184,16,39). This method gives good results in about half the volunteers. Good sera can also be produced by injecting rabbits with A and B cells and absorbing (16). Anti-A and anti-B sera are available commercially.

Agglutinins for M and N are rarely encountered in human serum, and to produce them it is generally necessary to immunize rabbits and absorb the diluted serum with M and N cells. Descriptions of the somewhat exacting technic have been given by Wiener (173), Boyd (154,16), and Race and Sanger (140). Anti-M and anti-N sera are available commercially.

No usable anti-S has yet been produced in animals; the only practical sources are the sera of human beings who have become immunized to this antigen by transfusion or pregnancy. Good anti-S sera are not common.

The only practical source of anti-Rh sera is also the serum of sensitized individuals. Such sera are usually discovered in laboratories where the abnormal agglutinins in the sera of patients are routinely checked and identified. Satisfactory anti-C, anti-D, anti-E, and anti-c (and occasionally anti-e) sera are available commercially.

Few of the other agglutinins used in blood groupings are available commercially. The researcher is mostly dependent upon good fortune in running across them in the serum of patients, and upon the kindness of other workers in the field.

Some of the agglutinins, in particular certain examples of anti-Rh sera, have been made by the deliberate stimulation of volunteers with incompatible blood. This method has not been successful in the case of anti-d and various other agglutinins such as anti-S.

10. Lectins

It was discovered by Boyd (17,18) and Renkonen (144) independently that saline extracts of the seeds of certain plants specifically agglutinate erythrocytes of certain blood groups. Some of these extracts are now widely used, and some of them are available commercially. The substances responsible for this specific hemagglutination are called lectins (42).

Strong anti-A agglutinins are found in certain lima beans (41,42), and the legumes *Vicia cracca* (12) and *Dolichos biflorus* (8a). The latter reacts so much more strongly with A_1 than with A_2 that it is virtually specific for A_1. A powerful and specific anti-A has been found in the expressed body fluids of the snail *Otala lactea* (35,36). An anti-N has been found in *Vicia graminea* (132) and, more recently, in *Bauhinia purpurea,* var. *alba* (112,37). An anti-M is on the market, prepared apparently from *Iberis amara.* The anti-N of *Vicia graminea* is actually better than the absorbed anti-N prepared from immune rabbit serum and would doubtless be used routinely if more of the tiny seeds of this South American plant were available. This lectin has already proven valuable in clarifying the MN system in chimpanzees (105). The anti-N of Bauhinia is not quite as good, but may nevertheless come into routine use because the seeds are available in many parts of the world (37).

No good anti-B lectin is routinely available. Extracts of seeds of *Sophora japonica* agglutinate bloods of group B more strongly than group A, but react too strongly with A to be satisfactory as a laboratory anti-B reagent (88). *Eunonymus europeus* extracts contain anti-B and anti-H (156). *Marasmius oreades,* which sometimes furnishes a satisfactory, though weak, anti-B, is a small mushroom not commercially available (64). The best plant anti-B is said to be that from *Bandeiraea simplicifolia* (113), although the samples of these seeds I have tested have been disappointing.

It has recently been discovered (54) that extracts of *S. japonica* can be converted into satisfactory anti-B reagents by inhibiting the anti-A activity with privine [2-(1-naphthylmethyl)-imidazoline].

Perhaps because of the absence of a good available anti-B, lectins are not routinely used in the determination of the ABO blood groups, in spite of the fact that satisfactory anti-A is available from several plants. However, the anti-A_1 of *Dolichos biflorus* and the anti-H of *Ules europeus* make an ideal combination for the routine determination of the subgroups of A and AB (44), as shown in Table 5-10. Anti-A lectins, particularly that from lima beans, have had a number of applications in special experiments where a large amount of anti-A agglutinin is needed (3). Testing for the H substance in saliva by inhibition of the anti-H of *Ulex* (43) has become the preferred method of diagnosing secretors and nonsecretors (Table 5-20). Lectins have been used by Morgan and Watkins (123) to show that the blood group antigen of group AB individuals is not a mixture of A and B substances, but a unique molecule containing both A and B specificities.

There is now a large literature on lectins. The subject has been re-

TABLE 5-20

Inhibition of Anti-H (Ulex) by Salivas of Secretors and Nonsecretors (43)

Blood groups	Reaction of Ulex lectin with group O cells Saliva, diluted				
	1:2	1:4	1:8	1:16	1:32
A (secretor)	0	0	0	0	0
A (nonsecretor)	++++	++++	++++	++++	++++
B (secretor)	0	0	±	+	++
O (secretor)	0	0	0	0	0
O (nonsecretor)	++++	++++	++++	++++	++++

viewed by Krüpe (89), Mäkelä (112), Saint-Paul (149), Boyd (27,28), and Tobiska (168).

General References

The best book on the blood groups is *The Blood Groups in Man,* by R. R. Race and R. Sanger (141). The anthropological data have been summarized by Mourant; *The Distribution of the Human Blood Groups,* Blackwell, 1954; *The ABO Blood Groups,* Blackwell, 1958.

References

1. Aird, I., *et al., Brit. Med. J.,* 11, 315 (1954).
2. Aminoff, D., W. T. J. Morgan, and W. M. Watkins, *Biochem. J. (London),* 46, 426 (1950).
3. Atwood, K. C., and S. L. Scheinberg, *J. Cellular Comp. Physiol.,* 52, Suppl., 1, 97 (1958).
4. Aubert, E. F., K. E. Boorman, B. E. Dodd, and J. F. Loutit, *Brit. Med. J.,* 1, 659 (1942).
5. Baronowski, T., E. Lisowska, A. Mordwiecki, E. Romanowska, and K. Strózecka, *Arch. Imm. i Terap. Dóswiadezalneg.,* 7, 15–27 (1959).
6. Bendich, A., E. A. Kabat, and A. E. Bezer, *J. Exptl. Med.,* 83, 485 (1946).
7. Bernstein, F., *Z. indukt. Abstammungs. u. Verebungsl.,* 37, 237 (1925).
8. Bernstein, F., *Z. indukt. Abstammungs. u. Verebungsl.,* 56, 233 (1930).
8a. Bird, G. W. G., *Current Sci. (India),* 20, 298 (1951).
9. Boorman, K. E., *et al., Brit. Med. J.,* 11, 535 (1942).
10. Boursnell, J. C., R. R. A. Coombs, and V. Rizk, *Biochem. J.,* 55, 745 (1953).
11. Boyd, W. C., *Tabulae Biologicae,* 17, 113 (1939).
12. Boyd, W. C., *J. Immunol.,* 37, 65 (1939).
13. Boyd, W. C., *Clinics,* 1, 1536 (1943).
14. Boyd, W. C., *Ann. N. Y. Acad. Sci.,* 46, 927 (1946).
15. Boyd, W. C., *J. Criminal Law Criminol.,* 36, 455 (1946).
16. Boyd, W. C., *J. Lab. Clin. Med.,* 32, 1275 (1947).

17. Boyd, W. C., *Fundamentals of Immunology*, 2nd ed., Interscience, New York, 1947, p. 40.
18. Boyd, W. C., *Am. J. Phys. Anthropol.*, **7**, 519 (1949).
19. Boyd, W. C., *Genetics and The Races of Man*, Little Brown, Boston, 1950.
20. Boyd, W. C., *Am. J. Phys. Anthropol.*, **13**, 37 (1955).
21. Boyd, W. C., *J. Immunol.*, **65**, 281 (1950).
22. Boyd, W. C., *Am. J. Human Genet.*, **6**, 1 (1954).
23. Boyd, W. C., *Am. J. Human Genet.*, **6**, 303 (1954).
24. Boyd, W. C., *Am. J. Human Genet.*, **6**, 1, 426 (1954).
25. Boyd, W. C., *Am. J. Human Genet.*, **7**, 229 (1955).
26. Boyd, W. C., *J. Med. Educ.*, **34**, 398–399 (1959).
27. Boyd, W. C., *Introduction to Immunochemical Specificity*, Interscience, New York, 1962.
28. Boyd, W. C., *Vox. Sang.*, **8**, 1–32 (1963).
29. Boyd, W. C., and I. Asimov, *Races and People*, Abelard-Schuman, New York, 1955.
30. Boyd, W. C., H. M. Bhatia, M. A. Diamond, and S. Matsubara, *J. Immunol.*, **89**, 463–470 (1962).
31. Boyd, W. C., and L. G. Boyd, *J. Immunol.*, **26**(6), 489 (1934).
32. Boyd, W. C., and L. G. Boyd, *J. Immunol.*, **32**, 307 (1937).
33. Boyd, W. C., and L. G. Boyd, *J. Immunol.*, **33**, 159 (1937).
34. Boyd, W. C., and L. G. Boyd, *Am. J. Phys. Anthropol.*, **12**, 393 (1954).
35. Boyd, W. C., and R. Brown, *Nature*, **208**, 593 (1965).
36. Boyd, W. C., R. Brown, and L. G. Boyd, *J. Immunol.*, **96**, 301 (1966).
37. Boyd, W. C., D. L. Everhart, and M. H. McMaster, *J. Immunol.*, **81**, 414 (1958).
38. Boyd, W. C., M. Heisler, and E. Orowan, *Nature*, **190**, 1123–1124 (1961).
39. Boyd, W. C., and F. C. Lowell, *Blood*, **1**, 584 (1946).
40. Boyd, W. C., M. H. McMaster, and E. Waszczenko-Zacharczenko, *Nature*, **184**, 989 (1959).
41. Boyd, W. C., and R. M. Reguera, *J. Immunol.*, **62**, 333 (1949).
42. Boyd, W. C., and E. Shapleigh, *J. Immunol.*, **73**, 226 (1954).
43. Boyd, W. C., and E. Shapleigh, *Blood*, **9**, 1195 (1954).
44. Boyd, W. C., and E. Shapleigh, *J. Lab. Clin. Med.*, **44**, 235 (1954).
45. Boyd, W. C., and E. R., Warshaver, *J. Immunol.*, **50**, 101 (1945).
46. Bray, H. G., H. Henry, and M. Stacey, *Biochem. J. (London)*, **40**, 124 (1946).
47. Broman, B., *Acta Paediat.*, **31**, Supplementum II (1944).
48. Brown, D. H., E. L. Bennet, G. Holzman, and C. Niemann, *Arch. Biochem.*, **13**, 421 (1947).
49. Calvin, M., R. S. Evans, V. Behrendt, and G. Calvin, *Proc. Soc. Exptl. Biol. Med.*, **61**, 416 (1946).
50. Candela, P. B., A. S. Wiener, and L. J. Gross, *Zoologica*, **25**, 513 (1940).
51. Castle, W. B., M. W. Wintrobe, and L. H. Snyder, *Science*, **107**, 27 (1948).
52. Cazal, P., and M. Lalaurie, *Acta Haematol.*, **8**, 73 (1952).
53. Chattoraj, A., and W. C. Boyd, *Nature*, **206**, 837 (1965).
54. Chattoraj, A., and W. C. Boyd, submitted to *Nature* (1965).
55. Cohen, A. S., W. C. Boyd, S. Goldwasser, E. S. Cathcart, and M. Heisler, *Nature*, **200**, 1215 (1963).
56. Coombs, R. R. A., A. E. Mourant, and R. R. Race, *Lancet*, **II**, 15 (1945).
57. DeGowin, E. L., *J. Am. Med. Assoc.*, **108**, 296 (1937).
58. DeGowin, E. L., and C. W. Baldridge, *Am. J. Med. Sci.*, **188**, 555 (1934).

59. Diamond, L. K., N. M. Abelson, *J. Lab. Clin. Med.*, **30**, 204 (1945).
60. Diamond, L. K., K. D. Blackman, and J. M. Baty, *J. Pediat.*, **1**, 269 (1932).
61. Diamond, L. K., and R. L. Denton, *J. Lab. Clin. Med.*, **31**, 821 (1945).
62. Dodd, M. C., N. J. Bigley, and V. B. Geyer, *J. Immunol.*, **90**, 518–525 (1963).
63. Dujarric de la Rivière, and A. Eyquem, *Les Groupes Sanguins Chez Les Animaux*, Flammarion, Paris, 1953.
64. Elo, J., E. Estola, and N. Malmström, *Ann. Med. Exptl. Biol. Fenniae (Helsinki)*, **29**, 297 (1951).
65. Filitti-Wurmser, S., et al., *Ann. Eugen.*, **18**, 183 (1954).
66. Fisher, R. A., *Ann. Eugen.*, **13**, 150 (1946).
67. Fisher, R. A., *Ann. Eugen.*, **13**, 223, 224 (1947).
68. Friedenreich, V., *Deut. Z. ges. gerichtl. Med.*, **25**, 358 (1936).
69. Friedenreich, V., and G. Hartmann, *Z. Immunitätsforsch.*, **92**, 141 (1938).
70. Friedenreich, V., and A. Lavridwen, *Acta Pathol. Microbiol. Scand.*, **38**, 155 (1938).
71. Friedenreich, V., and G. Thyssen, *Comp. rend. soc. biol.*, **126**, 801 (1937).
72. Friedenreich, V., and S. With, *Z. Immunitätsforsch.*, **78**, 152 (1933).
73. Furuhata, T., *Japan Med. World*, **7**, 197 (1927).
74. Greenbury, C. L., D. Moore, and L. A. C. Nunn, *Brit. Soc. Immunol. Abstracts*, Nov. 16, 1963.
75. Haberman, S., J. M. Hill, B. W. Everist, and J. W. Davenport, *Blood*, **3**, 682 (1948).
76. Hackel, E., *Vox. Sang.*, **9**, 56–59 (1964).
77. Hartmann, G., *Group Antigens in Human Organs*, Munksgaard, Copenhagen, 1941.
78. Hirschfeld, J., *Science*, **148**, 968–971 (1965).
79. Hirszfeld, L., and H. Hirszfeld, *Lancet*, **II**, 197, 675 (1919).
80. Hooker, S. B., and L. M. Anderson, *J. Immunol.*, **6**, 419 (1921).
81. Hotta, K., and G. F. Springer, *Sangre*, **9**, 183–187 (1964).
82. Javert, C. T., *Am. J. Obstet. Gynecol.*, **43**, 921 (1942).
83. Kabat, E. A., *Blood Group Substances, Their Chemistry and Immunochemistry*, Academic Press, New York, 1956.
84. Kabat, E. A., H. Baer, R. I. Day, and V. Knaub, *J. Exptl. Med.*, **91**, 433 (1950).
85. Kabat, E. A., A. Bendich, A. E. Bezer, and S. M. Beiser, *J. Exptl. Med.*, **85**, 685 (1947).
86. Keckwick, R. A., and P. L. Mollison, *Vox. Sang.*, **6**, 398–408 (1961).
87. Kosyakov, P. N., *Immunologia, Izoantigeni, Izoantitel*, Izdatel'stvo Meditsina, Moscow, 1965 (Russian).
88. Krüpe, M., *Z. Hyg. Infektionskrankh.*, **318**, 167 (1953).
89. Krüpe, M., *Blutgruppenspezifische Pflanzliche Eiwieszkorper (Phytagglutinine)*, Ferdinand Enke Verlag, Stuttgart, 1956.
90. Landsteiner, K., *Wien. Klin. Wochschr.*, **14**, 1132 (1901).
91. Landsteiner, K., *Münch. med. Wochschr.*, **49**, 1905 (1902).
92. Landsteiner, K., in *The Newer Knowledge of Bacteriology and Immunology*, E. O. Jordan and I. S. Falk, eds., University of Chicago Press, Chicago, 1928.
93. Landsteiner, K., *The Specificity of Serological Reactions*, Harvard University Press, Cambridge, 1945.
94. Landsteiner, K., and P. Levine, *Proc. Soc. Exptl. Biol. Med.*, **24**, 600, 941 (1927).
95. Landsteiner, K., and P. Levine, *J. Exptl. Med.* **47**, 757; **48**, 731 (1928).
96. Landsteiner, K., and C. P. Miller, *J. Exptl. Med.*, **42**, 841, 853, 863 (1925).
97. Landsteiner, K., and A. S. Wiener, *J. Immunol.*, **33**, 19 (1937).
98. Landsteiner, K., and A. S. Wiener, *Proc. Soc. Exptl. Biol. Med.*, **43**, 223 (1940).

99. Landsteiner, K., and A. S. Wiener, *J. Exptl. Med.*, **74**, 309 (1941).
100. Landsteiner, K., and D. H. Witt, *J. Immunol.*, **11**, 221 (1926).
101. Lattes, L., *The Individuality of the Blood in Biology and in Clinical and Forensic Medicine*, Oxford University Press, London, 1932.
102. Leading Article, *Brit. Med. J.*, **11**, 347 (1954).
103. Leskowitz, S., H. V. Vunakis, and E. A. Kabat, *J. Am. Chem. Soc.*, **74**, 5538 (1952).
104. Levine, P., *et al.*, *Am. J. Obstet. Gynecol.*, **42**, 925 (1941).
105. Levine, P., *et al.*, *Am. J. Phys. Anthrop.*, **13**, 29 (1955).
106. Levine, P., *et al.*, *Nature*, **177**, 40 (1956).
107. Levine, P., A. S. Kuhmichel, M. Wigod, and E. Koch, *Proc. Soc. Exptl. Biol. Med.*, **78**, 218 (1951).
108. Levine, P., and J. Mabee, *J. Immunol.*, **8**, 425 (1923).
109. Levine, P., and S. H. Polayes, *Ann. Internal Med.*, **14**, 1903 (1941).
110. Levine, P., and R. E. Stetson, *J. Am. Med. Assoc.*, **113**, 126 (1939).
111. Lombard, J. F., *Massachusetts Practice*, Vol. 3, *Adoption, Illegitimacy and Blood Tests*, Boston Law Book, Boston, 1952.
112. Mäkelä, O., *Studies in Hemagglutinins of Leguminosae Seeds*, Weilin and Göös, Helsinki, 1957.
113. Mäkelä, O., and P. Mäkelä, *Ann. Med. Exptl. Biol. Fenniae (Helsinki)*, **34**, 402 (1956).
114. Mandelbaum, H., *Ann. Internal Med.*, **12**, 1699 (1939).
115. Mann, J. D., A. Cahan, A. G. Gelb, N. Fisher, J. Hamper, P. Tippet, R. Sanger, and R. R. Race, *Lancet*, **I**, 8–10 (1962).
116. Masouredis, S. P., Paper presented at 14th Annual Meeting, Am. Assoc. Blood Banks, Chicago, October 26, 1961.
117. Masouredis, S. P., *Transf.*, **2**, 363–374 (1962).
118. Mollison, P. L., *Post. Grad. Med. J.*, **20**, 17 (1944).
119. Morgan, W. T. J., *Chem. Ind. (London)*, **19**, 722 (1941).
120. Morgan, W. T. J., and H. K. King, *Biochem. J. (London)*, **37**, 640 (1943).
121. Morgan, W. T. J., and R. van Heyningen, *Brit. J. Exptl. Pathol.*, **25**, 5 (1944).
122. Morgan, W. T. J., and W. M. Watkins, *Brit. J. Exptl. Pathol.*, **29**, 159 (1948).
123. Morgan, W. T. J., and W. M. Watkins, *Nature*, **177**, 521 (1956).
124. Morgan, W. T. J., and W. M. Watkins, *Brit. Med. Bull.*, **15**, 109 (1959).
125. Morton, J. A., and M. M. Pickles, *Nature*, **159**, 779 (1947).
127. Mourant, A. E., *The Distribution of the Human Blood Groups*, Charles C Thomas, Springfield, Illinois, 1954.
128. Mourant, A. E., A. C. Kopec, and K. Domaniewski-Sobczak, *The ABO Blood Groups*, Blackwell, Oxford, 1958.
129. Muller, M., and E. Balgairies, *Comp. rend, soc. biol.*, **121**, 1447 (1936).
130. Oliver-Gonzalez, J., *J. Infect. Diseases*, **74**, 81 (1944).
131. Oliver-Gonzalez, J., and M. V. Torregross, *J. Infect. Diseases*, **74**, 173 (1944).
132. Ottensooser, F., and K. Silverschmidt, *Nature*, **172**, 914 (1953).
133. Paterson, J. L., R. R. Race, and G. I. Taylor, *Brit. Med. J.*, **II**, 37 (1942).
134. Pike, I. A., and A. M. Dickins, *Brit. Med. J.*, **II**, 321 (1954).
135. Pirofsky, B., and M. S. Cordova, *Brit. J. Haemat.*, **10**, 320–326 (1964).
136. Pirofsky, B. M., Cordova, and T. I. Imel, *J. Immunol.*, **89**, 767–774 (1962).
137. Prager, M. D., and M. A. Fletcher, *Proc. Soc. Exptl. Biol. Med.*, **111**, 722–725 (1962).
138. Prager, M. D., M. A. Fletcher, and K. Efron, *J. Immunol.*, **89**, 834–840 (1962).
139. Putkonen, T., *Acta Soc. Med. Fennicae "Duodecim,"* **A14**, F2, 1 (1930).

140. Race, R. R., and R. Sanger, *Blood Groups in Man*, 2nd ed., Blackwell, Oxford, 1954.
141. Race, R. R., and R. Sanger, *Blood Groups in Man*, 4th ed., Blackwell, Oxford, 1962.
142. Race, R. R., R. Sanger, S. D. Lawler, and D. Bertinshaw, *Heredity*, **3**, 205 (1949).
143. Race, R. R., G. L. Taylor, K. E. Boorman, and B. E. Dodd, *Nature*, **152**, 563 (1943).
144. Renkonen, K. O., *Ann. Med. Exptl. Biol. Finniae (Helsinki)*, **26**, 66 (1948).
145. Rife, D. C., *Ohio J. Sci.*, **48**, 116 (1948).
146. Romanowska, E., *Polska Akademia Nauk.*, **15**, 375–376 (1960).
147. Ruffié, J., *Les Groupes Sanguins chez l'Homme*, Masson, Paris, 1953.
148. Rule, A., and W. C. Boyd, *Transf.*, **4**, 449–456 (1956).
149. Saint-Paul, M., *Trans.*, **4**, 3–37 (1961).
150. Sanger, R., and R. R. Race, *Nature*, **160**, 505 (1947).
151. Sanger, R., R. R. Race, and J. Jack, *Brit. J. Hematol.*, **1**, 375 (1955).
152. Schatkin, S. B., *Disputed Paternity Proocedings*, Mathew Bender, Albany, 1953.
153. Schiff, F., and L. Adelsberger, *Z. Immunitätsforsch.*, **40**, 335 (1924).
154. Schiff, F., and W. C. Boyd, *Blood Grouping Technic*, Interscience, New York, 1942.
155. Schmidt, F., and H. Sasaki, *Klin. Wochschr.*, **11**, 1426 (1932).
156. Schmidt, G., *Z. Immunitätsforsch.*, **III**, 432 (1954).
157. Smith, M., *Science*, **131**, 699–702 (1960).
158. Springer, G. F., *Bacteriol. Rev.*, **27**, 191–227 (1963).
159. Springer, G. F., and N. J. Ansell, *Proc. Nat. Acad. Sci.*, **44**, 182–189 (1958).
160. Springer, G. F., R. E. Horton, and M. Forbes, *Ann. N. Y. Acad. Sci.*, **78**, 272–275 (1959).
161. Springer, G. F., and K. Hotta, *Abstr. 6th Int. Congr. Biochem.*, New York, 1964.
162. Springer, G. F., and H. Tegtmeyer, *Nature*, **293**, 298–299 (1964).
163. Stevens, W. L., *Ann. Eugen.*, **8**, 362 (1938).
164. Stone, W. H., and M. R., Irwin, *Adv. Immunol.*, **3**, 315–350 (1963).
165. Struthers, David, *Brit. J. Soc. Med.*, **5**, 223 (1951).
166. Szulman, A. E., *J. Exptl. Med.*, **111**, 785–800 (1960).
167. Taylor, W. W., and W. C. Boyd, *Year Book of the Am. Phil. Soc.*, (1943) pp. 178–180.
168. Tobiska, J., *Die Phythämagglutinine*, Akademie-Verlag, Berlin, 1964.
169. Walsh, R. J., and C. Montgomery, *Nature*, **160**, 504 (1947).
170. Watkins, W. M., and W. T. J. Morgan, *Nature*, **175**, 676 (1955).
171. Wiener, A. S., *J. Immunol.*, **34**, 11 (1938).
172. Wiener, A. S., *Science*, **96**, 407 (1942).
173. Wiener, A. S., *Blood Groups and Transfusion*, 3rd ed., Charles C Thomas, Springfield, Illinois, 1943.
174. Wiener, A. S., *Am. J. Clin. Pathol.*, **16**, 477 (1946).
175. Wiener, A. S., *Lancet*, **I**, 343 (1948).
176. Wiener, A. S., *Rh-Hr Blood Types*, Grune and Stratton, New York, 1954.
177. Wiener, A. S., *An Rh-Hr Syllabus*, Grune and Stratton, New York, 1954.
178. Wiener, A. S., and S. Forer, *Proc. Soc. Exptl. Biol. Med.*, **47**, 215 (1941).
179. Wiener, A. S., and I. Kosofsky, *J. Immunol.*, **42**, 381 (1941).
180. Wiener, A. S., and H. R. Peters, *Ann. Internal Med.*, **13**, 2306 (1940).
181. Wiener, A. S, and E B. Sonn, *Genetics*, **28**, 157 (1943).
182. Wigmore, J. H., *Treatise on the Anglo-American System of Evidence in Trials at Common Law*, Little Brown, Boston, 1940.
183. Witebsky, E., and N. C. Klendshoj, *J. Exptl. Med.*, **73**, 655 (1941).
184. Witebsky, E., N. C. Klendshoj, and C. McNeil, *Proc. Soc. Exptl. Biol. Med.*, **55**, 167 (1944).

CHAPTER 6

Antibody–Antigen Reactions

The reaction between antibody and antigen is a chemical one. However, since the reaction between antibody and antigen, and that between proteins and proteolytic enzymes, are the only instances which have been well studied of reactions occurring in nature between molecules of very large size, it should not be surprising if some apparently new features emerge. Reserving for later discussion the reaction with haptens, which are usually much smaller molecules, and the combination of antibody with intact cells such as bacteria or erythrocytes, what do we find to be the salient characteristics of the reaction? Several features stand out.

1. Basic Facts

a. The reaction is specific. This point has already been discussed, and it will not be necessary to give examples here. We shall have to keep in mind the specificity of the reaction when we come to discuss the mechanism of union, that is, the nature of the forces holding antibody and antigen together.

b. The entire molecules react, not some fragment split off from them. This is clearly shown by ultracentrifugal experiments (see 111,181).

c. The antibody molecule, and the molecules of protein antigens, at any rate, behave in these reactions more or less like ellipsoids of greater or less eccentricity. They probably behave like rigid ellipsoids, but this is less certain. Boyd and Hooker (30,32) found that the composition of antibody–antigen precipitates they studied was compatible with the idea that antigen molecules are roughly spherical and antibody molecules be-

305

have as elongated units, such as ellipsoids, or chains of connected spheres. It was also found that in antibody–antigen reactions between films of the reagents (*e.g.,* see 194) the thickness (30 to 50 A.) of the films is such as to suggest that the molecules are behaving like ellipsoids lying on their sides. Evidence that protein molecules act as fairly rigid spheres or ellipsoids comes from their behavior in intense gravitational fields (212) and their possession of a definite electric moment (225). See also (166,223).

Early workers apparently supposed that the antibody spread as a thin film (about 10 A. thick) over the surface of the antigen. Such a film would resemble a condensed protein film and, having the polar groups turned away from the surrounding water, could account for the hydrophobic character of the compound.

The evidence, however, indicates that antibody does not behave as such a film. Also, the amount of antibody observed to combine with a molecule of antigen does not correspond to a film, but to a layer more than 30 A. thick (see p. 356). Also, the electrokinetic properties of the antibody–antigen complex are still those of protein, and do not suggest that all the polar groups are turned away from the surface.

d. No splitting, digestion, or other profound chemical alteration takes place in the reacting molecules after they have combined.

There are numerous observations which support this statement. It is well known that toxin is not permanently detoxified, but simply neutralized, by combination with antitoxin. Severe reactions occurred in members of two communities following the injection of toxin–antitoxin mixtures (of a formula not used at present) which had been frozen, apparently with resulting damage to the antitoxin and consequent release of some of the toxic properties of the toxin (198). Venoms can be recovered after neutralization with antivenins, by destroying the antibody (44,169).

Similarly, various workers (see Chapter 2) have been able to recover unaltered antibody from antibody–antigen precipitates or "agglutinates." It is evident that if any alteration takes place, it is pretty much reversible (46). It used to be thought that antibody was denatured after combination with antigen. Probably without fully sharing this idea, Eagle (69) and Mudd (see 170) emphasized the similarity in properties of combined antibody and denatured globulin. This similarity certainly exists and is probably significant for theories of serological reactions, but it does not mean that the antibody actually is denatured when it combines.

Not only is the antibody not immediately denatured, but it has been found (18) that the solubility of ovalbumin–antiovalbumin precipitates in excess of antigen was not altered by storage (see p. 321). Since this is a specific reaction, the result indicated that no progressive loss of specific reactivity of either of the reagents had taken place during that time.

There is other evidence that the serological specificity of the antigen and antibody is not altered by their combination. Precipitates will specifically sensitize animals to the antigen and to the serum proteins of the animal from which the antibody was derived; nonprecipitating (inhibition zone) compounds of antibody and antigen can be precipitated, after the lapse of an indefinite time, by the addition of more of the deficient reagent or by the addition of a different antibody directed against either the antigen or the first antibody. This again indicates that no significant denaturation takes place.

e. The combination of antibody and antigen takes place at the *surface* of the molecules or cells. This follows from the third point discussed above. Also, Marrack (155) pointed out that no molecule larger than the lower fatty acids could pass between the constituent atoms of a protein molecule, in view of their known distances from each other. Evidence for the role of surface in serological reactions has been brought out in the preceding chapters; it was stressed by Hooker (121). The experiments of Marrack suggest that when the antibody molecule is unfolded, thus producing a new "surface," it loses its power of specific combination, and the experiments of Porter and Pappenheimer (194) indicated that the reactive capacity of the antitoxin molecule is restricted to a portion of its surface.

It has been suggested (6,11) that the protective action of antipneumococcus antibodies, for instance, is due to their combination with the surface of the bacteria, and Bjørneboe (11) suggested that the greatest effect is obtained when the antibodies are evenly distributed over the surface.

f. The union between antibody and antigen is a *firm* one but is *reversible.* Numerous lines of evidence show that the union is firm. It is well known that it is quite difficult to dissociate diphtheria antitoxin and toxin after their combination. It is possible to dissolve the precipitate formed by the conjugated protein, arsanilic-acid–azocasein, and its antibody by the addition of dilute alkali; addition of dilute acid to this solution, which would not precipitate the antibody alone, throws down the antibody and antigen together, with hardly a trace of antibody left in the supernatant fluid (25). Studies on the heat of serological reactions (29) indicate a considerable energy change, implying a rather firm combination.

The reversibility of serological reactions is shown by several lines of evidence, such as dissociation of antibody from precipitates and agglutinated cells, and solution of precipitates in excess of antigen. This evidence is presented more fully on page 322.

g. Both antibody and antigen enter into the specific precipitate or into the specific "agglutinate." There is now abundant evidence for this statement, but before the introduction of quantitative methods into immunology the question was sometimes debated.

h. Antibody and antigen can combine in varying proportions. This is an obvious consequence of the multivalency of one or the other of the reagents, and has been shown by numerous analyses. Once it was realized that either antigen or antibody, or possibly both, were multivalent, the observation that antibody–antigen compounds may vary in composition became understandable. Credit for insisting on this point, and providing evidence for it, must go largely to Heidelberger and collaborators.

2. The Two Stages of Serological Reactions

It is customary to consider serological reactions as occurring in two stages. Such a subdivision should not be taken as implying that the two stages do not overlap, for it is quite likely that the second stage sets in before the first is entirely completed.

These two stages are: the specific combination between specific groups of the antibody and corresponding groups of the antigen or hapten; and the secondary, observable reactions which may follow this, such as precipitation, agglutination, and complement fixation.

There are several features of these reactions which make it convenient for us to retain this division into stages. (*a*) The first stage proceeds without visible alteration and can be detected only indirectly, whereas the second may be quite conspicuous and easily detected; (*b*) in the case of small haptens, as a rule, no second stage follows at all; (*c*) under some conditions, as in the absence of salts, the first stage can take place, but the second cannot; (*d*) their speeds are very unequal, the first stage being extremely rapid, and the second sometimes very slow; (*e*) the energy change seems to take place during the first stage, the second being accompanied by little energy change; (*f*) there is some evidence (see below) that the specificity of the second stage, or the latter part of it, may sometimes be of a lower order than that of the first stage.

A. FIRST STAGE: COMBINATION

1. Mode of Combination Between Antibody and Antigen

Because of the chemical basis of serological specificity, it is logical to suppose that the union between antibody and antigen is a chemical one, dut to combination of the specific reactive groups of the two reagents. This is supported by such facts as the power of specific simple chemical substances (haptens) to react with antibodies, and by the analogy with enzyme reactions, known to be chemical in nature.

For a long time the principal question in this connection was: is the union solely due to coulomb forces (attraction between positive and negative charges, *e.g.*, $-NH_3^+$ and $-COO^-$) or are other forces involved? If the forces acting are coulomb forces, we should suppose that the combination between antibody and antigen is chiefly due to attraction between amino and carboxyl groups. The possibility of such an ionic mechanism was pointed out by Heidelberger and Kendall in 1929 (103). There are points in support of this idea, such as the rapidity of the primary reaction, and the strong influence of polar groups observed in studies of specificity. In particular the immunological equivalence of such groups as

and the acidic (and therefore polar) character of many serologically reactive nonprotein antigens, such as some of the pneumococcal polysaccharides, are suggestive. Goebel and Hotchkiss (91) found that antipneumococcus horse sera of types I, III, and VIII gave vigorous precipitation with artificial antigens containing benzene carboxylic and sulfonic acid radicals, which are quite unrelated in chemical constitution to the pneumococcus polysaccharides. Chow and Goebel (45) suggested that combination between the pneumococcus polysaccharides and the corresponding antibodies might largely be due to attraction between the ionized uronic acid groups, containing $-COO^-$, and the ionized amino groups, $-NH_3^+$, of the protein. In support of this idea, it was found that treatment of the antibody with formalin, which reacts with the amino groups, destroys the precipitating power of the antibody, and that acetylation, also affecting the amino groups, is almost equally effective.

Landsteiner (146), in favor of the idea that such a mechanism, which he referred to as the formation of salt-like compounds, may operate, listed the following: the prominent influence of acid groups (see p. 146), the change in specificity following esterification of aromatic acids or proteins, and the similarity of hemagglutination and hemolysis produced by serological agents and by colloidal inorganic acids.

It has been objected that such a simple mechanism could not account for the specificity of serological reactions, but this is perhaps not a necessary difficulty. If a number of amino and carboxyl groups in the antibody together form one specific determinant group for a determinant group of the antigen, the specificity might be due to the spatial arrangements of

these groups. The weaker union observed with related heterologous antigens could be explained by a failure of the oppositely charged groups
to correspond perfectly in position.

It is, however, likely that other forces also play a role in serological
reactions (185,188). It does not seem likely that the covalent bond is
concerned, for, as Landsteiner said (146): ". . . in velocity and easy
reversibility antigen–antibody reactions differ from those due to primary
valences and resemble the formation of ionic and molecular compounds;
and a strong argument against the assumption of covalent bonds is the

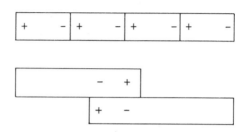

Schemes of dipole association

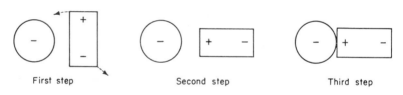

First step   Second step   Third step

Attraction of a dipole by an ion

Fig. 6-1. Possible ways in which forces between dipoles and dipoles and ions might
enter into the reaction between antibody and antigen (modified from Haurowitz).

fact that quite different substances, regardless of their chemical nature,
are capable of reacting with antibodies all in like manner." It is likely
that similar objections apply against the coordinate link or semipolar
double bond (see 183). Other types of bonds which may possibly play
some role in serological reactions are dipole–dipole bonds, dipole–ion
bonds [shown schematically in Fig. 6-1; see (96)], van der Waals forces, and
the hydrogen bond (185,186). The latter consists essentially of a hydrogen atom which is attacted simultaneously to two different atoms, as in

salicylaldehyde. The hydrogen bond, which has been discussed, for example, by Pauling (183), and Huggins (129), appears to be one of the forces keeping proteins in their characteristic configuration (see cut).

Electronic van der Waals attraction (151) is the most general sort of intermolecular attraction and operates between every two molecules of any sort. A molecule which has no permanent dipole moment (*e.g.*, methane, CH_4) may have an instantaneous electric dipole moment, as the center of charge of the electrons, as they swing rapidly around the nucleus, moves to one side or the other of the center of charge of the nuclei. This instantaneous dipole moment produces an instantaneous electric field which would act to polarize any other molecule in the neighborhood; as a result the electrons of the second molecule would move relative to the nuclei in such a way as to produce a force of attraction to the first molecule.

The van der Waals attraction increases very rapidly with decreasing interatomic distance, being inversely proportional to the seventh power of the distance. Consequently this attraction is not important when the molecules are separated very much, but quite strong when two molecules can bring parts of their surfaces into such close contact that a number of atoms of one are in contact with atoms of the other.

Modern opinion inclines to the view that of all these possible forces the van der Waals forces are probably the most important in holding antibody and antigen together.

2. Size of Reacting Groups

The size of the specific determinants in natural proteins is not known exactly (see p. 131), but in the case of artificial antigens we can form some idea of the extent of the reacting group. The total reacting group in conjugated antigens is probably somewhat larger than the introduced group, which chiefly determines the specificity, because of some effect of adjacent groups of the native protein. The specificity of proteins can be altered by introducing the phenylazo group:

into them by treating them with diazotized aniline, but antigens containing this group differ but little from those containing chlorophenylazo,

$$Cl\!\!-\!\!\langle\ \rangle\!\!-\!\!N\!:\!N\!-$$

and methylphenylazo,

$$CH_3\!\!-\!\!\langle\ \rangle\!\!-\!\!N\!:\!N\!-$$

(see p. 142). It was found that the reaction with such an antigen was not inhibited by aniline itself, in contrast to the results obtained with haptens containing polar groups. Jacobs (131) found that although introduced naphthalene residues:

and anthracene residues:

[both coupled through the azo (—N:N) link] conferred a new specificity on the conjugated protein, the two antigens differed but little serologically in spite of the considerable structural differences between these haptens. These facts suggest that in such cases the groups of the antigen which enter into combination with the antibody are probably native groups, possibly altered somewhat in composition, in the conjugated protein, lying near the introduced hapten. It is possible that the antibody reacts either not at all, or only to a limited extent, with such "neutral" haptens alone. If the specific active groups of the antibody are directed, not towards the hapten alone, but also towards the tyrosine and histidine nuclei with which diazonium compounds couple in a conjugated protein, we should expect that such antisera would be inhibited most effectively, not by the hapten alone, but by the hapten coupled to tyrosine or histidine, or some other phenolic or imidazole compound; and this has, in fact, been observed by several workers.

This idea is supported by the observation of Mutsaars and Grégoire (172) that synthetic antigens in which the determinant group (D) is coupled to the protein (Pr) through the lysine by a ureido link, DNHCOPr, are not equivalent to those in which it is attached by an azo link, DN:NPr. Hooker and Boyd (123) found similar evidence while studying antisera to egg-white–arsanilic-acid and gelatin–arsanilic-acid.

Since gelatin contains no tyrosine, or but a negligible amount, it would be expected that the antibodies to this compound would have predominantly an arsanilic-acid–azohistidine specificity, whereas those to the egg white compound would be directed also partly towards tyrosine-like structures. Consistent with this prediction they considered their observations that the dye:

$$\text{N}\diagdown_{\text{N}}^{\text{N}} \diagdown \text{N:N} \diagdown \bigcirc$$
$$\text{AsO}_3\text{H}_2$$

designated as H, was about three times as effective as another:

$$\bigcirc \diagdown \text{N:N} \diagdown \bigcirc$$
$$\text{OH} \qquad \text{AsO}_3\text{H}_2$$

called T, in inhibiting the reaction of the anti-egg-white–arsanilic antibodies with casein–arsanilic serum. The sodium salt of arsanilic acid alone (atoxyl) would also inhibit these sera, but much larger amounts were required. In later work Hooker and Boyd (122) found that antisera against *p*-aminobenzoic-acid-coupled antigens were inhibited much more efficiently by 2,4-dihydroxy-4′-carboxyazobenzene:

$$\text{OH}$$
$$\text{HO}\langle\bigcirc\rangle\text{N:N}\langle\bigcirc\rangle\text{COOH,}$$

than by 4,4′-dicarboxyazobenzene:

$$\text{HOOC}\langle\bigcirc\rangle\text{N:N}\langle\bigcirc\rangle\text{COOH}$$

indicating presumably the influence of the greater similarity of the former to the structures beyond the azo group in the coupled protein. The above facts may be taken as indicating that the reactive groups in serology are of about the dimensions of a synthetic chemical compound like some of those represented here, or perhaps in some cases a bit larger.

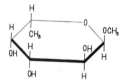

Fig. 6-2. α-Methyl-L-fucopyranoside.

Morgan and Watkins (168) found that α-methyl-L-fucopyranoside (Fig. 6-2) specifically inhibited the hemagglutinin anti-H, whether the anti-H came from animals (eels) or plants (*Lotus tetragonolobus*). Even fucose itself had considerable inhibitory activity. Although on a molar basis α-methyl-L-fucopyranoside did not inhibit so effectively as H substance itself (about 1000 times as many molecules being required), this suggests that the specific determinant in H substance is not very much more complicated than a molecule of this sugar, and consequently the corresponding combining group in the antibody (or lectin) would not need to involve more than perhaps 30 atoms, if we assume the combining forces to be mainly van der Waals attractions. Later studies of Kabat and Leskowitz (137) on the relative inhibiting efficiency of various sugars led them to suggest that the specifically active oligosaccharide chains in blood group A and B substances may be of the order of tri- to penta- to hexasaccharides. The complete specific combining group of the antibody might thus be as much as six times as large as the minimal structure we have just deduced, and up to 200 atoms of the antibody structure might be involved in the combination with each molecule of blood group substance.

3. Nature of the Reactive Group

We may suppose, according to the above, that the specifically active "patches" on the surface of the antibody are adapted to react with a considerable area of the determinant group. The reaction is therefore likely to be a complex one, with several chemical groups which together form the "active patch," being involved, not all of them, perhaps, exerting the same sort of forces. The specificity conferred by a small introduced chemical group would be due partly to its own structure and partly to alteration in the neighboring structures in the protein molecule. Marrack (155) said: "The effect of changes such as the introduction of, for example, a Cl atom into the benzene ring of a determinant group may be ascribed both to a local effect on the electric field, affecting the local adaptation to the receptor site, and to an electron drift in the benzene ring, which affects the adaptation of the whole ring or of any dominant group attached to it, to the receptor site."

A purely schematic representation of how an extremely simple case of correspondence between the specific groups in the antibody and those in the antigen might be based on distribution of positive and negative groups and hydrogen bonds is shown in Fig. 6-3. The H in this drawing may be taken to represent either a hydrogen atom capable of taking part in hydrogen bond formation, or a site capable of attracting such a hydrogen. No attempt has been made to represent the more generalized van der Waals attractions.

If the antibody-combining groups are chemically complex, as supposed here, we shall not expect to find that antibody molecules always carry a positive charge, say, while antigen molecules are always negative, or anything so simple. Landsteiner (146) said: "While experiments by Michaelis and Davidsohn and de Kruif and Northrop contradict the 'idea that the combination (of antibody and antigen) is caused by opposite electric charges' they do not preclude that among the combining groups involved in the reactions, there are acid and basic groups, interacting with each other." If we provisionally accept this point of view, we should

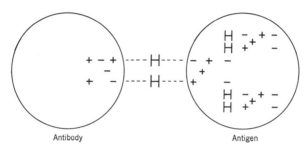

Fig. 6-3. Hypothetical way in which charges of opposite sign and groups capable of entering into hydrogen bond formation might determine the specific reaction between antibody and antigen.

probably assume that acidic and basic groups enter in roughly equal numbers into the reaction, as most protein antigens are not notably either acidic or basic, and Smith and Marrack (208) found no pH change following an antibody–antigen reaction nor did Boyd and Baskys (26). Singer and Campbell (204,205) deduced from a study of the effect of pH on the reactions of bovine serum albumin and ovalbumin with their antibodies that a single ionized carboxyl group was involved in each antibody–antigen bond. The work of Boyd and Baskys, although these authors believed they could have detected the liberation or absorption of as little as one or two equivalents of hydrogen ion per mole of antibody (or lectin), is not necessarily in contradiction with the work of Singer and Campbell, for the ionization of the single carboxyl group postulated by the latter authors would probably not be completely suppressed as a result of the combination, and the absorption of hydrogen ion would be less than one equivalent per mole.

If any considerable part of the forces uniting antibody and antigen are coulomb forces, it might be expected that an antibody to a strongly acidic antigen, such as one of the pneumococcus polysaccharides, would have more free amino groups (and perhaps more imidazole and guanidino groups) than normal globulin, but it is not necessary to suppose that the increase would be readily detectable chemically. In the first place, since antibody contains only two reactive groups per molecule (see Chapter 2), the change might be of the order of but two amino groups out of some one hundred. Marrack (155) calculated that even if antipneumococcus antibody contained enough extra amino groups to combine with all the carboxyl groups of the polysaccharide, this would involve an increase in the total amino content of the protein of only 14 per cent.

There is no evidence that antibodies contain prosthetic specific reactive groups, and it is generally supposed that the reactive group of the antibody is simply a patch of the surface in which the various groups are arranged so as to correspond in some way, perhaps electrically, to those of the antigenic determinant. Haurowitz (96) supposed that the surface of the antibody corresponds to the surface of the antigen as an electrotype to an electrode of complicated shape. Hooker and Boyd (127) and Pauling (184) suggested that a hapten or antigenic determinant fits into a pocket in the antibody and that the fit is a close one. See Fig. 2-10. Pauling pointed out the importance of a close fit if van der Waals forces are to play an important role. This correspondence must be brought about, if these ideas are correct, by adjustments of the spacing and arrangement of the amino acids in the antibody (see Fig. 3-2) while it is being synthesized.

Haurowitz (96) also gave a schematic representation of how the groups in the reactive portion of the antibody surface might be arranged to correspond to an artificial determinant, in this case metanilic acid. This is shown in Fig. 6-4 (redrawn). It was of course realized by Haurowitz that any such picture is a gross oversimplification. We do not yet know enough of the structure of any antibody to attempt an accurate picture for an actual case. On the basis of pictures such as these, however, it is possible to understand how the spatial arrangement of the groups in the active patch of the antibody would make it possible to differentiate steric isomers. Such an active patch would have to contain at least three reactive chemical groups (121); it would probably contain a good many more.

The role of coulomb forces in holding antibody and antigen together was clarified by the experiments of Singer (203). This worker pointed out that if a negatively charged group is involved in an antibody–antigen

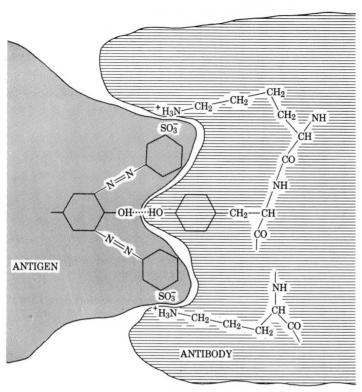

Fig. 6-4. Hypothetical manner in which surface structure of antibody and molecule might correspond to part of the surface of a synthetic conjugated antigen, in this case a native protein coupled with diazotized metanilic acid.

bond, it is possible to calculate the effect of pH on antibody–antigen combination. The assumption is made that, if the negative group is in the antigen, the antibody contains a corresponding positively charged group, and vice versa. For our present purposes it is immaterial which molecule contains the negative group. Singer and Campbell (203) suggested that, if there is one negative group characterized by an intrinsic hydrogen ion association constant K_H and if we neglect the nonspecific repulsion between antibody (Ab) and antigen (AG) molecules, the following relation should hold in the acid region:

$$\log (1/K - 1/K_0) = \log (K_H/K_0) - p\text{H} \qquad (1)$$

where K is the apparent equilibrium constant at a given pH for the reaction

$$\text{Ab} + \text{Ag} \rightleftharpoons \text{AbAg}$$

318 FUNDAMENTALS OF IMMUNOLOGY

and K_0 is the value of K at neutral pH where both the positive and the negative group are fully ionized. A similar relation would apply in the alkaline region. If two negative and two positive groups were critically involved in each Ab—Ag bond, the expected relation would now contain a $(p\mathrm{H})^2$ and a $2(p\mathrm{H})$ term.

Singer tested this relation by ultracentrifugal observations on Ab—Ag mixtures at different pH. Typical results are shown in Fig. 6-5, which

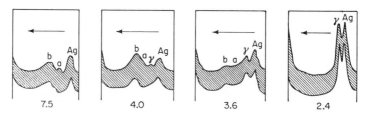

Fig. 6-5. Ultracentrifugal diagrams of mixtures of bovine serum albumin and its antibody at various pH. Sedimentation is proceeding in the direction of the arrow. Ag stands for antigen, a for an antibody–antigen complex thought to be Ag_2Ab, b represents a complex thought to be Ag_3Ab_2, and γ is gamma globulin. At pH less than 4.5, progressively larger amounts of free gamma globulin (antibody) appear, while the amounts of the complexes diminish (203).

shows the sedimentation diagrams of mixtures of bovine serum albumin and rabbit anti-bovine serum albumin. As the pH falls, more and more free gamma globulin (antibody) appears in the mixture while the amount of the antibody–antigen complexes decreases. The changes are clearly a function of pH* and were found to be entirely reversible.

Enough results at different pH were obtained to show that the linear relation predicted by the equation holds quite well (Fig. 6-6). This was found to be true for both systems studied, namely, ovalbumin–antiovalbumin and bovine serum albumin–antibovine-serum-albumin. The constant K_H had in both cases a value of about 10^5, which is consistent with the idea that a carboxyl group. $-COO^-$, is critically involved in the antibody–antigen bond in these systems, and must be ionized for maximum bond strength. Singer concluded that the attraction of this group for its com-

* Habeeb *et al.* (95), however, concluded from chemical modification studies that "the removal of the positive charge on the same amino groups of Ab by an increase of the pH of the solution, instead of by acetylation, might have the same effect on the Ab molecule and its capacity to precipitate with a large Ag molecule. The generally-observed dissociation of Ag–Ab bonds in alkaline solution might therefore be attributable to such a deformation of the Ab molecule, rather than . . . to titration of specific critical groups within the Ab sites."

plementary positive group accounts for about half of the strength of the antibody–antigen bond in these cases. The remainder is presumably due to some or all of the other forces mentioned above.

In the case of the attraction of antibody to p-(p'azophenylazo)-benzene arsonate, Nisonoff and Pressman (175) found that the negatively charged —COO⁻ group contributed over 4.8 kcal./mole to the binding energy, again indicating the presence of a positive charge in the combining group of the antibody. The uncharged p-phenylazo group contributed 2.3 kcal./mole.

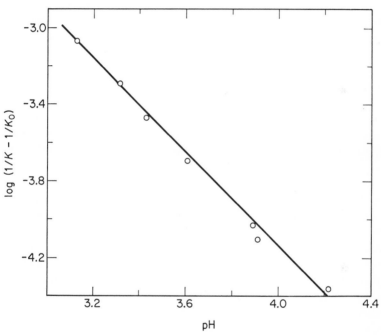

Fig. 6-6. Effect of pH on antibody–antigen equilibrium in the bovine serum albumin system. The slope of the line is − 1.2 (203).

There are a number of reasons for believing that the van der Waals forces are among the most important of the non-coulomb forces. One of the arguments supporting this belief derives from the fact that the strength of the antibody–antigen bond is greatly decreased if the hapten or antigen combining group is slightly changed in shape. This is shown by work with haptens of known chemical constitution, such as the experiments discussed in Chapter 1, and by measurements of the bond strength for groups of related haptens, discussed below. The strong influence of shape suggests that close contact between the various atoms of the combining group of the antibody and the atoms of the haptens or antigenic combining group is necessary for a strong antibody–antigen bond. Such closeness of contact accords well with the suggestion, made by Hooker and Boyd (127), Pauling and Pressman (187) (Fig. 2-9), and Karush (139), that the combining group of the antibody may in fact be a cavity into which the hapten or antigen combining group fits snugly. Close fit would make the van der Waals forces strong, and any change in the hapten or antigen combining group that lessened that fit would markedly weaken the strength of the bond, which is precisely what we observe.

Although in the two systems studied by Singer the non-coulomb forces (which, if the argument in the preceding paragraph is valid, may be second in importance) were thought to account for only about half the strength of the antibody–antigen bond, there are cases where the non-coulomb forces presumably account for the entire bond strength. These cases apply to antigens which do not contain positively or negatively charged groups in their specifically reactive portions. Here, no positive or negative groups are present, at least not in the portions responsible for the antigenic specificity. Yet the blood group antigens combine firmly and typically not only with antibody but with the blood group-specific plant proteins I have called lectins (Chapter 5). These reactions have been studied quantitatively (136,35). Karush (140) believes that the forces between antibody and carbohydrate antigens are mainly hydrogen bonds.

Wurmser and Filitti-Wurmser (226) suggested that the combining energy of the isohemagglutinins with their receptors on the human erythrocyte is equivalent to that of about four hydrogen bonds or twenty van der Waals bonds. Before we can discuss such quantitative estimates further it will be necessary to go into some of the concepts of thermodynamics (pp. 324 ff).

4. Reversibility of Serological Reactions

By treating the antibody–antigen reaction as if it attained equilibrium, as we have been doing (above), we have tacitly been assuming that the reaction is reversible. It is perhaps time to ask what evidence exists to support that assumption.

It has been found possible to dissociate considerable antibody from certain antibody–antigen complexes (46,79,102,107,130). The actual proportion recovered depends on the method and the kind of antibody, antipneumococcal antibodies appearing to be particularly easy to recover. Some normal antibodies, such as normal hemagglutinins, human isoagglutinins, and particularly "cold agglutinins," can be separated rather easily from the antigen.

It is a common observation that a mixture of a precipitin and a protein antigen will not result in the formation of a specific precipitate if the antigen is present in too great proportion ("antigen excess"). As would be expected from this, it is found that if excess antigen is added to a specific precipitate, it will dissolve. It is very difficult to see how this could take place except by reversal of at least some of the reactions involved in the formation of the precipitate.

There are some observations in the literature (see 12,18) suggesting an increasing firmness of union, or "stabilization," between antibody and antigen with the passage of time. In some cases the evidence for this seems fairly convincing; in others it is possible to think of other explanations for the results obtained. Well-founded or not, the conclusions based on such experiments have probably influenced opinion in regard to the similar but independent question of the solubility of precipitates in excess antigen, which probably involves the reversal of some of the reactions which took place during the formation of the precipitate. Boyd (18) found no evidence that the solubility of ovalbumin–antiovalbumin precipitates was diminished by storage for ten months in the icebox; the reversibility of the reaction, as judged by the solubility (and rate of solution) of the precipitate in antigen, remained unchanged.

On the assumption that serological reactions are reversible, mathematical treatment of the problem shows that there ought to be a linear relationship between the logarithm of the ratio of antibody to antigen in the precipitate, and the logarithm of the concentration of antibody (or antigen if this is in excess) in the supernatant. Figures 6-7a and 6-7b show that there is in fact a beautifully linear relation.

The reversibility of serological reactions is shown by the experiments of Eisen and Karush (73) in which hapten and antibody were dialyzed against hapten, and by the experiments of Doty and Epstein (63,75) in which the soluble compounds formed in mixtures of antibody and hapten were observed by light scattering. Both of these teams of workers observed that there was a definite equilibrium which could be approached from either direction. In addition, Doty and Epstein observed a shift in the equilibrium when the mixtures were diluted, as would be demanded by the idea that a dynamic equilibrium exists between hapten, antibody, and compounds containing one, two, and three molecules of antibody.

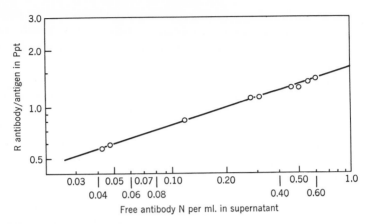

Fig. 6-7a. Linear relation between ratio of antibody to antigen (R) in precipitates and concentration of free antibody in supernatant (antibody being in excess) when plotted logarithmically. Data from (188b).

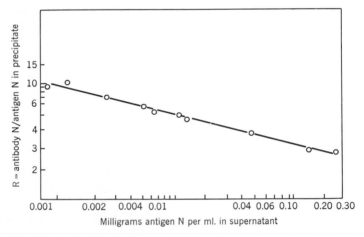

Fig. 6-7b. Linear relation between ratio of antibody to antigen in precipitates and concentration of antigen in supernatant (antigen in excess) when both are plotted logarithmically.

Studies with radioactive tracer-labeled lectin (28) and antibodies (14) have shown that the combination with cellular antigens is also reversible.

When precipitin and antigen are mixed, the precipitate often appears instantaneously, so far as can be observed. Heidelberger, Treffers, and Mayer (113) found that combination between antibody and egg albumin, even at 0°C., was apparently complete in 20 seconds. Eagle (69) stated that in the flocculation test for syphilis the combination between the reagin and the lipoid "antigen" is more than 95 per cent complete within 1 minute after mixing (see 222). Mayer and Heidelberger (161) obtained evidence that combination between pneumococcus polysaccharides and their antibodies is at least 90 per cent complete in less than 3 seconds at 0°C. Goldberg and Campbell (93), observing the reaction between bovine serum albumin and its antibody by means of light scattering, found the reaction to be complete in a few minutes. The rate at which heat is evolved when antibody and antigen react (see below) also suggests a very rapid reaction. If we suppose that the union takes place only when a molecule of antibody collides with (or approaches sufficiently near) a molecule of antigen or a cell, these results are not surprising, for it may be calculated that antibody molecules have velocities of the order of half a meter per second at room temperature, owing to Brownian motion (31).

However, not all serological reactions run so rapidly to completion, particularly if antigen is in excess (*i.e.,* antibody is deficient). •

Agglutination reactions often seem to require time for their completion, particularly when the concentration of antibody is low, as with Rh sera, where it is standard practice to incubate at 37°C. for an hour before centrifuging and reading. Reactions with strong agglutinating sera, such as anti-A, anti-B, anti-M, and anti-N, seem to go so fast that the mixtures can be centrifuged and read immediately. It is of course possible that the first stage (attachment of antibody to cells) of agglutination reactions is rapid, but the second stage is sometimes slow.

Cromwell (58) reported that the amount of hemolysin fixed by erythrocytes did not increase after 15 minutes, but Dreyer and Douglas (64) found there was some increase in the amount of agglutinin fixed by bacteria up to 4 hours after mixing.

Smith *et al.* (206), studying the neutralization of carboxypeptidase by specific antibody, found the reaction to be slow, requiring about an hour for completion at 25°C. At 6°C. it was incomplete even after 4 hours. The sera used by these workers were evidently weak.

From these observations it seems that antibody–antigen reactions can go quite fast when there is plenty of antibody for the amount of antigen used, but when antibody is relatively deficient and perhaps when certain other conditions obtain, the reactions can take some hours for completion, at least for completion of both stages.

5. Heat of Serological Reactions

Direct Calorimetry

In the early days of immunochemistry, methods were not available for measuring the amounts of free antigen or antibody, or both, remaining after antibody and antigen have reacted. Therefore calculation of the free energy change from direct measurements of the equilibrium constant was not possible. The earlier estimates of the strength of the antibody-antigen bond were based on attempts to measure the heat of reaction ΔH. It will be seen from equation (1)

$$\Delta F^\circ = \Delta H^\circ - T \Delta S^\circ \quad (T = \text{const.}) \tag{1}$$

that if the entropy change ΔS were zero, ΔH° would equal ΔF°, and such a measurement would be an adequate measure of the strength of the antibody–antigen bond. In fact, we may regard equation (1) as a statement that in order to make ΔH° a reliable index of the tendency of the reaction to take place, we have to correct it by allowing for the entropy change ΔS°. A positive entropy change will make a negative ΔF° still more negative, a negative entropy change will make it less negative or even positive. Somewhat unexpectedly, in serological reactions ΔS° is, in fact, not large, though usually not zero.

Nevertheless, not too much has been learned about antibody–antigen reactions by direct calorimetry. The first attempt, by Bayne-Jones (8), gave results that we now know were nearly a million times the correct value. Two later determinations, the first by Kistiakowsky and his group (29), and the second by Steiner and Kitzinger (210), gave −40 and −6 kcal. per mole of antibody, respectively. This difference might have been due to experimental error; but more likely it should be traced to differences in features between the two very different antibody–antigen systems used. Steiner and Kitzinger's result agrees better with values of ΔH° calculated indirectly for other serological reactions, as we shall see below.

Free Energy from Equilibrium Measurements

Various methods have been used to measure the equilibrium between free antibody and antigen and their compounds, or between antibody and hapten and their compounds, including (i) equilibrium dialysis, (ii) direct analyses of precipitates and supernatants, (iii) electrophoretic and ultracentrifugal observations, and (iv) light scattering. Details of the experimental procedures will be found in the references cited. All are methods of determining or calculating the concentrations at equilibrium of free antibody, free antigen, free hapten, or compounds thereof. From such measurements the equilibrium constant K and therefore ΔF° can be calculated. If measurements can be made at more than one temperature, ΔH° and ΔS° can also be estimated.

Of the above methods, (i) and (iv) are applicable only to simple antibody–hapten systems, the former only to univalent hapten systems. Method (iii) can be applied to systems in which the antibody is reacting with a protein, but application of the method may in some cases disturb somewhat the very equilibrium which it is desired to measure. Method (iv) does not disturb the equilibrium.

In applying method (iii), allowance must be made for the fact that antibody is divalent, at least usually, and protein antigens are multivalent (76). Therefore, if we measure the equilibrium in which each antibody is combined with as many antigen molecules as possible (two in the case of divalent antibody), in the presence of free antigen and the compound AG, where A represents antibody and G represents antigen, our equilibrium constant corresponds to

$$(AG_2)/(G)\,(AG) = K \qquad (2)$$

What we are interested in as chemists, however, is the strength of a single antibody–antigen bond. The compound AG_2 contains two such bonds, and each mole of free antigen G contains v moles of free combining sites, where v is the valence of the antigen. Consequently, we want to obtain the value of K', where K' is the equilibrium constant corresponding to the equilibrium.

(antibody–antigen bonds)/
(free antigen sites) (free antibody sites) $= K'$ (3)

by writing

$$2(AG_2)/v(G)\,(AG) = K'$$

or

$$K' = (2/v)K \qquad (4)$$

Therefore, the standard free energy of a single antibody–antigen bond ΔF°_i equals

$$- RT \ln K' = - RT \ln K - RT \ln(2/v), \text{ or}$$
$$\Delta F^\circ_i = - RT \ln K + RT \ln(v/2) \qquad (5)$$

The exact value of the correction will depend on the valence of the antigen and the exact nature of the reaction the equilibrium state of which is being studied.

As an illustration, let us consider the results of Baker et al. (7) on the reaction of anti-benzenearsonic acid antibodies with benzenearsonic acid-azo-bovine serum albumin (bovine serum albumin coupled with diazotized arsanilic acid). The reaction studied by these workers was

$$AG + G \rightleftharpoons AG_2$$

and their bovine serum albumin contained thirteen introduced benzenearsonic acid azo groups per molecule. They calculated a $\Delta F°$ of -5.2 kcal. per mole. From the above this is equivalent to a bond free energy change $\Delta F_i°$ of

$$- 5.2 + RT \ln(13/2)$$

or

$$- 5.2 + 1.1 = -4.1 \text{ kcal./bond}$$

Contrary to expectations, this value is less (*i.e.*, more positive) than the value of -7.4 kcal. per bond found by Epstein, Doty, and Boyd (76) for the reaction of anti-benzenearsonic acid antibodies with the divalent hapten T (terephthalanilide-*p,p′*diarsonic acid) (Fig. 6-8).

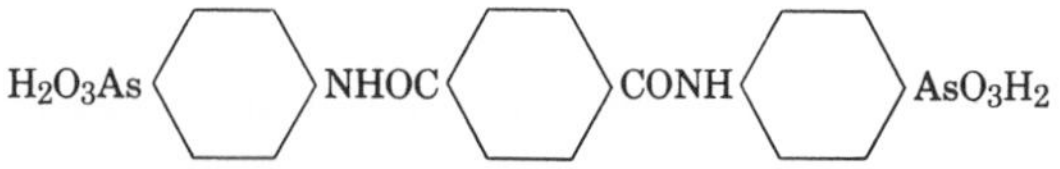

Fig. 6-8.   Divalent hapten used by Epstein, Doty, and Boyd (76).

It would have been expected that the benzenearsonic acid groups in the coupled bovine serum albumin, being coupled through the azo linkage with tyrosine and histidine residues just as in the coupled protein used for immunization, would correspond to the combining sites of the antibody better than the amide-coupled benzenearsonic acid groups of the hapten T. Epstein, Doty, and Boyd suggested that the decreased bond strength was due to some unfavorable feature in the orientation of the groups in the coupled protein.

In dealing with multivalent antigens which may combine simultaneously with a number of molecules of antibody, the mathematical problems of formulating the reaction become formidable unless we introduce simplifying assumptions. The simplest assumption is that the free energy of combination of an antibody molecule with a combining site of the antigen is the same for all such sites and is not affected by the number of antibody molecules which have already combined with the antigen. With the aid of this assumption, which can hardly be strictly true but which is certainly adequate as a first approximation, we can easily solve the problem, as shown by Linderstrøm-Lang (150), von Muralt (171), Fowler (83), Wyman (228), and Klotz (143). If we let the association constant for the formation of a single antibody–antigen bond be K, and the number of combining sites on the antigen molecule (or cell) be m,

TABLE 6-1

Thermodynamic Values Reported for Serological Reactions

Antigen or hapten[a]	Reaction studied[b]	Methods[c]	Reference	$\Delta F°$, kcal./mole	$\Delta H°$, kcal./mole	$\Delta S°$, e.u.
1. Hcy	A	DM	(2)	-10[d]	-40	-100
2. HSA	C	DM + (iii) + (iv)	(12)	-7.5–8.0	-3.66	13.1–14.8
3. BSA	D	(iii)	(9)	-5.5 ± 0.2	0 ± 2	20 ± 8
4. O	D	(iii)	(10)	-5.6 ± 0.2	0 ± 2	20 ± 8
5. Carboxy peptidase	B	(ii)	(11)	-9	-7	7
6. R-BSG	B	(ii)	(5)	$ca. -8.5$	-2	21
7. R-BSA	D	(i)	(1)	-5.2 ± 0.2	0 ± 2	18 ± 8
8. S-BSA	B	(ii)	(5)	-8.5	-2.8	21
9. Hapten T	F	(iv)	(4)	-7.4 ± 0.2	-0.8 ± 2.6	22 ± 9
10. DNP	E	(i)	(3)	-6.8	-1.6	17
11. D-1	E	(i)	(7)	-7.24	-7.1	0.3
12. Lac	E	(i)	(8)	-7.25	-9.7	-8.8
C. Dye B		(i)	(6)	-6.54	-3.93	8.75

[a] Hcy = hemocyanin, HSA = human serum albumin, BSA = bovine serum albumin, BSG = bovine serum globulin, DNP = e-dinitro-phenyllysine, O = Ovalbumin. Structure of R, S, and other haptenic groups was shown in Fig. 6-2. The antibody used in study 1 was horse antibody, rabbit antibody was used in other studies. Study C was on the binding of benzoic acid dye (B, Fig. 6-2) by normal BSA.

[b] See Table 6-1a.

[c] DM = direct measurement; other methods as described in text, p. 328.

[d] Assumed value.

we find the ratio r of antibody molecules combined with an antigen molecule (or cell) to be

$$r = mK(A)/[1 + K(A)] \qquad (6)$$

where (A) is the concentration of free antibody.

A summary of the principal thermodynamic studies on the antibody–antigen or antibody–hapten reaction is given in Table 6-1.

TABLE 6-1a

Reactions for which Data Are Presented in Table 6-1

A.	$nA + G \rightleftharpoons A_nG$
B.	$A + A_{n-1}G \rightleftharpoons A_nG$
C.	$A + 2G \rightleftharpoons AG_2$
D.	$AG + G \rightleftharpoons AG_2$
E.	$A + 2H \rightleftharpoons AH_2$
F.	Haptenic group + antibody site $\rightleftharpoons$ hapten-antibody bond

A = antibody, G = antigen, H = hapten.

References for Table 6-1

1. Baker, M. C., D. H. Campbell, S. I. Epstein, and S. J. Singer, 1956, *J. Am Chem. Soc.*, **78**, 312.
2. Boyd, W. C., J. B. Conn, D. C. Gregg, G. B. Kistiakowsky, and R. M. Robert, 1941, *J. Biol. Chem.*, **139**, 787.
3. Carsten, M. E., and H. N. Eisen, 1955, *J. Am. Chem Soc.*, **77**, 1273.
4. Epstein, S. I., P. Doty, and W. C. Boyd, 1956, *J. Am. Chem. Soc.*, **78**, 3306.
5. Haurowitz, F., C. F. Crampton, and R. Sowinski, 1951, *Federation Proc.*, **10**, 560.
6. Karush, F., 1950, *J. Am. Chem. Soc.*, **72**, 2705.
7. Karush, F., 1956, *J. Am. Chem. Soc.*, **78**, 5519.
8. Karush, F., 1957, *J. Am. Chem. Soc.*, **79**, 3380.
9. Singer, S. J., and D. H. Campbell, 1955, *J. Am. Chem. Soc.*, **77**, 3499.
10. Singer, S. J., and D. H. Campbell, 1955, *J. Am. Chem. Soc.*, **77**, 4851.
11. Smith, E. L., et al., 1952, *J. Biol. Chem.*, **199**, 789.
12. Steiner, R. F., C. Kitzinger, and T. H. Benzinger, 1956, *Research Rept. Naval Med. Research Inst.*, **14**, 73.

Significance of Thermodynamic Constants

The figures in Table 6-1 present some unexpected features. Most surprising, perhaps, is the fact that $\Delta F°$ is generally not large; -9 kcal. per mole seems to be about an upper limit. This is not a large value for standard free energy changes. The free energy of formation of water, for example, is -54.65 kcal. per mole (for two hydrogen–oxygen bonds); that of carbon monoxide is -33.0 kcal. per mole (for one carbon–oxygen bond). On the other hand, it can be seen from Fig. 6-10 that the free-

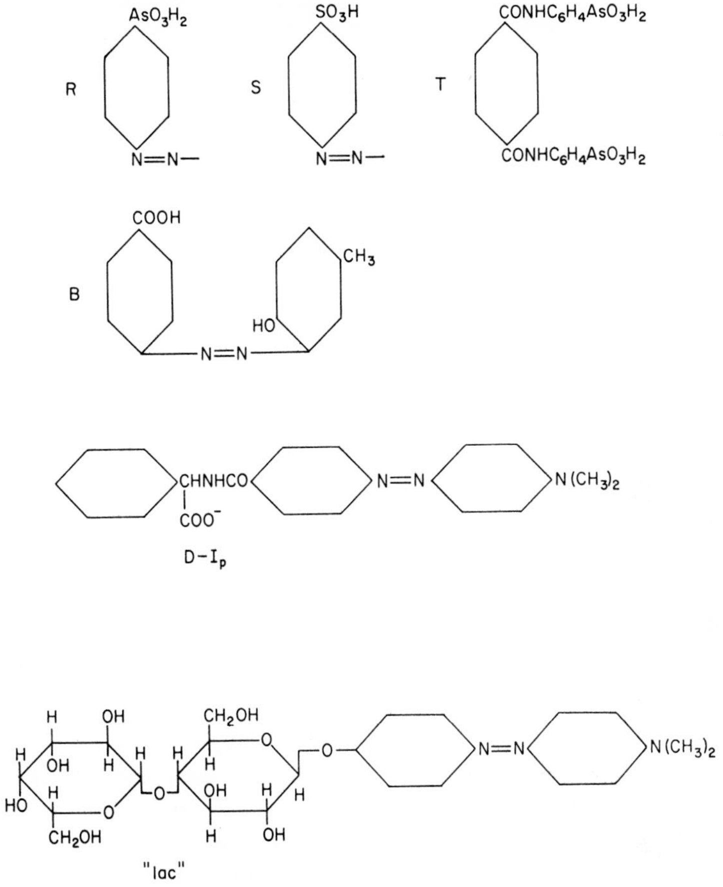

Fig. 6-9. Structures of haptens referred to in Table 6-1.

energy changes involved in the formation of the antibody–antigen bond are sufficient to cause the reaction to go substantially to completion if the reagents are concentrated. (This figure shows the relation between the equilibrium constant K and the free energy change. Also shown is the per cent of product B at equilibrium in a hypothetical reaction A ⇌ B.)

Not only are the values of $\Delta F°$ small by physical and chemical standards, but the values for the different reactions are surprisingly alike, suggesting that no antibody–antigen reaction is likely to have a large free-energy change. If antibody is formed through contact with a molecule or portion of a molecule of antigen or with some intracellular template which causes part of the new molecule to have a configuration comple-

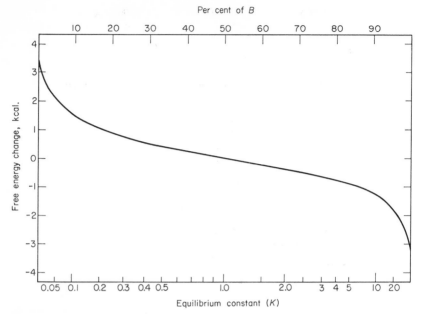

Fig. 6-10. Relation between standard free-energy change ($\Delta F°$) of a reaction $A \rightleftharpoons B$ and the equilibrium constant. Also shown is relation between $\Delta F°$ and the per cent composition of the equilibrium mixture with respect to B. (Slightly modified from H. B. Bull, 1951, *Physical Biochemistry*, 2nd ed., Wiley, New York, by permission.)

mentary to the antigenic determinant, a small value for $\Delta F°$ is understandable. An antibody molecule that possessed too strong an affinity for the fixed antigen molecule or intracellular template would have difficulty leaving its place of formation and getting into the circulation, as was pointed out by Pauling (184) and Singer (203)

Another unexpected feature of Table 6-1 is that the values of $\Delta S°$, with two exceptions, are positive instead of negative. When antibody molecules combine with a molecule of antigen, their freedom of motion is restricted, and this loss of freedom constitutes a loss of "configurational entropy." Therefore, one would expect antibody–antigen reactions to be accompanied by a decrease in entropy. The positive values reported therefore demand explanation.

It has generally been supposed that the positive values for $\Delta S°$ are due to the fact that in most cases there is mutual neutralization of positive and negative charges (see p. 309), with resulting loss of attraction for water molecules. Restoring freedom of motion to water molecules previously bound to the antigen or antibody surface causes an increase in entropy, and this might be more than enough to compensate for the loss of entropy due to the decreased mobility of the antibody molecules. For instance, Epstein, Doty, and Boyd (76) calculated that in the reaction studied by them the release of about twenty-four water molecules accounted for the observed $\Delta S°$. In line with this argument, Karush (140) found a negative entropy change of about nine units for the reaction of antibody with his lactose–hapten "lac," where there is no charge to be neutralized.

The one large negative entropy change in study 1 of Table 6-1 is harder to explain. However, it should be remembered that, in the first place, it is based on a value of $\Delta F°$ which was merely assumed and, in the second place, hemocyanin is a rather special antigen in a number of ways, being much larger and more multivalent than most antigens and constituting an associating and dissociating system. Steiner and Kitzinger (210) suggested that a change in the state of association of the hemocyanin might account for the large enthalpy change observed and for the large negative entropy change calculated from this value.

A third feature of the results of Table 6-1 is that the enthalpy (heat content) changes are small, with the exception, again, of that found in study 1. Aside from this perhaps atypical value, the largest enthalpy change in the table is the -9.7 kcal. per mole calculated by Karush (140) for the reaction of antibody with the "lac" hapten. This is definitely on the small side when compared with the $\Delta H°$ of -94.03 kcal. per mole for the reaction of hydrogen and oxygen to form water, or the -26.4 kcal. per mole for the reaction of carbon and oxygen to form carbon monoxide. It is also of interest that, in all cases where $\Delta H°$ is not zero, or so close to zero that its exact magnitude is not known, it is negative, i.e., the reaction is exothermic.

The enthalpy changes of all the antibody–antigen or antibody–hapten reactions studied, with the exception of that in study 1, are too small to account for the firmness of the bond and the fact that the reaction goes to substantial completion. Obviously, in many, perhaps most, cases the major portion of the driving force of the reaction's $\Delta F°$ is contributed by the term $T \Delta S°$ and is thus due to the positive entropy change.

In spite of the relative weakness of the antibody–antigen or antibody–hapten bond, antibodies display very sharp specificity, as we have already seen. For instance, when Karush compared the reactions of anti-"lac" antibody with lactose with the reaction of the same antibody with cellobiose, he found a value for $\Delta F°$ of -5.52 kcal. per mole for lactose and only -1.96 kcal. per mole for cellobiose, although the only difference between the two sugars is the arrangement of the hydrogen and hydroxyl groups on carbon number 4 of the terminal hexose unit (Fig. 6-11). This again accords with the notion that the hapten fits quite precisely into a portion of the antibody.

The importance of close fit of antibody to hapten is also shown by the work of Nisonoff and Pressman (175) who found that substitution of an iodine atom ortho to the carboxy group of the benzoate ion decreased the antibody–hapten combining energy by 2.4 kcal. per mole. Substitution of an iodine in the meta position decreased the binding energy by about 0.7 kcal. per mole.

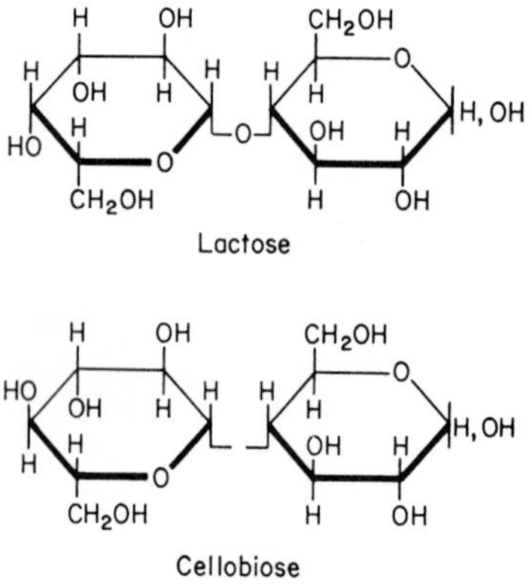

Fig. 6-11. Lactose and cellobiose.

Heat of Reaction of Isohemagglutinins

The thermodynamic constants for the reaction of the human isoagglutinins have been estimated by Wurmser and Filitti-Wurmser (80,227), who devoted a great deal of penetrating thought and experimental skill to the problem. The methods they used are somewhat different from those involved in the studies discussed above and deserve a little space to themselves.

Wurmser and co-workers showed that the combination of isoagglutinins with human erythrocytes is reversible, so that equilibrium considerations apply. We can therefore use the equation

$$\ln (K_2/K_1) = - (\Delta H^\circ/R)(1/T_1 + 1/T_2) \tag{7}$$

which gives us a relation between the equilibrium constant K and the concentration of free antibody at equilibrium. Equation (6) on p. 328, above, contains two unknown constants: the number of combining sites on a red cell (m), and the association constant K. Precise values of

m are not yet available, but Wurmser and Filitti-Wurmser devised methods of calculation which did not require a knowledge of m.

If we invert both sides of equation (6), we obtain

$$1/r = 1/m + 1/mK(A) \qquad (8)$$

This means that if we plot the reciprocal of the number of moles of agglutinin combined with a mole of red cells against the reciprocal of the concentration of free agglutinin, we should get a straight line with slope $1/mK$. If we make such determinations at two different temperatures, the ratio of the slopes $(1/mK_2)/(1/mK_1)$ gives us the ratio of the association constants at these two temperatures, K_1/K_2. From this we may calculate $\Delta H°$ from van't Hoff's equation (7).

The amount of isoagglutinin remaining free in equilibrated mixtures of erythrocytes and serum cannot be estimated with sufficient accuracy by the method of serial dilutions generally used to estimate the strength of an agglutinating serum, and the quantitative methods of Heidelberger and his school are not sensitive enough either. But the Wurmsers hit

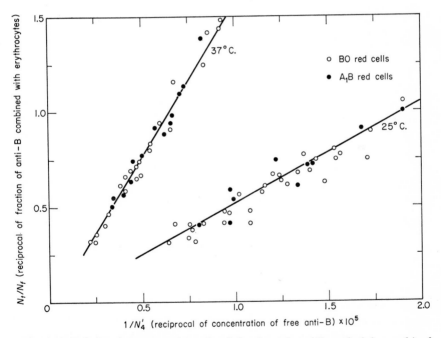

Fig. 6-12. Relation between reciprocals of fraction of anti-B agglutinin combined with erythrocytes and concentration of free anti-B agglutinin, at 37°C. and 25°C., showing linear relationship and different slopes at the two temperatures (80).

upon the device of expressing the agglutinin content of their sera in terms of the maximum number of red cells they agglutinate, and of determining the free agglutinin in the supernatant of erythrocyte–agglutinin mixtures in the same way. This enabled them merely by cell counting to obtain the data for determining the requisite slopes and ratios of slopes described in the last paragraph (Fig. 6-12).

The values of $\Delta H°$ calculated by these methods are shown in Table 6-2. It will be seen that these values of $\Delta H°$ are in several cases larger than the rather small values calculated by other workers for other antibody–antigen and antibody–hapten systems. The most surprising feature

TABLE 6-2

Heat of Combination of Isohemagglutinins with Erythrocytes (227)

Isoagglutinin	Agglutinogen	Genotype of donor	$\Delta H°$, kcal./mole
Anti-B	B	A_1O	-16 ± 2
Anti-B	B	A_1A_1	-6.5 ± 1.1
Anti-B	B	A_2O	-9
Anti-B	B	OO	-1.7 ± 0.4
Anti-A	A_1	BO	-10 ± 3
Anti-A_1	A_1	BO	-33 ± 2.5

of Table 6-2, however, is the marked differences in the anti-B isoagglutinin values obtained from the blood of persons of different blood group and even of different genotype. This has been confirmed by the examination of the serum of 36 A_1O individuals, six of group A_1A_1, and eight of group OO. The anti-B in the serum of any given individual appeared to be homogeneous. This homogeneity is, if real, in marked contrast to the heterogeneity found for immune antibodies (p. 52). The results of the Wurmser group have been criticized by Kabat, but their work seems to have been confirmed experimentally (199,72). See Filitti-Wurmser, Jacquot-Armand, and Wurmser (81).

6. Effect of Varied Conditions on the First Stage of Antibody–Antigen Reactions

Since the first stage of a serological reaction is usually followed by a second stage, it is difficult to distinguish between the effects of altered conditions on the two stages. If we make a change in the conditions of a precipitin reaction and obtain less specific precipitate, for instance, does this mean that less antibody and antigen have combined, or that less of the antibody–antigen compound has precipitated? In only a few cases has it been possible to study the effect on the two stages separately.

pH has an effect: it seems that antibody–antigen combination takes place best in the range pH 4–7.5. The effect of pH on antibody–hapten association was studied by Epstein and Singer (77). Salt (NaCl) is needed for the second stage. Increased temperature, below the limits where it would damage the (protein) reagents involved, accelerates the reaction.

B. SECOND STAGE: NEUTRALIZATION, COMPLEMENT FIXATION, PRECIPITATION, ETC.

When antibody reacts with simple monovalent haptens, no second stage is observable, and perhaps the primary stage of combination completes the reaction. When divalent haptens are used, small aggregates can be observed by suitable technics, and in some cases precipitation occurs. When toxins react with antitoxins, the toxin is found to be wholly or partially neutralized, which is probably an immediate consequence of being combined with antibody. But when conditions are right the combination with antibody results, in the case of some haptens and toxins and other antigens, in another, visible phenomenon, the formation of a precipitate. This usually follows the combination of antibody with carbohydrate and protein antigens. Antigenic cells after combination with antibody often stick together in visible clumps, or are observed to be lysed by the action of complement.

1. Complement Fixation

A discusion of the mechanism of this second-stage serological reaction will be more profitably postponed to Chapter 7.

2. Lysis

The first observations of specific lysis were made with bacteria, but the greater ease of demonstrating the lysis of red blood corpuscles has led to more intensive study of the latter, and it will be advantageous to discuss hemolysis first.

Hemolysis is the release of the hemoglobin from the inside of the erythrocyte. This is called "laking" of the cells. The cell stromata remain undissolved, although altered in size and shape and osmotic properties (13). Nonspecific organic and inorganic substances, or even too low a salt concentration, as well as antibody plus complement, can produce lysis.

The amount of antibody required to sensitize a cell for lysis is extremely small. Brunius (40) calculated that only about 30 molecules of antibody were required to sensitize an erythrocyte for hemolysis, and that the fraction of the surface covered was only about 0.001 per cent. Heidelberger and Mayer (110) calculated a larger number, 400 to 600 molecules of lysin, covering 0.05 to 0.5 per cent of the cell surface. Nevertheless, it is probably incorrect to think of lysis as resulting from punching one or two holes in the cell membrane. By use of hypotonic salt solutions, erythrocytes can be partially hemolyzed, right down to the stage found in completely lysed suspensions and commonly called "ghosts." Partially hemolyzed cells, put back into isotonic saline, seem to retain their remaining hemoglobin indefinitely. This behavior is not compatible with the simple picture of a ruptured membrane, and the mechanism is evidently more complex than that. In this connection it may be remembered that studies of erythrocytes have shown that the lipoprotein matrix extends throughout the cell, although it is much more concentrated near and at the surface, and hemoglobin is correspondingly less concentrated there. The hemoglobin is embedded in the lipoprotein matrix in such a way that the ghosts resulting from hemolysis are not hollow (190).

Specific hemolysis does not occur without the preliminary union of antibody with the cell, but antibody alone does not produce it. The cooperation of other constituents of serum, called collectively complement (or alexin), is needed. The nature of these substances will be considered in the following chapter.

Complement is not specific, for the same source of complement may be satisfactory for lysis of a number of serologically different cells by the appropriate antibodies. Guinea pig serum is the commonest source, but complement is present to some degree in other fresh sera. The sera of different species may, however, differ considerably in their complement activity for any particular lytic system.

Complement does not combine with the cell until the latter has been sensitized by combination with antibody. The degree of lysis depends both on the amount of complement available and on the amount of antibody.

The mechanism of specific lysis will be discussed in more detail in Chapter 7.

3. Bacteriolysis

Although in some instances, as in Pfeiffer's original observations with the cholera vibrio, gross degenerative changes analogous to hemolysis have been observed in bacteria, observation by the naked eye is not in general satisfactory to detect bacteriolysis. Although we speak of measuring the bacteriolytic power of a serum, it is the bactericidal effect which we actually measure.

This is estimated by mixing a light suspension of bacteria with complement and antiserum which has been inactivated (heated to 56°C.) to destroy any complement present in it. The proportion of organisms killed is estimated by culturing the surviving bacteria.

Not all bacteria are killed by such a combination of antiserum and complement. The cholera vibrio, the typhoid bacillus, and most Gram-negative bacilli are readily killed and lysed, but other bacteria, such as the Gram-positive cocci, are not susceptible. This is known not to be due to any failure of complement to combine with the sensitized cells.

It has been found (174) that the serum of patients or animals with syphilis contains an antibody which immobilizes virulent *Treponema pallidum* and destroys their capacity to infect rabbits. This antibody is distinct from the antibody which gives the Wassermann test, and Miller *et al.* (165) claimed that the treponemal immobilization test is highly accurate in the diagnosis of human syphilis.

A prezone is often observed in such experiments, *i.e.,* strong concentrations of serum may fail to kill, while lower concentrations may kill. It may be that when too much antibody is combined with the cell surface, the surface properties are too much like those of uncombined antibody, and complement is not attracted. It has been reported that complement was not fixed when antigen was precipitated with excess of antibody (see Chapter 7). In some such cases, perhaps, although complement combines, the surface is effectively screened from its lytic action by the heavy coating of antibody.

4. Neutralization of Toxins and Viruses

In the processing of neutralizing toxins, antibody combines with them, in varying proportions, dependent on the ratio in which the reagents are mixed, as claimed by Danysz, denied by Ehrlich, and experimentally shown by Healey and Pinfield (99) and Pappenheimer and Robinson (180), (see Table 6-3). Ehrlich early demonstrated that an antibody to the vegetable toxin, ricin, would neutralize its hemolytic power *in vitro.* Similarly it has been found that neutralizing antibodies for vaccinia virus can be adsorbed by the elementary bodies (43), which points to union between the virus and the antibody.

It is not known how the combination with antibody neutralizes toxins and viruses. Toxins are evidently not permanently changed by combination with antitoxin, for it has been found that some toxins, snake venoms,

TABLE 6-3

Toxicity of Tetanolysin after Addition of Antilysin (4)

Antilysin, ml.	Toxicity
0	100
0.05	82
0.1	70
0.15	52
0.2	36
0.3	22
0.4	14.2
0.5	10.1
0.7	6.1
1.0	4.0
1.3	2.7
1.6	2.0
2.0	1.8

for instance, can be recovered from the combination by destroying the antitoxin (44,169,219). Similarly, it has been shown by Todd (218), Andrewes (31), and others that neutral mixtures of antibody and virus can in some cases be made active again by simple dilution or centrifugation (191). Perhaps the action of the antibody is simply to cover the toxin or virus and thus prevent it from coming in effective contact with the susceptive tissue. The development of our knowledge of antitoxins has been well summarized by Pope (192).

Combination of antienzyme antibodies with enzymes sometimes does not destroy or even very much decrease the activity of the enzyme. In other cases the activity is decreased or abolished. A summary of some such results is given in Table 6-4. (See 48,49,37,50.)

It does not necessarily follow that when inhibition is observed the antibody has combined with the enzymatically active sites, for when the substrate is a big molecule, such as a protein, it might be prevented mechanically by the antibody present from approaching close enough to the enzymatically active sites, even though these might be uncombined.

Since the flocculation of toxins by horse antitoxins was not at first known (being missed because of the narrow zone in which precipitation is obtained), and because the point of primary clinical interest is the toxicity of the mixtures, most of the studies on toxin–antitoxin reactions have been made by mixing toxin and antitoxin in varying proportions and testing the toxicity on animals. It is probable that in such reactions we have an opportunity to study the characteristics of the primary stage of serological reactions, practically independently of the complications introduced by any second stage.

TABLE 6-4

Inhibition of Enzymes by Specific Antibodies (47,202)

Enzyme	Substrate	Inhibition, %
Catalase	H_2O_2	None
Tyrosinase	Tyrosine	0–100
Peroxidase	Pyrogallol	56
Laccase	Guaicol	90
Urease	Urea	55–80
β-Galactosidase	Lactose	None
β-Glycosidase (emulsion)	Amygdalin	56
β-Amylase (barley)	Starch	95
α-Glycosidase (sucrase)	Sucrose	36.4
Polysaccharidases (bacterial)	Types III, VII pneum. polysaccharides	100
Hyalurinidase	Mucoprotein	100
Lysozyme	Mucopolysaccharide	100
Thrombin	Plasma (fibrinogen)	100
Rennin	Milk	100
Papain	Gelatin, casein	58–73
Protease (cl. welchii)	Gelatin	52
Lecithinase	Lecithin	100
Lipase (bacterial)	Lipide	100
d-Ribonuclease (pancreas)	PNA	20–30
d-Ribonuclease (venom)	PNA	ca. 100
Deoxyribonuclease	DNA	100
Phosphatase	α-Glycerophosphate	100
D-Glyceraldehyde-3-phosphate dehydrogenase	DPN	90–95
Luciferase	Luciferin	100
Pyruvic acid reductase	DPN-H_2	44–75
Hexokinase	Glucose-ATP	100
Carboxylase	Pyruvate	100
Tryptophanase	Tryptophane	100
Carboxypeptidase	Carbobenzoyglycyl-L-tryptophane	70–100
Penicillinase	Penicillin	100

From the nature of the tests made, it was natural to study the relation of the amount of bound toxin to the amount remaining free. The resulting data when plotted give smooth curves. For example, see Fig. 6-13.

The early workers were often puzzled by the quantitative relations they observed. From Fig. 6-13, we see that the addition of 0.2 ml. of antilysin to the amount of tetanolysin used lowers the toxicity to about 35 per cent of its initial value. The addition of another 0.2 ml. of antilysin has a much smaller relative effect, for the toxicity is still nearly 15 per

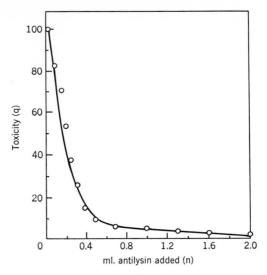

Fig. 6-13. Relative toxicity (*q*) of a constant amount of tetanolysin after addition of varying amounts (*n*) of antibody.

cent of the initial value. In the experiment of Arrhenius (Table 6-3), we find that the addition of 0.1 ml. of antiserum has neutralized 30 per cent of the toxin. It might have been expected that the addition of three times as much (0.3 ml.) would neutralize 90 per cent, but actually it neutralized only 78 per cent, and the addition of 1.0 ml, which we might have expected to neutralize three times as much toxin as was used altogether, actually neutralized only 96 per cent of that present, leaving 4 per cent still free.

Similarly, Ehrlich found that the amount of toxin which, mixed with one standerd antitoxin unit, would just kill a guinea pig, was not 101 times, but of the order of 150 times as much as that contained in one MLD (minimum lethal dose) of toxin. Since he did not consider combination in multiple proportions, Ehrlich was led to the unnecessary assumption that toxin contains a variety of substances of different degrees of combining power (or avidity) for the antitoxin.

We now know that these results are a natural consequence of the fact that the toxin can combine with antitoxin in multiple proportions, and this sort of behavior will be observed whenever one reagent is multivalent for another. The subject has been well discussed by Klotz (143).

A simple mathematical treatment of the problem, assuming reversible combination of antibody with each of a number of combining sites on the toxin, leads to equations formally identical with one or the other of the so-called "adsorption" equations. The solid line in Fig. 6-13 shows the excellent fit to the observed data obtained by using the equation of Ghosh (85), who was the first to treat the subject of quantitative toxin–antitoxin reactions in a sound manner.

Danysz Phenomenon

Danysz (59) observed that when toxin is added to antitoxin, the toxicity of the mixture depends partly on the way in which the toxin is added. If an equivalent amount of toxin is added all at once, the mixture is nontoxic, but, if it is added at intervals, in fractions, the final mixture is generally toxic. This suggests that the antibody in the serum was all expended in neutralizing the first portions added, and not enough was left to neutralize the final portion. From the above discussion of toxin–antitoxin combination it is clear that the explanation of this is, as Danysz thought, connected with the ability of toxin to combine with antitoxin in multiple proportions. If the reaction were reversible, however, we should expect such a toxic mixture, on standing, to become nontoxic; this has been observed (99), indicating that the reaction is at least partly reversible. Heidelberger and Kendall (104) reported an analogous experiment, using SIII and antipneumococcus antibody. It has been objected (155,180) that combination in multiple proportions can hardly be the whole explanation of the original Danysz effect, as in toxin–antitoxin generally no precipitate forms. Therefore, for the toxin–antitoxin compounds a further change, after combination, to less soluble forms was postulated. This may be correct in some instances, although it might be that low dissociability of the compounds first formed could account for the Danysz effect, without any additional assumptions. Healey and Pinfield (99), however, suggested that any persistent Danysz effect must be due to the toxid content of the toxin used and the use of *in vivo* methods for the determination of the antitoxin equivalent of the toxin–toxoid mixture.

The Danysz effect has been studied with enzyme antigens by Cinader (48,49).

Avidity

Early observations suggested that the *curative* effect of antitoxic sera, as judged by experiments on animals, did not always parallel the antitoxin content as determined by the Ehrlich technic. Kraus suggested that, in addition to the actual content of antitoxin units, antitoxic sera possessed another characteristic which determined the rate of neutralization, and for this he proposed the name *avidity*. It was found later that the antitoxin content of a serum, as determined by the Ehrlich *in vivo* and the Ramon *in vitro* titrations, is not always the same. An antitoxin may show in the animal several times the protective power which would be expected from its antibody content, estimated by the Ramon test tube titration (see Chapter 16). Glenny (90) and his colleagues found *in vitro/in vivo* ratios varying from 0.4 to 2.0, and have observed that, when the *in vivo* strength seems to be greater, the antitoxin flocculates more rapidly.

Glenny and his colleagues (88) suggested that the therapeutically important thing is a difference not so much in rate of combination as in firmness of union between toxin and antitoxin. It is not known whether these are related, but it may be suspected that there is some connection. It is apparent that this characteristic of avidity might have considerable bearing on the therapeutic value of antitoxins. It might be for this reason that the Ramon titration, though easier, has not displaced the Ehrlich method for final standardization of antitoxic sera.

In some experiments of Long, reported by Miles (164), the ability of different batches of antitoxin to neutralize toxin was found to be strictly proportional to their strength as measured by flocculation, and was not affected by their avidities.

With precipitating sera it is often observed that some antisera give rapid flocculation, whereas others, apparently possessing the same content of antibody in terms of milligrams per milliliter, flocculate more slowly. Partial absorption of the antibodies also reveals that the antibodies present are not all alike in their flocculative characteristics. It is natural to suppose that these antibodies differ in much the same way as do the antitoxins of different avidity found in antitoxic sera, and we may distinguish different degrees of avidity among them.

In a number of cases (106,113,179) serum has been found to contain, in addition to precipitating antibody, antibody which has the power of combining with antigen but which does not form a precipitate. Such antibody has been variously referred to as low-grade, incomplete, and "univalent" (see Chapter 2). Also, agglutinating sera of nearly the same antibody content may vary widely in the speed with which they agglutinate (24). We might perhaps speak of such differences in antibody as principally differences in avidity. It has been suggested that the differences between these antibodies are due to a smaller number of combining groups on the "low-grade" antibody, but it is perhaps equally probable that they are mainly due to other factors, such as different solubilities, or to less complete specific correspondence between the combining groups of such antibody and those of antigen (19,22,23).

Differences in avidity of hemagglutinating sera have been estimated on the basis of the speed of agglutination (24).

The question of avidity has been well discussed by Jerne (132).

Neutralization of Viruses

The serum of men or animals who have recovered from a virus or rickettsial infection generally contains neutralizing antibodies for the virus. They may be demonstrated by mixing the serum with the specific infectious material and inoculating the mixture into a susceptible host. This provides a method of detecting small amounts of antibodies and has been much used for viruses, but has not proven of quite the same value for rickettsiae. The end point may be death of the experimental animal, production of the specific disease, or the production of some characteristic lesion, as in the use of the dermal lesion in the rabbit in testing for neutralizing antibodies for vaccinia.

Although there has been much controversy about the nature of the reaction involved in the neutralization of viruses by antisera, it seems probable that the mechanism is basically the same as that of the neutralization of toxins (197).

5. Agglutination

If a specific antiserum is added to a uniform suspension of bacteria or red blood corpuscles, the cells are observed, after a certain time, to have stuck together in clumps. In strong reactions these may include practically every cell in the preparation. This is the phenomenon of agglutination. See page 49.

There is no doubt that the combination of agglutinating antibody with red cells and bacteria causes the agglutination which is observed, although the presence of electrolytes is also thought to be essential. The older view of Bordet (12) supposed that the antibody, by its presence, merely sensitized the cells to the agglutinating action of the electrolytes, but the "lattice" theory supposed that the cells are held together primarily by the links formed by bivalent antibody, one end of which is combined with one cell, and the other end of which is combined with another. The weight of evidence is in favor of the newer theory, but certain experiments indicate that the nonspecific mechanism may play a role under certain special conditions, as towards the end of the second stage (149).

Amount of Antibody Involved in Agglutination Reactions

It has been customary to estimate the strength of agglutinating sera by the method of limiting dilution, diluting the serum, and keeping the amount of cell suspension constant. This method gives only comparative values and is subject to the uncertainties discussed on page 102. In some cases, as with erythrocytes, it is still the only method available, and consequently has to be used. If due allowance is made for its relative inaccuracy, it can be very helpful. Miles (163) found that if both serum and suspension were diluted, optimal proportion titrations could be carried out as with precipitins and their antigens (see pp. 229 and 362). Some success was obtained in differentiating strains of *Brucella* by this method.

The accurate quantitative determination of the actual amount of antibody involved in bacterial agglutination was first made possible by the method of Heidelberger and Kabat (101). They found that pneumococci, in amounts which removed most of the agglutinin from the serum, took up from 0.2 to 1.9 g. of antibody nitrogen per gram bacterial nitrogen. Smaller amounts, perhaps of the order of 1/100 of these amounts, will still bring about agglutination.

Jones and Little (133) found that the volume of agglutinated bacteria was increased by amounts which ranged from values too small to measure to 60 to 80 per cent of the original volume. It will be seen that these results are in fair agreement with those found by Heidelberger and Kabat, but Jones and Little in their own determinations did not find enough protein taken up by the organisms to account for the observed volume increases, but found instead only one-fourth to one-sixth as much as expected. They suggested that possibly the excessive volume increase is due to nonuniform distribution of antibody over the surface of the bacteria, preventing close packing of the bacteria when centrifuged.

Filitti-Wurmser *et al.* (80) found that for human group B erythrocytes to be agglutinated by the anti-B agglutinin from group A_1O serum, about 1600 molecules of agglutinin had to be combined with each single erythrocyte at 4°C., and about 4000 at 37°C. This corresponds to about 10^{-15} g. protein per erythrocyte, or about 10^{-4} g. agglutinin nitrogen per gram erythrocyte nitrogen.

Zones in Agglutination

If an agglutinating serum is sufficiently diluted, it no longer agglutinates the cell suspension. If we view the array of test tubes in which the tests are carried out, with the serum dilutions increasing towards the right, we shall find that at some point on the right we enter a "zone" in which agglutination is absent, owing to the lack in those and succeeding tubes of sufficient antibody to cause the cells to agglutinate (Fig. 6-14).

With some antisera a more puzzling observation is made. In addition to the zone just described, which we may call the "postzone," we find that at the left, just where the serum concentrations are highest, agglutination fails. This is called the prezone, or "prozone." Coca and Kelley (51) found one such serum (against *Klebsiella capsulata*) which showed this phenomenon to a very marked degree. This serum would even suppress the agglutinating action of other antisera for *Klebsiella,* when it was

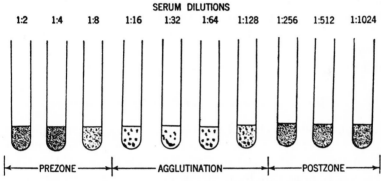

Fig. 6-14. Diagrammatic representation of zones in agglutination.

added to them. The inhibiting action was specific. The inhibiting substance could be absorbed out by treating the serum with homologous organisms, leaving considerable agglutinin; on storage the inhibitory property diminished and finally disappeared. It has also been found possible to give such properties to antisera by artificial means, as by heating. Jones and Orcutt (134) made a careful study of the prezone in bacterial agglutination. They found that it was apparently due to a film of some substance, which interfered with agglutination by reducing the cohesiveness, for direct measurement of the cohesive force between smears of bacteria showed that the presence of this film reduced the cohesion to the value for normal organisms, whereas the surface charge did not seem to be significantly altered. Such treated films, after washing, regained the cohesiveness of others treated with noninhibitory serum; and treated bacteria, after washing, would then agglutinate. It is interesting that no extra increase in volume was observed to accompany the presence on the sensitized cell of this inhibiting film, which seems to imply that the film is either very thin, or consists of a few molecules at scattered loci on the bacterial surface. Treatment of agglutinating sera in ways which destroy their agglutinating activity does not always produce such inhibiting antibodies (22,23).

In some hemagglutinating sera, especially anti-Rh sera, specific inhibiting substances are often found, and when these are present in just the right amount, the serum shows a prezone. As already mentioned, it has been suggested that these inhibiting substances are univalent antibodies, capable of combining but not of linking two cells together. If this were so, the mechanism of the prezone in such cases would be different from that of the case of Jones and Orcutt. However, there are a number of persuasive arguments against the theory that these inhibitors are univalent antibodies (see Chapter 2). The similarity of the "blocking antibodies" to the inhibitor of Jones and Orcutt may be closer than was at first thought.

For further discussion of blocking antibodies and zones, see p. 357.

Effect on Agglutination of Changes in Conditions

A certain amount of electrolyte seems to be necessary for agglutination, but higher concentrations diminish the effect of agglutinating antibodies. Agglutination can take place over a rather wide range of pH (176). Agglutination is promoted by higher temperatures at least up to 37°C. Increase in temperature at the same time decreases the firmness of union of agglutinins with cells (80). Shaking and stirring speed up agglutination, and automatic shaking devices, or centrifugation, are commonly used in blood grouping work.

Nonspecific Serum Proteins. As Marrack (155) pointed out, in view of the protecting or precipitating effects which proteins exert on various suspensions, it would be expected that nonspecific proteins may affect agglutination and flocculation, and it would be expected that they might either promote or partially inhibit these reactions. The effect is generally not very great. Dean (60) found agglutination increased by euglobulin from guinea pig serum. Eagle (68) found that a fraction of fresh normal serum, precipitated by dilution and carbon dioxide, accelerated agglutination. He found this to parallel the complement "mid-piece" activity (see Chapter 7). Duncan (67) found a retarding action of normal serum. The increased rate of sedimentation of erythrocytes observed in certain clinical conditions, such as infections, results from "rouleaux" formation, not true agglutination.

A different sort of influence of nonspecific proteins was brought to light when Diamond discovered that anti-Rh sera of the nonagglutinating type ("incomplete," "univalent," or "blocking" antibodies) in slide tests would agglutinate cells suspended in their own serum. Wiener showed that this would also work in the test tube and proposed it as a routine technic. Diamond and Denton (62) showed that agglutination would occur when the cells were suspended in 20 per cent human or bovine albumin solution. This was an important addition to clinical technics, as it enabled the presence of the "blocking" antibodies to be more easily demonstrated, and these antibodies are the more important ones in the production of *erythroblastosis fetalis*.

Wiener (221) has suggested calling this the conglutination test, although this involves a change (perhaps justifiable) in the original meaning of the term conglutinin (see p. 49).

The mechanism of this action of albumins is not known. See, however, Pirofsky and Cordova (189).

Hemagglutination by Viruses

It was found in 1941 that the influenza virus has the power of agglutinating chicken red cells (120,162). Since then a number of other viruses have been found to have a similar power. These viruses include (*a*) influenza, mumps, Newcastle disease; (*b*) variola, vaccinia, ectromelia, meningopneumonitis; and (*c*) encephalomyocarditis virus, mouse encephalomyelitis, Japanese encephalitis, St. Louis encephalitis, West Nile fever, Russian spring summer encephalitis, foot-and-mouth disease, and fowl plague. It will be seen that this is a very heterogeneous group of viruses.

To demonstrate the phenomenon, suspensions of red cells and virus are mixed and allowed to stand. As the cells settle out they aggregate into clumps of moderate size which are macroscopically visible. The cohesion between the cells is much weaker than in ordinary hemagglutination, and the clumps are very easily broken up by gentle shaking.

Hemagglutination by viruses provides a rapid and simple method for assaying the virus content of a tissue suspension, although it is not nearly so sensitive as the virus neutralization technic (197).

Virus hemagglutination has also been used for the measurement of antibody concentration, since it is found that neutralizing antibody for these viruses also neutralizes their hemagglutinating activity.

It has been shown that the agglutination is a result of the attachment of virus particles to the surface of the red cell, in the cases of viruses of groups (*a*) and (*c*), but in the case of viruses of group (*b*) the agglutinating agent is a soluble substance which is separable from the virus particle.

The viruses of group (*a*) exhibit an interesting behavior. When one of them is mixed with suitable red cells, almost all of the virus becomes attached to the cells within a few minutes. Then the virus particles begin to elute spontaneously from the cells, and under proper conditions will do so completely. The eluted virus seems the same as before, but the red cells will no longer absorb fresh virus of this particular strain, nor will they usually absorb viruses of different strains of the same type, though they will absorb unrelated strains. The charge on the cells, as shown by measurements of electrophoretic mobility, is found to have changed markedly, and immunological tests show that a hitherto undetectable antigen has appeared on the surface of these cells (42).

These phenomena suggest that the virus has an enzymatic action on the cell, and make it probable that the union of the virus with the cell is brought about by the usual forces which unite enzyme and substrate. Once the red cell receptor, which is thought to be mucoprotein in nature, is destroyed, the combining forces no longer exist, and the virus spontaneously elutes.

Mechanism of Agglutination

It is now generally believed that agglutination is brought about by the Marrack-Heidelberger (154,100) "lattice" mechanism, with divalent molecules of antibody, one end combined with one cell and the other end with another cell, acting as links to hold the cells together. See Figs. 6-23 and 6-24.

Unlike the older Bordet theory, this theory of agglutination says nothing about the role of electric forces, which are known to be active in keeping bacterial cells and erythrocytes from contact with each other in unagglutinated suspensions. Under the microscope, for example, the cells of an erythrocyte suspension are seen to be arranged, not in random fashion, but almost exactly equidistant from each other; they look as if they were held apart by electric repulsion. The first sign of incipient agglutination is often just a modification of this equidistant arrangement in the direction of a truly haphazard arrangement. Measurements of the surface potential of bacteria (see 155) have shown that agglutination begins when the potential falls below about 15 mv. From observations of this sort it was concluded that one of the conditions which permit agglutination is a diminution of the charge on the cells.

The studies of Brody (38), however, threw considerable doubt on the role of reduced surface charge in agglutination. He found that red cells could have their charge reduced by 80 per cent or more (as by treatment with extracts of certain pneumococci) without a trace of agglutination. The isoagglutinins did sometimes lower the charge (25 to 35 per cent) but sometimes affected it very little. Anti-Rh antibodies changed the charge only about 6 to 8 per cent, irrespective of whether they were of the agglutinating or nonagglutinating (blocking) type. Furthermore, treatment of cells with charge-lowering agents did not increase the sensitivity of the cells to isoagglutinins.

Agglutinated cells sometimes stick to the walls of the test tube, so firmly that only a mechanical wiping, or washing with water, will remove them. This is especially likely to happen if the cells are agglutinated by chicken serum (146) or plant agglutinins (lectins) (25). Boyd found such cells would even stick to silicone-treated tubes. This phenomenon looks at first sight like a nonspecific stickiness of the sort demanded by the Bordet theory (p. 375), but Landsteiner (146) suggested that the phenomenon might result from the attachment of the cells to antibody adsorbed on the glass and this seems to be the case (33).

Immune Adherence

It was observed a long time ago that parasites, in the presence of specific antibody, could attach themselves to cells of the host (173).

Immune adherence (IA) (174) has proved to be a very sensitive method of detecting antibody (as little as 0.005 to 0.01 μg.) It has wide potential application as an immunological tool in clinical and research laboratories (173).

6. The Precipitin Reaction

The formation of a precipitate when antibody and soluble antigen are mixed is one of the most striking phenomena of serological reactions; some of the older and many of the more recent studies of it have yielded results of great interest and importance.

Amount of Precipitate; Zones

Either the amount of antiserum or the amount of antigen can be varied; it is usual to keep the concentration of one reagent constant and add various amounts of the other. The precipitates obtained were at first generally analyzed for nitrogen by some modification of the micro-Kjeldahl technic divised by Parnas and Wagner (182), apparently first applied to serological reactions by Heidelberger and Kendall. The amount of protein was calculated by multiplying by the traditional factor 6.25 (equivalent to assuming 16 per cent nitrogen in the protein). When the antigen was not a protein, particularly if it were a nitrogen-free polysaccharide, these analyses sufficed to determine the amount of antibody in the precipitates directly. If the antigen was a protein, the nitrogen due to the antigen had to be first subtracted. In regions of the precipitin reaction where not all the antigen was precipitated, some method of determining the antigen separately was needed, as by the determination of some inorganic atom naturally present or artificially introduced. The ratio in which antibody and antigen were mixed could be varied to produce precipitates of different composition, and the absolute amounts adjusted so as to give a precipitate containing about the amount of nitrogen which was optimal for the Parnas-Wagner method (about 1 mg.).

This amount of nitrogen, in precipitates consisting, as is usual, mostly of antibody, called for the use of some 6 mg. of antibody in each precipitate, and there have been many attempts to develop more sensitive and less laborious analytical methods which will accurately determine smaller amounts. Heidelberger and McPherson (109) described a method, using the Folin-Ciocalteu phenol reagent, which will estimate very small amounts (as little as 10 μg.) of protein. The use of ultraviolet absorption photometry has been described (160), the use of the biuret method has been studied (160,35), and Kunkel and Ward (144) have described a method, utilizing the color reaction of ninhydrin with amino groups, which is stated to be five times as sensitive as the method of Heidelberger and MacPherson.

Advantage has also been taken of the newer radio-isotope labeling techniques (160,97). Radioactive iodine (158) can be introduced into either the antibody or the antigen, and studies have shown that small amounts of such introduced iodine do not much affect the immunochemical behavior of these proteins. Such labeled antibody has also been used in a study of the agglutination reaction (15), and to follow the localization in the body of injected antiorgan antibodies (195). Antibody labeled by coupling with fluorescein isocyanate has been used to study the localization of injected antigens and antibody in the tissues (57).

The whole subject of the use of labeled antigens and antibodies has been reviewed by Coons (56).

Most of the precipitating antisera that have been studied quantitatively thus far were obtained from the horse or the rabbit (Pennell and Huddleson used goat serum). In the horse there seems to be a striking difference in the behavior of antibodies against proteins (such as antitoxins) and antibodies against bacterial polysaccharides; in the rabbit this difference is not found, but both kinds of antibodies behave more or less alike, resembling in their precipitating behavior the anticarbohydrate antibody of the horse.

As already mentioned in Chapter 2, with horse antisera to proteins it is generally found that, if more than a certain relative amount of antibody is added, no precipitate is produced, soluble compounds being formed, whereas carbohydrates are precipitated even with large excess of antibody. In the language of our discussion of agglutination, horse antiprotein sera exhibit a prezone. Rabbit antibodies, whether against protein or carbohydrate, do not show a prezone with excess antibody. It may be suspected that the difference is at least partly due to a difference in solubility of the various antibodies, for it will be recalled that the anticarbohydrate antibodies in the horse, and most antibodies of the rabbit, are predominantly found in the euglobulin (least soluble) fraction of the serum proteins, while the antiprotein antibody in the horse is mostly of pseudoglobulin (more soluble) character.

All precipitating systems exhibit the phenomenon of the postzone which is unfortunately usually called the prezone (since in precipitin reactions it is usually the antigen which is diluted, so that the strongest antigens solutions come first) (see Fig. 6-15); for this reason and for others, it seems best to use Heidelberger's term "inhibition zone." We may define this as the zone in which there is insufficient antibody to precipitate the antigen present. The antibody in this zone forms soluble compounds with the antigen.

The actual amount of precipitate obtained from a given amount of antiserum depends in the first place on the amount of precipitating antibody present, and in the second place on the amount of antigen added. As increasing amounts of antigen are added, the amount of precipitate increases up to a maximum, then declines as the inhibition zone is reached. This is brought out by Figs. 6-15a and 6-15b (drawn to the same scale), which are based on results of Heidelberger and Kendall (106,108), Pappenheimer and Robinson (180), Pappenheimer (179), and Hooker and Boyd (122). Figure 6-15a illustrates typical results obtained with rabbit antisera, and Figure 6-15b those with horse antiprotein sera. As has already been mentioned, horse anti-carbohydrate sera have been found to behave in this respect much like rabbit antisera. The precipitating zone may be somewhat broader, however, in some cases, with rather a flat plateau on top (100,104). We may mention also that horse antiprotein sera, when sufficiently strong, may show a much broader zone of precipitation than those shown in Figure 6-15b; the breadth of the zone may even exceed (122) that of the rabbit sera shown in Figure 6-15a.

If the supernatants from such precipitates are tested for antibody and

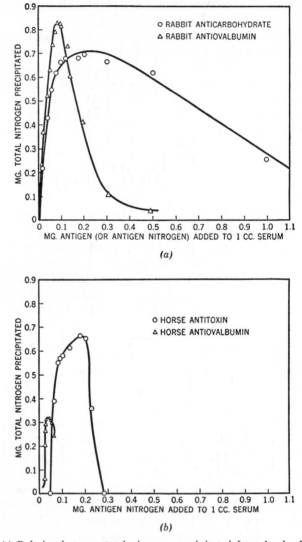

Fig. 6-15. (a) Relation between total nitrogen precipitated from 1 ml. of rabbit antiserum and amount of antigen added (106,108); (b) relation between total nitrogen from 1 ml. of horse antiprotein serum and amount of antigen added (122,179,180).

antigen, it is found that antibody is present in the first tube (where insufficient antigen was added), and antigen is present in the last tube (where excess antigen has been added). In the central part of the range, one or more tubes will be found where there is either no antibody and no antigen, or small traces of both, in the supernatant. This is called the equivalence zone (Heidelberger). In some systems this zone may coincide with, or lie near, the point of maximal precipitation of antibody. In other systems (105,152), however, the point where the maximal precipitate is obtained may lie in the region of antigen excess.

It has been found convenient to divide the whole range of the reaction of rabbit precipitin with antigen into the following five zones in order of increasing antibody-to-antigen ratio: complete inhibition, partial inhibition, antigen excess, equivalence, and antibody excess. In the case of horse antiprotein precipitin it would be necessary to add two more zones, partial antibody inhibition and complete antibody inhibition. A schematic presentation of this arrangement, which also serves to indicate approximately the meaning to be attributed to each term, is given in Figs. 6-16a and 6-16b.

The precipitin reaction has also been studied by following photometrically the turbidity which develops (193,36) and by studying the light scattering of antibody–antigen mixtures (87,93). The light-scattering method enables the sizes of the aggregates to be estimated at any time in the course of the reaction.

Light-scattering methods have also been used to study the reaction of antibody with haptens (63).

Composition of the Precipitate

The precipitate contains both antibody and antigen; with the majority of antigens the greater part of the precipitate consists of antibody; with the antigens of high molecular weight the reverse may be true. Precipitates may contain lipide; in addition minor constituents such as complement are usually present (see Chapter 7). There is definite evidence that the washed precipitate does not contain any large amount of nonspecific serum proteins (104,122,157), although small amounts of complement, even when aged sera are used, are present.

The antibody and antigen are found in the precipitate in varying proportions, depending on the ratio in which the serum and antigen solution are mixed (and also on the final concentration in the supernatant of the reagents (see p. 322)) and on other factors such as the molecular weight of the antigen.

Influence of Molecular Weight of the Antigen

Boyd and Hooker (30,32) called attention to the fact that the ratio of antibody to antigen in precipitates made at the equivalence point (mid-

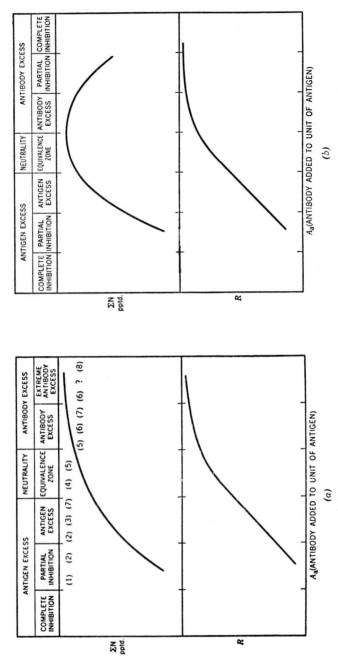

Fig. 6·16. (a) Zones into which the precipitin reaction with rabbit antibody can be divided. Curves show schematically the relation between total nitrogen precipitated (above) and ratio of antibody to antigen (r) in the precipitate (below) observed when increasing amounts of antibody (A_a) are added to a constant amount of antigen (G); (b) zones of precipitin reaction with horse antiprotein antibody.

point of equivalence zone) depends on the molecular weight of the antigen. The dependence is not absolute, as will be seen in Fig. 6-17, but
it was found that there was at least a highly significant degree of correlation between the two variables. Boyd and Hooker interpreted this
tentatively as due to the fact that at the equivalence point the surface of
the antigen molecule is just covered with molecules of antibody, each

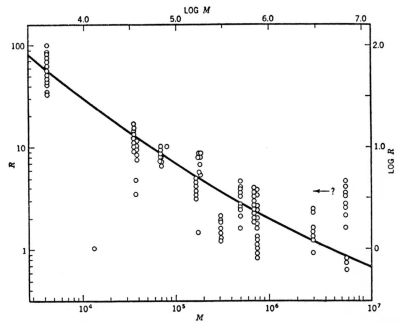

Fig. 6-17. Calculated relation between ratio of antibody to antigen (R) in precipitates, and molecular weight (M) of antigen, shown by curve. Experimental values
shown by circles.

such molecule supposedly acting as a chain of four roughly spherical units
of molecular weight about 35,000 (Fig. 6-18). It would do equally well
for this purpose, and perhaps accord better with our ideas of the shape
of antibody molecules, to suppose that antibody behaved as a long flexible
ellipsoid.* On the basis of such a picture it was possible to calculate by
spherical geometry that the theoretical relation between molecular weight

* Flexibility of antibody molecules is suggested by electron micrographs by Almeida,
Cinader, and Howatson (2,176a) showing antibody molecules attached by both ends to
the same antigenic surface, and bent into the shape of an inverted U.

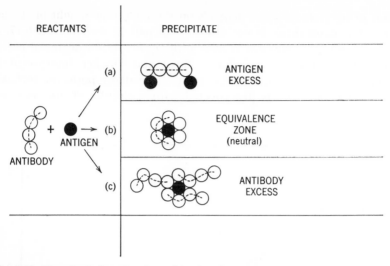

Fig. 6-18. Hypothetical mode of combination between antibody—assumed to consist of four linked units of about 40,000 molecular weight each—with an antigen of about the molecular weight of egg albumin (about 40,000), in three different zones of the precipitin reaction.

of the antigen (M) and ratio by weight of antibody to antigen (R) in the precipitates ought to be approximately:

$$R = 37,800M^{-0.8} + 179M^{-0.35}$$

In Fig. 6-17 this theoretical relation, shown by the solid line, is seen to fit the data rather well, considering the roughness of many of the measurements. It is doubtful, however, if we are justified in considering the polysaccharide molecules, here plotted at the value, $M = 4000$, to have molecular weights this low, or to be spherical, so it may be that part of the agreement is fortuitous. Also it is perhaps doubtful if antibody molecules are as flexible as required by the above picture. In any case, it can be seen that the ratio does tend to diminish with increasing molecular weight of the antigen, falling from values of around 10 for antigens of molecular weight 35,000 to 40,000 to values of less than 1.00 for the large hemocyanin molecules of molecular weight of about 7,000,000 to 10,-000,000.

Landsteiner (147) pointed out that this model, however, improbable it may be in some ways, does predict a coating of antibody of about the thickness (about 40 A.) that is actually found. How (128) derived an improved formula giving somewhat better agreement with the data.

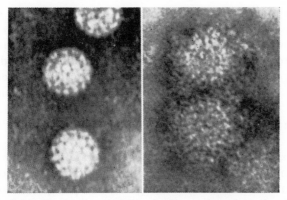

Fig. 6-19. On left, polyoma virus, 280,000 ×. The outline of the virus is smooth; the capsomeres can be clearly seen. On right, polyoma virus combined with divalent rabbit antibody. The virus particles are completely surrounded by a halo of antibody molecules, standing out radially from the virus surface. The halo is approximately 300 A. wide, in good agreement with the calculated dimensions of antibody (Table 2-3 in Chapter 2). From Almeida, Cinader, and Naylor (2a) with permission.

When less than the equivalent amount of the antibody is used, the precipitate contains less antibody, and we may suppose the surface to be only partly coated. When more antibody is used, the ratio of antibody to antigen in the precipitate goes up. If antibodies are really to be visualized as just suggested, it is necessary to suppose that some of the molecules in this case are not in complete contact with the antigen surface, and when there is a considerable excess of antibody we should have to visualize them as "standing on their heads." This concept is illustrated in Fig. 6-18, drawn more than 20 years ago. For an actual photograph, see Fig. 6-19.

Influence of Proportion in Which Reagents Are Mixed

It has already been pointed out that if serological reactions are reversible and follow the usual laws of chemical equilibrium, then the composition of the antibody–antigen compound formed ought to depend on the final concentration of antibody (or antigen) in the supernatant, and we have seen that a simple relationship between these two variables does in fact exist. The logarithm of the ratio of antibody to antigen in the compound is a linear function of the logarithm of the concentration of antibody (or antigen) in the supernatant.

Not much use has been made of such relations, or of this equation, in modern immunochemistry, because few data of this sort are available.

It is not easy to measure the concentration of antibody in the supernatant of a precipitate, and such determinations are not generally attempted. Usually all we know is how much antibody and how much antigen were mixed to produce a precipitate, which on analysis is found to have a certain composition. So the theoretical relation desired is one between the ratio in which the reagents are mixed and the composition of the precipitate. This is a more difficult relation to derive, and attempts to solve it have given rise to a series of mathematical theories of the precipitin reaction.

When mixtures are made containing more antibody than is required for equivalent proportions, the resulting precipitate will be richer in antibody. The ratio of antibody to antigen in the precipitate does not continue to increase at the same rate as more and more antibody is used, but the curve flattens out, and the ratio appears to approach an upper limit asymptotically. In the case of most horse antiprotein sera these compounds with higher antibody-to-antigen ratio are soluble, and precipitation does not occur with any considerable excess of antibody. With other antisera the compounds of higher ratio are all insoluble and therefore precipitate.

If we keep the amount of antibody constant, and add varying amounts of antigen, we find that more than the equivalent amount of antigens gives compounds with an antibody-to-antigen ratio lower than that formed in the equivalence zone. Below a certain point these compounds are soluble, and no precipitate is formed, in the case of all systems. This gives rise to what we may refer to as the "zone of complete inhibition," or prezone. The ratio of antibody to antigen in the *precipitate* therefore never falls below a certain limiting value, which if it could be measured would give the approximate composition of the compound having the smallest proportion of antibody which will still precipitate. For small antigen molecules, this is estimated at about 2 molecules of antibody to 1 of antigen, but for larger molecules as many as 30 to 40 molecules of antibody may be required to precipitate 1 molecule of antigen. This is shown in Table 6-6.

The adjoining Table 6-5 gives two examples of the variation in the composition of precipitate with variation in the proportion in which the reagents were mixed. The first, from Heidelberger and Kendall (104), shows the results for the system horse antipneumococcus type III and the specific polysaccharide SIII. The second, from Pappenheimer and Robinson (180), is from a study of the reaction of diphtheria toxin and horse antitoxin.

In both of the examples in Table 6-5, as in the majority of the early

TABLE 6-5

Ratio of Antibody to Antigen in Precipitates Made with Varying Proportions of Antibody to Antigen for Two Different Systems

Horse antipneumococccus SIII				Horse antidiphtheria toxin			
S added (mg.)	ΣN pptd. (mg.)	r = (N/S) × 6.25	Reagent present in excess	Toxin N added (mg.)	ΣN pptd. (mg.)	r = antibody N/toxin N	Reagent present in excess
0.02	0.45	140	A	0.023	0	—	A
0.04	0.79	124	A	0.046	0	—	A
0.05	0.97	121	A	0.069	0.386	(6.9)	(A)
0.06	1.08	112	A	0.081	0.554	5.8	(A)
0.08	1.29	101	A	0.092	0.564	5.1	—
0.10	1.54	96	A	0.103	0.579	4.6	—
0.12	1.68	87	A	0.138	0.612	3.4	—
0.15	1.71	71	A	0.184	0.661	2.6	(T)
0.20	1.75	?	S	(0.196)	—	(2.4)	(T)
				0.207	0.652	—	(T)
				0.230	0.359	—	T
				0.276	0	—	T

One milliliter of antiserum used for all experiments. A = antibody, T = toxin, S = specific capsular polysaccharide of type III pneumococcus, N = nitrogen. Figures in parentheses somewhat uncertain.

quantitative studies on the precipitin reaction, the ratio of antibody to antigen was calculated on the assumption that in the absence of any way to determine the amount of antigen directly in the precipitate, all the antigen was precipitated. This assumption has been shown to be allowable, but it precludes a study of the region where only part of the antigen is precipitated (region of antigen excess). For a study to be carried any distance into the region of antigen excess, it is necessary to have some way of determining the antigen separately from the antibody. When the proportion of antigen remaining unprecipitated is small, serological methods (196,125) can be used to estimate it, but the only analytical methods of general applicability to this problem depend on the use of antigens which are colored, or contain a "tracer" atom, or which contain some introduced prosthetic group which enables them to be detected (105,126,152,211,224, 225). There have been only two investigations which were at all extensive into the region of antigen excess (105,152).

Broadening of the Equivalence Zone

It was found by Heidelberger and Kendall (106) and Heidelberger Treffers, and Mayer (113) that the equivalence zone is broader in sera from animals after prolonged immunization than in sera from animals after a brief course of injections. Malkiel and Boyd (152) made an observation which is probably related, that the difference between the midpoint of the equivalence zone and the point of optimal proportions was greater in the sera of animals having had longer courses of injections. All of these workers observed that the ratio of antibody to antigen in precipitates from sera such hyperimmunized animals might be higher.

Molecular Composition of Precipitates

The application of quantitative methods to the study of the precipitin reaction, plus the determination of molecular weights of various proteins, including antibodies, by the ultracentrifugal technic, have made it possible to calculate the actual molecular composition of precipitates made under various conditions. In Table 6-6 are given the results of the studies of

TABLE 6-6

Molecular Composition of Specific Precipitates

Antigen	Antibody	Empirical composition of precipitate at				
		Extreme[a] antibody excess	Antibody excess end of equivalence zone	Antigen excess end of equivalence zone	Zone of partial inhibition	Composition of soluble compound in zone of partial inhibition
Ovalbumin	Rabbit	A_5G	A_3G	A_5G_2	A_2G	(AG)
Dye-ovalbumin	Rabbit	(A_5G)	(A_3G)	A_5G_2	A_3G_4	(AG_2)
Serum albumin	Rabbit	A_6G	A_4G	A_3G	A_2G	(AG)
Thyroglobulin	Rabbit	$A_{40}G$	$A_{14}G$	$A_{10}G$	A_2G	(AG)
Viviparus hemocyanin	Rabbit	—	$A_{120}G$	$A_{83}G$	$A_{35}G$	—
Tobacco mosaic virus	Rabbit	$A_{900}G$	$A_{450}G$	—	—	—
Diphtheria toxin	Horse	A_8G	A_4G	A_3G_2	AG	(AG_2)
Ovalbumin	Horse	(A_4G)	A_2G		AG	(AG_2)

A = antibody, G = antigen.

Formulas in parentheses are somewhat uncertain.

[a] For meaning of this and similar terms, see Figs. 6-16a and 6-17b.

Heidelberger (100) and collaborators, to which have been added results calculated from the data of Malkiel and Boyd (152), Pappenheimer (179), Heidelberger, Treffers, and Mayer (113), Pappenheimer, Lundgren, and Williams (181), and Kabat (135).

From Table 6-6 it may be concluded, since the ratio of antibody to antigen in precipitates is observed experimentally to vary continuously, that, if the above formulas really represent the composition of all the various antibody–antigen compounds possible, the precipitate obtained at any particular point is likely to be a mixture of two or more of these compounds.

Solubility of the Precipitate

It is the custom of all workers to wash precipitates two or three times with saline before analysis. The amount of serum protein removed during these washings may be two or three times the amount remaining in the precipitate, but, by tacit agreement, only that which remains after washing is defined as antibody. Later washings remove comparatively little from the precipitate; in other words, the solubility of the precipitate is low. When very small precipitates are being analyzed, it is necessary to correct for the amount which dissolves in the wash liquid. The use of chilled saline reduces this loss. Various workers (see references in (155) have found solubilities of the order of 0.05 to 0.005 mg. nitrogen per milliliter saline; the solubility found with the first washings is larger, falling asymptotically towards a minimum as washing is continued. This suggests that the precipitates are not homogeneous, as was mentioned above. There is perhaps also the possibility of gradual denaturation, but such precipitates still dissolve in excess antigen. Typical results (25) are shown in Table 6-7.

TABLE 6-7

Solubility in Saline (Milligrams Nitrogen per Milliliter) of Thrice-Washed Precipitates (Hemocyanin of *Busycon canaliculatum* and Horse Anti-*Busycon*)

Extraction	Volume of extractant (milliliters saline per gram precipitate nitrogen)		
	333	878	1660
1	0.0379	0.0210	0.0211
2	0.0169	0.0032	0.0036
3	0.0082	0.0038	0.0024
4	0.0056	0.0021	0.0026
5	0.0036	—	0.0011
6	0.0044	—	0.0001

The question arises: Does the precipitate in these experiments dissolve in the form of undissociated compound, or is the dissolved precipitate more or less completely dissociated into antibody and an antibody–antigen compound containing less antibody? Since we believe the mass law to apply to antibody–antigen reactions, it is obvious that some dissociation will result when the precipitate is transferred from the supernatant in which it was formed to a wash liquid. The available tests for antigen and antibody are often not delicate enough to detect the small amounts of dissociation which might be expected to occur. A further difficulty arises because of the general nonhomogeneity of antibodies. Even in those experiments in which both antibody and antigen are detected in the supernatant, and in which pure antigens were used (which is not always the case), it is hard to be sure that antibody found in solution is the same as that which precipitated. In fact, according to Heidelberger (personal communication), there is plenty of evidence that the antibody in solution is different. One can only observe that some workers have found both antibody and antigen in the supernatant in the equivalence zone, whereas others have failed to find either. Different systems may vary in this respect.

Effect of Altered Condition on Amount and Composition of Precipitate

Although antibody and antigen evidently can combine in the absence of electrolyte, some salt seems to be necessary for precipitation (82). High salt concentrations will diminish precipitation, or actually dissociate antibody from antigen to some degree, in some systems (112). Within the "physiological" range (6.6 to 8.0) pH has little effect on most systems (158). Higher temperatures accelerate precipitation, unless high enough to denature one of the reagents, although in some cases less precipitate is formed (113).

Velocity of the Reaction. Zones and Optima

The reader will already have gathered that the velocity of precipitate formation is different in the different zones defined above. The practical use of velocity observations, in the form of the Ramon titration and the Dean and Webb method of optimal proportions, has also been referred to in Chapter 2, in the sections devoted to methods of measuring antibody concentration. The technic of carrying out such titrations is described in Chapter 16. We must now take up the question of the differences between these two procedures.

In the Ramon technic, varying amounts of antiserum are added to a constant amount of antigen (toxin), and the most rapidly flocculating mixture is observed. This has been called the β procedure by English writers (see 155). In the Dean and Webb technic, the amount of antiserum is held constant, and the amount of antigen is varied (α procedure). If another amount of antiserum is taken, and varying amounts of antigen again are used, it is found that the ratio (dilution of antigen)/(dilution of antiserum) is the same, or nearly the same, as was obtained with the first amount. Thus in the α procedure, if most rapid flocculation occurs in the case of antiserum diluted 1:5 and antigen diluted 1:200, then we shall find with antiserum diluted 1:10 that the optimal dilution of antigen will be 1:400. This constant of dilutions is referred to as the "optimal proportions" ratio. The question now arises, will the optimal proportions ratios obtained by α and β procedures be the same? It might possibly be expected that they would. A number of experimenters have tested this, however, and have found that in general the two points are not the same (66,163,213–215).

The proper examination of this question involves extensive "checkerboard" experiments, in which all practicable dilutions of serum are tested with all practicable dilutions of antigen. If this is done, a table of times of flocculation, one entry for each combination of antibody dilution and antigen dilution, will be obtained. The result of a typical experiment is shown in Fig. 6-20.

In this experiment, the time of particulation, *i.e.*, the time required for particles to become just visible to the unaided eye of the operator, was recorded. The reactions were carried out with the tubes one-third immersed in water at 40°C. so as to obtain strong convection currents, which greatly accelerate the reaction, probably proportionally in all tubes (125).

The sort of result obtained in the α procedure can be found by following along one of the horizontal rows, where antigen concentration varies and antibody concentration remains the same. A minimum appears in the times recorded in this row. In the row above or the row below, there will also be a minimum; and the ratio of the concentrations (or dilutions) will in each case be the same, though in the lower rows the total time, since both reagents are more dilute, will be greater even at the optimum.

The results which would have been obtained if the β procedure had been used are obtained by following one of the columns vertically. In the above experiment, in several of the columns at least, a minimum is also observed. However the ratio of the dilutions at the optimum is not as constant as it was in the case of the α procedure.

Mathematically, the set of data shown in Fig. 6-20 define a surface, where time is the third dimension, and antigen dilution and serum dilution are the two independent variables. (Note that we are plotting these on a logarithmic scale; this is the result of giving simply the tube numbers

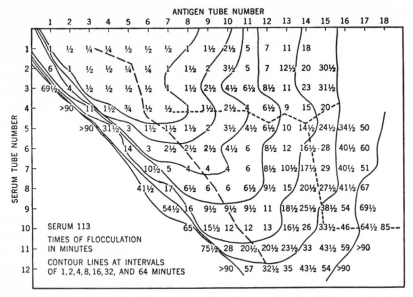

Fig. 6-20. Table of times of flocculation of mixtures of various dilutions of *Limulus* hemocyanin (top) and various dilutions of antiserum 113 (left), showing method of drawing lines of approximately equal times. Dilutions of antigen (reading left to right) and serum (reading down) successively 1.5 times greater.

instead of actual concentrations, but is in any case necessary in order to achieve sufficient compactness.) This surface could be modeled in three dimensions, and the model would summarize the flocculative behavior of the system. Such a model is not easy to show in two dimensions, but the essential characteristics can be shown by making use of conventions similar to those used in topographic maps. Lines can be drawn through points of equal time, at appropriate intervals, and the position and distance apart of these contour lines (isochrones) serve to characterize the surface. A number of such experiments were carried out by the present author (19).

The contour lines cannot be drawn at equal intervals; therefore the intervals have been successively doubled. The line of dashes connects the minima obtained by the α procedure, while the line of dots connects those of the β procedure. For a constant "optimum" to be obtained by either method, the corresponding line should be straight, with a slope of 45°.

Classes of Antibodies. It has been suggested (19) that sera may be divided roughly into two classes designated as R and H. It will perhaps make the distinction between these different types of antisera clearer if

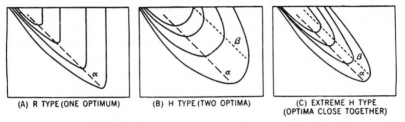

Fig. 6-21. Ideal isochrones for antisera of various types (see text).

we present a set of ideal contour lines illustrating them where the non-essential irregularities have been smoothed out. This is done in Fig. 6-21, which shows the ideal behavior of the R type, the H type, and the extreme H type as typified by diphtheria antitoxin.

In the R type only one optimum, that obtained by the α procedure, is possible. In sera of the H type, two optima are possible, depending on the procedure, and it is clear from Fig. 6-21 that these two optima can never actually coincide. See also Teorell (217). In the H system, the contour line passes through a minimum and then curves over to the left, so as to create another minimum under the conditions of constant antigen. This may be seen by turning Fig. 6-21 clockwise through 90°, so that the right-hand side as viewed in the usual way becomes the bottom. In these sera, apparently, combination of more than a certain amount of antibody with a given amount of antigen does not leave the rate of flocculation at its maximum, but actually diminishes it. Duncan (67), Miles (163), and Taylor (213) have reported experiments in which this behavior of certain rabbit sera is even clearer.

Horse antitoxin of course furnishes the classical example of what is meant here by an H serum. In such sera (extreme H type), where the change in slope of the curves is extremely rapid near the point of inflection, the difference between the two optima will be slight. This has been observed in titrations of diphtheria antitoxin, where the optima are so close together that there is only a 10 to 15 per cent difference between them (217a). A number of workers, working with rabbit serum, have found well-marked optima with both the α and β procedures (65,66,213).

Relation of Flocculation Optima to Neutralization

Dean and Webb (61) found that at the optimum obtained by their (α) procedure, in the case of the system with which they worked (antibody = rabbit antihorse serum, antigen = horse serum), there were no more than traces of antibody and antigen in the supernatant. Similar results have been obtained with ovalbumin, azoproteins, yeast gum, and pneumococcus polysaccharide type I [references in (19) and (155)]. This suggested that the flocculation optimum had in addition to its practical utility some theoretical significance.

The fact that the β optimum seems to correspond in at least some cases to some point in the equivalence zone may be accidental, but is more likely due to the fact that in both cases the deciding factor is approximately complete coverage of the surface of the antigen by antibody. This is conceivable on the basis of either the older or newer theories of reaction mechanism, as can be seen by the remarks of Pauling (184). The studies of Boyd and Hooker (30,32) on the ratio of antibody to antigen in precipitates suggest that the antibody covers more surface than if it behaved as a sphere, and purely chemical and physical evidence suggests that antibody molecules are elongated ellipsoids. In the case of ovalbumin, the antigen surface is calculated to be about completely covered by three molecules of antibody. The studies of Heidelberger (100) and collaborators suggested that the compound formed in this system at the antibody excess end of the equivalence zone is mostly A_3G (Table 6-6).

In the case of diphtheria toxin, the β optimum and neutralization sometimes coincide. Pappenheimer and Robinson (180) failed to detect, even by the sensitive rabbit intracutaneous test, any appreciable toxin or antitoxin in the supernatant from such mixtures. Glenny (89), however, found considerable variation in precipitates of toxin and antitoxin in the most rapidly flocculating proportions, reporting some to be neutral, some overneutralized, and some underneutralized. Duncan (66) and Taylor, Adair, and Adair (215) found instances where the Ramon optimum was in the region of antibody excess. Burnet (41) and a number of others found most rapid flocculation of staphylococcal toxin and antitoxin in mixtures containing some excess of antibody. Malkiel and Boyd (152) found in two hemocyanin–antihemocyanin systems that most rapid flocculation occurred in mixtures where antigen was in excess.

Interpretation of Flocculation Optima

Attempts to account for the difference between the α and β optima will be found in papers by Brown (39), Boyd and Purnell (34), and Teorell (217). They are based chiefly on the assumption that different classes of antibodies and antibody–antigen compounds have different solubilities. Boyd and Purnell (34) also pointed out the α and β optima can never really coincide, even theoretically, since the two procedures are essentially different. This can be seen from the diagrams of Fig. 6-20, for the α optima are obtained by drawing parallel horizontal lines tangent to the isochrones, and the β optima by drawing vertical tangent lines. A horizontal line which just touches a given isochrone corresponds to the use of a constant amount of antibody with varying antigen, and the point at which it touches the isochrone corresponds to the combination of antibody and antigen which gives the shortest flocculation time for this particular amount of antibody. Similarly, a vertical line corresponds to a certain amount of antigen and varying amounts of antibody, and the point at which it touches the isochrone corresponds to the shortest flocculation time for this amount of antigen. It is apparent that as long as the isochrones have the shape they are observed to have, *i.e.*, do not run to a sharp point, the two optima will never be quite the same.

The reasoning of Boyd and Purnell as to the essential nonidentity of the two optima ran as follows: the α and β optima are different *because the two experimental procedures ask different questions of nature* (which is in this case the flocculating system). The α procedure takes a constant amount of antibody and asks: what is the amount of antigen (volume remaining constant) which will give maximum speed of flocculation? The β procedure takes a constant amount of antigen, and asks instead, what is the amount of antibody (volume constant) which gives maximum speed of flocculation? In the former case we are treating antibody as the precious commodity involved in attaining speed of flocculation, with no limit to the amount of antigen we may care to use; in the latter we are treating antigen as the precious commodity, allowing ourselves as much antibody as we like. It is not surprising that the two questions get different answers since both reagents, within limits, speed flocculation.

We may illustrate the situation by the following hypothetical analogy. Suppose we have a submarine which is running on the surface and consequently has an unlimited supply of oxygen. It will burn in its motors that mixture of oil and oxygen which gives maximum energy from a given weight of oil. This corresponds to one of our optima, say the α optimum. The same submarine on some hypothetical planet, running submerged in an ocean of fuel oil (supposing problems of exhaust and so forth solved) and carrying its oxygen in compressed form, would burn that mixture which gave maximum energy from a given weight of *oxygen*. This might be a rather different mixture from the first, and could be said to correspond to the β optimum.*

---

* We do not have at hand any data on the performance of the motors of preatomic submarines. That the hypothetical situation outlined corresponds to something real may, however, be learned from sources such as (78), where it is stated on page 102 that maximum efficiency (in the use of gasoline) is attained by modern 6-cylinder automobile engines when the ratio by weight of air to gasoline is about 16.3 to 1. Greatest power, however (economy of gasoline being disregarded), is obtained when the ratio is 13.1 to 1.

The work of Boyd and Purnell was confirmed by Bowen and Wyman (16,17). These authors emphasized the fact, implicit in the data of Boyd and Purnell, that the total concentration is an important factor in determining the velocity of flocculation. Thus there remains no question but that the Ramon and the Dean-Webb optima are different, even for the toxin–antitoxin system.

If more than one antigen and its corresponding antibody are present in a precipitating system, it is obvious that it would happen only by accident that the point of optimal proportions for one of the systems would correspond with the optimal point for another. Therefore one might expect to find more than one optimum in such systems, each optimum representing the ratio in which one of the various sets of reagents precipitates fastest. (This should not be confused with the existence of two optima, α and β, which result from different technics of performing the experiment; we are assuming that the same technic is employed throughout.) If two antigens, A and B, are mixed and optimal proportions determined against a mixture of the corresponding antisera anti-A and anti-B, two optima are in fact generally observed, and it seems quite certain that when a natural antigen and its antiserum show multiple optima this is an indication of the presence of more than one antigen or more than one antibody, or both.

Linear Relation of Velocity and Antigen Concentration

Hooker and Boyd (125) observed that, when there was a considerable excess of antibody (three to four times the (α) optimal amount), the times of flocculation varied inversely as the concentration of the antigen, so that on plotting them a straight line was obtained. At the time Hooker and Boyd were inclined to interpret this in the light of the older Bordet theory of serological reactions, by applying the mathematical treatment which von Smoluchowski (125,217) developed for the flocculation of colloids. There has not been any attempt to interpret the linear relation between flocculation time and antigen concentration in terms of more modern theories, although this could doubtless be done. In any case there is no doubt the relation exists, and has some practical usefulness.

One application of the relation permits the rapid and accurate estimation of extremely small quantities of antigen. A measured portion is added to an excess of antibody, and the time of flocculation is determined. The concentration of antigen in the sample can be read off from a graph of times and concentrations, constructed by determinations of the time of flocculation of known amounts of antigen.

Effect of Changes in Conditions on Velocity

Electrolytes seem to be necessary for flocculation, but if the concentration is too high flocculation may be delayed (200,201). Flocculation seems to be possible at any pH between 5.5 and 9.0 (200,201), with an optimum of perhaps something in the vicinity of 6. Raising the temperature accelerates flocculation considerably until temperatures are reached that begin to denature proteins. Shaking and stirring (and centrifuging) markedly accelerate the process, and if such mixing processes are prevented by putting the antibody–antigen mixtures in a thermostated chamber, the rate of flocculation is greatly slowed down, but the addition of a small amount of untreated specific serum restored flocculative ability, although the addition of untreated heterologous serum, 20 per cent bovine albumin, or horse serum did not. The amount of precipitating antibody proved not to have been changed by lipide extraction. Orlans proposes as possible explanations of these rather puzzling observations the hypotheses that the extraction procedure somehow weakens one of the combining groups of the antibody, or that the extraction somehow diminishes the hydrophobic character of the antibody–antigen compound.

Nonspecific Serum Proteins. The effect of proteins other than antibody or antigen on the velocity of precipitation is probably rather variable, as it is in agglutination, but not many observations have been reported. Hooker and Boyd (122) found that mixtures of ovalbumin and antiovalbumin, containing normal rabbit serum instead of saline as a diluent, flocculated somewhat more slowly. It was not tested if this was simply due to the increased viscosity of the solution. Hooker (unpublished) found that normal horse serum had a considerable retarding effect on the flocculation of *Busycon* hemocyanin and a horse antihemocyanin.

Other Substances in the Serum. It is not impossible that substances as yet unidentified may be found to affect the velocity of precipitation. Diphtheria antitoxin, when purified by precipitation with sodium sulfate, has been reported not to flocculate, although it still neutralizes (155). The possibility of some denaturation of the antibody has to be considered. Pappenheimer and Robinson (180) obtained flocculation with antitoxin purified by ammonium sulfate precipitation. It has been found (27,124) that partially absorbed* sera, even in cases where the amount of antibody remaining is nearly as great as before, may show greatly increased flocculation times. These observations, however, could perhaps be ex-

---

* Or "partially exhausted" *(i.e.,* sera from which part of the antibody had been removed by precipitation with an amount of antigen insufficient to combine with all the antibody for a certain antigen).

plained by removal of lecithin or cephalin, a possibility that was not investigated.

Precipitin Reactions in Gels

The use of gels as media for the precipitin reaction is not new (177); such technics have become important in immunology. In 1946 Oudin (178) proposed a new procedure, which involved placing agar, containing an appropriate amount of immune serum, to solidify in small tubes, then pouring appropriate dilutions of the antigen over the agar. Under proper conditions specific precipitates appeared in the form of more or less definite rings in the gel. A separate zone of precipitate developed for each antibody–antigen pair present in sufficient amount.

In 1947 Ouchterlony (177) developed another gel diffusion method which permitted the diffusion of both the antibody and the antigen. In this method, a shallow layer of agar is allowed to solidify in a dish in which stands a metal matrix of the appropriate design; the antibody and antigen are then poured into wells left in the agar. When the antibody and antigen have diffused to meet each other, there will be a narrow line at which the relative concentrations permit a precipitate to be formed. If more than one antigen, and corresponding antibodies, are present, then several lines, each corresponding to one antibody–antigen system, will be formed. This technic makes it possible to detect that a certain antigen is in fact a mixture.

If the agar contains three wells arranged at the corners of a triangle, antibody is placed in one well, and two antigen solutions, which may or may not be identical, are placed in each of the other two wells, different patterns of precipitate result in different cases. This makes the gel technic valuable when it is desired to compare two preparations from different sources. A photographic record of the reactions can be obtained by placing photographic paper under the gel and exposing with light from above. A diagrammatic representation of the sort of result that might be obtained is shown in Fig. 6-22. The curves of part *a* and the upper curves of part *b* illustrate the "reaction of difference," and the lower curves of part *b* illustrate the "reaction of identity."

These gel technics have been used to analyze the antigenic complexity of natural antigens such as toxins (177,9,207), and have been extensively applied by Elek in England (74), Björklund in Sweden (10), and Grabar in France (94). Grabar has also developed a very useful technic of electrophoresis of antibody (or antigen) in gels (see 188a). A theoretical treatment of this reaction has been given by Aladjem, Jaross, Paldino, and Lackner (1).

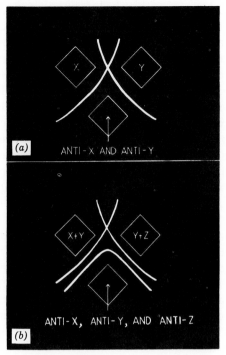

Fig. 6-22. Diagrammatic representation of antibody–antigen by the Ouchterlony technique. (a) Reaction of difference. (b) Reaction of difference (above) and reaction of identity (below).

A micro method has been described by Vyazov, Konyukhov, and Lishtyan (218a).

Flocculation Tests for Syphilis

If the blood of syphilitic patients contained antibodies for the spirochete, it ought to be possible to demonstrate them by the precipitin test, using a suitable extract of the organisms which might contain specific proteins, carbohydrates, or possibly lipide (142). But one serious difficulty immediately presents itself: according to several authorities (71,229), no pathogenic strain of *Treponema pallidum* has been cultivated, and the latter authors (229) state that there is no relation, serologically and immunologically, between the virulent and the cultured organisms. They suggest that the cultivated organism has, in the language of the laboratory, gone "rough" (lost a surface antigen), and such organisms would not be expected to furnish specific extracts.

Nevertheless it is possible to test serologically for syphilis, and such procedures have much clinical importance. The antigens first used for such tests were made from organs of syphilitic human beings, but it was soon found by Landsteiner that extracts of normal organs, even from animals, would do. It is now known that these active extracts consist of various normal lipides. At first this seemed to prove that the reactions obtained with the bloods of syphilitic patients were biologically non-specific, but clinical experience has shown that on the contrary they are practically specific for syphilis. It is now thought, at least by some workers (71) that there is a real serological relationship between some antigen in the spirochete and some of these lipides. This is supported by the observation that absorption of syphilitic sera with washed spirochete suspensions (of certain strains) removes the "reagin" for these lipide-containing extracts.

At the same time that it was considered that the "antigens" used in the serological tests for syphilis had nothing to do with the spirochete, it was doubted if antibody ("reagin") in the patient's serum responsible for the reaction bore any relation to antibodies against the spirochete. The observations of Eagle and Hogan (71) however, tended to support the thesis that the serum change in syphilis is primary an antibody response to *T. pallidum*. The reactivity which these antibodies display for the tissue extracts are, according to these workers, due to a serological similarity between some of the normal tissue lipides and antigens of the spirochete. (This recalls the observations on the Forssman antigen; see Chapter 4.) In support of this contention they cite the above observation on the absorption of syphilitic serum with spirochetes, and also the very suggestive observation that immunization of rabbits with tissue lipides will produce agglutinins and complement-fixing antibodies for the spirochetes (148). Other workers (220), however, still do not support this view that the Wassermann antigen is spirochetal in origin. Weil (220) seemed to think the Wassermann antigen may come from either the spirochetes or the host's own tissues.

Having, however, an antibody of some sort to the spirochete in syphilitic serum, and having available a serologically related antigen in the form of the lipide-containing tissue extracts used, it might be possible to observe a specific precipitation reaction between them.

If we accept the above notions, this is apparently essentially what the flocculation tests for syphilis consist in. A suitable preparation of the lipide-containing tissue extracts is mixed with serum from the patient, and in positive cases a flocculation or precipitation is obtained (Sachs-Georgi, Kahn, Eagle, etc.). The extract generally used is an alcoholic extract of beef heart, to which cholesterol is usually added. According to Eagle (69,70), the function of the cholesterol is to serve as centers of adsorption for the tissue lipides, so that the particles of "antigen" will be larger, and hence more suitable for precipitation (and complement fixation), when the mixture is added to water. See page 397.

Examination of purified syphilitic reagin indicates that it is associated with two components with sedimentation constants of 7 and 19 svedbergs, and has an electrophoretic mobility between that of the β and γ globulins (135).

The mechanism of reaction is supposed (69,70) to consist in the combination of the protein reagin (or antibody) from the serum of the patient with the particles of lipide-coated cholesterol, thus sensitizing the particles to agglutination by the electrolyte present. The reaction is therefore in all respects similar to other antibody–antigen reactions.

Various hypotheses of the Wassermann reaction are discussed by Weil (220). The Wassermann reaction itself will be discussed in the next chapter.

Inhibition of Second Stage of Serological Reactions

We have mentioned in Chapter 2 that certain haptens which do not themselves give any visible reaction with antibody will, when present in sufficient amounts, prevent the antibody from reacting with an antigen with which it would ordinarily give a precipitate. Similarly, we have seen in discussing zones of serological reactions that excess antigen will prevent a precipitate from forming. Antibody and antigen still combine in mixtures containing excess antigen, but the compounds formed are soluble and do not precipitate.

We have also seen that antibody of the H type (typically, horse antitoxin) will prevent precipitation if present in excess—again due to the formation of soluble compounds—but we have also seen that this is in general not true or antibodies of the R type (typically, rabbit antiprotein or anticarbohydrate). However, it is probable that all animals can, and on occasion do, produce antibodies which, although they have the power of combining, have no power of causing precipitation (or agglutination). These antibodies have been variously described as incomplete or univalent, but this is pure speculation (see p. 285); it seems more likely that their peculiar behavior is due to their greater solubility or some other physical chemical characteristic. These nonprecipitating (or nonagglutinating) antibodies not only do not bring about the characteristic second stage when they combine with an antigen, they will prevent the production of this second stage by normal antibody, if they are mixed with the antigen simultaneously. Because of this they are often called "blocking antibodies."

The best known examples are the blocking anti-Rh antibodies, which when combined with appropriate erythrocytes not only do not agglutinate them but prevent their being agglutinated by the ordinary sort of agglutinins. The reason for this action is unknown, but that it is not because the blocking antibodies are univalent is shown by the fact that if the cells are suspended in 25 per cent bovine albumin solution, or treated with trypsin and washed, they will be agglutinated by such antibody. It is clear that exposure of the *erythrocytes* to an enzyme which is then washed off can hardly suddenly double the valence of the antibody which is added later.

It has also been reported (209) that exposure of blocking antibody to certain enzymes gives it agglutinating properties in saline. It is hard to see how an enzyme could create a new combining group on a "half-antibody." It might perhaps release a "masked" second combining group in a molecule of full-sized antibody (see Chapter 2, p. 80).

Nonprecipitating antibody is often found in a precipitating serum along with ordinary antibody, and if present in sufficient amount may inhibit or markedly alter the form of the precipitin curve (138). It seems that the skin-sensitizing antibody produced in allergic conditions (see Chapter 8) is of the nonprecipitating type, and that precipitating antibodies do not have the characteristic affinity for tissues which is possessed by the nonprecipitating antibodies.

A number of aliphatic aminocarboxylic acids have been found to inhibit precipitin reactions, but it is not yet certain whether this inhibition is completely nonspecific or partly specific (5).

Artificial Production of Second Stage (Coombs Reaction)

After the discovery of nonagglutinating antibodies in the sera of mothers of erythroblastotic infants (p. 275), it occurred to Coombs, Mourant, and Race (53–55) that the employment of an antibody to this nonagglutinating antibody might cause the cells to stick together and produce visible agglutination. Since the nonagglutinating antibody encountered in such cases is of human origin, a rabbit serum against human gamma globulin is appropriate for this test. Addition of such serum (Coombs reagent) to cells previously treated with nonagglutinating antibody, or naturally sensitized in vivo, then carefully washed free of uncombined protein, causes the cells to agglutinate. This is somewhat more laborious than the albumin or "conglutination" test (p. 347) but has the advantage of being more sensitive. It will detect the presence of antibodies in some cases where the albumin technic would fail.

It has also been found (196) that treatment of erythrocytes with trypsin causes them to be agglutinated by nonagglutinating antibodies.

Mechanism of the Precipitin Reaction

Several hypotheses have been proposed to account for the second stage of serological reactions in which precipitation or flocculation is produced.

Theories of Bordet. Perhaps the chief credit for insisting on the power of antibodies and antigens to combine in varying proportions goes to Bordet (12), although others had proposed the idea previously (see 100). Bordet stressed the similarity of serological to "adsorption" reactions, and went so far as to deny the applicability of the laws of ordinary chemical union to serological reactions.

We now know that there is no such fundamental distinction between adsorption and ordinary chemical reactions. Practically any reversible chemical reaction taking place at a surface where there are many reactive groups will follow a course similar to that of adsorption reactions (see 83). Consequently this difference between the views of Bordet and of Ehrlich or Arrhenius has reduced simply to the insistence of the former on combination in multiple proportions.

It was Bordet who insisted on the division of serological reactions into two stages, which still seems convenient, if perhaps not so fundamental as Bordet believed. He pointed out the importance of salts in the reaction. He looked upon agglutination and precipitation as fundamentally analogous, and in the section on precipitation in his book (12) spoke of the formation of a layer of antibody over the surface of a particle, rendering if susceptible to the flocculating influence of electrolytes.

The "Lattice" Theory

Marrack (155) pointed out that if the antibody has more than one combining group it might be possible for antibody and antigen to be bound together in the form of a coarse "lattice," which is shown diagrammatically in Fig. 6-23. This involves a new concept, in that the aggregation is ascribed not to a loss of attraction for water but to specific attraction between the particles. "This mutual attraction is due to the link provided by further antigen molecules" (155). Marrack further stated: "If only two determinant groups are attached to one molecule an aggregate of unlimited size (AGAGAG—) can be built up," and thus seems to

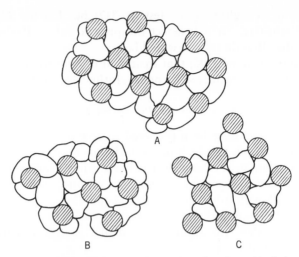

Fig. 6-23. Diagrams of hypothetical arrangements of antigen (shaded) and antibody (white) molecules in antibody–antigen complex: (*A*) primary aggregate, (*B*) complex structure at optimal proportions, (*C*) antigen excess. Such aggregates are not to be supposed to possess a structure as regular as that of a crystal lattice, but are to "be compared rather with a glass such as silica glass, in which each silicon atom is surrounded tetrahedrally by four oxygen atoms and each oxygen atom is bonded to two silicon atoms, but which lacks further orderliness of arrangement" (Pauling).

expect lattice, and therefore precipitate, formation even with a simple hapten, provided it contains two reactive groups in its molecule.

A very similar theory was developed by Heidelberger and Kendall (100) and later taken up by Pauling (184) and various other workers.

Heidelberger (100) said: "the process of aggregation as well as the initial hapten–antibody combination is considered to be a chemical reaction between definite molecular groupings . . . . the entire course of these instances of specific bacterial agglutination could be accounted for. . . . . . ."

Heidelberger's concept of the mechanism of the precipitin reaction (100) was based on certain assumptions and simplifications; in nearly his own words, they are: (*1*) Antigen (G) and antibody (A) are chemically and immunologically ultivalent with respect to each other; that is, each substance possesses two or more groupings capable of reacting with the other. (*2*) The antibody may be treated mathematically as if its average behavior were that of a single substance. (*3*) The reaction is considered as a series of successive bimolecular reactions which take place before precipitation occurs. (*4*) The mass law applies, so that the rates of formation of the reaction products are proportional to the concentrations of the reacting substances.

The first reaction postulated is:

$$G + A \rightleftharpoons GA \qquad (1)$$

followed, for example, in the region of excess antibody, by competing bimolecular reactions due to the mutual multivalence of the components:

$$GA + A \rightleftharpoons GA \cdot A$$
$$GA + GA \rightleftharpoons GA \cdot GA \qquad (2)$$

A third step follows, in which the competing bimolecular reactions would be:

$$GA \cdot A + A \qquad \rightleftharpoons GA \cdot A \cdot A,$$
$$GA \cdot G + A \qquad \rightleftharpoons GA \cdot GA,$$
$$GA \cdot A + GA \cdot A \rightleftharpoons GAA \cdot GAA,$$
$$GA \cdot A + GA \cdot GA \rightleftharpoons GAA \cdot GA \cdot GA, \text{ and}$$
$$GA \cdot GA + GA \cdot GA \rightleftharpoons GAGA \cdot GAGA$$

in which the first two reactions are supposed to occur only in the presence of enough A to carry the composition of the reaction product beyond the GA_2 stage. Similarly, each compound formed in the third step would react with each other compound, or with more A, if present, to form still more complex substances, and the reaction is supposed to continue until particles are formed large enough to settle from the solution. Precipitation would take place at this point, "doubtless facilitated by the mutual discharge, with loss of affinity for water, of ionized or polar groupings brought together by the series of chemical reactions."

If A and G are mixed in equivalent proportions the reaction is supposed to consist simply of polymerization of the GA formed in reaction [1], in steps [2], [3], etc. The precipitate would be $(GA)_n$.

For the region of excess G similar expressions are proposed if G and A are interchanged in [3], [4], etc. In the presence of a large excess of G (in the inhibition zone), a soluble compound, G_xA, containing one more molecule of G in combination than the last insoluble compound, is supposed to be present in solution.

The final precipitate in each case is supposed to consist of antibody molecules held together in three dimensions by antigen molecules, which Heidelberger represented two-dimensionally as:

$$
\begin{array}{cc}
\cdot\cdot\dot{A}\cdot GA\cdot\ddot{G} & \cdot AA\cdot\cdot AA\cdot \\
\cdot\cdot\ddot{G}A\cdot\dot{G}\dot{A}\cdot GA\cdot\cdot & \cdot\ddot{G}\cdot A\cdot\ddot{G}\cdot A\cdot \\
& \text{or} & \\
\dot{A}\cdot\dot{A}\cdot GA\cdot & \ddot{A}A \quad \ddot{A}A\cdot \\
\dot{A}\cdot & \cdots\dot{G}\cdots\cdot
\end{array}
$$

"The process of aggregation as well as the initial hapten–antibody combination is considered to be a chemical reaction between definite molecular groupings."

In attempts to test this theory, divalent haptens have been tested, and did in some cases precipitate with antibody, as expected (186). However, this did not always happen, and Epstein, Doty, and Boyd (76) found that if care was taken to exclude aggregation of the hapten and the antibody, precipitation generally did not take place, although light-scattering observations showed that small aggregates were formed.

That antibody molecules do link up particles of antigen in much the way Marrack envisaged is shown by the electron micrographs of Almeida, Cinader, and Howatson (2), one of which is shown in Fig. 6-24.

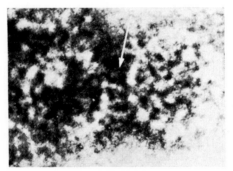

Fig. 6-24. Electron micrograph showing two particles of wart virus held together by three distinct antibody molecules. From Almeida, Cinader, and Howatson (2), by permission.

Teorell's Theory. Teorell (216,217) published a theory in which he assumed that antibody *behaves* as if it were univalent, and that the reaction of A and G results in the establishment of the following simultaneous equilibria:

$$
\begin{aligned}
A + G &\rightleftharpoons AG, \text{ with dissociation constant } K_n \\
A + AG &\rightleftharpoons A_2G, \text{ with dissociation constant } K_{n-1} \\
A + A_2G &\rightleftharpoons A_3G, \text{ with dissociation constant } K_{n-2} \\
A + A_{n-1}G &\rightleftharpoons AG, \text{ with dissociation constant } K_1
\end{aligned}
\tag{4}
$$

Precipitation was ascribed simply to insolubility of compounds such as AG or A_2G, and not to a "lattice" formation. Teorell further assumed that the mass law applies, even to the insoluble compounds, since he supposed that the combining groups of the antigens and antibodies composing them are still freely accessible.

The "Occlusion Theory." Boyd (20) offered an alternative theory of the precipitin reaction (which by implication would apply to other serological reactions), which he called the "occlusion theory." This attempted to explain the initiation of precipitation (or agglutination) as due to the lowering of the solubility (in the $0.15M$ sodium chloride in which all these reactions are carried out) of the antibody–antigen compound, owing to mutual neutralization of polar (*i.e.*, solubilizing) groups of antibody and antigen, and concomitant steric hindrance of other polar groups of antibody molecules, as a result of their being brought into such close apposition. That is, the molecules of antibody, when in combination with a molecule of antigen, are supposed to be so near each other that they literally get into each other's way, and many of their polar groups are nonspecifically turned aside from their business of attracting water (127), with the result that as a whole the antibody–antigen complex does not have enough free polar groups to keep it in solution. Kleczkowski (141) evidently held a very similar theory.

Marrack has recently expressed himself (156) as not entirely satisfied with his own (lattice) theory, and has stated that we are now "back to Boyd's occlusion theory." I, on the other hand, believe there is considerable truth in the lattice theory.

Mathematical Theories

There have been a number of mathematical theories of the precipitin reaction (21,216,217,85,86,105,114–119,167,92), but their usefulness is doubtful. One would expect that a valid theory would enable the experimenter, knowing the amounts of the two reagents, antibody and antigen, he has put together, and consequently the ratio in which they are mixed, to predict the amount and composition of the precipitate. This the theories referred to do not generally do, but predict, when they predict anything, something such as a relation between the composition of the precipitate and the amount of antigen *precipitated.* Even here one or two adjustable parameters were used. All these theories ignored the known heterogeneity of antibody.

Since none of these theories have contributed significantly to our understanding of immune processes, it hardly seems necessary to discuss them here.

References

1. Aladjem, F., R. W. Jaross, R. L. Paldino, and J. A. Lackner, *J. Immunol.*, **83**, 221–231 (1959).
2. Almeida, J., B. Cinader, and A. Howatson, *J. Exptl. Med.*, **118**, 327–340 (1963).

2a. Almeida, J. D., B. Cinader, and D. Maylor, *Immunochemistry*, Pergamon, New York, 1965, pp. 169–176.

3. Andrewes, C. H., *J. Pathol. Bacteriol.*, **31**, 671 (1928).

4. Arrhenius, S., *Immunochemistry*, Macmillan, New York, 1907.

5. Atchley, W. A., and N. V. Bhagazan, *Science*, **138**, 528–529 (1962).

6. Avery, O. T., and M. Heidelberger, *J. Exptl. Med.*, **42**, 367 (1925).

7. Baker, M. C., D. H. Campbell, S. I. Epstein, and S. J. Singer, *J. Am. Chem. Soc.*, **78**, 312 (1956).

8. Bayne-Jones, S., *J. Immunol.*, **10**, 663 (1925).

9. Becker, E. L., *Federation Proc.*, **12**, 717 (1953).

10. Björklund, B., *Intern. Arch. Allergy Appl. Immunol.*, **4**, 340 (1953).

11. Bjørneboe, M., *Z. Immunitätsforsch.*, **99**, 160 (1940).

12. Bordet, J., *Traité de l'Immunité*, Masson, Paris, 1920.

13. Bordet, J., *Traité de l'immunité dans les maladies infectieuses*, 2nd ed., Masson, Paris, 1939.

14. Boursnell, J. C., *Immunology*, **7**, 127–141 (1964).

15. Boursnell, J. C., R. R. A. Coombs, and V. Rizk, *Biochem. J.*, **55**, 745 (1953).

16. Bowen, H. E., and L. Wyman, *J. Immunol.*, **70**, 235 (1953).

17. Bowen, H. E., and L. Wyman, *J. Immunol.*, **71**, 86 (1953).

18. Boyd, W. C., *J. Immunol.*, **38**, 143 (1940).

19. Boyd, W. C., *J. Exptl. Med.*, **74**, 369–386 (1941).

20. Boyd, W. C., *J. Exptl. Med.*, **75**, 407 (1942).

21. Boyd, W. C., *Fundamentals of Immunology*, 1st ed., Interscience, New York, 1943.

22. Boyd, W. C., *J. Exptl. Med.*, **83**, 221 (1946).

23. Boyd, W. C., *J. Exptl. Med.*, **83**, 401 (1946).

24. Boyd, W. C., *Ann. N. Y. Acad. Sci.*, **46**, 927–937 (1946).

25. Boyd, W. C., *Fundamentals of Immunology*, 2nd ed., Interscience, New York, 1947.

26. Boyd, W. C., and B. Baskys, *Experientia*, **13**, 238 (1957).

27. Boyd, W. C., and H. Bernard, *J. Immunol.*, **33**, 111–122 (1937).

28. Boyd, W. C., H. M. Bhatia, M. A. Diamond, and S. Matsubara, *J. Immunol.*, **89**, 463–470 (1962).

29. Boyd, W. C., J. B. Conn, D. C. Gregg, G. B. Kistiakowsky, and R. M. Roberts, *J. Biol. Chem.*, **139**, 787 (1941).

30. Boyd, W. C., and S. B. Hooker, *J. Gen. Physiol.*, **17**, 341 (1934).

31. Boyd, W. C., and S. B. Hooker, *Proc. Soc. Exptl. Biol. Med.*, **39**, 491 (1938).

32. Boyd, W. C., and S. B. Hooker, *J. Gen. Physiol.*, **22**, 281 (1939).

33. Boyd, W. C., and M. H. McMaster, *J. Immunol.*, **82**, 151–152 (1959).

34. Boyd, W. C., and M. A. Purnell, *J. Exptl. Med.*, **80**, 289–298 (1944).

35. Boyd, W. C., E. Shapleigh, and M. McMaster, *Arch. Biochem. Biophys.*, **55**, 226 (1955).

36. Boyden, A., *Systematic Zoology*, **2**, 19 (1953).

37. Branster, M., and B. Cinader, *J. Immunol.*, **87**, 18–38 (1961).

38. Brody, O. V., "Microelectrophoretic studies on human erythrocytes," Ph.D. Thesis, Harvard University, 1954.

39. Brown, A. M., *Brit. J. Exptl. Pathol.*, **16**, 556 (1935).

40. Brunius, F. E., *Chemical Studies on the True Forssman Hapten, the Corresponding Antibody, and Their Interaction*, Aktiebolaget, Fahlcrantz Boktryckeri, Stockholm, 1936.

41. Burnet, F. M., *J. Pathol. Bacteriol.*, **34**, 471–492 (1931).

42. Burnet, F. M., and S. G. Anderson, *Australian J. Exptl. Biol. Med. Sci.*, **25**, 213 (1947).
43. Calaman, M. H., *Proc. III Intern. Congr. Microbiol., New York*, 356, **1940**.
44. Calmette, A., *Ann. inst. Pasteur*, **9**, 225 (1895).
45. Chow, B. F., and W. F. Goebel, *J. Exptl. Med.*, **62**, 179 (1935).
46. Chow, B. F., and H. Wu, *Chinese J. Physiol.*, **11**, 139 (1937).
47. Cinader, B., *Biochem. Soc. Symposia (Cambridge, Engl.)*, **10**, 16 (1953).
48. Cinader, B., *Ann. Rev. Microbiol.*, **11**, 371–390 (1957).
49. Cinader, B., *Brit. J. Exptl. Pathol.*, **38**, 362–376 (1957).
50. Cinader, B., K. J. Lafferty, *Immunology*, **7**, 342–362 (1964).
51. Coca, A. F., and M. F. Kelley, *J. Immunol.*, **VI**, 87–101 (1921).
52. Colwell, C. A., and G. P. Youmans, *J. Immunol.*, **42**, 79–89 (1941).
53. Coombs, R. R. A., A. E. Mourant, and R. R. Race, *Brit. J. Exptl. Pathol.*, **26**, 255–266 (1945).
54. Coombs, R. R. A., A. E. Mourant, and R. R. Race, *Lancet*, **II**, 15 (1945).
55. Coombs, R. R. A., A. E. Mourant, and R. R. Race, *Lancet*, **I**, 264–266 (1946).
56. Coons, A. H., *Ann. Rev. Microbiol.*, **8**, 333 (1954).
57. Coons, A. H., and M. H. Kaplan, *J. Immunol.*, **91**, 1 (1950).
58. Cromwell, H. W., *J. Immunol.*, **7**, 461 (1922).
59. Danysz, J., *Ann. inst. Pasteur*, **16**, 331 (1902).
60. Dean, H. R., *Proc. Roy. Soc. (London)*, **B84**, 416 (1912).
61. Dean, H. R., and R. A. Webb, *J. Pathol. Bacteriol.*, **29**, 473–492 (1926).
62. Diamond, L. K., and R. L. Denton, *J. Lab. Clin. Med.*, **30**, 821 (1945).
63. Doty, P., and S. I. Epstein, *Nature*, **174**, 89 (1954).
64. Dreyer, G., and J. S. C. Douglas, *Proc. Soc. (London)*, **B82**, 185–205 (1910).
65. Duncan, J. T., *Brit. J. Exptl. Pathol.*, **13**, 489 (1932).
66. Duncan, J. T., *Brit. J. Exptl. Pathol.*, **13**, 498 (1932).
67. Duncan, J. T., *Brit. J. Exptl. Pathol.*, **15**, 23–44 (1934).
68. Eagle, H., *J. Immunol.*, **18**, 393–417 (1930).
69. Eagle, H., *J. Phys. Chem.*, **36**, 259 (1932).
70. Eagle, H., *The Laboratory Diagnosis of Syphilis*, Mosby, St. Louis, 1937.
71. Eagle, H., and R. B. Hogan, *J. Exptl. Med.*, **71**, 215 (1940).
72. Eigel, M., *Untersuchungen über die Unterscheidungsmoglichkeit der Genotypen der Blut gruppe, A durch Bestimmung des $N_4/_{37}$ Quotienten*, Inaugural-Dissertation, Bonn, 1960.
73. Eisen, H. N., and F. Karush, *J. Am. Chem. Soc.*, **71**, 363 (1949).
74. Elek, S. D., *Brit. J. Exptl. Pathol.*, **30**, 484 (1949).
75. Epstein, S., *Science*, **118**, 756 (1953).
76. Epstein, S. I., P. Doty, and W. C. Boyd, *J. Am. Chem. Soc.*, **78**, 3306 (1956).
77. Epstein, S. I., and S. J. Singer, *J. Am. Chem Soc.*, **80**, 1274–1283 (1958).
78. Faires, V. M., *Applied Thermodynamics*, Macmillan, New York, 1938.
79. Felton, L. D., *J. Immunol.*, **22**, 453 (1932).
80. Filitti-Wurmser, S., Y. Jacquot-Armand, G. Aubel-Lesure, and R. Wurmser, *Ann. Eugen.*, **18**, 183 (1954).
81. Filitti-Wurmser, S., Y. Jacquot-Armand, and R. Wurmser, *Rev. d'Hématol.*, **15**, 201–261 (1960).
82. Follensby, E. M., and S. B. Hooker, *J. Immunol.*, **37**, 367 (1939).
83. Fowler, R. H., *Statistical Mechanics*, Cambridge University Press, Cambridge, 1936.
84. Furuhata, T., *Japan Med. World*, **7**, 197 (1927).

85. Ghosh, B. N., *Indian J. Med. Research*, **23**, 285 (1935).
86. Ghosh, B. N., *Indian J. Med. Research*, **23**, 837 (1936).
87. Gitlin, D., and H. Edelhoch, *J. Immunol.*, **66**, 67 (1951).
88. Glenny, A. T., and M. Barr, *J. Pathol. Bacteriol.*, **35**, 91 (1932).
89. Glenny, A. T., and C. C. Okell, *J. Pathol. Bacteriol.*, **27**, 187 (1924).
90. Glenny, A. T., C. G. Pope, and H. Waddington, *J. Pathol. Bacteriol.*, **28**, 279 (1925).
91. Goebel, W. F., and R. D. Hotchkiss, *J. Exptl. Med.*, **66**, 191 (1937).
92. Goldberg, R. J., *J. Am. Chem. Soc.*, **74**, 5715 (1952).
93. Goldberg, R. J., and D. H. Campbell, *J. Immunol.*, **66**, 79 (1951).
94. Grabar, P., *Bull. soc. chim. biol.*, **36**, 65 (1954).
95. Habeeb, H. F. S. A., *et al.*, *Biochim. Biophys. Acta*, **34**, 439 (1959).
96. Haurowitz, F., *Fortschr. Allergielehre*, **1939** 19.
97. Haurowitz, F., *Ann. Rev. Microbiol.*, **7**, 389 (1953).
98. Haurowitz, F., and F. Breinl, *Z. physiol. Chem.*, **214**, 111 (1933).
99. Healey, M., and S. Pinfield, *Brit. J. Exptl. Pathol.*, **16**, 535 (1935).
100. Heidelberger, M., *Bacteriol. Rev.*, **3**, 49 (1939).
101. Heidelberger, M., and E. A. Kabat, *J. Exptl. Med.*, **60**, 642 (1934).
102. Heidelberger, M., and E. A. Kabat, *J. Exptl. Med.*, **65**, 885 (1937).
103. Heidelberger, M., and F. E. Kendall, *J. Exptl. Med.*, **50**, 809 (1929).
104. Heidelberger, M., and F. E. Kendall, *J. Exptl. Med.*, **61**, 559 (1935).
105. Heidelberger, M., and F. E. Kendall, *J. Exptl. Med.*, **62**, 467 (1935).
106. Heidelberger, M., and F. E. Kendall, *J. Exptl. Med.*, **62**, 697 (1935).
107. Heidelberger, M., and F. E. Kendall, *J. Exptl. Med.*, **64**, 161 (1936).
108. Heidelberger, M., and F. E. Kendall, *J. Exptl. Med.*, **65**, 647 (1937).
109. Heidelberger, M., and C. F. C. MacPherson, *Science*, **97**, 405 (1943); **98**, 63 (1943).
110. Heidelberger, M., and M. M. Mayer, *Advances in Enzymol.*, **8**, 71 (1948).
111. Heidelberger, M., and K. O. Pedersen, *J. Exptl. Med.*, **65**, 393 (1937).
112. Heidelberger, M., F. E. Kendall, and T. Teorell, *J. Exptl. Med.*, **63**, 819 (1936).
113. Heidelbrgeer, M., H. P. Treffers, and M. M. Mayer, *J. Exptl. Med.*, **71**, 271–282 (1940).
114. Hershey, A. D., *J. Immunol.*, **45**, 39–50 (1942).
115. Hershey, A. D., *Science*, **95**, 280–282 (1942).
116. Hershey, A. D., *J. Immunol.*, **46**, 249–261 (1943).
117. Hershey, A. D., *J. Immunol.*, **47**, 77–87 (1943).
118. Hershey, A. D., *J. Immunol.*, **48**, 381–401 (1944).
119. Hershey, A. D., G. Kalmanson, and J. Bronfenbrenner, *J. Immunol.*, **46**, 276 (1943).
120. Hirst, G. K., *Science*, **94**, 22 (1941).
121. Hooker, S. B., *J. Immunol.*, **33**, 57 (1937).
122. Hooker, S. B., and W. C. Boyd, unpublished data.
123. Hooker, S. B., and W. C. Boyd, *J. Immunol.*, **25**, 61 (1933).
124. Hooker, S. B., and W. C. Boyd, *J. Immunol.*, **26**, 469 (1934).
125. Hooker, S. B., and W. C. Boyd, *J. Gen. Physiol.*, **19**, 373 (1935).
126. Hooker, S. B., and W. C. Boyd, *J. Immunol.*, **30**, 33 (1936).
127. Hooker, S. B., and W. C. Boyd, *J. Immunol.*, **42**, 419 (1941).
128. How, Alfred E, *J. Immunol.*, **37**, 77 (1939).
129. Huggins, M., *Am. Scientist*, **50**, 485–496 (1962).
130. Huntoon, F. M., and S. Etris, *J. Immunol.*, **6**, 123 (1921).
131. Jacobs, J., *J. Gen. Physiol.*, **20**, 353 (1937).
132. Jerne, N. K., *Avidity*, Ejnar Munksgaard, Copenhagen, 1951.

133. Jones, F. S., and R. B. Little, *J. Exptl. Med.*, **57**, 721 (1933).
134. Jones, F. S., and M. Orcutt, *J. Immunol.*, **27**, 215 (1934).
135. Kabat, E. A., *Ann. Rev. Biochem.*, **15**, 502 (1946).
136. Kabat, E. A., *Blood Group Substances*, Academic Press, New York, 1956.
137. Kabat, E. A., and S. Leskowitz, *J. Am. Chem. Soc.*, **77**, 5159 (1955).
138. Kabat, E. A., and M. M. Mayer, *Experimental Immunochemistry*, Charles C Thomas, Springfield, Illinois, 1961.
139. Karush, F., *J. Am. Chem. Soc.*, **78**, 5519 (1956).
140. Karush, F., *Trans. N. Y. Acad. Sci.*, **20**, 581 (1958).
141. Kleczkowski, A., *Brit. J. Exptl. Pathol.*, **26**, 41 (1945).
142. Klopstock, F., *Deut. med. Wochschr.*, **52**, 226, 1460 (1926).
143. Klotz, I. B., "Protein Interactions," in *The Proteins*, H. Neurath and K. Bailey, eds., Vol. 1, Part B, Academic Press, New York, 1953, p. 727.
144. Kunkel, H. F., and S. M. Ward, *J. Biol. Chem.*, **182**, 597 (1950).
145. Landsteiner, K., *Biochem. Z.*, **104**, 280 (1920).
146. Landsteiner, K., *The Specificity of Serological Reactions*, Charles C Thomas, Springfield, Illinois, 1936.
147. Landsteiner, K., *The Specificity of Serological Reactions*, 2nd rev. ed., Harvard University Press, Cambridge, 1945.
148. Landsteiner, K., and J. van der Scheer, *J. Exptl. Med.*, **45**, 465–482 (1927).
149. Lanni, F., *J. Exptl. Med.*, **84**, 167 (1946).
150. Linderstrøm-Lang, K., *Compt. rend. trav. lab. Carlsberg Ser. chim.*, **15** [7] (1924) .
151. London, F., *Z. Physik*, **63**, 245 (1930).
152. Malkiel, S., and W. C. Boyd, *J. Exptl. Med.*, **66**, 383 (1937).
153. Maltaner, F., and E. Johnston, *J. Immunol.*, **6**, 349–354 (1921).
154. Marrack, J. R., *The Chemistry of Antigens and Antibodies*, 1st ed., H. M. Stationery Office, London, 1934. Revised ed., see ref. 155.
155. Marrack, J. R., *The Chemistry of Antigens and Antibodies*, Med. Research Council (Brit.) Spec. Rept. Ser., No. **230** (1938).
156. Marrack, J. R., in *Immunochemical Approaches to Problems in Microbiology*, M. Heidelberger, O., J. Plescia, and R. A. Day, eds., Rutgers University Press, New Brunswick, 1961, pp. 43–48.
157. Marrack, J. R., and F. C. Smith, *Brit. J. Exptl. Pathol.*, **12**, 30 (1931).
158. Mason, V. R., *Bull. Johns Hopkins Hosp.*, **33**, 116 (1922).
159. Masouredis, S. P., *J. Clin. Invest.*, **39**, 1450 (1960).
160. Mayer, M. M., *Ann. Rev. Biochem.*, **20**, 415 (1951).
161. Mayer, M. M., and M. Heidelberger, *J. Biol. Chem.*, **143**, 567–574 (1942).
162. McClelland, L., and R. Hare, *Can. Public Health J.*, **32**, 530 (1941).
163. Miles, A. A., *J. Exptl. Pathol.*, **14**, 43 (1933).
164. Miles, A. A., *Federation Proc.*, **13**, 799 (1954).
165. Miller, J. L., *et. al.*, *J. Am. Med. Assoc.*, **149**, 987 (1952).
166. Mirsky, A. E., and L. Pauling, *Proc. Natl. Acad. Sci. U. S.*, **22**, 439 (1936).
167. Morales, M. F., J. Botts, and L. Hill, *J. Am. Chem. Soc.*, **70**, 2339 (1948).
168. Morgan, W. T. J., and W. M. Watkins, *Brit. J. Exptl. Pathol.*, **34**, 94 (1953).
169. Morgenroth, J., *Berlin klin. Wochschr.*, **42**, 1550 (1905).
170. Mudd, S., R. L. Nugent, and L. T. Bullock, *J. Phys. Chem.*, **36**, 229–258 (1932).
171. von Muralt, A., *J. Am. Chem. Soc.*, **52**, 3518 (1930)
172. Mutsaars, W., and T. E. Grégoire, *Compt. rend. soc. biol.*, **123**, 144 (1936).
173. Nelson, D. S., *Adv. Immunol.*, **3**, 131–180 (1963).

174. Nelson, R. A., and M. M. Mayer, *J. Exptl. Med.*, **89**, 369 (1949).
175. Nisonoff, A., and D. Pressman, *J. Am. Chem. Soc.*, **79**, 1616 (1957).
176. Northrop, J. H., and P. H. de Kruif, *J. Gen. Physiol.*, **4**, 655 (1933).
176a. Nossal, G. J. V., *Sci. Am.*, **211**, No. 6, 106 (1964).
177. Ouchterlony, Ö., Paper presented at the VI International Congress for Microbiology, Rome, September, 1953.
178. Oudin, J., *Methods in Medical Research*, Vol. 5, Year Book Publishers, Chicago, 1952, p. 335.
179. Pappenheimer, A. M., *J. Exptl. Med.*, **71**, 263 (1940).
180. Pappenheimer, A. M., and E. S. Robinson, *J. Immunol.*, **32**, 4 (1937).
181. Pappenheimer, A. M., H. P. Lundgren, and J. W. Williams, *J. Exptl. Med.*, **71**, 247 (1940).
182. Parnas, J. K., and R. Wagner, *Biochem. Z.*, **125**, 253 (1921).
183. Pauling, L., *The Nature of the Chemical Bond*, Cornell University Press, Ithaca, New York, 1939.
184. Pauling, L., *J. Am. Chem. Soc.*, **62**, 2643–2657 (1940).
185. Pauling, L., "Molecular structures and intermolecular forces," in K. Landsteiner, ed., *The Specificity of Serological Reactions*, Harvard University Press, Cambridge, 1945.
186. Pauling, L., *et al.*, *J. Am. Chem. Soc.*, **64**, 2944–3003, 3003–3009, 3010–3014, 3015–3020 (1942).
187. Pauling, L., and D. Pressman, *J. Am. Chem. Soc.*, **67**, 1003 (1945).
188. Pauling, L., D. H. Campbell, and D. Pressman, *Physiol. Rev.*, **23**, 203–219 (1943).
188a. Pectoom, F., *The Agar Precipitation Technique and Its Application as a Diagnostic and Analytical Method*, Charles C Thomas, Springfield, Illinois, 1963.
188b. Pennell, R. B., and I. F. Huddleson, *J. Exp. Med.*, **68**, 73 (1938).
189. Pirofsky, B., and M. S. Cordova, *Vox. Sang.*, **9**, 17–21 (1964).
190. Ponder, E., *Blood*, **9**, 227 (1954).
191. Pope, C. G., *Brit. J. Exptl. Pathol.*, **38**, 207–216 (1957).
192. Pope, C. G., *Brit. Med. Bull.*, **19**, 230–234 (1963).
193. Pope, C. G., and M. Healey, *Brit. J. Exptl. Pathol.*, **19**, 397 (1938).
194. Porter, E. F., and A. M. Pappenheimer, *J. Exptl. Med.*, **69**, 755 (1939).
195. Pressman, D., and B. Sherman, *J. Immunol.*, **67**, 21 (1951).
196. Race, R. R., and R. Sanger, *Blood Groups in Man*, Blackwell, Oxford, 1962.
197. Rivers, T. M., *Viral and Rickettsial Infections in Man*, Lippincott, Philadelphia, 1952.
198. Robinson, E. S., *New Engl. J. Med.*, **213**, 208 (1935).
199. Salmon, C., and M. Hautenauve, "Thermodynamic study of the anti-B antibody of subjects of Ax phenotype," *Noev. Rev. Franc. Hemat.*, **1**, 847–871 (1961).
200. Schmidt, S., *Z. Immunitätsforsch.*, **67**, 197 (1930).
201. Schmidt, S., *Compt. rend. soc. biol.*, **103**, 101 (1930).
202. Sevag, M. G., *Ergeb. Hyg. Bakteriol. Immunitätsforsch. u. Exptl. Therap.*, **28**, 423 (1954).
203. Singer, S. J., *J. Cellular Compt. Physiol.*, **50**, Suppl. 1, 51 (1957).
204. Singer, S. J., and D. H. Campbell, *J. Am. Chem. Soc.*, **77**, 3499 (1955).
205. Singer, S. J., L. Eggman, and D. H. Campbell, *J. Am. Chem. Soc.*, **77**, 4855 (1955).
206. Smith, E. L., *et al.*, *J. Biol. Chem.*, **199**, 789 (1952).
207. Smith, E. L., and B. V. Jager, *Ann. Rev. Microbiol.*, **6**, 207 (1952).
208. Smith, F. C., and Marrack, *Brit. J. Exptl. Pathol.*, **11**, 494 (1930).

209. Spielmann, W., *Z Immunitätsforsch.*, 111, 460 (1954).
210. Steiner, R. F., C. Kitzinger, and T. H. Benzinger, *Research Rept. Naval Med. Research Inst.*, 14, 73 (1956).
211. Stokinger, H. E., and M. Heidelberger, *J. Exptl. Med.*, 66, 251 (1937).
212. Svedberg, T., and K. O. Pedersen, *The Ultracentrifuge*, Clarendon, Oxford, 1940.
213. Taylor, G. L., *J. Hyg.*, 31, 56 (1931).
214. Taylor, G. L., *J. Hyg.*, 33, 12–27 (1933).
215. Taylor, G. L., G. S. Adair, and M. E. Adair, *J. Hyg.*, 34, 118 (1934).
216. Teorell, T., *Nature*, 151, 696 (1943).
217. Teorell, T., *J. Hyg.*, 44, 277 (1946).
217a. Timmerman, W. A., *Ann. inst. Pasteur*, 52, 146 (1934).
218. Todd, C., *Brit. J. Exptl. Pathol.*, 9, 244 (1928).
218a. Vyazov, O. E., B. V. Konyukhov, and L. L. Lishtvan, *Byul. Exp. Biol. i Med.*, 5, 117–120 (1959) (Russian).
219. Wassermann, A., *Z. Hyg. Infektionskrenkh.*, 22, 263 (1896).
220. Weil, A. J., *Bacteriol. Rev.*, 5, 293–330 (1941).
221. Wiener, A. S., *The Rh-Hr Blood Types*, Grune and Stratton, New York, 1954.
222. Winkler, A., and O. Westphal, *Z. Immunitätsforsch.*, 105, 154–164 (1944).
223. Wu, H., *Chinese J. Physiol.*, 5, 321 (1931).
224. Wu, H., L. H. Cheng, and C. P. Li, *Proc. Soc. Exptl. Biol. Med.*, 25, 853 (1928).
225. Wu, H., P. P. T. Sah, and C. P. Li, *Proc. Soc. Exptl. Biol. Med.*, 26, 737 (1929).
226. Wurmser, R., and S. Filitti-Wurmser, *Biochem. Biophys. Acta*, 4, 238 (1950).
227. Wurmser, R., and S. Filitti-Wurmser, *Progr. Biophys.*, 7, 88 (1957).
228. Wyman, J., in *Proteins, Aminoacids and Peptides*, E. J. Cohn, and J. T. Edsall, eds., Reinhold, New York, 1944.
229. Zinsser, H., J. F. Enders, and L. D. Fothergill, *Immunity: Principles and Application in Medicine and Public Health*, Macmillan, New York, 1939.

CHAPTER 7

Complement and Complement Fixation

1. Complement

Important as antibodies are in resistance, they are by no means the whole story. We must now consider the role of another constituent of blood, called complement, or alexin, more frequently the former. Actually complement seems to consist of at least six components (64,65,71). Complement is essential for the lytic action of certain antibacterial antibodies, and may aid the opsonizing action of antibodies. The action of complement is conveniently studied through its role in hemolysis. To give a specific example, if the complement of an immune rabbit serum which is hemolytic for sheep erythrocytes is removed or destroyed, the serum no longer will produce lysis when added to sheep cells. Antibody is still present and active, however, as is shown by the fact that such a serum will usually still agglutinate the cells, or by absorption experiments it can be shown that the antibody present is still capable of combining with the cells. If fresh normal serum is added to the mixture of serum and cells, lysis may be obtained, of a degree indicating that destruction of the complement did not decrease the amount of antibody present. In many cases fresh serum even of a different species will thus restore hemolytic power to such a treated serum. Lysis will also be observed if the cells are removed from the "inactivated" serum and the fresh normal serum is added to them, without the presence of any uncombined antibody.

Ehrlich believed that in lysis the antibody acted only as a go-between for the complement, which he believed to be the cause of lysis. He conceived the antibody as having two combining groups, one for the cell and one for the complement, and therefore called it an "amboceptor." Bordet denied that the antibody thus acted as a link, and considered that the complement united (by adsorption) because of some physical change in the sensitized cell.

Heidelberger and Mayer (44) believed that the complement components possess one or more groupings capable of forming loose dissociable unions

387

with individual antibody (and perhaps antigen) molecules, but that these unions become stable enough to detect only when the complement molecules are more or less surrounded by antibody (and perhaps antigen) molecules.

That the combination of complement with the sensitized cell may in part be due to nonspecific physicochemical forces is indicated by observations that complement will lyse red cells after they have been treated with colloidal silicic acid (7,54), tannin (83), etc.

Hybrid univalent 6.5S antibody molecules, formed by recombination of half-molecules of rabbit antibody to ovalbumin with those of normal rabbit γ_G-globulin, fail to fix complement in reactions with homologous antigen. Such hybrid molecules, however, block complement fixation by intact antibody to ovalbumin. Molecules of antibody reconstituted in the absence of other protein retain the capacity to fix complement. The data suggest that small complexes containing excess univalent antibody do not fix complement and that lattice formation is required for fixation (30).

2. Mechanism of Action

The mechanism by which complement produces its effects is still not really understood. The sequence of events as at present conceived is outlined below (Section 9).

3. Species Differences

Complement is not a product of an immune reaction; it is present in normal serum. It might be supposed, therefore, that it is entirely nonspecific in its action, and it is a fact that complement from the same serum can often be used to activate a variety of reactions involving a number of different antibodies and antigens. Nevertheless, complements are not all alike, and more or less well-marked species differences can be observed—a fact already known to Bordet and Ehrlich.

Muir (69) studied the power of activation possessed by various complements (fresh serum) with antisera from the rabbit, cat, goat, duck, and ox. The antigenic cells in each case were the erythrocytes of the ox; the antibody in the ox serum was thus an isolysin. All of the antisera, except that of the duck, were activated by all the complements except those of the ox, pigeon, and horse. The horse complement was effective with cat serum. Muir considered that failure of sensitized corpuscles to lyse with a given complement might be due either to failure of the complement to combine, or to insensitivity of these particular corpuscles to its action. Thus horse complement failed to give lysis with ox cells sensitized with rabbit antiox serum, but it could be shown that nevertheless a considerable amount of the horse complement had combined.

Dingle, Fothergill, and Chandler (16), in studying the bactericidal action of antisera of the horse, rabbit, and guinea pig against *Hemophilus influenzae*, found that in the case of horse antiserum, of the complements tried (guinea pig, human, and rabbit), only the human complement would activate the killing power; in the case of rabbit antiserum both rabbit and human complements activated, while, with guinea pig antiserum, guinea pig complement was also effective, although not more effective than the human complement. Most striking of all, horse complement did not activate horse antiserum.

Some individual differences in complement content of the blood have been found. Apparently these are sometimes hereditary, for a complement-deficient strain of guinea pigs has been investigated (49). It was found that this inactive guinea pig serum could be activated with fresh human and guinea pig sera, and to a less extent with dog, rabbit, and cat sera, but not at all with the sera from a large number of other species. It could be activated by heated human serum about as readily as by fresh, but five times as much heated normal guinea pig serum was needed, and other heated sera had no activating effect. The observation of Horsfall and Goodner (48) that antibodies for pneumococcus polysaccharide could be divided into classes, according to whether or not they fixed guinea pig complement, has been referred to in Chapter 2.

Even the complement from a given individual of a given species may vary in its efficacy when tested with different systems. In general one of the best sources of complement for hemolytic systems is guinea pig serum, but we have just seen that this was found to be inefficient in the *H. influenzae* system. It is also a poor activator for the lysis of guinea pig corpuscles by anti-guinea-pig serum. It is in fact often found that an animal's complement is weak in activating the lysis of the blood cells of its own species, although this cannot be stated as a general rule. The relationships of the complements of different species have been discussed by Cushing (11,12). See also page 388.

4. Origin

It was early suggested that complement might be found in the leukocytes, but attempts to extract it from leukocytes failed, and present-day evidence indicates that complement is composed of normal constituents of circulating blood plasma. Since it is apparently a mixture of globulins and a mucoprotein (see p. 390), it may be supposed that its origin is in the main the same as that of other globulins. Possible participation of the reticuloendothelial system in the formation of complement is suggested by the experiments of Jungeblut and Berlot (51) who found a fall in the complement content of the blood following "blockade" with India ink. However, the level came back to normal in 24 hours. Early work such as that of Ehrlich and Morgenroth (27) and Dick (15) with poisons affecting the liver suggested that this organ takes part in the formation of complement. According to Coons (9) however the liver is not a site of globulin synthesis.

5. Nature of Complement

The lability of complement early suggested that it might be protein in nature. It has been found (22) that as much as 90 per cent of the complement activity of fresh guinea pig serum can be separated in a fraction which proved to be a constituent of the serum globulins. Contrary to the opinion of some earlier workers, Ecker *et al.* (22) did not believe that any of the serum albumins are intimately associated with the complement function. The fraction called "albumin" by earlier workers was said by Ecker and Pillemer (21) to consist of a mucoeuglobulin. These experimenters were able to separate complement into four fractions, of which two could be well characterized as proteins.

6. Effect of Various Reagents

One of the most striking things about complement is that heating to 56°C. for half an hour destroys its activity, although most of the serum proteins resist this treatment. The inactivation may not be entirely irreversible, for Gramenitzki (34) found a gradual return to an active condition after moderate heating.

Complement is also inactivated readily by various other treatments, such as prolonged shaking and addition of various salts. The activity is permanently destroyed by the addition of any considerable amount of acid or alkali, and in fact complement seems to have maximal stability only within the pH ranges 6.0 to 6.5 (10). It has also been observed to be destroyed by ultraviolet rays and α-particles. Other more or less destructive agents are proteolytic ferments, cobra venom, mustard gas, shaking with ether or chloroform, alcohol, alcoholic tissue extracts, bile salts, soaps, and some alkaloids. Complement activity also disappears if the serum is simply allowed to stand. Under ordinary conditions of icebox storage, as much as 90 per cent of the activity may disappear in 3 to 4 days. Even in old sera, however, some protein that can fix to specific precipitates remains. Maurer and Weigle (62) believed it is a part of the complement.

The components C′2 and C′4 (see Section 7) of human complement are inactivated by streptokinase-activated plasmin (79,57). This process is potentiated by calcium ions (56) and required the cooperation of another plasma factor which differs from plasminogen and which is believed to be identical with C′1 (55). Lepow, Wurz, Pillemer, and Ratnoff (55) suggested that the inactivation of C′2 and C′4 by plasmin and by antibody–antigen aggregates is the result of conversion of an enzyme precursor (C′1) to an active enzyme.

Complementary activity may be removed by absorption with many substances in the particulate or colloidal state, such as casein, cholesterol, kaolin, shellac, kieselguhr; inactivation also follows filtration through a Berkefeld (references in 7a).

The disodium salt of ethylenediamine tetra-acetic acid (EDTA) sometimes called versene, if present in high enough concentrations to chelate the Ca^{++} and Mg^{++}, inhibits the fixation of guinea pig complement (and some human complement) by specific precipitates (59,62). It does not seem to have this effect on rabbit complement (62).

7. "Splitting" of Complement

It was found (references in 85a) that, as electrolytes were removed from serum, its complementary activity was lost. Under these conditions the euglobulins are precipitated, and it is logical to suppose the complement has gone into the precipate. However, if the precipitate is redissolved in saline, it alone does not have complement activity. But, if the dissolved precipitate is added to the supernatant from which it was precipitated, the mixture is active, although either component alone was inactive. It was found that the fraction precipitated would unite with sensitized red cells, although it did not cause hemolysis, while the fraction remaining in solution would not unite directly with the sensitized cells. Therefore the precipitated fraction was designated as "midpiece" and the soluble fraction as "endpiece." Heidelberger (43), in agreement with Pillemer and Ecker (73), designated these as C′1 and C′2, respectively.* The midpiece is adsorbed by lead phosphate and by titanium dioxide (21). Kaolin and magnesium hydroxide adsorb both midpiece and endpiece. It was also shown that it is the midpiece which is chiefly absorbed when antibody–antigen reactions take place, most of the endpiece

---

* The symbol C′, instead of C, is used because the latter symbol is used for certain bacterial antigens.

remaining free. Both of these fractions are destroyed by heat. Saturation with carbon dioxide has also been used to separate these two fractions.

One of the agents which will absorb complement activity from serum is yeast cells. Zymin (dried, powdered, ether–acetone extracted yeast) will do the same thing. It was found by Coca (8a) that a serum so treated could be rendered active again by adding a serum which had been inactivated by heating to 56°C., which we have just seen destroys both endpiece and midpiece. Thus a relatively heat-stable fraction of complement appeared to be demonstrated (C′3). It seems to be part of the midpiece (20). According to Ecker and Pillemer (21), it is destroyed by heating to 63°C. and 30 minutes. The hereditary complement deficiency of certain guinea pigs (see p. 355) is apparently due to lack of this fraction.

Pillemer (74,80,81) showed that the inactivation of C′3 by yeast is due to the presence of an insoluble constituent, which is predominantly carbohydrate in nature, and is called zymosan. The inactivation by zymosan requires the presence of Mg^{++} and properdin.

Gordon, Whithead, and Wormall (33) reported the presence of a fourth complementary factor, also heat-stable, but not absorbed by yeast (C′4). It is inactivated by treating the serum with ammonia, hydrazine, and certain other amines. This factor was found by Gordon et al. to be essential for lysis, but not for opsonic (see p. 15) action. Ecker and Pillemer (21), however, found that removal of C′4 destroyed the opsonizing action.

Pillemer et al. (21,75) were able to obtain C′1 (midpiece), C′2 (endpiece), and C′4 in purified form, as well-defined proteins, by fractional precipitation of guinea pig serum with ammonium sulfate and dialysis. C′1 proved to be a globulin, with a sedimentation constant of 6.4 and an isoelectric point of pH 5.2 to 5.4. It was destroyed by heating of 50°C. for 30 minutes. C′2 and C′4 were obtained together in the form of an apparently pure mucoeuglobulin, containing 10.3 per cent carbohydrate, with an isoelectric point of pH 6.3 to 6.4. The C′2 activity was destroyed by heating to 50°C. for 30 minutes, the C′2 activity by heating to 66°C. for 30 minutes. C′3 was found in all the globulin fractions, even to some extent in albumin. It seemed to be a phospholipide or phosphoprotein.

Of these fractions, C′1 was found to comprise 0.72 per cent of the total serum proteins, and the mucoeuglobulin corresponding to C′2 and C′4 comprised 0.17 per cent of the total serum proteins. Chromatography shows that C′1 consists of three components, C′1q, C′1r, and C′1s (57a). C′3 of guinea pig serum consists of four separate factors, called C′3a, C′3b, C′3c, and C′3d (59a).

The properties of some isolated complement components are shown in Table 7-1 (68a).

TABLE 7-1
Some Properties of Isolated Complement Components

	C'1q (11S Component)	C'4 (β 1E-Globulin)	C'3 (β 1C-Globulin)	C'5 (β 1F-Globulin)
Sedimentation constant	11.1	10.0	9.5	9.4
Electrophoretic mobility	γ_2	β_1–α_2	β_2–β_1	β_1–α_2
Concentration in serum (μg./ml.)	20–30	30–50	300–400	30–50
Receptor	EA	EAC'1a	EAC'a,4,2a	EAC'1a,4,2a,3
Temperature requirement	0	0	+	
Inactivated by	heat	N_2H_2	N_2H_2	heat

N_2H_2 = hydrazine.

Mayer (64,65) stated in 1961 that "Although I believe that the dark days of complementology are behind us, we are still a long way from understanding what complement is and how it acts."

8. Preservation of Complement

Since complement is unstable, methods of preservation are of practical importance. Some methods which have proved successful consist in the addition of sodium chloride up to 10 per cent, addition of boric acid, drying in the lyophilizing apparatus, or freezing in solid CO_2 (53).

9. Complement Fixation

For complement to combine effectively with a cell, antibody must be present. Borsos and Rapp (2a) believe that a single molecule of 19S antibody on the cell surface is sufficient, whereas two molecules (a doublet) are required in the case of 7S antibodies.

The first step in the complement reaction is thought to be uptake of the components C'1q, C'1r and C'1s. Then the progesterase C'1s is activated, presumably by the action of C'1q and C'1r (57a). As a result of this reaction, EAC'1a, we have a cell (E) or a cellular site that contains antibody (A) and the active first component of complement (C'1a), which is now ready to react with the next component. Completion of the whole process of complement fixation requires the participation of calcium ions, although C'q can combine with gamma globulin in the absence of bivalent cations.

Activated C'1 can move from site to site and from cell to cell and like an enzyme can react with many molecules of substrate (2α). Removal of calcium ions from the reaction mixture reverses the reaction between sensitized cells and the first component (1a).

Although it is an enzyme, C'1 esterase is not involved in the actual process of cell lysis. The natural substrate of C'1 esterase is not the cell membrane but apparently two of the other components of complement, C'4 and C'2.

The next event in the complement reaction therefore seems to be uptake by the complex, EAC'1a-cell, of C'4. The latter then attaches itself firmly to the cell, from which it does not come off even if the C'1 is later removed by treatment with EDTA (1a).

Following attachment of C'4, C'2 reacts with the complex, EAC'1a,4-cell to produce a complex containing the activated form of the second component, C'2a. This step requires magnesium ions. C'2a may be an enzyme acting on C'3.

The complex EAC'1a,4-cell is still not ready to undergo hemolysis, and at least four other serum factors are required to convert it to such a state (59a). When these have acted, the cell is irreversibly damaged in some way, and spontaneously undergoes lysis.

The fatal event (for the cell) is the action of C'8; after this the integrity of the cell membrane (or some part of the cell structure that effectively keeps the hemoglobin inside the cell) is doomed. As already stated, we still do not know exactly how this irreparable damage is brought about.

Müller-Eberhard (68a) summarizes the whole sequence of events as follows:

$$
\begin{array}{lll}
(1)\ \text{E} & +\text{A} \xrightarrow{\quad\quad\quad\quad} \text{EA} & \\
& \quad\quad\quad Ca^{++} & \\
(2)\ \text{EA} & +\text{C}'1\text{q,r,s} \xrightarrow{\quad\quad\quad} \text{EAC}'1\text{a} & \\
(3)\ \text{EAC}'1\text{a} & +\text{C}'4 \xrightarrow{\quad\quad\quad\quad} \text{EAC}'1\text{a,4} & \\
& \quad\quad\quad Mg^{++} & \\
(4)\ \text{EAC}'1\text{a,4} & +\text{C}'2 \xrightarrow{\quad\quad\quad} \text{EAC}'1\text{a,4,2a} & \\
\uparrow & \text{_____|} & \\
(4a) & & \\
(5)\ \text{EAC}'1\text{a,4,2a} & +\text{C}'3 \xrightarrow{\quad\quad\quad} \text{EAC}'1\text{a,4,2a,3} & \\
(5a)\ \text{EAC}'1\text{a,4,3} \leftarrow & & \\
(6)\ \text{EAC}'1\text{a,4,2a,3} & +\text{C}'5,6 \xrightarrow{\quad\quad} \text{EAC}'1\text{a,4,2a,3,5,6} & \\
(7)\ \text{EAC}'1\text{a,4,2a,3,5,6} & +\text{C}'7 \xrightarrow{\quad\quad\quad} \text{EAC}'1\text{a,4,2a,3,5,6,7} & \\
(8)\ \text{EAC}'1\text{a,4,2a,3,5,6,7} & +\text{C}'8 \xrightarrow{\quad\quad\quad} \text{E}^* & \\
\end{array}
$$

E^* = damaged cell

In the early days of complement study, Heidelberger, Weil, and Treffers (46) proposed the hypothesis that complement molecules, through groupings capable of loose dissociable union with antibody molecules combine with antibody–antigen complexes in a purely chemical way. The unions were supposed to become progressively firmer because the complement molecules are gradually surrounded by antibody (and antigen) molecules as larger aggregates of antibody and antigen molecules are formed. These authors suggested that stabilization of the originally loose complement bonds "might result either through the attraction of approaching ionized groupings of opposite sign, through hydrogen bonding, through spatial accommodation of large groupings on C′1 (combining component of complement) and A (antibody), or through the presence, on C′1, as on antigen and antibody, of more than one grouping capable of reacting with A molecules brought into apposition." They made the suggestion that possibly such union could be demonstrated without the presence of an antibody–antigen compound, or even with normal globulin, if there were any way of bringing a sufficient number of such molecules into suitable apposition and holding them there. The anticomplementary power of purified γ-globulin (13) seems in accord with this suggestion.

A schematic representation of Heidelberger's ideas on the way complement combined with antibody–antigen compounds is shown in Fig. 7-1, modified from Heidelberger and Mayer (44).

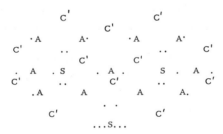

Fig. 7-1. Hypothetical mode of combination of complement with antibody–antigen compounds. From Heidelberger.

The release of hemoglobin from the erythrocyte, once C′8 has combined, takes about two minutes, and is faster at 37°C. than at lower temperatures (71).

The power of antibody–antigen compounds to combine with complement evidently depends on a number of factors. It has been mentioned previously that the species origin of the antibody and complement may have an important influence. The size of the antibody–antigen complex seems also to be a determining factor. Most precipitin reactions involving rabbit antibody fix complement as they progress, but it is not necessary that a precipitate should form for complement to be fixed, for this may occur in zones where there is no visible precipitation. Goldsworthy (31), who investigated this question, found that, as aggregation proceeded in precipitating systems, the power of fixing complement rose to a maximum, then declined, and, if complement was not added until precipitation was complete, little fixation occurred. Heidelberger *et al.* (45), however, observed that resuspended, finely divided specific precipitates took up complement from guinea pig sera almost as well as did precipitates allowed to form in the presence of complement, and Mayer and Levine (67) found that preformed precipitates had considerable power of fixing complement. Evidence was obtained which suggested that the maximal power of fixation was possessed by particles large enough to cause opalescence, but not visible to the eye. Mixtures in which antigen was in excess and in which the particles never grew to the opalescent stage, fixed poorly or not at all. Dean (14) had previously observed failure to fix when antigen was in excess. Goodner and Horsfall (32) found no fixation when an antiserum against aminobenzylglucoside-protein was mixed with the uncoupled glucoside, although with the conjugated protein fixation was obtained. That is, the (invisible) hapten–antibody reaction did not fix complement.

Pressman, Campbell, and Pauling (82) found that complement was fixed when antibody combined with a multivalent hapten to form a precipitate, but not when antibody combined with a univalent hapten which did not precipitate.

Goldsworthy suggested that complement fixation is a function of the size of the particles of a precipitate. On this basis it is quite understandable that mixtures in which antigen is in excess, or deficient, so that the size of the particles increases only gradually, reach their maximal fixing power more slowly. Thus it was found that the relation of the complement-fixing optimum to the precipitating optimum (point of most rapid precipitation) depended on the interval allowed to elapse after the antibody and antigen were added, before the addition of complement. If complement was added simultaneously with the other two reagents (the usual technic), the fixation optimum was found either at the precipitation optimum (with weak or medium strength sera) or in a tube having somewhat less antigen (with very strong sera). If, however, an interval (20 minutes to 4 hours), was allowed to elapse before the addition of complement, the fixation optimum shifted in the direction of increased antigen, and was to be found in a zone where the particles had not grown too large to fix before the complement was added.

Eagle (17,18) tried to explain the sensitization of the Wasserman "antigen" by serologically unreactive sterols as also simply a matter of particle size. He supposed the sterol to act as a nucleus around which are deposited reactive lipides of the antigen, resulting in the formation of larger particles which, when coated with reagin, fix complement better than the smaller particles formed in the absence of sterol. This is illustrated in Fig. 7-2.

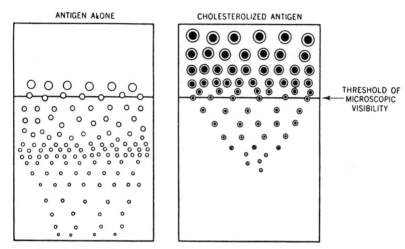

Fig. 7-2. The effect of cholesterol on size, number, and composition of particles in Wassermann antigen (diagrammatic) (17). The core (black) represents cholesterol of a cholesterol–antigen mixture, the clear area represents (lipoid) antigen.

It is difficult to test whether fixation is influenced by the proportion of antibody to antigen in the aggregates, as well as by their size. It has been observed that the proportion of antiserum to antigen in the mixture may be widely varied, sometimes as much as 1000-fold, without notably lessening the degree of fixation. Experiments are on record in which a fixation optimum was observed with a constant amount of antigen; however, in such experiments the complement was usually added simultaneously with the other reagents, so that the deciding factor might still have been particle size. With horse antihemocyanin antibody, where the antigen molecule is large, Hooker and Boyd (47) observed fixation in mixtures containing so much antigen that neither precipitation nor clouding would occur. In some of these mixtures there was only about one antibody molecule for each seven molecules of antigen; it is not known how far secondary aggregation might have proceeded in such a mixture, surely not far.

Combination of complement with antibody–antigen mixtures is rapid at first, but becomes slower with the lapse of time. The velocity, were it not for the deterioration of complement as the mixtures stand, would not fall to zero within less than about 8 hours at 37°C. (17). The actual time of incubation of complement allowed with the antibody–antigen mixtures (usually 60 minutes at 37°C., or 4 hours in the icebox) is essentially a compromise between the rate of fixation and the rate of destruction of complement.

The quantitative formulation of fixation reactions is complicated by the fact that the number of variables is large. It is possible to vary three different time intervals: the time elapsing after mixing the antibody and antigen before complement is added, the time of incubation with complement before the indicator (sensitized red cells–hemolytic system) is added, and the time of incubation following this addition before readings of the degree of lysis are made. (In practical work the first interval is usually zero, or negligible.) In addition, the amounts of five different reagents, the antibody, the antigen, the complement itself consisting of a number of components, the cells, and the sensitizer, may be varied.

The time intervals are, however, not usually varied much in work of this kind, so results of different experiments fortunately are comparable in this respect. The amounts of reagents are subject to more variation.

A certain minimal concentration of antigen is requisite, but in the usual volumes fixation may be obtained with amounts of antigen of the order of 10^{-7} g., or less. A certain minimal amount of antibody must be combined with this antigen. More antibody than this does not usually prevent fixation, even in the case of horse antiprotein antibodies, where an inhibition zone with excess serum is observed in precipitation (47); but the fixation technic is such that large excesses of antiserum cannot be tried, as serum alone usually has some "anticomplementary" effect. With any given amount of (rabbit) antiserum, it is usually found that only amounts of antigen within a certain range will give fixation. With the lower concentrations of serum, this optimal zone contracts markedly, until with the smallest amounts it may be found that only one particular proportion of antibody to antigen will give complete fixation.

The more complement is used, naturally, the less complete the fixation is likely to be (i.e., more remains free in the mixture). The degree of hemolysis, if any, which is observed when the sensitized cells are added, depends upon the amount of complement remaining. However, the degree of hemolysis also depends upon the amount of sensitizer (hemolytic antibody) previously combined with the indicator cells.

To a certain extent, complement and sensitizer (sometimes called amboceptor) can supplement each other in hemolysis. This is shown schematically in Fig. 7-3, modified from Eagle (18). Of course, complete hemolysis

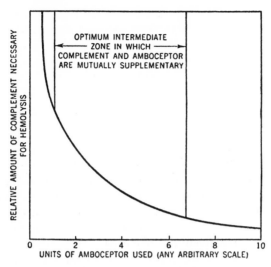

Fig. 7-3. Mutually supplementary activity of complement and lysin in hemolysis (diagrammatic). From Eagle.

cannot be obtained with less than a certain minimal amount of either; there is a certain optimal range of proportions for practical work, shown by the lines in Fig. 7-3.

If too much sensitizer is used, hemolysis may be retarded (*Neisser-Wechsberg phenomenon,* or complement deviation). This is still unexplained.

10. Titration of the Components of Complement

Methods of titrating the components of complement were worked out by Heidelberger *et al.* (2,44), following the principles enunciated by Hegedüs and Greiner (41). A separate reagent is required for the titration of each component. This reagent should not contain the component to be titrated, but should contain an excess (*i.e.,* more than one unit per dose employed) of each of the remaining components. Four reagents were used: reagent 1 (R 1) containing C'2,3,4, for the titration of C'1; reagent 2 (R 2) containing C'1,3,4, for the titration of C'2; reagent 3 (R 3) containing C'1,2,4, for the titration of C'3; and reagent 4 (R 4), containing C'1,2,3 for the titration of C'4. A reagent should produce no lysis of sensitized red cells when used alone in several times the quantity employed in the actual titrations. R 1 was prepared by combining "endpiece," which furnished C'2 and some C'3 and C'4 with heated serum

TABLE 7-2

Average Titers of Complement and Its Components in Guinea Pig and Human Sera (2)

Source	Whole C'	C'1	Units per ml. C'2	C'3	C'4
Guinea pig	350	2300	450	370	6000
Human	100	3700	170	250	4000

which supplied extra C'3 and C'4. R 2 consisted of "midpiece" plus heated serum. "Zymosan"-treated complement was employed as R 3, and ammonia- or hydrazine-treated complement was employed as R 4.

As a control on the adequacy of the amounts of the components contained in the reagents, each reagent was tested in mixture with every other reagent. The reagents were judged adequate if addition of any one of these mixtures caused complete hemolysis of sensitized cells. By adding measured amounts of an unknown serum to these reagents and testing with sensitized cells, the number of units of each component in the unknown could be determined. Average results for guinea pig and human sera are shown in Table 7-2.

Since volume units are used in all these titrations, the data are purely relative and give no clue to the actual content by weight or the concentration of any component.

11. Actual Weight of Complement Involved in Fixation

Haurowitz (37) showed by determinations of the weights of precipitates made with and without complement that complement did not enter into the precipitate in anything like as large a ratio as one molecule of complement per one of antibody. Heidelberger (42,43), using large excesses of complement, found that the presence of complement increased the amount of nitrogen in the precipitate by an amount corresponding roughly to 1 molecule per 4 molecules of antibody, if we assume complement and antibody to have the same molecular weight. This is in contrast to the approximate ratio of 35 molecules of complement to 1 of antibody which seem to act in hemolysis (see above).

Pillemer et al. (77) believed that the complement nitrogen which added to specific precipitates of pneumococcus polysaccharide S3 and its antibody came from components C'1, C'2, and C'4.

In terms of a "hemolytic unit," determined as the amount required for complete hemolysis of 0.2 ml. of a minimally sensitized 2 to 2.5 per cent sheep red cell suspension, Heidelberger estimated that 1000 units corresponded to 0.10 to 0.14 mg. of complement nitrogen. If all the nitrogen comes from globulins, this would correspond to about 0.75 mg. of protein. It was concluded that guinea pig serum containing 200 to 250 units contains about 0.04 to 0.06 mg. of complement nitrogen per cubic centimeter, or about 0.4 to 0.7 per cent of the total protein content of guinea pig serum. Some sera were found to have as much as 0.07 mg. of complement nitrogen per milliliter. Haurowitz and Yenson (38) computed that 1.5 $\times 10^{-14}$ g. of complement is required to hemolyze a single erythrocyte.

12. Anticomplementary Effect

Most antisera, in sufficient amounts, and also some antigens, even without the addition of the other reagent, antigen or antiserum as the case may be, have the power of nonspecifically removing or inactivating some complement. This is called anticomplementary action, and often sets a limit to the concentration of one or both reagents which can be used. The anticomplementary effect of the reagents used must always be carefully tested for by setting up proper controls.

There are probably a number of causes of anticomplementary action. It has been pointed out on page 396 that particulate matter often adsorbs complement. Sera which are old or contaminated with bacteria may be anticomplementary, and this property also may be induced by presence of soaps, acid, alkali, oxalate, etc. It has been found that absorption of antisera with bacteria (in operations designed to remove certain antibodies) may render them anticomplementary. Sera of syphilitic patients are likely to be intrinsically somewhat anticomplementary.

Hayes and Sachs (40) found that heating syphilitic sera tended to make them anticomplementary. They reported that addition of about eight volumes of 0.03N hydrochloric acid precipitated out the anticomplementary fraction, leaving the syphilitic antibodies in solution.

The anticomplementary properties of human γ-globulin, and the inhibition of this action by other substances, have been studied by Davis et al. (13). The anticomplementary action was decreased by heating to 56°C. for half an hour, and was abolished by the addition of approximately equal amounts of serum albumin or β-globulin.

Olhagen (70) made an extensive study of anticomplementary effects. Electrophoretic study of strongly anticomplementary sera revealed an extra component "X" which migrated between the β- and γ-globulins. In some cases an abnormal γ-component was observed which was termed "Y_r." It was possible to isolate the relatively thermostable anticomplementary globulin. It appeared to be a pseudoglobulin with a molecular weight of about 170,000, which Olhagen considered higher than that of normal gamma globulin. Olhagen believes that the anticomplementary effect is due to a sort of denaturation of the globulin of serum which results in a change in dispersion, which leads to adsorption of complement.

Streptokinase inactivates human complement (79). It may be that this explains why contaminated sera often become somewhat anticomplementary.

13. Quantitative Formulation of Course of the Fixation Reaction

The relation between the degree of hemolysis and the amount of complement used has been studied by a number of workers. Wadsworth, Maltaner, and Maltaner (86,87) reported that, if to a given amount of antigen there is always added that amount of antibody which gives maximum fixation, there is observed a linear relationship between the concentration of antiserum and the concentration of complement required to give 50 per cent hemolysis of the sensitized cells. Or, if a constant amount of antiserum is used, and the amount of antigen which gives maximum fixation is used each time, there is a linear relation between the concentration of the antigen and that of complement giving 50 per cent hemolysis.

Wadsworth, Maltaner, and Maltaner constructed tables based on the "logistic formula," whereby from two readings of hemolysis the ratio c_{s+a}/c_s can be calculated, where c_{s+a} is the amount of complement required for 50 per cent hemolysis with serum and antigen and c_s is the amount required with serum alone. The numerical value of this ratio was taken as a measure of the fixing power of the serum, and of course made automatic allowance for any anticomplementary activity of the serum.

It has been shown that the S-shaped curve, which is obtained when the degree of hemolysis is plotted against the amount of complement used, can be explained on the basis of plausible hypotheses as to the mechanism of hemolysis, and that the mathematical predictions of these hypotheses fit the data as well as, or better than, the empirical logistic function.

Waksman (88) pointed out that the sigmoid curve could be predicted from the assumption that all cells are not identical, but that there is a distribution of sensitivities to lysis which obeys the normal Gaussian curve. He then finds that the probit transformation (p. 713) of the cumulative normal curve gives a straight line which fits the observed data quite well. Since the normal curve is better understood and has found application to so many kinds of biological data, Waksman properly believed that it was to be preferred in this instance also. Furthermore, it seems likely that the red cells of an animal, being of various ages, would in fact differ in sensitivity to lysis.

14. Other Effects of Complement

The hemolytic effects of complement are chiefly emphasized here, because lysis is the most convenient way of detecting and measuring complement activity. The value of complement in resistance, however, depends upon its other roles in immune reactions. Among these we may list: opsonizing activity which accelerates phagocytosis of invading microorganisms, lysis of certain microorganisms, possible adjuvant role in virus neutralization, and various effects on the precipitin and agglutinin reactions.

Lysis *in vivo* can occur in the case of the chlorera vibrio, some of the Gram-negative enteric bacilli, and probably *Brucella* and *H. influenzae*. The smooth virulent forms of these bacteria are less easily lysed than the rough avirulent forms, so the actual importance of this role of complement in immunity is perhaps not great. There is evidence (19) that the complement involved in bactericidal and bacteriolytic processes is the same as that which brings about hemolysis.

Opsonization greatly increases phagocytosis, and is thus of great significance in the mechanism of acquired resistance. Both antibody and complement seem to be involved for opsonization (19,60,44). Removal or inactivation of $C'1$, $C'2$, or $C'4$ results in a loss of opsonic activity, and the addition of the missing complement component restores activity. Calcium ions are also needed. It is possible that the part played by complement in opsonization is its most important protective role.

Complement has been shown to effect the precipitin reaction, not only by adding to the precipitate (p. 353), but in other ways. Using crystallized bovine serum albumin and rabbit antibody, Maurer and Talmage (61) found that rabbit complement caused more of the antigen to be precipitated, and less antibody. They postulated that the rabbit complement causes some of the soluble antibody–antigen complexes to become insoluble, thus shifting the equilibria existing in the region of antigen excess.

It has been reported (68) that complement is essential for the lysis of human leukocytes which takes place in the presence of tuberculin and a protein factor from tuberculous serum, but Waksman (89) and Stineberg and Flick (85) could not confirm this.

15. Effect of Altered Conditions and Various Reagents

Temperature

Fixation is slow at 0°C. and increases rapidly with rise in temperature. The rate of deterioration of complement also increases very rapidly with higher temperatures, however, so that a limit is put to the temperature which can be used in practice. There are indications that a longer period of fixation at icebox temperatures gives a more sensitive reaction than incubation at 37°C. According to Eagle (17) this depends on four main factors: (1) the time may be prolonged beyond that possible at 37°C., (2) there is less inhibiting effect of the serum at low temperatures, (3) the anticomplementary action of serum is more pronounced in the prolonged low temperature incubation, favoring development of a positive reaction, (4) complement may deteriorate in the prolonged test, again favoring positive reactions.

It is apparent that these factors would be in favor of sensitivity, which may be desirable in a test for syphilis, for example, but might not necessarily make the test more reliable, which may be the important point in other instances where complement fixation is employed.

Time of Incubation

Fixation goes on rapidly at first, then more slowly, so that the amount of fixation increases with time. Here too, however, complement deterioration comes in as a limiting factor. Complement is destroyed with prolonged incubation, especially at room temperature and higher. Consequently, according to Eagle, the time allowed for fixation at 37°C. should not exceed 30 minutes. Longer times at lower temperatures favor the detection of weak positive reactions, as just mentioned, and are therefore favored by some for the Wassermann test.

Electrolytes

Complement is not fixed in the absence of electrolyte, and fixation is inhibited by excess electrolyte, e.g., over 1.5 per cent sodium chloride. The optimal salt concentration, according to Eagle (17), is that commonly used in "physiological saline," viz., 0.85 per cent sodium chloride. Some bivalent cations, even in traces, have a marked inhibiting effect. Calcium and magnesium ions, however, in small amounts are essential to fixation and lysis (see Section 9).

Hydrogen Ion Concentration

The optimal *p*H is substantially the *p*H of serum, falling in the narrow zone of 6.3 to 7.8. Complement itself is rapidly and irreversibly destroyed at *p*H values less than 5.5, or greater than 8.0.

16. Forensic Complement Fixation Tests

We have previously said that the fixation of complement in a mixture can be used as an indication that an antibody–antigen reaction has gone on. The way this is used is shown schematically in Fig. 7-4.

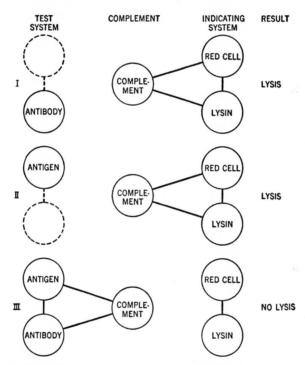

Fig. 7-4. Diagrammatic representation of complement fixation test: (I) test system contains antibody but no antigen, complement remains free and lyses sensitized cells added as indicating system; (II) test system contains antigen but no antibody, again complement is not fixed; (III) test system contains both antigen and antibody, complement is fixed, and sensitized cells added are not lysed. After Hooker (unpublished).

The value of this technic in cases where no visible reaction follows the combination of antibody and antigen is obvious, but the reaction has actually proved more sensitive than direct observation even in cases where visible precipitation could result. It has been found possible to detect by complement fixation amounts of a protein much too small to be demonstrated by direct precipitation with an antiserum. Therefore the method has found application in the determination of the species origin of foreign proteins, such as blood stains, in medicolegal cases. Anyone familiar with the technic of the Wassermann test, which is outlined below, can readily devise the appropriate modifications.

17. Applications to Diagnosis of Disease

Complement fixation has found valuable applications in diagnosis. The principle involved is the same as before. The question to be answered is, generally, does the serum of the patient contain antibodies for the disease-producing agent that we suspect is causing his malady? By testing for complement fixation when the serum is mixed with the infectious agent or a suitable preparation from it, valuable information may be obtained. Of course since fixation is only a secondary reaction, consequent on the union of antibody and antigen, the fixation technic can not be expected to be more specific than other methods of detecting antibody-antigen reactions. Consequently cross reactions with related organisms, and (rarely) with antigens not closely related, may be found here as in other cases. Application of this technic to specific diseases will be mentioned in Chapter 15.

18. The Wassermann Test

Although developed before the flocculation tests for syphilis, the Wassermann reaction is best understood by referring to these reactions, which we have already discussed in Chapter 6. Wassermann et al. (90) used in their first work extracts of syphilitic organs as "antigen," but it was soon found that suitable "antigen" could be prepared from normal organs.

We may regard the Wassermann test as simply an application of the complement fixation technic to detect the reaction between the lipoid "antigen" and the "reagin" in syphilitic serum. The reagents are mixed in the presence of complement, and, after suitable incubation, the indicating system, red cells sensitized by combination with hemolysin (amboceptor), is added. If hemolysis takes place, complement must still have been free when the sensitized cells were added, and no fixation had previously taken place during the incubation, or was not complete; if there is no hemolysis, fixation was complete, and we infer the presence of syphilitic reagin in the patient's serum.

In actual practice, the reaction must be carried out in a quantitative manner, with careful controls on all the reagents.

Mechanism of the Wassermann Reaction

Whether the reagin in syphilitic serum is a true antibody or not, we know that it combines with the lipoid "antigen" used. This can be demonstrated by adding an excess of the antigen to a Wassermann-positive serum and removing the lipoid particles (by high-speed centrifugation or Berkefeld filtration). The serum will be found to have lost its positive reaction or to have it much reduced (17).

The lipoid particles after combination with reagin aggregate, as has been observed under the microscope by dark-field illumination (8,50), even though no change visible to the eye alone is seen. The surface properties of the particles are found to be profoundly altered after combination with reagin. Their isoelectric point shifts towards that of serum protein, and their critical potential and the electrolyte concentration required to cause aggregation become the same as for particles of heat-coagulated protein. On the basis of these facts, Eagle (17) suggested that the reagin forms a sensitizing layer of globulin around each particle. He believed that it is probably this sensitizing film which fixes the complement.

19. Applications to Other Diseases

The complement fixation technic can be applied to the diagnosis of various diseases. It is particularly valuable when the antibodies present refuse to manifest their activity in any other way (or only by neutralizing the infectious agent). Examples are furnished by the work of Enders (28) on mumps and of Witebsky *et al.* (91) on trichinosis. Fixation has also been used in influenza (29) and neurotropic viruses (39).

References

1. Alberty, R. A., and R. L. Baldwin, *J. Immunol.,* **66,** 725 (1951).
1a. Becker, E. L., *J. Immunol.,* **84,** 299–308 (1960).
2. Bier, O. G., *et al., J. Exptl. Med.,* **81,** 449 (1945).
2a. Borsos, T., and M. M. Mayer, in *Mechanisms of Cell and Tissue Damage Produced by Immune Reactions,* P. Grabar and P. Miescher, eds., Schwabe, Basel-Stuttgart, 1962.
2b. Borsos, T., and J. Rapp, *Science,* **150,** 505–506 (1965).
3. Borsos, T., H. J. Rapp, and M. M. Mayer, *J. Immunol.,* **87,** 310–325 (1961).
4. Borsos, T., H. J. Rapp, and M. M. Mayer, *J. Immunol.,* **87,** 326–329 (1961).
5. Borsos, T., H. J. Rapp, and C. T. Cook, *J. Immunol.,* **87,** 330–336 (1961).

6. Bowman, W. W., M. M. Mayer, and H. J. Rapp, *J. Exptl. Med.*, **94**, 87 (1951).
7. Browning, C. H., *Immunochemical Studies*, Wood, New York, 1925.
7a. Browning, C. H., "Complement," in *A System of Bacteriology*, **6**, 332, London (1931).
8. Chevrel-Bodin, M. L., and M. Cormier, *Compt. rend. soc. biol.*, **109**, 1152 (1932).
8a. Coca, A. F., *Z. Immunitatsforsch.*, **21**, 604 (1914).
9. Coons, A. H., *Ann. Rev. Microbiol.*, *Stanford*, **8**, 333 (1954).
10. Coulter, C. B., *J. Gen. Physiol.*, **3**, 771 (1921).
11. Cushing, J. E., Jr., *J. Immunol.*, **50**, 61–74 (1945).
12. Cushing, J. E. Jr., *J. Immunol.*, **50**, 75–89 (1945).
13. Davis, B. D., *et al.*, *J. Immunol.*, **49**, 223–233 (1944).
14. Dean, H. R., *Z. Immunitätsforsch.*, **13**, 84 (1912).
15. Dick, G. F., *J. Infect. Diseases*, **12**, 111 (1913).
16. Dingle, J. H., D. Fothergill, and C. A. Chandler, *J. Immunol.*, **34**, 357 (1938).
17. Eagle, H., *J. Exptl. Med.*, **52**, 747 (1930).
18. Eagle, H., *The Laboratory Diagnosis of Syphilis*, Mosby, St. Louis, 1937.
19. Ecker, E. E., *Ann. Rev. Microbiol.*, **2**, 255 (1948).
20. Ecker, E. E., C. B. Jones, and A. O. Kuehn, *J. Immunol.*, **40**, 81 (1941).
21. Ecker, E. E., and L. Pillemer, *Ann. N. Y. Acad. Sci.*, **43**, 63 (1942).
22. Ecker, E. E., L. Pillemer, C. B. Jones, and S. Seifter, *J. Biol. Chem.*, **135**, 347 (1940).
23. Ecker, E. E., L. Pillemer, and S. Seifter, *J. Immunol.*, **47**, 181–193 (1943).
24. Ecker, E. E., and S. Seifter, *Proc. Soc. Exptl. Biol. Med.*, **58**, 359–361 (1945).
25. Ecker, E. E., S. Seifter, and T. F. Dozois, *J. Lab. Clin. Med.*, **30**, 39–50 (1945).
26. Ecker, E. E., *et al.*, *Science*, **98**, 43–44 (1943).
27. Ehrlich, P., and J. Morgenroth, *Berlin klin. Wochschr.*, **37**, 453, 681 (1900).
28. Enders, J. F., and S. Cohen, *Proc. Soc. Exptl. Biol. Med.*, **50**, 180–184 (1942).
29. Friedewald, W. F., *J. Exptl. Med.*, **78**, 347–366 (1943).
30. Fudenberg, H. H., R. Hong, and A. Nisonoff, *Science*, **148**, 91–93 (1965).
31. Goldsworthy, N. E., *J. Pathol. Bacteriol.*, **31**, 220 (1928).
32. Goodner, K., and F. L. Horsfall, *J. Exptl. Med.*, **64**, 201 (1936).
33. Gordon, J., H. R. Whitehead, and A. Wormall, *Biochem. J. (London)*, **20**, 1028 (1926).
34. Gramenitzki, M., *Biochem. Z.*, **38**, 501 (1912).
35. Hambleton, A., *Can. J. Res.*, **7**, 583 (1932).
36. Hambleton, A., *Can. J. Res.*, **7**, 596 (1932).
37. Haurowitz, F., *Z. Immunitätsforsch.*, **95**, 200 (1939).
38. Haurowitz, F., and M. M. Yenson, *J. Immunol.*, **47**, 390 (1943).
39. Havens, W. P., Jr., *et al.*, *J. Exptl. Med.*, **77**, 139–153 (1943).
40. Hayes, W., and H. Sachs, *J. Pathol. Bacteriol.*, **51**, 455–458 (1940).
41. Hegedüs, A., and H. Greiner, *Z. Immunitätsforsch.*, **92**, 1 (1938).
42. Heidelberger, M., *Science*, **92**, 534 (1940).
43. Heidelberger, M., *J. Exptl. Med.*, **73**, 681 (1941).
44. Heidelberger, M., and M. M. Mayer, *Advan. Enzymol.*, **8**, 71 (1948).
45. Heidelberger, M., M. Rocha e Silva, and M. M. Mayer, *J. Exptl. Med.*, **74**, 359 (1941).
46. Heidelberger, M., A. J. Weil, and H. P. Treffers, *J. Exptl. Med.*, **73**, 695 (1941).
47. Hooker, S. B., and W. C. Boyd, *Ann. N. Y. Acad. Sci.*, **43**, 107–122 (1942).
48. Horsfall, F. L., and K. Goodner, *J. Immunol.*, **31**, 135 (1936).
49. Hyde, R. R., *J. Immunol.*, **8**, 267 (1923).
50. Jacobsthal, E. *Z. Immunitätsforsch.*, **8**, 107 (1910).
51. Jungeblut, C. W., and J. A. Berlot, *J. Exptl. Med.*, **43**, 797 (1926).
52. Kabat, E. A., *J. Exptl. Med.*, **69**, 103 (1939).

53. Kabat, E. A., and M. M. Mayer, *Experimental Immunochemistry*, Charles C Thomas, Springfield, Illinois, 1948.
54. Landsteiner, K., *Münch med. Wochschr.*, **51**, 1185 (1904).
55. Lepow, I. H., *J. Immunol.*, **73**, 146 (1954).
56. Lepow, I. H., L. Pillemer, and O. D. Ratnoff, *J. Exptl. Med.*, **98**, 277 (1953).
57. Lepow, I. H., and L. Pillemer, *J. Immunol.*, **75**, 63 (1955).
57a. Lepow, I. H., *et al.*, *J. Exp. Med.*, **117**, 983–1008 (1963).
58. Levine, L., A. G. Osler, and M. M. Mayer, *J. Immunol.*, **71**, 374 (1953).
59. Levine, L., *et al.*, *Federation Proc.*, **12**, 451 (1953).
59a. Linscott, W. D., and K. Nishioka, *J. Exp. Med.*, **118**, 795–815 (1963).
60. Maaløe, O., *On the Relation between Alexin and Opsonin*, Einer Munksgaard, Copenhagen, 1946.
61. Maurer, P. H., and D. W. Talmage, *J. Immunol.*, **70**, 435 (1953).
62. Maurer, P. H., and W. Weigle, *J. Immunol.*, **71**, 284 (1953).
63. Mayer, M. M., Proc. VI Intern. Congr. Microbiol., Rome, Sept. 6–12, 1953.
64. Mayer, M. M., *Cancer Res.*, **21**, 1262–1269 (1961).
65. Mayer, M. M., *Immunochemical Approaches to Problems in Microbiology*, Rutgers University Press, New Brunswick, 1961.
66. Mayer, M. M., and L. Levine, *J. Immunol.*, **72**, 511 (1954).
67. Mayer, M. M., and L. Levine, *J. Immunol.*, **72**, 516 (1954).
68. Miller, J. M., J. H. Vaughan, and C. B. Favour, *Proc. Soc. Exptl. Biol. Med.*, **71**, 592 (1949).
68a. Müller-Eberhard, H. J., in *Bacterial and Mycotic Infections of Man*, R. J. Dubos and J. G. Hirsch, eds., Lippincott, Philadelphia, 1965.
69. Muir, R., *J. Pathol. Bacteriol.*, **16**, 523 (1911–1912).
70. Olhagen, B., *Acta Med. Scand.*, Suppl. **162** (1945).
71. Osler, A. G., *Advan. Immunol.*, **1**, 131–210 (1961).
72. Pillemer, L., *Chem. Rev.*, **33**, 1–26 (1943).
73. Pillemer, L., and E. E. Ecker, *Science*, **94**, 437 (1941).
74. Pillemer, L., and E. E. Ecker, *J. Biol. Chem.*, **137**, 139 (1941).
75. Pillemer, L., E. E. Ecker, J. L. Oncley, and E. J. Cohn, *J. Exptl. Med.*, **74**, 297–308 (1941).
76. Pillemer, L., *et al.*, *J. Exptl. Med.*, **76**, 93–101 (1942).
77. Pillemer, L., F. Chu, S. Seifter, and E. E. Ecker, *J. Immunol.*, **45**, 51 (1942).
78. Pillemer, L., *et al.*, *J. Immunol.*, **47**, 205 (1943).
79. Pillemer, L., *et al.*, *J. Exptl. Med.*, **97**, 573 (1953).
80. Pillemer, L., *et al.*, *J. Immunol.*, **71**, 331 (1953).
81. Pillemer, L., I. H. Lepow, and L. Blum, *J. Immunol.*, **71**, 339 (1953).
82. Pressman, D., D. H. Campbell, and L. Pauling, *Proc. Natl. Acad. Sci. U. S.*, **28**, 77 (1942).
83. Reiner, L., and O. Fischer, *Z. Immunitätsforsch.*, **61**, 317 (1929).
84. Seifter, S., T. F. Dorzois, and E. E. Ecker, *J. Immunol.*, **49**, 45–49 (1944).
85. Stinebring, W. R., and J. A. Flick, *Federation Proc.*, **13**, 513 (1954).
85a. Topley, W. W. C., and G. S. Wilson, *The Principles of Bacteriology and Immunity*, 5th ed., by G. S. Wilson and A. A. Miles, Wm. Wood, Baltimore, 1964.
86. Wadsworth, A., F. Maltaner, and E. Maltaner, *J. Immunol.*, **35**, 93 (1938).
87. Wadsworth, A., F. Maltaner, and E. Maltaner, *J. Immunol.*, **35**, 105 (1938).
88. Waksman, B. H., *J. Immunol.*, **63**, 409 (1949).
89. Waksman, B. H., *Federation Proc.*, **10**, 423, No. 1, pt. 1 (1951).
90. Wassermann, A. A., Neisser, and C. Bruck, *Deut. med Wochschr.*, **32** 745 (1906).
91. Witebsky, E., *et al.*, *N. Y. State J. Med.*, **42**, 431 (1942).

CHAPTER 8

Immediate Hypersensitivity

A. INTRODUCTION TO HYPERSENSITIVITY

The word immunology in the title of this book may have led some unwary readers to suppose that we were going to be interested only in mechanisms which increase the resistance of an animal to disease or help protect him against the effect of deleterious foreign substances. Actually we shall not so restrict ourselves; immunology includes the study of a number of conditions in which the animal is actually more, not less, susceptible. This is traditional and proper; the study of heightened susceptibility belongs to our field, because such states are conditioned in most, if not all, cases by mechanisms which show the closest similarity to those we have investigated above. For example, they exhibit the same high degree of specificity, can often be shown to depend on the presence of antibodies, and, like the ordinary sorts of immunity, often result from infection with a specific organism or from exposures to a specific foreign substance. It is not extending the meaning of the term too much to call these phenomena immunological.

A certain extension of the word *immune* has already been introduced, for we have spoken of a rabbit which has been repeatedly injected with egg albumin, for example, as immunized, although egg albumin is not a toxic substance for a normal rabbit, and although the "immunized" rabbit has not been particularly protected by the treatment. Indeed, as we shall soon see, an animal which has been injected with a harmless protein may actually become, not resistant, but highly susceptible to it, so that the later injection of a small dose may kill him with great rapidity. It may also be found that an animal which has been infected with a certain disease-producing agent, although apparently more resistant to a subsequent infection, may be definitely less resistant than the normal animal to injection of certain substances derived from the infectious agent or to reinfection with massive doses of the living agent.

We shall also include a consideration of hypersensitive* conditions in man. Many of these conditions, as, for example, hay fever, have, so far as we can tell, no connection with infection. Patients suffering from these complaints find, to their great annoyance, that they have acquired an altered way of responding to certain constituents of their environment. These persons are more, not less, susceptible, yet their difficulties are produced by reactions which are essentially the same (in mechanism) as those which do come into play in defense against disease.

The phenemonon of human hypersensitivity has obviously been known for a long time, as shown by the quotation from the great Latin poem given at the beginning of this chapter. *De Rerum Natura* (On the Nature of Things) was apparently written in the years 95 to 55 B.C. (and never considered finished by the author).

Although we define immunological processes as those concerned in increasing resistance to disease, still we claim the right to treat under this heading processes which may actually reduce the resistance of the individual, or cause him to have a disease which would otherwise not exist at all. This apparent paradox probably depends fundamentally on two facts: *(1)* In many of the cases in which an individual suffers as the result of a newly acquired altered reactivity to some agent, the conditions are artificial. We may perhaps say poetically that Nature did not intend that human beings should have horse serum injected into their veins and tissues, and we should not be surprised that the results of doing so are sometimes disconcerting as well as undesirable. The guinea pig is extremely easy to kill by an immunological reaction we call anaphylaxis, but it may be doubted if many guinea pigs under natural conditions ever died of anaphylactic shock. When we perform such an experiment we are setting up conditions which are essentially artificial; as Hill (70) has put it, we are "stacking the cards" against the guinea pig. *(2)* Immunological mechanisms are teleologically not perfect, and some of the disadvantageous effects of specifically altered reactivities are due to overfunction, or misdirected function, of one or another of these mechanisms. This is not a unique state of affairs; there are analogies for it in ordinary pathology. We may suppose that allergic disease, in cases where there can clearly be no question of advantage to the allergic subject, is the result of the miscarriage of a process which under other circumstances, as in bacterial infection, may be of actual service to the organism; it may be an exaggeration of normal mechanisms of defense.

* The words "hypersensitive," "sensitive," and "hypersusceptible" are all to be found in the literature, apparently meaning much the same thing as the common usage of "allergic." Briefly, we may say that the hypersensitive patient responds to substances which provoke no visible response in normal individuals, or responds to much smaller quantities, or responds in an exaggerated manner.

An exaggeration of the body's normal mechanism is of course not always a good thing. The body ordinarily maintains itself in homeostasis, thereby exhibiting what Cannon (24) called "The Wisdom of the Body." But these homeostatic mechanisms can go wrong and end up by being unhomeostatic—a phenomenon which Richards (130) has called *hyperexis,* or "The Stupidity of the Body." The body is certainly a marvelous machine but, like any machine, it is capable of functioning at an unwelcome time or in an undesirable manner, as when a machine for sewing on buttons suddenly sews a button on your finger.

There is good reason to believe that heredity in many cases markedly affects the type of serological reactivity of which an animal is capable, and in particular some types of human allergy are probably the result of definite inherited tendencies to become hypersensitive. So, when we speak of such conditions as the results of the malfunction of a normal mechanism, we should keep in mind the role of heredity in accentuating or possibly initiating this departure from the normal.

The phenomena of immediate hypersensitivity, like the processes we have just been studying, are caused by antibody–antigen reactions, although the amounts of antibody involved are perhaps in general rather less. But the most important point to notice is that when we embark upon the study of hypersensitivity reactions we shift our point of view in regard to antibody–antigen reactions. Heretofore we have been interested mainly in what happened to the antigen. From now on we shall not be so much interested in this as in a hitherto neglected *dramatis persona,* the tissues of the body in which the antibody–antigen reaction takes place. The union of antibody and antigen *in vivo* can have, and often does have, beneficial effects, as we shall see in the chapters concerned with practical applications of immunology. However, the union may sometimes have harmful effects, apparently due to disturbances of the cells in the area in which antibody and antigen combine, or disturbances of cells not in the immediate area, or due to cellular damage caused by toxic substances released as a consequence of antibody–antigen combina-

	Reaction	Effect on Antigen	Effect on Body
Acquired immunity	Antibody and antigen	Neutralization	Indirectly beneficial i antigen is toxin or infectious agent.
Immediate hypersensitivity	Antibody and antigen	(Neutralization may occur but it is a side issue.)	Harmful effects on various tissues. Possibly sometimes beneficial when mild?

tion, or damage due to other mechanisms. The difference between our old and new points of view is shown by the scheme on p. 413 (123).

Hypersensitivity may be defined as an altered or heightened way of reacting to an antigen or hapten which has harmful effects on the body. The word allergy is often used as a synonym, but the original meaning of this word, which was coined by von Pirquet (118), was " changed or altered reactivity," and von Pirquet intended the word to embrace immunity as well as hypersensitivity. This use of the word is now seldom encountered. The modern tendency is to use allergy to denote certain types of hypersensitivity, although different writers do not always agree in their use of the word.

Allergy, if we accept von Pirquet's definition, should include anaphylaxis, serum sickness, the Arthus reaction, the delayed sensitivities, and immunohematologic diseases, all being examples of altered reactivity on immunologic grounds. The concept can include or exclude the Shwartzman phenomenon, anaphylactoid shock, and atopic symptoms (urticaria, asthma, rhinitis) due to physical agents, i.e., all phenomena which may share the final common path of well-known allergic reactions but apparently do not have an immunologic basis.

Hypersensitive reactions can be divided into two types: immediate and delayed (or early and late). The difference between the two types of hypersensitivity is, however, much more fundamental than a mere difference in the promptness with which a reaction is observed. The first, or immediate, type of hypersensitivity can be produced by ordinary antigens introduced in the usual way, although it may result from inhalation of foreign materials such as pollen. It is associated with circulating antibody, and the sensitivity can be passively transferred by the serum of a hypersensitive individual. The reactions can be evoked only in vascularized tissues, and depend largely upon changes which occur in the blood vessels, smooth muscle, and collagen. No hypersensitivity of the tissue cells as such can be demonstrated in tissue cultures (unless we consider the isolated guinea pig uterus, in a bath of Ringer's solution, a tissue culture (pp. 436, 437).

In contrast to this, induction of the delayed type of hypersensitiveness requires the presence of entire infectious agents, or prolonged contact of a nonliving antigen (here called an allergen) with the skin, or deliberate administration of an allergen plus adjuvants. In this type of hypersensitivity no circulating antibody has been certainly demonstrated, and passive transfer of sensitivity by serum is probably not possible, but passive transfer can be accomplished by transfer of certain types of cells. Cellular sensitivity can be demonstrated in tissue cultures, and the reaction can be elicited in nonvascular tissues. This type of hypersensitive reaction is probably not restricted to any particular type tissue, but almost any cells of the body may suffer injury or destruction following exposure to the antigen.

One or the other of these types of hypersensitivity, or both, may be present versus the same allergen in the same animal. Guinea pigs can be sensitized by intradermal injection or sometimes by mere application to the skin of simple chemicals such as picryl chloride, so that the animals show a local reaction of the delayed type when the chemical is painted on the skin (63). Such animals nearly always show reactivity of the immediate type (anaphylaxis) when injected with a conjugate of the sensitizer with protein. But these two types of immunization are concomitant and not identical, as shown by several observations. Firstly, transfer of serum from such an animal to a normal guinea pig results in the transfer of the anaphylactic sensitivity but not the skin sensitivity. Secondly, anaphylactic desensitization of an animal, occurring as the result of recovery from shock or protection from shock, has no effect on the intensity of the skin reaction. Thirdly, immunization with the "full" antigen, such as picryl-guinea-pig serum, which leads to the production of precipitins, makes the animals anaphylactically sensitive but does not make their skin sensitive to contact with the hapten.

The early or immediate type of hypersensitivity has been further subdivided by some according to the type of antibody involved, and the de-

TABLE 8-1

Hypersensitivity

1. Immediate			2. Delayed	
Circulating antibody. No cellular sensitivity in tissue culture. Passive transfer with serum. Sensitization with usual antigens by usual routes. Can be elicited only in vascularized tissues.			No circulating antibody. Cellular sensitivity in tissue culture. Passive transfer with cells. Sensitization by special routes or with special (waxy) adjuvants. Can be elicited in nonvascular tissues.	
(Due to precipitating antibody)	(Due to either type of antibody)	(Autoantibodies, antibodies against drugs, isoantibodies)		
a. Arthus reaction (+ periarteritis nodosa?)	b. Urticaria, anaphylaxis, atopy	c. Blood dyscrasias	d. Allergy of infection (TB type)	e. Contact allergy
	f. Serum disease = mixture of above types. (Symptoms suggest mainly b and d.)			

layed type can be subdivided into two main types, allergy of infection and contact allergy. We shall use here a classification such as that shown in Table 8-1 based on unpublished lecture notes of Dr. B. H. Waksman.

1. Main Types of Hypersensitivity

a. Arthus reaction (and possibly periarteritis nodosa). The symptoms of this type of hypersensitivity are edema, polymorphonuclear leukocyte infiltration, hemorrhage. These are followed by secondary necrosis which reaches a maximum in 8 to 24 hours. This type of hypersensitivity is due to precipitating antibody only and requires a large amount of antibody. Horse, rat, and avian antibody will bring about the reaction. The antibody is not fixed to the tissues. The symptoms of the Arthus reaction are virtually the same in most animals, including man. Histamine does not duplicate the symptoms, and antihistamines do not suppress the reaction.

b. Urticaria, anaphylaxis, and atopy (in man). The symptoms are edema and smooth muscle contraction, which become maximal in 1 to 20 minutes, decrease in blood coagulability, in blood pressure, and in temperature, slowing of the heart beat, decreased leukocyte count and platelet count. The reaction is due to nonprecipitating antibody, in relatively small amounts. Horse antibody fails to produce the condition. The antibody is fixed to the tissues in some species, as shown by the need for a latent period after passive transfer, by tests at intervals of sensitized skin sites, and by the reactivity *in vitro* of isolated smooth muscle such as uterus. The symptoms vary in different species, depending upon the histamine sensitivity of the species and upon the distribution of histamine in the various organs. Histamine duplicates most details of the reaction, and antihistamines prevent the symptoms. Heparin, acetyl choline, serotonin, K+, are also factors (see p. 436). Horse, rat, and avian antibody do not work. The phenomena can be produced by nonprecipitating antibody, but precipitating sera work, and Waksman (167) thinks precipitating antibody probably works.

c. Certain blood discrasias. This very special type of hypersensitivity is perhaps better considered along with the autoimmune diseases (Chapter 13). There is still uncertainty about the types of antibody involved, and even as to whether they are antibodies at all. The erythrocytes, leukocytes, or platelets may be uniquely damaged. The antigens involved determine the cell type which is affected, and the antigens apparently may be cell antigens or external antigens which attach to the cell.

d. Allergy of infection. This type of hypersensitivity, typified by the hypersensitivity of tuberculosis, apparently does not involve any circulating antibody. It can be produced artificially by injection of protein antigents, usually in association with adjuvants.

e. Contact allergy. Here the incitant is a relatively simple chemical which probably first couples with skin proteins. The reaction can be elicited in the skin. Sensitivity of cells in tissue culture has apparently not been demonstrated.

f. Serum disease. Serum disease cannot be neatly classified. The evidence suggests that it is due to a mixture of the above mechanisms, and the symptoms suggest mostly those of (*b*) atopy and (*d*) allergy of the tuberculin type.

All of these types of hypersensitivity will be discussed more in detail below.

B. ANAPHYLAXIS

Portier and Richet (120) reported that toxic extracts of the tentacles of certain sea anemones, in doses so small that they produced no symptoms in normal animals, would, if injected into a dog which had recovered from a previous—sublethal—dose, cause violent illness and often death. To characterize the *lowering* of resistance thus evidenced, they coined the phrase, anaphylactic action (*action anaphylactique de certains venins*), thus calling attention to its antithesis to the prophylactic or protective effects following other forms of treatment.

Other workers (Magendie, Flexner, Richet, and Hericourt) had previously observed what was doubtless anaphylaxis; and Arthus, Theobald Smith, and Rosenau and Anderson subsequently noticed similar phenomena. It was discovered that the substance provoking anaphylaxis need not be toxic in itself; on the contary, normal animal serum from a different species, or a harmless substance, such as egg white, could produce the effect. It was only necessary to "sensitize" the animal by one or more previous injections, and then, after an appropriate interval, administer the anaphylaxis-provoking, or "shocking," dose.

1. Production of Anaphylactic Sensitivity

Suitable animals can be sensitized by most antigens. The majority of these are proteins or carbohydrates, but Landsteiner and Jacobs (88) induced anaphylaxis by injection of arsphenamine (which has occasionally been observed to sensitize human beings), and Landsteiner and Chase

(87) were able to sensitize animals anaphylactically by the cutaneous administration of simple compounds such as picryl chloride and 2,4-dinitrochlorbenzene. It had formerly been believed that haptens might shock but would not sensitize. It is probable that it is a protein–hapten complex that actually sensitizes.

Administering the sensitizing antigen (called the anaphylactogen) by any route which avoids its destruction by the digestive enzymes may be effective, just as in the case of antibody production. Sensitization has been obtained by administration of the antigen intravenously, subcutaneously, intracutaneously, and following absorption through the placenta, the skin, and the respiratory passages. Some sensitization is occasionally produced even by feeding the anaphylactogen, especially to scorbutic guinea pigs.

The amount of antigen required for sensitization varies widely. All that is necessary is enough to start antibody formation. Rosenau and Anderson (138,139) found that 10^{-6} ml. of horse serum (about 7×10^{-8} g. protein) would sensitize a guinea pig, and Wells (172) got definite sensitization of small guinea pigs with 5×10^{-8} g. of crystallized egg albumin. These amounts appear to represent about the limits in this direction. Larger doses may be necessary to sensitize sufficiently for fatal shock; a single subcutaneous dose of 0.01 ml. of horse serum (about 0.001 g. protein) may be taken as a typical amount for practical work. Larger doses have been found successful, up to 5 to 10 ml. of serum. If the dose is too large, however, especially if it is repeated, the animal may be protected, in some cases for weeks, from the effects of the shocking dose; this may perhaps be due to the persistence of antigen in the circulation so that the animal is in effect desensitized (see p. 419). In animals such as rabbits, dogs, and cats, larger doses than those used for guinea pigs (1 or 2 ml. of serum), repeated several times at 2- or 3-day intervals, are better, and in the rabbit the minute amounts found to be sufficient for guinea pigs are quite ineffective.

The time factor is important. With the standard dose of about 0.01 ml. of foreign serum, guinea pigs begin to be sensitive in about 8 days, and the sensitization reaches a maximum in about three weeks. In the mouse sensitivity is at a maximum in 7 to 14 days. After this it declines but remains sufficient for fatal shock, provided a large enough shocking dose is used, for about six months. It is possible that the animal remains somewhat sensitive for life. In rabbits, which should be injected repeatedly, a 10-day to three-week interval should be allowed to elapse before attempting to elicit anaphylaxis; in dogs and mice the optimal interval is about three weeks.

2. Induction of Anaphylactic Shock

In addition to the method of sensitization, and the time allowed to elapse before test, the amount and mode of administration of the shocking dose are important. The most severe symptoms occur when the antigen comes suddenly in contact with the sensitive tissues. Therefore the best method of eliciting anaphylactic symptoms is intravenous injection. In animals which are not particularly sensitive to anaphylactic reactions, such as rabbits and dogs, this is the only way in which death can be obtained with any regularity. In the guinea pig as little as 0.01 ml. of serum given intravenously may produce fatal shock. Guinea pigs may be killed by injecting the shocking dose intraabdominally or even subcutaneously, but in this case considerably larger amounts are needed. The actual amount required will depend upon the degree of sensitization of the animal, and partly, therefore, upon the size of the sensitizing dose and the interval which has elapsed. If the degree of sensitivity is less, larger shocking doses are required. In all cases the shocking dose must be considereably larger than the minimal quantities which have sometimes been observed to sensitize.

It was once thought that shock could be produced only by protein antigens, but this is not so; Landsteiner and van der Scheer (89,90), followed by later workers (22,116), were able to produce anaphylactic shock by injecting azodyes. Carbohydrates and certain drugs, such as penicillin (p. 431), will produce anaphylaxis.

3. Desensitization

If the administration of the shocking dose does not result in death, after recovery the animal is temporarily refractory. It is no longer sensitive to similar injections of the antigen and is said to be desensitized. Similarly, the onset of sensitivity in injected animals may be postponed by injections of moderate quantities of the antigen in the period just preceding development of hypersusceptibility. Adminstration of the antigen by a method allowing gradual penetration to the sensitized tissues will desensitize, as will the repeated administration of minute doses too small to produce any symptoms.

The desensitized state is only temporary. In guinea pigs it lasts two weeks or more, and in rabbits a much shorter time (144,145), perhaps because of the greater rapidity of antibody production in the latter animal. Afterwards the animal becomes equally sensitive or even more sensitive than before.

It is logical to suppose that one of the reasons for the refractory state

following specific desensitization is temporary saturation of tissue antibodies by antigen, so that further administration of antigen is ineffective,
although exhaustion of histamine, production of a refractory state in the
tissue, etc., may also play a role.

4. Nonspecific Desensitization

It has been found that anesthesia, or injection of large quantities of
an unrelated antigen, or of one or more of a variety of substances (see
list in 147), may depress the degree of anaphylaxis obtainable by injection
of the shocking dose of the specific antigen. The desensitization is not
absolute, for larger doses of the antigen will still shock. A number of
workers have reported being able to desensitize with histamine (references
in (78)); Karady (78) was able thus to prevent anaphylactic death in many
guinea pigs sensitized to horse serum but, remarkably, not in those sensitive to egg white. Doerr suggested that nonspecific desensitization depends upon alterations in the condition of the smooth muscle. Others
(181) have pointed out the similarity of such phenomena to the disappearance of cutaneous hypersensitivity to tuberculin and foreign proteins
at the time of the rash in measles.

5. Specificity of Anaphylaxis

The specificity observed in this reaction is of the same order as that
found in other serological reactions. After sensitization to an antigen,
an animal reacts anaphylactically only to this antigen or to one chemically
related. Animals may be made sensitive to a number of antigens at the
same time, and will react separately to each of them. After desensitization
with one antigen the animal still remains reactive to the others; consequently anaphylaxis is useful in experimental investigations of specificity. It was used extensively by Wells and others, notably in studies
on the specificity of plant antigens. The *symptoms* of anaphylaxis, however, in a given species of animals, are not dependent on the antigen used.

6. Passive Anaphylaxis

It has been implied already that anaphylactic sensitivity is due to the
development of antibodies, and this is strongly confirmed by the observation that a normal animal can be rendered susceptible to anaphylactic
shock by transferring to it serum from a sensitive animal. This serum
need not necessarily come from another individual of the same species;
in fact a very convenient experimental technic uses the guinea pig as
the test animal, but sensitizes the animal with immune serum from rabbits.

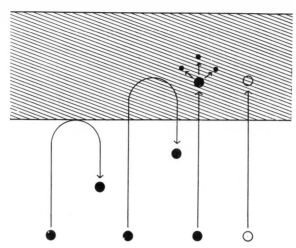

Fig. 8-1. Diagram showing rejection of ungulate antibody by guinea pig smooth muscle. Modified from Brambell. Solid circles = ungulate antibody; open circles = other (*e.g.,* rabbit) antibody.

The guinea pig can usually be sensitized quite easily in this way (76), even though the rabbit which provided the serum might suffer no shock if the test dose of antigen were injected into it.

Under suitable conditions, it is possible to produce typical symptoms of anaphylaxis in guinea pigs by injecting the antigen, followed by the antiserum (see 82). This is called reversed passive anaphylaxis. In this case also an appropriate incubation period (4 to 24 hours) must be allowed to elapse. It has also been found that such animals can be specifically desensitized by subshocking injections of the antiserum.

Although it is clear that passive sensitization with immune serum is due to the transfer of some sort of antibody, the animal does not usually become sensitive immediately following the injection of serum from a sensitive or immune animal. It is generally found that before typical shock can regularly be obtained, an interval of a few hours must elapse, and maximal sensitization was not found by Kellaway and Cowell (80) before 4 to 6 days. Kabat *et al.* (9a) found only 3 to 6 hours. Apparently the antibody must be allowed to "settle down" in the tissues or to cross certain membranes (14) before the animal becomes reactive. The failure of antibodies from certain species to sensitize the guinea pig might perhaps be due to their inability to attach themselves appropriately to the guinea pig tissues (see Fig. 8-1).

However, Zinsser and Enders (180), studying the phenomenon of reversed passive anaphylaxis, observed that some guinea pigs could be shocked by antibody within a few minutes after the adminstration of the antigen.   Only certain stocks of guinea pigs exhibited this behavior, which thus appears to be hereditary.   The same stock was also susceptible to shock in the ordinary way (antiserum followed by antigen) even when an interval of only a few minutes had elapsed between the injections (17). In rabbits the reaction is apparently entirely within the blood stream, so there is no latent period, as there are no membranes to cross.

Species differences are observed in passive sensitization experiments. Rabbit antisera will usually sensitize guinea pigs passively, but horse antisera have not usually been observed to do so (7,17,56), although Bailey (8) was able to sensitize with antipneumococcal serum.   It has also been observed that guinea pigs cannot be sensitized with antiserum from fowl (58), and pigeons cannot be sensitized with antiserum from rabbits (64, 146,160).

Brambell *et al.* (14,15) suggested that ungulate antibodies are either excluded from the cells of guinea pig smooth muscle, or if permitted to enter, not retained in a reactive form.   This conception is represented diagrammatically in Fig. 8-1.

Also relevant are studies of the penetration of antibodies from the maternal circulation into the circulation of the fetus.   Brambell, Hemmings, and Henderson (14) found that the yolk-sac splanchnopleure of the 24-day-old rabbit fetus admits rabbit antibodies (even the large molecular weight antisheep cell hemolysins) to its circulation, while it virtually excludes cow or horse antibodies.   They believed that this is a cellular phenomenon (for which the cells of the endothelium are mainly responsible) similar to the rejection of cow and horse antibodies by guinea pig smooth muscle.

Guinea pig antibodies to soluble protein antigens consist of two types, both 7S (see Chapter 2), but of diffierent electrophoretic mobilities (173a, 10a) .   Only one of these, called $7S_{\gamma 1}$, seems to fix to tissues and mast cells and make passive anaphylaxis possible (112a).

The optimal anaphylactic reaction in passive anaphylaxis is obtained (77) when the relation of antigen to antibody is such that, by the standards of the precipitin test, antigen is in large excess.

It will be informative to compare the main features of the three main types of immediate hypersensitivity in three experimental species and in man.   For that purpose we offer Table 8-2, based on unpublished lecture notes of Dr. B. Waksman.

Guinea Pig.   The symptoms of anaphylactic shock in the guinea pig have been extensively studied, and have been vividly described by Seegal

(147): "After a pig has been injected intravenously with the . . . shocking dose of antigen, it shows signs of distress within a minute. The hair on the head and back of the neck begin to ruffle. The animal becomes restless, coughs and retches, rubs its nose, and seems to choke. Respirations, which were at first increased in frequency, become slower and labored and soon the animal is gasping for breath and making tremendous inspiratory efforts. The mucous membranes become cyanotic. The animal defecates and urinates. If the anaphylactic shock is destined to end fatally the animal soon becomes weak and rolls over on its side, gives a few convulsive kicks, gasps, and stops breathing. In very severe shock this symptomatic cycle may all be over within minutes. In a less sensitive animal the symptoms of restlessness, peripheral irritation, and respiratory distress are followed by considerable weakness and a marked drop in temperature. The pig huddles in a corner with hair ruffled and attention centered on its respirations, which are still accomplished with difficulty. After fifteen to thirty minutes it begins to shiver and improvement followed by recovery gradually sets in. The onset of shivering is usually an indication that the body temperature is rising again." If, instead of a sufficiently large injection of antigen to precipitate acute shock, a minute amount is injected, of the order of 0.000001 ml. of serum, guinea pigs develop an elevation of temperature (Friedberger and Mita).

"When the shocking dose of antigen is given intraperitoneally the most marked symptom is generally weakness. The animal lies on its side or drags itself around feebly, while the respiratory difficulties are not so marked although never absent. Death may not occur for 30 minutes or more, and indeed animals may finally recover from very grave symptoms."

The blood pressure rises from the normal of 80 mm. to 90 to 140 mm., then gradually (in around 10 minutes) falls to 10 to 20 mm. Asphyxia is the immediate cause of death in the guinea pig, and immediately after death the heart is still beating. The lungs are markedly inflated, owing to constriction of the bronchial musculature. Small hemorrhages are common on the under side of the diaphragm and in the viscera. The coagulation time of the blood is found to be prolonged, and Zuntz and LaBarre (182) have reported hyperglycemia and increase in blood lactic acid during the first minutes of shock. Examination of the blood often discloses leukopenia and thrombocytopenia.

The anaphylactic reaction of guinea pig lung has been studied *in vitro* (6).

The Dog. The pioneer observations of Portier and Richet (120) were made using the dog as the test animal. Richet's (131) description is still a classic:

TABLE 8-2

Hypersensitivity = allergy	Immunohematologic diseases = blood dyscrasias	Immediate reactions 1. Anaphylaxis 2. Atopy 3. Urticaria (local cutaneous anaphylaxis)	"Early" (compared c delayed) or "late" (compared c immediate) reactions 1. Periarteritis nodosa 2. Arthus	Delayed reactions — Tuberculin-type (bacterial or infection) allergy	Delayed reactions — Contact allergy
Occurrence	Human disease: Sensitization and elicitation by: transfusions, pregnancy, infection, ingestion of food or drugs.	1). Humans injected more than once c foreign proteins. Animals sensitized by one or more A injections and shock c iv G. Atopics injected c sensitizing G. 2). Human disease: sensitization and elicitation by natural exposure to foods, pollen, etc. 3). Reactions to skin tests in (1) and (2).	1). Humans or animals sensitized by exposure to drugs, foreign infection, foreign protein → circulating, precipitating A. Elicit by massive doses of G, introduced in such a way as to avoid anaphylaxis. 2). Local reactions in same individuals following local injection.	Humans or animals sensitized by: infection, injection protein G c special (waxy) adjuvants, injection protein G (intradermally). Elicit by injection of G (usually in skin). Sensitivity affects character of reaction to infecting agent.	Humans or animals: sensitization & elicitation by contact of simple chemicals c skin.
Gross reactions	Anemia: Transfusion reactions; erythroblastosis; hemolytic reactions to drugs; acquired hemolytic anemia; blackwater fever. Leukopenia: Allergic agranulo-	1). Shock, c respiratory, vascular, & other symptoms, depending on species, often c death. 2). Asthma, hay fever & eczema. 3). Wheal & flare.	1). Generalized vascular symptomatology. 2). Local edematous hemorrhagic reaction.	Necrosis, induration, slow healing.	Eczematous reaction of skin.

cytosis; chronic leukopenia

Purpura:
Allergic thrombocytopenia; idiopathic thrombocytopenia; neonatal thrombocytopenia

	Minutes–hours	Minutes (0–60)	Hours (2–24)	Days (2–4)	Days (2–4)
Time course	Minutes–hours	Minutes (0–60)	Hours (2–24)	Days (2–4)	Days (2–4)
Histologic & physiologic components	Lysis of one cell type (rbc, polys, platelets), or agglutination c̄ mechanical destruction, uptake by phagocytic cells & destruction in spleen.	Damage mast cells (& others?), release of pharmacologic agents gives ↑ vascular permeability & edema, smooth muscle contraction, ↑ in coagulability of blood, ↓ blood pressure, etc.	Precipitate formation, poly & platelet thrombi, vessel occlusion, vessel wall damage, hemorrhage & edema, fibrinoid necrosis, poly & eosinophile exudation.	Exudation & proliferation of RE & other mesenchymal cells, c̄ necrosis at sites of high G concentration and 2° poly response.	Mesenchymal reaction, & epidermal spongiosis (2°?)
Participation of histamine, heparin, serotonin, etc.	0	+	0	Other unknown types of agents may play a role in these	
Release during typical reaction	0	+	0	0	0
Ability to mimic typical reaction	0	+	0	0	0
Effect of antihistaminic therapy	0	+	0	0	0

(*Table continued*)

TABLE 8-2 (*Continued*)

Hypersensitivity = allergy	Immunohematologic diseases = blood dyscrasias	Immediate reactions: 1. Anaphylaxis 2. Atopy 3. Urticaria (local cutaneous anaphylaxis)	"Early" (compared c delayed) or "late" (compared c immediate) reactions: 1. Periarteritis nodosa 2. Arthus	Delayed reactions	
				Tuberculin-type (bacterial or infection) allergy	Contact allergy
Antigens	Normal or altered cell surface Gs, drugs or toxins adherent to cells	1). All usual protein & carbohydrate Gs. 2). Ditto plus large peptides (in pollens).	All usual protein & carbohydrate Fs, toxins.	Proteins, possibly certain drugs combined c body proteins.	Simple chemical "allergens" combined c skin protein.
G fixation to tissue needed for reaction	+	0	0	0	0
Circulating A responsible for sensitivity				Special types reported to play role	
1. Correlation of A in serum c sensitivity	+	+	+	0	0
2. Passive transfer of sensitivity c serum to intact individual	+	+	+	0 (transfer only c cells).	0 (transfer only c cells).
3. to isolated tissue	+	+	0	0	0
Amount of A which can produce typical reaction	Probably little	Little (0.003 μg. A N for minimal reaction in gp or human skin)	Much (10.0 μg. A N for minimal reaction in gp skin)	—	—

Types of A which can produce typical reaction				
1. Precipitating	?	In some species +	—	—
2. Nonprecipitating	+	+	—	—
3. Horse-cattle-rat-avian antisera	?	0	+	—
A fixation to tissue needed for reaction	?	+*a	0	—
1. Latent period for passive sensitization	?	+	0	—
2. Diffusion of A from locally sensitized site	?	0	+	—
3. Duration of local sensitization	?	Days	Minutes	—
In vitro effects of G demonstrable on:				
Rbc[b]	+ (Agglutination, lysis, opsonization)	±	0	—
Polys[b]	+	+ (Lysis & release of histamine)	+ (stickiness, clumping, & – thrombi)	±
Platelets[b]	+	+ (contraction)	+	0
Mast cells (isolated organs)	—	+	0	0

(Table continued)

TABLE 8-2 (*Continued*)

Hypersensitivity = allergy	Immunohematologic diseases = blood dyscrasias	Immediate reactions 1. Anaphylaxis 2. Atopy 3. Urticaria (local cutaneous anaphylaxis)	"Early" (compared c delayed) or "late" (compared c immediate) reactions 1. Periarteritis nodosa, 2. Arthus	Delayed reactions	
				Tuberculin-type (bacterial or infection) allergy	Contact allergy
Smooth muscle (isolated organs; Schultz-Dale test)	—	+	0	0	—
RE cells (tissue culture)	—	0	0	+ (stimulation &/or necrosis)	?
Fibroblasts (tissue culture)	—	0	0	+	?
Epidermis (tissue culture)	—	—	—	0	0
Ability to elicit reaction in nonvascular tissue (cornea) *in vivo*	0	0	0	+	+
Nonimmunologic equivalents		Histamine injection Mechanical or chemical (including nervous) stimuli Anaphylactoid shock	Local Schwartzman reactions?	0	0

a See p. 389.

b Whole blood or isolated cells.

Abbreviations: A = antibody, G = antigen, Rbc = red blood cells, c = with, poly = polymorphonuclear leukocyte, 2° = secondary, RE = reticuloendothelial, iv = intravenous, + = yes, 0 = no, — = unknown.

"Dans la forme la plus légère, les seuls symptômes sont le prurit, une accélération des mouvements respiratoires, avec abiassement de la pression artérielle, fréquence augmentée des mouvements du coeur, diarrhée et ténesme rectal . . Tous ces symptômes disparaissent vite dans le cas d'anaphylaxie légère. Mais, si l'anaphylaxie est grave, ils prennent un aspect tout différent.

"D'abord il n'y a plus de prurit. Le premier effet, c'est le vomissement, premier symptôme, tellement rapide, tellement dominateur, que, dans nombre de cas, le vomissement survient au bout de dix secondes à peine après l'injection même d'une dose faible. Ce vomissement est si caractéristique je l'ai pris comme critérium . . .

"Les vomissements sont spumeux, avec mélange de bile; quelquefois ils sont fécalöïdes, quelquefois (dans les cas très graves) mêlés à du sang: car il y a dès le début une congestion gastro-intestinale intense.

"Presque aussitôt après, l'animal, étant détaché, est pris de ténesme rectal, avec diarrhée liquide, mêlée à du sang. Parfois il y a écoulement par le rectum de sang presque pur. En même temps, des coliques violentes et du ténesme rectal.

"Mais souvent le déchaînement des accidents nerveux est si soudain et si violent que les coliques et la diarrhée ne peuvent pas s'établir. Tout de suite il y a ataxie: l'animal chancelle comme s'il était ivre: il a de la paraplégie . . . la pupille se dilate; les yeux deviennent hagards; et, après quelques cris lamentables, l'animal tombe par terre, urinant et déféquant sous lui, épuisé, insensible. . . . La respiration est accélérée, dyspnéique; la pression artérielle est très basse (de 4 à 5 centimètres de mercure, à peine). Le coeur précipite ses battements, qui sont faibles, si faibles quelquefois qu'on a peine à les compter. . . . Bref l'état général est assez grave pour qu'on soit tenté de croire à la mort imminente. (En réalité la mort en moins de deux heures est extrêmement rare chez chein.)"*

* In the mildest form the only symptoms are pruritus, an acceleration of respiratory movements, with lowering of the arterial pressure, diarrhea and rectal tenesmus. . . . All these symptoms quickly disappear in the case of mild anaphylaxis. But if anaphylaxis is profound, they take on quite a different aspect.

First of all there is no pruritus. The first effect is vomiting, the first symptom, so rapid, so dominant, that in a number of cases vomiting comes on in barely ten seconds after the injection even of a weak dose. Vomiting is so characteristic that I have taken it as the criterion. . . .

The vomit is frothy and mixed with bile, sometimes it is fecal, sometimes (in the most serious cases) mixed with blood: for from the beginning there is an intense gastro-intestinal congestion.

Almost immediately afterwards, the animal, being let loose, is seized by tenesmus, with liquid diarrhea mixed with blood. Sometimes there is a flow of almost pure blood from the rectum. At the same time, violent colic and tenesmus.

(Footnote continued on page 430)

It has been observed that in the dog the liver is profoundly congested during shock, and that in fact most of the symptoms observed are due to what happens in the liver. The intense congestion of the liver has been explained as due to injury of the liver sinusoids and liver cells, allowing transudation of fluid, edema, and congestion with red cells, and to constriction of the hepatic veins, producing interference with the outflow of blood. The dog liver releases histamine, which it contains in relative abundance (34,47). The liberated histamine affects other tissues, and death may be due largely to increased capillary permeability throughout the body with loss of circulating volume (101).

The Rabbit. Death due to anaphylaxis is not so common in the rabbit. When it occurs it is usually rapid. The first sign appears to be a flush of the ears, followed by pronounced pallor. There is a drop in blood pressure and the coagulability of the blood is impaired. The animal lies with legs outstretched or falls on its side, gives a series of convulsive movements, often associated with the passage of urine and feces, and dies. The heart may continue to beat after respiration has ceased (147), or respiration may continue for a brief period after the heart has ceased to beat (156). Rabbits which have progressed to the stage of coma may sometimes recover. In nonfatal anaphylaxis the rabbit may show few symptoms other than an increase in respiratory rate. However, the blood pressure and body temperature fall.

In the rabbit the pathological symptoms are different from those observed in either guinea pig or dog. The pulmonary dilation found in the guinea pig is absent, and there are no marked hemorrhages in the splanchnic area, although some congestion of the liver and other viscera may be found. The most characteristic finding is the extreme dilatation of the right side of the heart and the inferior vena cava with blood, apparently due to constriction of the pulmonary arterioles (49,65).

A more complete description of anaphylaxis in the rabbit will be found in Doerr (44).

But often the production of nervous accidents is so sudden and so violent that colic and diarrhea cannot get established. Suddenly there is ataxia, the animal reels as if it were drunk, it has paraplegia . . . . the pupil dilates, the eyes become haggard, and, after mournful cries, the animal falls to the ground, urinating and defecating under it, exhausted, insensible. . . . The respiration is accelerated, dyspneic; the arterial pressure is very low (hardly 4 to 5 centimeters of mercury). The heart hurries its beats, which are weak, so weak that they can barely be counted. . . . In short the general condition is so serious that one would be tempted to believe death imminent. (In reality death in less than two hours is extremely rare in the dog.)

The Horse. The symptoms in the horse are dyspnea, rapid, feeble heart beat, and increased defecation and urination; and more important, urticaria, edema of the limbs, cyanosis, edema and petechial hemorrhages of the mucous membranes, lacrimation, and salivation.

Other Animals. Anaphylaxis in the mouse has been discussed by Weiser *et al.* (169). The intact mouse is difficult to sensitize anaphylactically, but if the antigen is injected mixed with *Pertussis* vaccine a degree of sensitization leading to fatal anaphylactic shock is relatively easy to produce (99,107). References to work on other animals will be found in (132,147,148,71).

Man. Acute anaphylactic shock in human beings can be very similar to the condition in one of the species described, or it may combine features shown by different species (83,124). It generally resembles the guinea pig type of anaphylaxis. Vance and Strassmann (161) reported finding marked inflation of the lungs due to bronchial spasm. In some cases they saw also edema of the brain and in others edema of the submucous layer of the upper portion of the larynx. Fortunately fatal anaphylactic shock in man is quite rare; Park reported 2 fatal cases out of 50,000 instances of injection of horse serum, but later statistics suggest a somewhat greater frequency (0.10 per cent) (83). In man as in other animals there is a fall in blood pressure and temperature with decreased blood coagulability and eosinophilia. Anaphylaxis in man may occur in an individual who has been sensitized by previous injections of an antigen such as foreign serum, or in individuals who have become sensitized by inhalation or ingestion of atopens (p. 447).

With increasing use of antibiotics, anaphylaxis due to hypersensitivity to these drugs is becoming commoner. It has been reported that about 1,000 anaphylactic reactions to penicillin occur in this country per year, and some 90 of these are fatal (171).

7. Cot Death

In the last decade or so there has been recognized a cause of death that is probably allergic in etiology. An apparently normal child, or one that has had a slight cold for the previous 2 or 3 days, 2 weeks to 2 years old, is fed, put to bed, and during the next 3 to 4 hours is found dead. No noise or struggle has been noticed by the parents. There is evidence that the cause of death is allergy, and that death is brought on by inhalation of cow's milk into the lungs of the sleeping child (115). In 1955 there were 1432 such deaths in England and Wales. A further argument, if any were needed, for mothers nursing their infants.

8. Pathological Changes

A synopsis of the pathological changes following anaphylactic shock in various animals will be found in Table 8-3, taken from an article by Seegal (147).

The pathological and physiological symptoms of anaphylaxis at first sight appear unrelated and surprisingly different in different species. However, it has been shown (147) that most of the observations can be referred to one or the other of two principal causes: contraction of smooth muscle and increased capillary permeability.

Other symptoms include edema, decreased coagulability of the blood, fall in blood pressure and temperature, thrombocytopenia, general leuko-penia with aggregation of leukocytes in the pulmonary bed, and quite often pulmonary eosinophilia. Humphrey and others found platelet lysis. Increased leukocyte fragility has been found (102, 177), and Waksman (165) was able to produce lysis of leukocytes by antibody (apparently of the nonprecipitating type) to such antigens as egg albumin and bovine gamma globulin. The similarity between this lysis and the cell damage which releases histamines, etc., is suggestive.

In the guinea pig and the rabbit the immediate cause of death is prob-ably contraction of smooth muscle in the bronchi and in the pulmonary arterial system, respectively. In the dog, cat, guinea pig, rabbit, horse, rat, pigeon, and sheep, any one or all of the following symptoms may occur: vomiting, diarrhea or frequency of defecation; all provide evi-dence of increased activity of the gastrointestinal tract. (Note, however, that rodents do not vomit.) The ruffling of the hair is presumably due to contraction of the *arrectores pilorum*.

Increase in capillary permeability may explain the hyperemia, hemor-rhages, edema and urticaria observed.

The fall in blood pressure may be explained partly by dilation of the capillaries. In the guinea pig the blood pressure changes may be largely due to the anoxemia, following contraction of the bronchioles.

Cannon *et al.* (27), studying anaphylaxis in rabbits, reported that the primary effect of the antigen–antibody reaction in the lungs was increased capillary permeability, followed later by severe vascular injury. In the liver Hartley and Lushbaugh (69) found massive areas of coagulative necrosis of the parenchyma.

The organs chiefly involved in anaphylaxis are called the "shock or-gans." The differences observed in various species may be due partly to differences in the amount of smooth muscle present in different organs in various animals, partly to intrinsic differences in the degree of sensi-

TABLE 8-3

Pathology of Anaphylaxis in Different Species ot Animals[a]

Animal	Congestion and hemorrhage	Edema	Liver	Lungs	Right-sided heart failure
Guinea pig	Hemorrhages of stomach, cecum, lungs, heart, etc. (Gay and Southard)	Lung, skin (Schultz and Jordan, Ramsdell)	Occasional local fatty changes	Emphysema due to constriction of bronchioles	Questionable
Dog	Liver, gall bladder, gastrointestinal tract, lungs, endocardium and pleura, auriculoventricular bundle (Dean et al., Richet)	Intestinal mucosa (Manwaring, Beattie, and McBride)	Congestion central necrosis (Weil)	Very occasional emphysema	
Rabbit	Liver and gastrointestinal tract (Scott)	Slight of lung	Marked engorgement of intralobular capillaries, central veins and portal vein	Very occasional emphysema. Proliferation and phagocytosis, endothelial cells (Domack)	Marked, due to constriction of pulmonary arterioles (Drinker and Bronfenbrenner, Gilbert)
Rat	Gastrointestinal tract, lymph gland, etc. (Parker et al.)		Congestion	Very occasional emphysema	
Mouse	Intestine and stomach (Ritz)			Moderate emphysema (Schultz and Jordan)	Present

[a] Modified as suggested by Dr. B. C. Seegal (147).

tivity which the same organ may acquire in various species, and partly to differences in distribution of histamine, sensitive vessels, and smooth muscle in various species.

9. Mechanism of Anaphylaxis

There can be no doubt that anaphylaxis is essentially the result of an antibody–antigen reaction. Evidence that antibodies play an essential role is overwhelming, and may be briefly summarized here: (*1*) only antigenic or haptenic substances will induce anaphylaxis; (*2*) the incubation period for active anaphylactic sensitivity is of similar length to that for antibody production; (*3*) the specificity of the reaction is exactly similar to that of other serological reaction; (*4*) specific desensitization of sensitive animals by injection of antigen is hard to explain except by the assumption that antibodies present are temporarily saturated with antigen; (*5*) sensitivity can be passively conferred on a normal animal by transfer of serum from a sensitized animal; (*6*) by suitable technic (25), antibody can be demonstrated in the serum of sensitive animals; (*7*) the ability of a serum to confer anaphylaxis passively is approximately proportional to its precipitin content (46).

Soluble antibody–antigen complexes can be quite toxic, and their injection into animals can produce reactions typical of hypersensitivity (21).

The failure of some workers to find precipitating antibodies in serum which would sensitize passively may now be explained in the light of recent indications that nonprecipitating (so-called "incomplete" or "univalent" antibody) will sensitize to anaphylaxis just as well as precipitating antibody (see p. 447). In some cases perhaps the tests made were not sufficiently delicate to detect the precipitating antibody present, for the amount needed to sensitize is not large. Kabat and Landow (77) reported that injection of 0.03 mg. of rabbit antibody nitrogen will sensitize a guinea pig sufficiently for fatal anaphylactic reaction, if the proper amount of antigen is used. This is not the "equivalent amount" as determined by the precipitin test but approximately 50 times as much, corresponding to amounts found in the "inhibition zone" (p. 357). An isolated guinea pig uterus will contract even though it contains amounts of antibody not exceeding 0.01 μg. of antibody nitrogen. This reaction is therefore much more sensitive than the precipitin or even the complement fixation test.

Fedorov and Gurvich (50) are quite convinced that anaphylactogenic antibodies are not identical with precipitins.

10. Site of Anaphylactic Reaction

There have been two theories as to the place where the reaction causing anaphylaxis occurs. According to one view, the reaction occurs in the circulation and causes the production of toxic substances (humoral theory). According to the other view, the reaction occurs with antibodies present in, or fixed to, the tissues (cellular theory).

The available evidence definitely shows that cells are involved in some of the reactions, and may be summarized thus: (1) An incubation period is almost always necessary for the development of passive sensitivity, suggesting that time is required for the introduced antibodies to become fixed in the tissues. If the reaction were purely a "humoral" one, there is no reason shock could not always be produced immediately after the transfer of the serum. It has been shown that during the incubation period a large proportion of the injected antibody does actually leave the circulation (168). (2) A sensitive animal can still be shocked readily even after its own blood has been replaced by that of a normal animal. (3) A large amount of circulating antibody actually tends to protect an animal against anaphylactic shock, probably by combining with antigen which would otherwise combine with "sessile" antibody in the sensitive tissues. (4) The smooth muscle of a sensitive animal, when removed and tested *in vitro*, even after thorough washing, reacts vigorously when brought in contact with the specific antigen.

Austen and Humphrey (6a) point out that the old argument as to the relative importance of the cellular and humoral mechanisms now seems pointless in many ways. The anaphylactic release of histamine and SRS-A from guinea pig lung is "cellular," the release of kinin-forming enzyme from guinea pig lung and the subsequent action on plasma proteins to produce active polypeptides is "cellular-humoral," the release of anaphylotoxin by antibody–antigen complexes or agar is "humoral-cellular," as are the cytoxic antibody, complement-requiring systems, and the action of immune aggregates to produce mechanical obstruction of the pulmonary capillaries in the rabbit, with histamine release, is "humoral."

11. Cause of the Reaction

From the work of Manwaring and associates it appeared that in the dog during anaphylaxis there is liberated from the liver a toxic substance, which is responsible for many of the phenomena of shock. If the liver is removed, or excluded from the circulation, shock is prevented, and if the liver of a sensitive animal is "transplanted" to a normal dog, the latter can be shocked by the injection of antigen. A normal piece of intestine or bladder transplanted to a sensitive animal shows typical contraction when the latter is shocked.

The pulmonary aspects of anaphylaxis in the guinea pig seem to be completely explainable on the basis of histamine release, and antihistaminic agents can block the reaction almost completely, but in the mouse antihistamines have little effect. This difference may be connected with the fact that mouse lung contains relatively large amounts of serotonin, whereas guinea pig lung contains little if any (170).

Geiger and Alpers (61) believed that at least three agents—histamine, serotonin, and acetylcholine—are involved in the anaphylactic reaction, but that the liberation of acetylcholine is a consequence, rather than a cause, of the contraction. A good article on serotonin was published in the *Scientific American* (114).

According to Chase (29), SRS-A ("Slow Reacting Substance of Anaphylaxis"), which Smith (149) suggests may be a mixture of glycosides of neuraminic acid, is formed in the tissues, and certain short peptides (including bradykinin) arise by enzymatic cleavage of certain of the plasma proteins. Chase believes that acetylcholine and heparin play minor roles.

The chemical nature of the "anaphylotoxin" and "leukotaxine" released during anaphylaxis is still unknown (29).

The general picture of the mechanism of anaphylaxis that is emerging seems to be (6a,29):

A number of pharmacologically active substances may be released. Their relative roles vary from one species to another, depending on the relative sensitivity of the various animals to the different agents, the abundance of the substances or their precursors in the tissues, the location of the sensitive tissues relative to the sites of antibody—antigen reaction, and the types of antibody involved.

As already suggested, serum enzymes and complement may be involved in anaphylaxis, but the subject seems too complicated to discuss further here. (See 6a, 29.)

The history of our knowledge of anaphylaxis has been summarized very well by Mongar and Schild (105).

Schultz-Dale Reaction

Smooth muscle (usually uterus or intestine) from an anaphylactically sensitized animal may respond by contraction when exposed *in vitro* to the antigen (37,42). This a simple and attractive technique that has been much used. Geiger, Hill, and Thompson (62), who investigated the mechanism, found that it could be blocked by urethane, Nupercaine, the lower aliphatic alcohols, and type D botulinum toxin, although these substances did not block the responses of the tissue to histamine or acetylcholine. These authors concluded that the reaction involves postganglionic cholinergic nerves.

Typical results of a test with sensitized guinea pig uterus are shown in Fig. 8-2. Note the sharp specificity of the reaction.

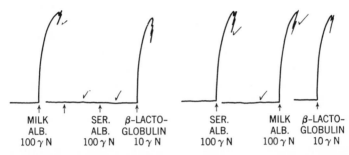

Fig. 8-2. Kymograph tracings illustrating the use of the Schultz-Dale technique in studying antigens. The tissue used was the uterus from a guinea pig sensitized to milk albumin. The two horns of the uterus were tested separately, resulting in the two tracings shown. Recorded on paper travelling 3 mm. per minute. Modified from Coulson.

The first horn of the uterus (Fig. 8-2, top) reacted to milk albumin and as a result was desensitized to serum albumin. The second horn (Fig. 8-2, bottom) reacted to serum albumin, as the first would have done also, but was not desensitized to milk albumin as a result, indicating that the milk albumin contained a further antigenic component. Test of the strips with another protein of milk, beta-lactoglobulin, produced contraction in both cases, indicating that there was sufficient beta-lactoglobulin in the milk albumin preparation to sensitize a guinea pig to this second protein. (But not enough, be it noted, for the dose of milk albumin capable of producing a reaction *in vitro* to desensitize the uterine horn to beta-lactoglobulin.)

12. Anaphylaxis and Nonprecipitating Antibody

It was formerly rather generally believed that skin-sensitizing, nonprecipitating antibody (reagin) would not passively sensitize guinea pigs to anaphylaxis (references in 85), although Ratner and Gruehl (125) showed that serum from a patient sensitive to horse dander would sensitize guinea pigs to anaphylaxis. Kabat and Benacerraf (75) demonstrated in 1949 that guinea pigs could be sensitized to fatal anaphylactic shock with approximately the same quantity of nonprecipitating or "univalent" rabbit antiovalbumin as with precipitating antiovalbumin. The amounts of either antibody required were equivalent to about 0.03 mg. protein N. In 1952 Kuhns and Pappenheimer (85) showed that the nonprecipitating "reagin" type of antitoxin produced by atopic individuals in response to injections of toxoid would sensitize guinea pigs passively to anaphylaxis. The amounts required to sensitize to fatal anaphylaxis were equivalent to about 0.023 mg. N.

From the experiments of Kabat and Benacerraf and Kuhns and Pappenheimer it is evident that the amounts of antibody required to sensitize guinea pigs to anaphylaxis are considerably greater than the amounts commonly present in the serum of atopic patients (p. 445). It is therefore possible that earlier workers had failed to sensitize guinea pigs with atopic serum merely because the amount of antibody present was insufficient for this purpose.

The symptoms of anaphylaxis due to nonprecipitating antibody do not appear to be any different from those due to precipitating antibody, described above.

C. ARTHUS PHENOMENON

It was found by Arthus and Breton (5) that if horse serum, which is harmless to normal rabbits, is repeatedly injected at intervals of several days, eventually the later injections will give rise to a characteristic reaction, involving infiltrations, edema, sterile abscesses, and in severe cases even gangrene. It is not necessary that the earlier injections be made in the same place as the later ones. This reaction is less easily obtained in guinea pigs and some other animals, but it is fairly common in man. It is specific.

The cells of the tissues at large are not sensitized (94), but the tissue death which results is due primarily to impairment of nutrition, resulting from vascular damage and clogging of the tissue spaces with exudate and hemorrhage. The studies of Opie (109), Cannon and Marshall (26), and Fishel and Kabat (55) indicate a definite relation between the degree of sensitivity and the precipitin titer of the serum. They suggested that the Arthus phenomenon is dependent upon the union within the tissues of circulating precipitin and its specific antigen. This suggestion is supported by the observation that it is necessary to inject a relatively large amount of antigen to elicit the reaction in its intense form.

Precipitating antibody is essential for the Arthus reaction: this was shown by Benacerraf and Kabat (10) with rabbit antibody in the guinea pig, and Kuhns (84) showed that even large amounts of nonprecipitating human antibody did not cause severe Arthus reactions even when large amounts of antigen were injected.

The amount of antibody nitrogen necessary to sensitize a guinea pig passively for a minimal Arthus reaction is about 0.56 mg. or about 14 times the amount sufficient to sensitize to fatal anaphylaxis (10). And almost 2500 times as much antibody is required for the induction of local passive Arthus reactivity in the rabbit's skin as for the sensitization of a strip of guinea pig smooth muscle for anaphylactic contraction (55). Horse, rat, and bird antisera will produce the Arthus reaction (Table 8-2).

The basic requirements of the Arthus reaction are the reaction of precipitating antibody with antigen, in adequate concentrations, and the presence of blood vessels in the tissue in which this combination takes place. The characteristic features of the Arthus reaction depend chiefly upon injury to blood vessels, although other effects such as swelling and degeneration of collagen fibers are also observed. Thus the Arthus reaction cannot ordinarily be produced in the avascular cornea, but can if the cornea is first vascularized by irritation (128).

Abell and Schenck (2) observed microscopically in the living animal the results of the combination of antigen and antibody in a local area of rabbit tissue. The primary result is contraction of the smooth muscle of the arterioles. The endothelium of these vessels and the leukocytes in them appear to become sticky, and the leukocytes stick to each other and to the walls of the arterioles. The resulting masses of cells may eventually stop up the vessels completely. This stickiness of the endothelium indicates an injury, which may go on to cause the death of this layer of the vessel wall; the resulting necrosis may then extend to the rest of the wall as well. A chain of pathological events is initiated which includes arteriolar spasm, endothelial damage, formation of leukocytic thrombi, and exudation of fluid and blood cells into the tissues. In a severe reaction an area is deprived of its blood supply, with resulting necrosis.

The Arthus reaction is definitely not identical with the wheal and flare reaction, with anaphylactic shock, nor with those allergies of man called "atopy" (p. 442). Waksman (166) has summarized the main differences: in the first place, the Arthus is a relatively slow reaction, reaching its peak only after some hours, while the other reactions have a time course measured in minutes or even seconds. The Arthus is characterized by edema with extensive cellular filtration, hemorrhage, and secondary necrosis, while the others are characterized only by smooth muscle contraction, increased vascular permeability, and such other events as are produced by the pharmacological agents released by the reaction. Some of these agents, such as histamine, have been identified (p. 487), and will duplicate essentially all the observed characteristics of these reactions, and antihistamines in general will prevent these reactions. Antihistamines have little or no effect on the Arthus reaction. It has been shown that the Arthus can be produced only by precipitating antibody, whereas urticaria and anaphylaxis can be produced by nonprecipitating antibody. The antisera of certain species of animals, notably the horse, will not produce passive anaphylaxis or urticaria in guinea pigs or rabbits in spite of a high titer of precipitating antibody, but are quite effective in sensitizing animals for the Arthus reaction (113). The actual amounts of antibody involved in the reactions of the urticaria—anaphylaxsis—atopy group are significantly less than those needed for the Arthus reaction. Finally, many types of evidence indicate that circulating antibody must be fixed in appropriate tissues before the introduction of antigen will cause anaphylaxis or any of its relatives, whereas no such fixation appears to occur in Arthus sensitivity.

Before the days of sulfa drugs and antibiotics, the use of foreign sera in therapy of various infections was relatively common. Large amounts of antibody were thus being introduced, and antigen (from the infecting organism) was present. It is not surprising that reactions which seem to have been Arthus in nature were sometimes observed (163). The surprising thing is that they were not much more frequent. However, it will be recalled that the reaction requires the presence of precipitating *antibodies* and, apparently, combination of antibody and antigen in the right proportions to give a precipitate. The usual source of such therapeutic sera was the horse, and many horse antibodies precipitate with antigen only within a rather narrow range of antibody/antigen proportions (p. 352). Raffel (123) suggested that this may be the reason the Arthus phenomenon was so seldom encountered in clinical practice.

1. Periarteritis Nodosa

Some of the pathological processes observed in periarteritis nodosa (necrotic changes, edema, local eosinophilia, and smooth muscle hypertrophy occurring in the arteries of the voluntary muscles, the liver, gall bladder, coronary vessels, lungs, and elsewhere) have been attributed to irreversible changes resulting from inflammation resulting from an allergic reaction (literature in 163). It has been suggested that the disease is the result of an Arthus reaction taking place in the vessel walls.

Rich (127,129) has in fact produced convincing evidence of this by clinical and pathological examination of patients with serum sickness and severe sensitivity to sulfonamides, and by experiments on rabbits.

Other authors, however, such as Zeek (179), believe that some cases are not due to hypersensitivity, mainly because cases of periarteritis nodosa are observed in which no clinical hypersensitiveness is found.

In Chapter 13 we shall examine the possibility that periarteritis nodosa is due to the formation of autoantibodies by the patient.

2. Passive Cutaneous Anaphylaxis (PCA)

Ovary (110,112), developed a very sensitive method of detecting small amounts of antibody or antigen. If we wish to study antibody, for example, we inject it intrademally into the back of a guinea pig. About three hours later the animal is given an intravenous injection of the antigen, mixed with a dye (0.5 ml. of 1 per cent Evans blue in saline). The vascular reaction at the intradermal injection site leads to escape of the dye into the skin, and a blue area develops that is easily seen. Under favorable conditions, this technique will detect as little as 0.02 μg. of antibody. It detects only 7S antibodies, however, since 19S antibodies are not fixed to the skin (72). Complement seems to be necessary for PCA (111).

D. ATOPY

"Atopy" is a term which embraces a group of human diseases which differ from anaphylaxis in certain aspects. They have in common the characteristic that they have been observed chiefly in man. It is likely, however, that this difference is in part due to our preoccupation, in clinical work, with the human species. Many of the conditions exist also in the lower animals (Fig. 8-3) or can be produced under suitable experimental conditions. These conditions were once classified under "clinical allergy."

1. Historical

The word "alergy," first defined by von Pirquet (see above), has been widely used, but usually in a slightly different sense by each author. It has even found its way, usually in an incorrect usage, into the advertising columns of our magazines and newspapers. Von Pirquet expressed the belief that an antibody—antigen reaction was the basis of the phenomenon. Doerr (43) extended the originator's definition to include all forms of changed reactivity, irrespective of whether an antibody—antigen reaction could be demonstrated. The subject has been reviewed by Talmage (154).

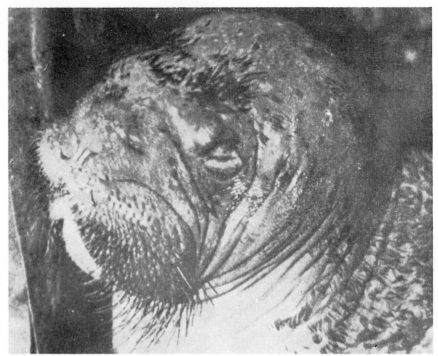

Fig. 8-3. Bottle-fed baby walrus with atopic allergy to cow's milk. Photograph shows almost total loss of hair, papular eruptions, swollen eyelids, and mucous accumulation in the nasal passages and oral cavity. **Courtesy C. R. Schroeder and the** *Journal of the American Veterinary Medical Association.*

2. Atopy

The term atopy, from the Greek ἄτοπος, meaning out of place, strange, odd, was proposed by Coca and Cooke (33) to denote certain clinical forms of human hypersensitiveness which are affected by a hereditary predisposition. It was once supposed that this condition did not occur in animals, but it has since been observed in dogs (20,119,162), cattle (15a), and other animals (18,28,73,175), including a walrus (141) (Fig. 8-3). See reference (176).

The basic element in atopy appears to be (85) the tendency to form reagin (nonprecipitating, nonagglutinating, etc., antibody) in place of the more usual type, and we might define atopic individuals as those persons who produce larger amounts than normal of reagins, or produce them in response to stimuli which would not cause a normal person to produce reagins. In this we depart somewhat from the original definition of

Coca in that we include some allergic conditions in which the hereditary element has not yet been clearly demonstrated.

Hay fever and asthma are classified under atopy; probably we should include also most forms of infantile eczema, and certain forms of drug and food idiosyncrasy. The hereditary factor involved in atopy is discussed on page 446. For individuals who inherit the tendency towards atopic allergy, a slight degree of exposure is sufficient to produce sensitivity. There is evidence that other "normal" individuals may, if continuously exposed to allergens, as in the course of their daily work, acquire some degree of sensitivity. Thus 30 to 40 per cent of bakers give skin reactions to rye, wheat, or other grains, and over 20 per cent of cavalrymen react to horse dander (see reference 70). Few such persons have clinical symptoms, however.

The word allergen, analogous to antigen, denotes the excitant of an allergic reaction. This is the term in common clinical use. An analogous word, atopen, was proposed by Coca. Allergens include some substances which are not antigenic in the ordinary sense. According to the route through which they produce their effects, they may be classified as inhalants, ingestants, contactants, injectants, and physical and nonspecific factors. Examples are pollens, dusts, danders; foods and drugs; poison ivy, formaldehyde; arsphenamine; heat and cold.

3. Mechanism

Just as there is good reason to think that anaphylaxis is an antibody–antigen reaction, so there is persuasive evidence that the reaction in the natural or atopic type of allergy is also a reaction between the allergen and an antibody, which in this case is called reagin. We may cite two main facts: (1) individuals with the atopic types of hypersensitiveness, such as hay fever, asthma, and eczema, have reagins in their blood which are specific for the allergen, and their concentration may parallel the degree of skin sensitivity. (2) The reagin content of the blood has been reported to increase to from two to four times its initial level following injection of pollen extracts, suggesting that the reagins are produced in response to the antigenic stimulus of the allergen.

It is also believed, again in analogy with anaphylaxis, that the allergic reaction is due to the combination of allergen with reagin in the tissues, and the immediate cause of the symptoms is believed to be the resulting liberation of histamine (79) or a histamine-like substance. (See p. 436.)

The differences in the symptoms of different atopic reactions in the same species appear to be due largely to the localization of the process in one or more of the "shock organs." The important sites of such reactions may be conveniently classified into: conjunctiva, nasal mucosa, bronchi, skin, gastrointestinal mucosa, and the nervous system (brain). Clarke, Donnally, and Coca (31) presented evidence indicating that the localization of the sensitivity is at least in some cases also determined by inheritance. The influence of other factors, such as the natural portal of entry of the allergen, is still in need of exploration.

White cell destruction, presumably from combination of antigen with reagin, has been implicated in the study of atopic allergy, as explaining the fall in white count observed after administration of the specific allergen, the so-called "hemoclastic crisis" or "leukopenic index" (165). Waksman (165) was able to produce lysis of leukocytes in rabbits by adding antigen to immune rabbit serum in the presence of fresh normal blood. The antibody involved seemed to be of the nonprecipitating type.

The pathological lesions of atopic reactions are much the same regardless of etiology or location. They consist of edema with cellular infiltration chiefly of histiocytes and eosinophiles, fibrinoid and colagen degeneration, in varying degrees. The histological picture in the skin of atopic patients is the same as that seen in lower animals or in the passively sensitized sites of normal human beings (11). Many eosinophiles are found, and histiocytes are believed to engulf the antigen. Fibrinoid collagen degeneration and edema are prominent findings.

In general, we may say that atopy has all the same pathophysiological characteristics as animal anaphylaxis: vessel permeability change, smooth muscle contraction, leukopenia, histamine release, and associated changes. If the allergen is injected intravenously, atopic individuals react with typical anaphylactic shock. There is no obvious reason to continue to regard atopy as different from anaphylaxis except that allergy occurs spontaneously and is elicited by the small doses of antigen that can penetrate the nasal mucosa, gastrointestinal tract, etc. (and is therefore less violent), in people unusually prone to form a highly active type of sensitizing antibody. The basic mechanisms seem to be the same as in anaphylaxis. Rackemann (121) published data concerning 50 deaths from asthma, and reported that in younger individuals with asthma traceable to a definite antigenic stimulus the pathological findings were comparable to those seen in anaphylaxis of the guinea pig.

4. Differences between Anaphylaxis and Atopy

Although the basic mechanisms of atopy and anaphylaxis appear to be the same, and we class them together under the headings of immediate hypersensitivity, many earlier writers believed there were considerable differences between them. These differences seem less striking today, as may be seen from Table 8-4, modified from Tuft (157). However, it is likely that we shall retain the two terms, one for the artificially induced phenomenon usually seen only in animals, one for the naturally occurring phenomenon which is more commonly seen in man, perhaps mainly because we do not ordinarily look for it in animals.

TABLE 8-4

Differences between Anaphylaxis and Atopy[a]

	Anaphylaxis	Atopy
Occurrence.	Artificially induced.	Usually naturally acquired.
Hereditary factor.	Perhaps less.	Often present; predisposition can be inherited through either mother or father (rarely congenital).
Duration of sensitization.	Relatively brief.	Long.
Nature of antigen.	Usually protein or carbohydrate.[b]	Induced by many nonprotein substances.
Characteristic antibodies.	Precipitins or nonprecipitating antibodies.	Reagins[c] (when present).
Symptoms.	Due to contraction of smooth muscle. Same irrespective of type of antigen.	Usually due to edema, but some reports indicating smooth muscle contraction. May differ with different antigens.
Pathological findings.	Shock organ variable in different species but constant in individual members (see p. 420).	Shock organ may differ in different individuals; even in same individual more than one may be involved.
Desensitization.	Relatively easy, at least in the guinea pig.	Difficult to produce, or to prove.

[a] Modified from Tuft (157).

[b] Landsteiner and Jacobs (88) reported anaphylactic sensitization to arsphenamine. However, Landsteiner (86) favored retaining the distinction between allergens and antigens, reserving the latter term for substances of high molecular weight. Arsphenamine probably acts by combining with proteins first.

[c] See text, p. 443.

5. Hereditary Factor

Observations indicating the existence of a hereditary predisposition, both in hay fever and in asthma, were made long ago. Modern work has established it practically beyond question. Later, vasomotor rhinitis and

Besnier's prurigo (atopic dermatitis) were added to the group. Studies on the heredity of these four conditions will be found in (32,157,163,143). The hereditary factor does not seem to be equally strong in all forms of allergy, however, and Coca originally used the hereditary factor as one justification for separating "atopy" from other types of allergy. As an example of a continued sceptical attitude towards the role of heredity, see Ratner and Silberman (126).

Wiener, Zieve, and Fries (174) suggested that the predisposition to atopic allergic disease may be transmitted by means of a single pair of allelomorphic genes, H and h, in which H determines nonallergy, and h determines allergy. Three different genotypes are possible: HH, pure normal; hh, allergic individuals whose symptoms are apt to begin before puberty; and Hh, individuals who may be normal transmitters, or develop allergic disease after puberty. This seems to be the best theory of the inheritance of a tendency to atopic allergy which has been proposed so far, and agrees well with such family data as are available. Figure 8-4

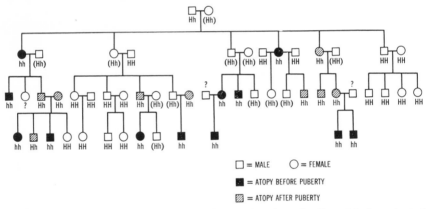

Fig. 8-4. Occurrence of atopic allergy in an American family, with hypothetical genotypes showing how the inheritance might be accounted for on the basis of Wiener's theory.

shows the inheritance of atopic tendencies in a typical American family, with the putative genotypes of some of the individuals involved.

It has been shown that a hereditary factor operates in the susceptibility. of guinea pigs to sensitization (74,29,30).

6. Importance of Contact

It should of course be realized that the role of heredity in these conditions is simply to predispose the affected individual to sensitization.

The hereditary predisposition alone is not enough to make the individual actually sensitive; contact with the active agent is also necessary. This is well shown by experiments of Grove (cited in 32) who tested with ragweed 35 patients suffering from timothy hay fever, residing in Berlin, where there is no ragweed. None of these patients had been in the United States, where ragweed is common. Grove found that none of the 35 reacted even to strong extracts of ragweed. Since about half the timothy hay fever patients in the United States are also subject to ragweed pollen hay fever, about 17 of the Berlin cases were, as Coca points out, *potentially* ragweed-sensitive, so that if the hereditary predisposition alone were sufficient, they should have reacted. This is supported by Grove's test of another timothy hay fever sufferer in Berlin who had been to the United States. This individual reacted to the ragweed pollen extract.

Contact is necessary, therefore, to make an individual sensitive, no matter what his heredity or background. It is evidently not sufficient, however, for in the types of allergy where the role of heredity is clearest, it has been found that even extensive and prolonged contact with an allergen will not render a "normal" individual sensitive, at least not to the same degree as one predisposed to sensitivity (11,54). Figley and Elrod (54), who traced an endemic focus of asthma to dust from a castor oil mill, considered that their study "apparently refutes Van Leeuwen's contention that asthma can occur in normal persons when the factors of irritation and prolonged contact are present."

In types of hypersensitiveness where the influence of heredity is less marked, apparently almost every individual can be sensitized by adequate contact. This is clearly suggested by the results of the administration of even small amounts of horse serum.

7. Atopic Antibodies (Reagins)

In a number of allergic conditions antibodies can be demonstrated in the patient's serum. Their behavior differs in a number of respects from that of ordinary antibodies, and some authors prefer to use the noncommittal term reagin. The chief differences between reagins and anaphylactic antibodies are shown in Table 8-5.

Although neutralizing antibodies have been found (see 93), it will be noted that *reagins* typically do not precipitate or neutralize the antigen. They may, however, be detected by their power of passively sensitizing the human skin. If a small amount (0.1 ml.) of the allergic patient's serum is injected into the skin of a normal individual, after a suitable interval (24 to 48 hours) the prepared site in the normal will now react (by reddening, itching, and edema) when injected with a small amount (0.02 ml.) of the specific excitant; it will also react when the excitant is introduced into the blood, although untreated sites on this person's skin still fail to react. It is said that a small number of normal individuals exist whose skin cannot be thus sensitized. This demonstration of reagins is apparently successful only in the skin of the larger "receptive" group.

Passive sensitization of the skin may also result from the transfusion of blood from a sensitive person into a normal (see 94).

It was originally believed, by Coca and others, that there were great differences between reagins and anaphylactic antibodies. For example, it was stated that reagins would sensitize the human skin, whereas anaphylactic antibodies would not. Many of these distinctions have broken down, and Table 8-5 has been considerably modified in the light of newer knowledge.

TABLE 8-5

Comparison of Reagins with Anaphylactic Antibodies[a]

Reagins	Anaphylactic antibodies
Sensitize human skin, often in very small quantity.	Some do not sensitize the human skin.
Quickly and permanently attached to body cells.	Some diffuse from injection site through the body.
Some do not sensitize the guinea pig.	Sensitize the guinea pig.
Not precipitating antibodies.	Sometimes precipitating antibodies.
Do not always neutralize the antigen.	Neutralize the antigen.
Heat-labile (largely destroyed, half hour at 56 °C.).	Heat-stable (slightly affected, half hour at 56 °C.).

[a] Modified from Coca (32).

One of the characteristics of reagins was said to be their failure to neutralize their antigen. This resulted in a peculiar nonreciprocal interrelation of allergen and reagin. It was reported that, if a mixture of egg white and serum (from an egg-sensitive patient) which contained reagins to egg white were incubated and injected into a site previously passively sensitized to egg, a positive reaction would be obtained, indicating that the inciting power of the antigen had not been destroyed. But at the same time it was claimed that such a mixture would not passively sensitize the skin of a normal person, suggesting that the sensitizing power of the reagin in the mixture had been lost. Loveless (93) reported that reagins to ragweed were never produced in nonsensitive subjects injected with ragweed extract, although the reagin titer of sensitive subjects was usually increased by such injection.

Our knowledge of the atopic type of antibody has been advanced by Kuhns and Pappenheimer (85), who showed that one of the essential differences between normal and atopic individuals is that the former produce ordinary precipitating antibodies, whereas the latter produce nonprecipitating reagins. They were able to study these antibodies, using diphtheria toxoid as the antigen, and obtained precipitating antitoxin in normal persons, and nonprecipitating antitoxin in the atopics. The nonprecipitating antibody could be quantitated by its power of neutralizing toxin.

The two sorts of antibody differed in a number of ways. The nonprecipitating (reagin) antitoxin would passively sensitize the human skin, persisting at the injection site for weeks, whereas the ordinary antibody diffused away from the site in about 100 minutes. The ordinary antibody exhibited a marked Danysz effect (p. 341), but the atopic antibody did not.

Heating the sera containing the atopic antitoxin to 56°C. for 4 hours destroyed its skin-sensitizing power, although it could be shown that the heated reagin nevertheless persisted at the site for weeks. Heating the ordinary antibody destroyed its precipitating power, but did not much diminish its neutralizing power, and the heated ordinary antibody still showed a Danysz effect, although somewhat diminished.

The atopic antitoxin, though it would not precipitate, would nevertheless coprecipitate when mixed with ordinary antibody and added to antigen, as would the heated normal antibody.

Both kinds of antibody would passively sensitize guinea pigs to anaphylaxis.

It is not known what physical and chemical differences account for the special behavior of the reagins, and it must be admitted that our knowledge of them is still quite unsatisfactory. They may be part of the IgA immunoglobulins (see Chapter 2). An extensive review has been published by Stanworth (150). (See also 29.)

Antibodies that possess, like reagins, the power of passively sensitizing the human skin, have been observed in the sera of rabbits and guinea pigs injected with pollen extracts (references in 164) and with purified egg albumin. This property of the sera did not appear to be correlated with the precipitin content; in most of the guinea pig sera no precipitins were found.

Vaughan and Kabat (164) verified the presence of sensitizing antibodies for human skin in the sera of rabbits injected with recrystallized egg albumin, but concluded that these antibodies were specific, not for albumin, but for some impurity which is not identical with conalbumin, ovomucoid, or lysozyme. They considered that their work invalidated the work of Kuhns, and Pappenheimer, Sherman *et al.*, and Waksman. Kuhns and Pappenheimer did not agree with this.

The concentration of reagin in the blood of atopic individuals seems to be proportional to the degree of skin sensitivity, but does not necessarily parallel the degree of clinical sensitivity (severity of symptoms). It has been reported that the titer of demonstrable antibodies in various organs correlates well with the occurrence of allergic reactions (59).

Statements about amounts of reagin present in the serum of atopic patients are only relative because reagin, being a nonprecipitating antibody, cannot be determined by micro-Kjeldahl analysis as can precipitating antibodies (p. 686). Consequently one is limited to methods involving comparative titers. The work of Kuhns and Pappenheimer (85) enables us to set an upper limit for atopic patients with the ordinary degree of sensitivity. After examining a number of patients who showed atopic reactions to diphtheria toxoid, they concluded that the serum of these individuals contained less than 1/50 unit of antitoxin per milliliter. By analysis of precipitates made with precipitating antitoxin in the presence of nonprecipitating human antitoxin of high titer, they found that one unit of nonprecipitating antitoxin was equivalent to about 1.6 μg. of antibody nitrogen per milliliter. Therefore, the ordinary atopic patients tested by them had less than 1.6/50=0.03 μg. of antitoxin reagin N per milliliter.

"Reversed" skin reactions (injection of the antigen into the skin, followed by injection of the serum of a sensitive individual) have been reported (178). This is reminiscent of "reversed passive anaphylaxis" (p. 421).

8. "Hay" Fever

The seasonal paroxysmal attacks of coryza, known as hay fever, are too familiar to require any extended description. The symptoms may be produced by pollens or mold spores, or both, in the air coming in contact with the upper respiratory membranes. The pollens come chiefly from three groups of plants, called popularly trees, grasses, and weeds. In the United States weeds are the most important cause of trouble, trees the least. Since ragweed produces pollen so profusely and the plant is so widespread, it provokes symptoms in a large number of people. It pollinates from about the first week in August to the first week in October. Although hay fever is usually caused by pollens, similar symptoms may be produced by other agents, such as house dust, orris root (once a constituent of many cosmetics), and danders.

There have been many chemical studies on the atopens of pollen. Abramson (3) believed that the electrophoretically homogeneous, colorless components trifidin (from giant ragweed) and artefolin (from dwarf ragweed) are polypeptides of molecular weight about 5000. However, pollen extracts are not simple solutions of one atopen. They are complex mixtures and contain a number of different electrophoretic components, some colored, many or all of which are active in hay fever patients.

Pollen extracts also contain many other substances; quercitin (a flavinol pigment), numerous enzymes, and various polysaccharides. All these are atopically inactive (117).

There can be little doubt that hay fever is due to an "immunization that does not immunize," in other words a sensitization of the susceptible individual by antigenic constituents of the pollen or other incitant. It has been demonstrated that pollen is antigenic for lower animals. Reagins are found in the blood of hay fever patients, usually in relatively large amounts. Pollen extracts produce marked skin reactions in sensitive subjects, and this is believed to be due to the combination between the pollen antigen and its specific reagin.

Since the pollen antigen is not neutralized by the reagin, as is shown by passive transfer (see p. 449), but seems to be held in some sort of loose combination, it is apparent that "desensitization" (see p. 454), by injection of pollen extracts, does not operate by neutralizing the reagin; it has in fact been found experimentally that the reagins in such cases are not neutralized.

As would be expected from our knowledge of specificity (see Chapter 3), overlapping reactions are obtained with the pollens of closely related plants. Some allergists, therefore, have advocated the use of an extract made of only one member of a plant group (instead of a mixture of the individual members), for "desensitization."

9. Asthma

This term designates a recurrent, periodic, or paroxysmal type of breathlessness or dyspnea. The symptoms include wheezing or whistling respiration, with prolongation of the expiratory phase. This is caused by obstruction of the smaller bronchioles, due to spasm of the bronchial muscles or swelling of the mucosal lining, or both. Asthma is not always caused by atopic factors, and the term asthma is really only a name for a symptom complex. Bronchial asthma may be subdivided into atopic and nonatopic types. Of the bronchial asthmas, we shall consider here only the atopic type, which includes by far the greater number of patients.

Atopic asthma may be produced by a variety of allergens; of these the most important are inhalants and ingestants. Asthma caused by inhalants may be regarded as essentially the same thing as hay fever, except for differences in the location of the susceptible tissue (shock organ). It may be due to house dust, orris root, pollens, animal danders (such as dust from feathers or epithelium from horses, cats, and dogs), glue in furniture, book bindings, straw hats, etc.

Nearly 50 per cent of asthmatics react to house dust (134). The atopen in house dust seems to be an unknown constituent which is not identical with any of the known atopens. House dusts from various parts of the world seem to be about equally potent. On the other hand, the ingredient which causes the skin reaction is absent from street dust and from the dust of unused lofts and empty buildings (152). The origin of this atopen has not been definitely established; experimental evidence does not support the logical hypothesis that it is a constituent of some microorganism which grows in the dust (134,97). The prevailing opinion today is that it results from disintegration, whether natural or bacterial is not known, of cellulose, particularly cotton and kapok (134,97). Chemical analyses of purified material from extracts of house dust indicate that the active material is not a protein but may be carbohydrate in nature (134).

Ingestants causing asthma include foods and drugs. Foods are particularly important when the patients are infants or young children; older persons seem to develop an increasing tolerance to foods, but they frequently become more sensitive to inhalants. A large number of different foods, especially wheat, eggs, and milk, may be allergenic for particular individuals. Drugs may cause asthma by ingestion (*e.g.*, aspirin, quinine, antipyrine, and members of the morphine group) or by inhalation, as in pharmacists and laboratory workers (ipecac, *p*-phenylenediamine, lycopodium, urease, peptone, etc.).

It is generally agreed that the shock organ in allergic asthma is the lining or the musculature of the bronchi. When the allergen comes in contact with the sensitive cells, the reaction may liberate histamine or a histamine-like substance, which is responsible for the attack. Serotonin may also be involved, although antiserotonin drugs do not help. For that matter antihistamine drugs do not help either (57). Heparin may be a factor; it exists in the mast cells that contain histamine. It must be confessed that there is still a lot we do not know about asthma (57). Asthma is a much more crippling condition than hay fever, although patients rarely die even during an acute asthmatic attack. Walzer and Frost (163) reported on five deaths occurring in asthmatic paroxysms. It is the *impression* of many who see large numbers of asthmatics that their span of life is not materially shortened, although the available statistics do indicate an increased death expectation (163).

10. Urticaria (Hives)

This condition, sometimes also known as nettle rash, is an edematous or inflammatory disorder of the skin. Whitish, pinkish, or reddish elevated spots, known as wheals or hives, appear, accompanied by an itchy or burning sensation. They tend to come and go, even within a period of an hour or less. There seems to be some evidence of a hereditary factor, but the condition is usually classified as nonatopic. The most frequent cause is probably allergy to foods; the frequency with which the condition results from eating strawberries is known to everyone. Drugs are probably also responsible in some cases, particularly phenolphthalein, which is a constituent of many proprietary laxatives.

Skin tests may help detect the specific excitant, but often fail in conditions due to food allergy. It is sometimes possible to determine the cause from the history of the complaint. Removal of the specific allergen or allergens in nonpsychogenic cases usually brings relief.

11. Atopic Dermatitis

When the skin is the shock organ in atopy, the picture produced may vary in infants and adults, presumably due to differences in the skin at various ages. In the infant the result is a noninfectious, erythematous, itching, scaly, and vesicular or oozing dermatitis, which is called "eczema" by most physicians. The word eczema is, however, used to denote a heterogeneous collection of inflammatory dermatoses and is not a proper disease entity.

The excitants of atopic dermatitis are mostly foods, but may include some inhalants such as dust, silk, orris root, and animal danders. In infants the most important are egg, milk, and wheat, probably in about this order.

Patients with atopic dermatitis often give positive skin tests to one or more (sometimes to a great many) allergens. Reagins can often be demonstrated in such persons.

12. Angioneurotic Edema

This is similar to urticaria, but the lesions are large, pale swellings which may involve whole areas, such as the lip, eyelid, genitals, or even the side of the face or a whole hand. The edema involves the deeper layers of the corium and subcutaneous tissues. The condition has been called "giant urticaria." It may be dangerous if the larynx is involved. It may occur in association with other atopic diseases, and the excitant in such cases is usually the same. The diagnosis and treatment are practically the same as for urticaria.

13. Migraine

This is a periodic, incapacitating type of headache, usually unilateral. It may be accompanied or preceded by sensory disturbances, and may end in nausea and vomiting. The layman knows it as bilious headache, sick headache, or blind headache. The symptoms seem to be due to cerebal vasodilatation. There is indication that some forms of migraine may be atopic in nature. The hereditary factor is undoubtedly present, and some foods occasionally seem to be the exciting factor. If the atopic hypothesis is correct, it may be supposed that the basic cause of such types of migraine is the same as in any other type of allergy, i.e., local edema resulting from capillary vasodilation and capillary permeability. An interesting observation tending to support this has been presented by Goltman (67, see 151).

14. Treatment of Atopic Allergy

Three basic measures are possible in the treatment of the various atopic allergies: (1) we may urge the patient to avoid or eliminate, if possible, the excitant or excitants; (2) we may attempt to remove or lessen the degree of susceptibility by "desensitization"; (3) in acute attacks, or where the specific excitant cannot be discovered, symptomatic treatment (e.g., adrenaline) may be given.

1. Elimination or avoidance of the excitant is always the preferable method, but may be difficult or impossible if the patient is sensitive to a large number of substances, or if his occupation requires his presence in places where the excitant cannot be avoided. In any case this method presupposes that the specific excitant is known or can be discovered (skin tests, etc.). If the sensitivity is to a single atopen which can be completely avoided, the results are completely satisfactory.

2. Desensitization might be spoken of as lessening of sensitization, or the term hyposensitization proposed by Cooke and Coca might be used. The process may really be an immunization (94). Desensitization in atopic conditions differs from that in anaphylaxis; it is rarely complete and, in atopy, desensitization does not lessen the antibody content of the blood. Nevertheless, the procedure has considerable value, for it lessens

or even abolishes (temporarily) the sensitivity of some patients. Desensitization may be specific or nonspecific. The latter term refers to the use of agents unrelated to the excitant, such as bacterial vaccines, peptone, and tuberculin. The mechanism of this procedure, if it is really very effective, is as yet unexplained.

Specific desensitization consists of the introduction of very small amounts of the specific allergen at frequent intervals, until the clinical susceptibility is diminished (see p. 454). Usually the dose is gradually increased. The first dose may be roughly gauged by the degree of skin reactivity to the allergen. Densensitization to ingestants is not often necessary, as the patient can avoid the food or drug. If it should be necessary, the administration by mouth of successively increasing amounts of the allergenic food is the method to be preferred.

Specific desensitization is most often undertaken in the case of allergy to inhalants. It is done by a series of subcutaneous injections of progressively larger doses of an extract of the allergen (see p. 419). The inhalants most frequently employed are pollens, molds, dust, and animal danders.

Loveless (93) pointed out that following the injection of pollen extracts into pollen-sensitive patients three changes occur: thermostable antibody is produced in the serum; a relative immunity to the administered antigen is achieved, as reflected in the behavior of the conjunctiva and skin; and clinical benefits result. She suggested that all three may be referable to one mechanism, which is production of a "blocking" antibody which has a binding action on the antigen.

The thermostable blocking antibody produced differs from reagin (which, in naturally sensitive patients, may be produced in increased amounts also) in that it resists heating to 56°C. for 5 hours, or 60°C. for half an hour, and has the power of combining with antigen in the tissues without causing the irritation which follows combination of reagin and antigen. If present, it will "block" (36) the reagin so that, if this antibody, reagin, and antigen are introduced into the skin, no urticarial reaction follows, unless more antigen is present than the blocking antibody is capable of combining with. Hampton et al. (68) reported that the thermostable antibody will also block rabbit antiragweed precipitating antibodies and that the method compares favorably with the passive transfer procedure. Since the tests with rabbit antibody are carried out entirely in vitro, this makes the new method potentially preferable.

Lowell (95,96) reported finding in the serum of an insulin-resistant patient two antibodies, one a heat-labile allergic antibody capable of conferring sensitivity on normal skins, the other a heat-stable neutralizing antibody, capable of preventing the normal physiological action of insulin.

Kuhns and Pappenheimer (85) observed that heating reagin-type anti-toxin to 56°C. destroyed its skin-sensitizing power but left its neutralizing power substantially intact. This led them to suggest that possibly the results which Loveless interpreted as evidence for the presence of two distinct antibodies were in reality merely indications that reagin had been converted by heating to a form of antibody with blocking properties.

3. Many patients require drug therapy at some time. Three groups of drugs, exemplified by adrenaline, atropine, and the synthetic antihista-mine substances (66,103,92,100) have been used. Of the available drugs adrenaline is the most useful, chiefly because of its immediate action. Ephedrine has a similar effect but takes longer to act; it has a more pro-longed effect, however. Atropine and similar drugs are helpful in asthma because of their action in dilating and drying the respiratory passages.

Evidence at hand suggests that the antihistamines block the action of histamine by competing for the same receptor sites on sensitized cells. The chemistry and pharmacology of these numerous drugs have been reviewed in a number of places (104,52).

Cortisone and ACTH are also used in treatment of atopy, mainly in conditions which do not yield to other treatment (163). They should not be used in patients who have severe or chronic infections.

15. Atopic Allergy to Parasites

Many parasitic infections give rise to the immediate type of hyper-sensitivity; the skin sensitivity can often be utilized in diagnosis. Ex-amples are schistosomiasis (13), many intestinal helminth infections (153), particularly *ascaris,* trichinosis [two or three weeks after infection (106)], echinococcus disease, and filariasis (29,30). It has in fact been suggested (see p. 465) that this is the basic type of response of animals to infections, since metazoon parasitic infection must have been of great importance in animal evolution, and that allergic reactions of the atopic type are essentially exaggerations and misdirected examples of this basic reaction (42).

Although bacterial allergy is generally of the delayed type (see p. 499), the immediate type of reaction has been seen. Thus Tillett and Francis (155) demonstrated an immediate reaction of the urticarial type in pneu-monia convalescents; this reaction was type-specific, and was thus elicited by the capsular polysaccharide. They also observed skin reactions analo-gous to the tuberculin reaction, which were not type-specific, when pneu-mococcus protein was injected.

E. "IMMEDIATE" HYPERSENSITIVITY DUE TO ANTIBODIES OF VARIOUS TYPES

Under this heading we include those blood dyscrasias which seem to be due to antibody action (acquired hemolytic anemia, leukopenias, and thrombopenias), and possibly various obscure diseases in which the role of antibodies is still doubtful.

In the blood dyscrasias the affected cell, whether erythrocyte, leukocyte, or platelet, is typically damaged, and it is possible by special technics such as the Coombs reaction (see p. 285) to demonstrate that antibody or an antibody-like substance is in combination with the affected cell. Which type of cell is affected seems to depend upon the antigen giving rise to the antibody. In some cases this is evidently part of the cell, and in others something coming from outside. In many cases where the responsible agent is from outside it does not seem to function as a complete antigen, but rather as a hapten which combines with constituents of the particular type of cell and renders them antigenic.

In our attempts to understand this group of hypersensitive reactions, a new concept has appeared, one long doubted by most immunologists, but one which increasingly seems of great significance today. This is the phenomenon of autoimmunization, the production of antibodies or hypersensitivity against tissue components of the individual producing the response. See Chapter 13.

Waksman (167) includes in this classification transfusion reactions and erythroblastosis, which are due to perfectly well-understood antibodies.

F. MECHANISM OF IMMEDIATE HYPERSENSITIVITY

We may attempt to summarize our current ideas on the mechanisms of immediate hypersensitivity somewhat as follows:

Immediate hypersensitivity, when it occurs, is produced in response to a complete antigen, or a hapten which is able to combine with tissue proteins to form an antigen. The route of absorption of the antigen is generally unimportant. The induction period is about 10 days, or sometimes less.

After a state of immediate hypersensitivity has been induced, a reaction will be produced if fresh antigen gains entrance to the body. Antibody now reacts with the antigen, in the circulation or perhaps on or in the cells. As a result of this combination, harmful substances such as histamine, acetylcholine, and heparin are released from the cells, and symptoms due to the pharmacologic action of these substances are observed.

Much antibody is not necessary in order that this mechanism may operate, and it need not be of the precipitating type. In some hypersensitive subjects the only way antibody can be detected is by passive transfer. When precipitating antibody is present, and the dose of injected antigen is large, the resulting precipitate may possibly directly damage walls of the blood vessels, as is thought by some workers to be the case in the Arthus reaction.

It is not known exactly how the antibody–antigen reaction causes the release of histamine from the cells. Substances such as bee and snake venoms, which cause symptoms similar to anaphylaxis in normal unsensitized animals, have been found to liberate histamine from lung tissue. This is apparently the result of the production from lecithin, by the lecithinase in these venoms, of lysolecithin, which can release histamine from tissue cells. Trypsin, which when injected also produces symptoms like those of anaphylaxis, liberates histamine from tissue cells. Rocha e Silva (135) believed that the antibody–antigen combination in hypersensitive reactions releases or activates a proteolytic enzyme of the cells, and that this enzyme in turn releases histamine which is bound to cell proteins through lysine or arginine.

Histamine, or histamine-like substance, does not seem to be the only harmful substance liberated in these reactions. There is evidence that a "slow-reacting substance" is also liberated during anaphylactic shock, and heparin liberated from the liver may account for the deficient coagulability of the blood during anaphylactic shock, although this may be partly due to a fall in number of the blood platelets. Acetylcholine may be liberated, and larger amounts of adenosine derivatives and potassium ions may be found in the circulation.

The Arthus reaction is produced only by precipitating antibody, anaphylaxis can be produced by either precipitating or nonprecipitating antibody, and atopic allergy is produced by nonprecipitating antibody (reagin). It is not known what chemical and physical differences account for the lack of precipitating power of reagin, or for its ability to sensitize the skin, but evidence is accumulating that reagins are β-globulins, whereas precipitins are mostly γ-globulins.

Many parasites give rise to the immediate type of hypersensitivity. Injection of antigens of *Ascaris,* for instance, will cause the formation of the reagin type of antibody in the majority of subjects, irrespective of any inherited atopic tendencies (122,19,39). It has even been suggested that atopy is just an exaggerated response of the type which is routine against metazoon parasites, another example of an essentially homeostatic mechanism acting in a nonhomeostatic manner (41) (p. 413). In mammalian evolution, metazoon parasites may have been as important, as causes of disease, as bacteria (42).

In their basic mechanism, atopic reactions seem to resemble anaphylactic reactions. Both are probably mediated by, among other substances, histamine liberated by the combination of antigen with antibody in the tissues. There are, however, some differences in the reactivity of the human skin to histamine and to injected atopens.

Hay fever, urticaria, and angioneurotic edema are all primarily manifestations of serous exudation from blood vessels, consequent upon the increased permeability which results from the antibody–antigen reaction. Asthma seems strikingly similar to anaphylaxis in many ways; yet there are reasons to doubt that smooth muscle contraction is a factor in all cases of asthma.

References

1. Abel, J. J., and S. Kubota, *J. Pharmacol. Exptl. Therap.*, **13**, 243 (1919).
2. Abell, R. G., and H. P. Schenck, *J. Immunol.*, **34**, 195 (1938).
3. Abramson, H. A., *Treatment of Asthma*, Williams and Wilkins, Baltimore, 1951.
4. Alexander, H. L., and D. Bottom, *J. Immunol.*, **39**, 457 (1940).
5. Arthus, M., and M. Breton, *Compt. rend. soc. biol.*, **55**, 1478 (1903).
6. Austen, K. F., and J. H. Humphrey, in *Mechanism of Cell and Tissue Damage Produced by Immune Reactions*, P. Grabar, and P. Miescher, eds., Benno Schwabe. Basel/Stuttgart, 1962.
6a. Austen, K. F., and J. H. Humphrey, *Advan. Immunol.*, **3**, 1 (1963).
7. Avery, O. T., and W. S. Tillett, *J. Exptl. Med.*, **49**, 251 (1929).
8. Bailey, G. H., S. Raffel, and J. H. Dingle, *Am. J. Hyg.*, **25**, 381 (1937).
9. Bartosch, R., W. Feldberg, and E. Nagel, *Pflügers Arch. ges. Physiol.*, **230**, 129 (1932).
9a. Benacerraf, B., and E. A. Kabat, *J. Immunol.*, **62**, 517 (1949).
10. Benacerraf, B., and E. A. Kabat, *J. Immunol.*, **64**, 1 (1950).
10a. Benacerraf, B., Z. Ovary, K. J. Bloch, and E. C. Franklin, *J. Exp. Med.*, **117**, 937 (1963).
11. Berger, W., and F. J. Lang, *Beitr. Pathol., Anat. u. allgem. Pathol.*, **87**, 71 (1931).
12. Best, C. H., and E. W. McHenry, *Can. Med. Assoc. J.*, **43**, 163 (1940).
13. Blair, D. M., and W. F. Ross, *Ann. Trop. Med. Parasitol.*, **42**, 46 (1948).
14. Brambell, F. W. R., W. A. Hemmings, and M. Henderson, *Antibodies and Embryos*, University of London, Athlone Press, London, 1951.
15. Brambell, F. W. R., et al., *Proc. Roy. Soc., (London)*, **B137**, 239 (1950).
15a. Bray, G. W., *Recent Advances in Allergy*, Churchill, London, 1937.
16. Brocklehurst, W. E., *Prog. Allergy*, **6**, 540 (1962).
17. Brown, R., *Proc. Soc. Exptl. Biol. Med.*, **31**, 700 (1934).
18. Brownlee, A. J., *J. Compt. Pathol. Therap.*, **53**, 55 (1940).
19. Brunner, M., *J. Allergy*, **3**, 521 (1934).
20. Burns, P. W., *J. Am. Vet. Med. Assoc.*, **83**, 627 (1933).
21. Campbell, D. H,. in *Allergology*, Pergamon, New York, 1962, pp. 61–70.

22. Campbell, D. H., and G. E. McCasland, *J. Immunol.*, **49**, 315 (1944).
23. Campbell, D. H., and P. A. Nicoll, *J. Immunol.*, **39**, 103 (1940).
24. Cannon, W. B., *The Wisdom of the Body*, Norton, Philadelphia, 1939.
25. Cannon, P. R., and C. E. Marshall, *J. Immunol.*, **38**, 365 (1940).
26. Cannon, P. R., and C. E. Marshall, *J. Immunol.*, **40**, 127 (1941).
27. Cannon, P. R., T. E. Walsh, and C. E. Marshall, *Am. J. Pathol.*, **17**, 777 (1941).
28. Chase, M. W., *J. Exptl. Med.*, **73**, 711 (1941)
29. Chase, M. W., "The Allergic State," in *Bacterial and Mycotic Infections of Man*, R. J. Dubos and J. G. Hirsch, eds., Lippincott, Philadelphia, 1965.
30. Chase, M. W., *Bacterial Proc.*, **M58**, 100 (1952).
31. Clarke, J. A., H. H. Donnally, and A. F. Coca, *J. Immunol.*, **15**, 9 (1928).
32. Coca, A. F., in *Practice of Medicine*, by F. Tice, Price, New York, 1920.
33. Coca, A. F., and R. A. Cooke, *J. Immunol.*, **8**, 163 (1923).
34. Code, C. F., *Am. J. Physiol.*, **127**, 78 (1939).
35. Cooke, R. A., *Allergy in Theory and Practice*, Saunders, Philadelphia, 1947.
36. Cooke, R. A., et al., *J. Exptl. Med.*, **62**, 733 (1935).
37. Dale, H. H., *J. Pharmacol. Exptl. Therap.*, **4**, 167 (1913).
38. Danielopolu, D., *Phylaxie-Paraphylaxie et Maladie Spécifique*, Masson, Paris, 1946.
39. Davidson, A. F., B. Baron, and M. Walzer, *J. Allergy*, **18**, 359 (1947).
40. Dean, H. R., R. Williamson, and G. L. Taylor, *J. Hyg.*, **36**, 570 (1936).
41. Dienes, L., and H. L. Naterman, *J. Infect. Diseases*, **60**, 279 (1937).
42. Dienes, L., personal communication, 1955.
43. Doerr, R., *Ergeb. Hyg. Bakteriol. Immunitätsforsch. u. Exptl. Therap.*, **5**, 71 (1922).
44. Doerr, R., *Die Immunitätsforschung. VI. Die Anaphylaxie*, Springer-Verlag, Vienna, 1950.
45. Doerr, R., *Die Immunitätsforschung. VII. Die Anaphylaxie. II*, Springer-Verlag, Vienna, 1951.
46. Doerr, R., and V. K. Russ, *Z. Immunitätsforsch.*, **3**, 181 (1909).
47. Dragstedt, C. A., *Physiol. Rev.*, **21**, 563 (1941).
48. Dragstedt, C. A., and E. Gebauer-Fuelnegg, *Am. J. Physiol.*, **102**, 512, 520 (1932).
49. Drinker, C. K., and J. Bronfenbrenner, *J. Immunol.*, **9**, 387 (1924).
50. Fedorov, H. A., and A. E. Gurvich, *Arkhiv. Patologii*, **6**, 52–55 (1956) (Russian).
51. Feinberg, S. M., *J. Am. Med. Assoc.*, **132**, 703 (1946).
52. Feinberg, S. M., S. Malkiel, and A. R. Feinberg, *The Anti-histamines*, Year Book Publishers, Chicago, 1950.
53. Feldberg, W., *J. Pharm. and Pharmacol.*, **6**, 281 (1954).
54. Figley, K. D., and R. H. Elrod, *J. Am. Med. Assoc.*, **90**, 79 (1928).
55. Fishel, E. E., and E. A. Kabat, *J. Immunol.*, **55**, 337 (1947).
56. Follensby, E. M., and S. B. Hooker, *J. Immunol.*, **49**, 353 (1944).
57. Frankland, A. M., in *Clinical Aspects of Immunology*, P. G. H. Gell and R. R. A. Coombs, eds., F. A. Davis, Philadelphia, 1963, pp. 338–359.
58. Friedberger, E., and O. Hartoch, *Z. Immunitätsforsch.*, **3**, 581 (1909).
59. de Gara, P. F., and D. M. Angevine, *J. Exptl. Med.*, **78**, 135 (1943).
60. Geiger, W. B., *J. Immunol.*, **68**, 11 (1952).
61. Geiger, W. B., and H. S. Alpers, *J. Allergy*, **30**, 316–328 (1958).
62. Geiger, W. B., E. M. Hill, and M. Thompson, *Proc. Soc. Exptl. Biol. Med.*, **92**, 793–796 (1956).
63. Gel, P. G. H., *Biochem. Soc. Symposia (Cambridge, Engl.)*, No. **10**, 63 (1953).
64. Gerlach, F., *Z. Immunitätsforsch.*, **34**, 75 (1922).

65. Gilbert, A. J., *J. Pharmacol. Exptl. Therap.*, **62**, 228 (1938).
66. Goldstein, H., *J. Pediat.*, **30**, 41 (1947).
67. Goltman, A. M., *J. Allergy*, **7**, 351 (1936).
68. Hampton, S., *et al.*, *J. Allergy*, **14**, 227 (1943).
69. Hartley, G., and C. C. Lushbaugh, *Am. J. Pathol.*, **18**, 323 (1942).
70. Hill, L. W., *J. Allergy*, **11**, 170 (1940).
71. Hochwald, A., and F. M. Rackemann, *J. Immunol.*, **53**, 355 (1946).
72. Humphrey, J. H., and R. G. White, *Immunology for Students of Medicine*, F. A. Davis, Philadelphia, 1963.
73. Hutyra, F., J. Mareck, and R. Manninger, *Special Pathology and Therapeutics of the Diseases of Domestic Animals*, Eger, Chicago, 1938.
74. Jacobs, J. L., J. J. Kelley, and S. C. Somners, *Proc. Soc. Exptl. Biol. Med.*, **48**, 639 (1941).
75. Kabat, E. A., and B. Benacerraf, *J. Immunol.*, **62**, 97 (1949).
76. Kabat, E. A., and M. H. Boldt, *J. Immunol.*, **48**, 181 (1944).
77. Kabat, E. A., and H. Landow, *J. Immunol.*, **44**, 69 (1942).
78. Karady, E. S., *J. Immunol.*, **41**, 1 (1941).
79. Katz, G., *Proc. Soc. Exptl. Biol. Med.*, **49**, 272 (1942).
80. Kellaway, C. H., and S. J. Cowell, *Brit. J. Exptl. Pathol.*, **3**, 268 (1922).
81. Kellaway, C. H., and E. P. Trethewie, *Quart. J. Exptl. Physiol.*, **30**, 121 (1940).
82. Kellett, C. E., *J. Pathol. Bacteriol.*, **41**, 479 (1935).
83. Kojis, F. G., *Am. J. Diseases Children*, **64**, 93, 313 (1942).
84. Kuhns, W. J., *J. Exptl. Med.*, **97**, 903 (1953).
85. Kuhns, W. J., and A. M. Pappenheimer, *J. Exptl. Med.*, **95**, 375 (1952).
86. Landsteiner, K., *The Specificity of Serological Reactions*, 2nd rev. ed., Harvard University Press, Cambridge, 1945.
87. Landsteiner, K., and M. W. Chase, *J. Exptl. Med.*, **66**, 337 (1937).
88. Landsteiner, K., and J. Jacobs, *J. Exptl. Med.*, **64**, 717 (1836).
89. Landsteiner, K., and J. van der Scheer, *J. Exptl. Med.*, **57**, 633 (1933).
90. Landsteiner, K., and J. van der Scheer, *J. Exptl. Med.*, **67**, 79 (1938).
91. Lewis, T., *The Blood Vessels of the Human Skin and Their Responses*, Chicago Medical Book, Chicago, 1927.
92. Loew, E. R., *Med. Clin. North America*, **34**, 351–368 (1950).
93. Loveless, M. H., *Southern Med. J.*, **33**, 869 (1940).
94. Loveless, M. H., *J. Immunol.*, **41**, 15 (1941).
95. Lowell, F. C., *Proc. Soc. Exptl. Biol. Med.*, **50**, 167 (1942).
96. Lowell, F. C., *J. Clin. Invest.*, **23**, 225, 233 (1944).
97. Lowell, F. C., personal communication, 1955.
99. Malkiel, S., *Atti congr. intern. microbiol. 6th Congr.*, Rome, **2**, 265 (1953).
100. Malkiel, S., S. M. Feinberg, and A. R. Feinberg, *The Antihistamines: Their Clinical Application*, Year Book, Chicago, 1950.
101. Manwaring, W. H., R. C. Chilcote, and U. M. Hosepian, *J. Am. Med. Assoc.*, **80**, 303 (1923).
102. Mauriac, P., and M. Moureau, *J. méd. franç.*, **9**, 243 (1920).
103. McElin, T. W., *et al.*, *Proc. Staff Meetings Mayo Clinic*, **20**, 417 (1945).
104. Meier, P., and K. Bucher, *Progr. Allergy*, **2**, 290 (1949).
105. Mongar, J. L., and H. O. Schild, *Physiol. Rev.*, **42**, 226–270 (1962).
106. Most, H., *Parasitic Infections in Man*, Columbia University Press, New York, 1951.
107. Munoz, J., L. F. Schuchardt, and W. F. Verwey, *J. Immunol.*, **80**, 77–84 (1958).

108. Nakamura, K., *Allergy and Anaphylaxis*, Nippon Medical School, Tokyo, 1954.
109. Opie, E. L., *J. Immunol.*, **9**, 231 (1924).
110. Osler, A. G., M. M. Hawrisiak, Z. Ovary, M. Siqueira, and O. G. Bier, *J. Exptl. Med.*, **106**, 811–834 (1957).
111. Osler, A. G., H. G. Randall, B. M. Hill, and Z. Ovary, in *Mechanisms of Hypersensitivity*, Little, Brown, 1959.
112. Ovary, Z., *Progr. Allergy*, **5**, 459–508 (1958).
112a. Ovary, Z. B. Benacerraf, and K. J. Bloch, *J. Exp. Med.*, **117**, 951 (1963).
113. Ovary, Z., and O. G. Bier, *J. Immunol.*, **71**, 6 (1953).
114. Page, I. H., *Sci. Am.*, **197**, 52–56 (1957).
115. Parish, W. E., and J. Pepys, in *Clinical Aspects of Immunology*, P. G. H. Gell and R. R. A. Coombs, eds., F. A. Davis, Philadelphia, 1963.
116. Pauling, L., D. H. Campbell, and D. Pressman, *Proc. Natl. Acad. Sci. U. S.*, **27**, 125 (1941).
117. Perlman, E., "Chemistry and standardization of pollen extracts," in *Treatment of Asthma*, H. A. Abramson, ed., Williams and Wilkins, Baltimore, 1951.
118. von Pirquet, C., *Münch. med. Wochschr.*, **53**, 1457 (1906).
119. Pomeroy, B. S., *Cornell Vet.*, **24**, 335 (1934).
120. Portier, and Richet, *Compt. rend. soc. Biol.*, **54**, 170 (1902).
121. Rackemann, F. M., *J. Allergy*, **15**, 249 (1944).
122. Rackemann, F. M., and A. H. Stevens, *J. Immunol.*, **13**, 389 (1927).
123. Raffel, S., *Immunity*, Appleton-Century-Crofts, New York, 1953.
124. Ratner, B., *Allergy, Anaphylaxis, and Immunotherapy*, Williams and Wilkins, Baltimore, 1943.
125. Ratner, B., and H. L. Gruehl, *Proc. Soc. Exptl. Biol. Med.*, **27**, 574 (1929–1930).
126. Ratner, B., and D. E. Silberman, *Trans. N. Y. Acad. Sci.*, **15**, 82 (1953).
127. Rich, A. R., *Harvey Lecture Ser.*, **42**, 106 (1947).
128. Rich, A. R., and R. H. Follis, *Bull. Johns Hopkins Hosp.*, **52**, 179 (1933).
129. Rich, A. R., and J. E. Gregory, *Bull. Johns Hopkins Hosp.*, **72**, 65 (1943).
130. Richards, D. W., *Sci. Monthly*, **77**, 289 (1953).
131. Richet, C., *L'Anaphylaxie*, Librairie Felix Ilcan, Paris, 1911.
132. Rienmuller, J., *Z. Immunitätsforsch.*, **102**, 74 (1942).
133. Riley, J. F., D. M. Shepherd, and G. B. West, *Nature*, **176**, 1123 (1955).
134. Rimington, C., "The chemical nature of dust allergen," in *Treatment of Asthma*, H. A. Abramson, ed., Williams and Wilkins, Baltimore, 1951.
135. Rocha e Silva, M., *J. Immunol.*, **40**, 399 (1941).
136. Rocha e Silva, M., O. Bier, and M. Aronson, *Nature*, **168**, 465 (1951).
137. Rose, B., and J. S. L. Browne, *J. Immunol.*, **41**, 409 (1941).
138. Rosenau, M. J. and J. F. Anderson, *U. S. Public Health Service, Hyg. Lab. Bull.*, No. **29** (1906).
139. Rosenau, M. J., and J. F. Anderson, *U. S. Public Health Service, Hyg. Lab. Bull.*, No. **45**, (1908).
140. Rosenthal, S. R., and M. L. Brown, *J. Immunol.*, **38**, 259 (1940).
141. Schroeder, C. R., *J. Am. Vet. Med. Asoc.*, **33**, 810 (1933).
142. Schultz, W. H., *J. Pharmacol. Exptl. Therap.*, **2**, 221 (1910).
143. Schwartz, M., in *Clinical Genetics*, Mosby, St. Louis, 1953.
144. Scott, W. M., *J. Pathol. Bacteriol.*, **14**, 147 (1909).
145. Scott, W. M., *J. Pathol. Bacteriol.*, **15**, 31 (1910).
146. Scott, W. M., *Med. Res. Council (Brit.) Spec. Rept. Ser.*, No. **6**, 457 (1931).

147. Seegal, B. C., in *Agents of Disease and Host Resistance*, F. P. Gay, ed., Charles C Thomas, Springfield, Illinois, 1935.
148. Sherwood, N. P., *Immunology*, Mosby, St. Louis, 1941.
149. Smith, W. G., *Life Sciences*, No. 4, pp. 133–140 (1962).
150. Stanworth, D. R., *Adv. Immunol.*, 3, 181–260 (1963).
151. von Storch, T. J. C., *Arch. Neurol. Psychiat.*, 44, 316 (1940).
152. Sutherland, C., *Med. J. Australia*, 1, 583 (1945).
153. Taliaferro, W. H., *The Immunology of Parasitic Infections*, Century, New York, 1929.
154. Talmage, D. W., *Ann. Rev. Med.*, 8, 239–256 (1957).
155. Tillett, W. S., and T. F. Francis, *J. Exptl. Med.*, 52, 561 (1930).
156. Topley, W. W. C., and G. S. Wilson, *The Principles of Bacteriology and Immunity*, Arnold, Baltimore, 1936; 5th ed. by G. S. Wilson and A. A. Miles, 1964.
157. Tuft, L., *Clinical Allergy*, Lea and Febiger, Philadelphia, 1949.
158. Tum Suden, C., *Am. J. Physiol.*, 108, 416 (1934).
159. Udenfriend, S., and T. P. Waalkes, in *Mechanisms of Hypersensitivity*, Little Brown, Boston, 1959.
160. Uhlenhuth, P., and Händel, Z. *Immunitätsforsch.*, 3, 284 (1909).
161. Vance, B. M., and G. Strassmann, *Arch. Pathol.*, 34, 849 (1942).
162. Vaughan, W. T., *Practice of Allergy*, Mosby, St. Louis, 1939.
163. Vaughan, W. T., and J. H. Black, *Practice of Allergy*, 3rd ed., Mosby, St. Louis, 1954.
164. Vaughan, J. H., and E. A. Kabat, *J. Exptl. Med.*, 97, 821 (1953).
165. Waksman, B. H., *J. Immunol.*, 70, 331 (1953).
166. Waksman, B. H., *Ann. N. Y. Acad. Sci.*, 59, 306 (1955).
167. Waksman, B. H., personal communication, 1955.
168. Weil, R., *J. Med. Research*, 27, 497 (1912–1913).
169. Weiser, R. S., O. J. Golub, and D. M. Hamre, *J. Infect. Diseases*, 68, 97 (1941).
170. Weissbach, H., T. P. Waalkes, and S. Udenfriend, *Science*, 125, 235–236 (1957).
171. Welch, H., C. N. Lewis, H. I. Weinstein, *Antibiotic Med. Clin. Therapy*, 4, 800 (1957).
172. Wells, H. G., *The Chemical Aspects of Immunity*, 2nd ed., Chemical Catalog Co., New York, 1929.
173. Went, S., *Proc III Intern. Congr. Microbiol. 1939*, New York, 1940.
173a. White, R. G., G. C. Jenkins, and P. C. Wilkinson, *Internat. Arch. Allergy*, 22, 156 (1963).
175. Wiener, A. S., I. Zieve, and J. H. Fries, *Ann. Eugenics*, 7, 141 (1936).
175. Wittich, F. W., *J. Allergy*, 12, 247 (1941).
176. Wittich, F. W., "Animal Allergy," in *Treatment of Asthma*, H. A. Abramson, ed., Williams and Wilkins, Baltimore, 1951.
177. Wittkower, E., *Z. ges. exptl. Med.*, 34, 108 (1923).
178. Wright, G. P., and S. J. Hopkins, *J. Pathol. Bacteriol.*, 53, 243 (1941).
179. Zeek, I., *Am. J. Clin. Pathol.*, 22, 77 (1952).
180. Zinsser, H., and J. F. Enders, *J. Immunol.*, 30, 327 (1936).
181. Zinsser, H., J. F. Enders, and L. D. Fothergill, *Immunity: Principles and Application in Medicine and Public Health*, Macmillan, New York, 1939.
182. Zuntz, E., and J. LaBarre, *Compt. rend. soc. biol.*, 91, 121, 802 (1924).

CHAPTER 9

Delayed Hypersensitivity

A. DELAYED HYPERSENSITIVITY IN INFECTIONS (TUBERCULIN TYPE)

The delayed type of reaction shows the following differences from the immediate: (*1*) The interval between contact with the antigen and the onset of symptoms is relatively long (several hours), the reaction reaches a maximum in 24 to 72 hours, and may persist for days. (*2*) Circulating antibody cannot be demonstrated (see below). (*3*) There do not seem to be specific shock tissues such as smooth muscle, blood vessels, or collagen. On the contrary, many of the cells of the body seem to be susceptible to injury by hypersensitive reactions of the delayed type.

In spite of these differences, delayed hypersensitivity is clearly immunological in character (74): (*1*) contact with an antigen is necessary to induce the hypersensitive condition, (*2*) the reaction occurs only when the sensitive subject is re-exposed to the antigen, (*3*) the incubation period necessary for the production of sensitization is of the same order of magnitude as in other immunological responses (a week or 10 days). (*4*) An anamnestic reaction may also occur. (After waning of sensitivity, re-exposure to the antigen re-establishes sensitivity in a much shorter space of time than was needed originally.) (*5*) Desensitization can be effected.

1. Allergy in Tuberculosis

For the induction of the delayed type of hypersensitivity in *infection*, it seems that there usually must be present, not merely the antigen to which the response is made, but also the intact infectious organism, or at least certain derivatives of it. Sensitization to chemical substances takes place by way of the skin, with few exceptions. We shall discuss these peculiarities more at length in connection with specific situations.

Koch (52) made the basic observation that "Tuberculin may be in-

465

jected into normal guinea pigs in considerable quantities without causing noticeable symptoms. Tuberculous guinea pigs, on the other hand, react to comparatively small doses in a very characteristic manner." Koch found that larger doses would kill tuberculous guinea pigs—a fact which he interpreted as due to the toxic property of tuberculin, supposing that the animal's tissues were already saturated with as much of the "poison" as they could tolerate. Work of later investigators has shown that the reaction has a different mechanism; the tissues of the tuberculous animal have become specifically altered by the infection. Tuberculin is entirely harmless to normal animals. It was thought for a long time that true tuberculin sensitization could be produced only by infection with living organisms, but there is evidence to the contrary. For example, Flahiff (26) reported the production of typical tuberculin sensitivity in children by heat-killed tubercle bacilli. Freund et al. (29) reported the production of local hypersensitiveness (and antibodies) by injection of heat-killed tubercle bacilli in paraffin oil. Tubercle formation in the animal seems essential in all cases. Tuberculoprotein from tuberculin will sensitize guinea pigs to anaphylactic shock, but will not produce the tuberculin type of sensitivity. The protein and wax from tubercle bacilli together will produce typical tuberculin sensitivity (70).

The distinguishing characteristics of the tuberculin type of reaction are: (1) there is an incubation period of several hours before the reaction shows itself, and it reaches its maximum in 48 to 72 hours; (2) the reaction is inflammatory in nature, and produces induration and necrosis; (3) hyperpyrexia is characteristic of the general reaction; (4) the symptoms are very similar in different species. Histologically the major response is that of the histiocyte elements. Edema and hemorrhage are not important in these reactions.

When tuberculin is injected into the skin, a local reaction is obtained; when it is injected subcutaneously a local reaction at the site of injection and a focal reaction (about the tuberculous lesions, wherever they are) are obtained. The reaction does not occur in the very early and in the last stages of infection.

Not only do tuberculous and normal animals respond differently to the (nonliving) tuberculin, but they also differ strikingly in their response to inoculation of living tubercle bacilli (the "Koch phenomenon"). When a normal guinea pig is injected with living tubercle bacilli, a localized nodule appears at the site of inoculation in 10 to 14 days. This nodule increases in size, involves the skin, and undergoes necrosis, leaving a persistent ulcer. In the meantime the disease is spreading through the lymphatics, eventually to lead to the animal's death. But, if living tubercle bacilli are injected into a guinea pig with an infection of one week's standing, the response is (1) more rapid; superficial inflammation appears in 1 to 2 days, followed by necrosis the next day, leaving a flat shallow ulcer which heals rapidly; and (2) is not followed by spread of the infection from the new site; for example, the regional lymph glands are not affected. The Koch reaction is due to the tubercle protein in the organisms responsible for the secondary infection; it is really a tuberculin reaction.

It will be seen that the tuberculin reaction is quite different in character from anaphylaxis; but in tuberculosis both anaphylaxis and allergy of infection can often be observed (see, e.g., 4,14,92). Injection of purified tuberculoprotein gives rise to circulating antibody and the Arthus type of skin reaction. The tuberculin type of sensitivity is thus not produced.

It has been shown that tuberculin sensitivity is not related to any of the kinds of antibody which can be demonstrated in tuberculosis (90); also it obviously depends neither on the factors promoting leukocyte lysis (63,64), or erythrocyte agglutination (62). These two antibodies may not be even correlated with tuberculosis (36).

Skin sensitivity is, however, correlated with inhibition of macrophages, fibroblasts, and liver cells from tubercular animals in tissue culture (88).

Differences between Allergy of Infection and Arthus Type of Hypersensitivity

According to Rich (73) allergy of infection differs from hypersensitivity of the Arthus type in the following ways: (1) the slow development of the reaction following contact in allergy of infection, contrasted to the prompt appearance of the reaction in the Arthus-sensitized body; (2) allergy of infection is not transferable passively by serum. (We have omitted one of Rich's points which hardly seems valid today.) From Table 8-1 we note that the tuberculin type of sensitivity is not dependent upon circulating antibody but can be transferred by certain types of living cells.

Relation of Tuberculin Allergy to Antibodies

It has not been found possible to transfer tuberculin sensitivity to normal animals by injection of serum from infected animals, so that no circulating antibodies responsible for the altered reactivity have been demonstrated. The altered reactivity of the tissues of the tuberculous animal might be ascribed either to an intrinsic alteration in the cells themselves, or to the production of sessile antibodies in or on the cells.

Until a method of deciding between these two alternatives is found, the difference remains largely a verbal one.

Diagnostic Value of Tuberculin Response

The characteristics of the tuberculin response make it of value in diagnosis. There are a number of methods of administering and preparing derivatives of the tubercule bacillus for this test. The "Old Tuberculin," prepared by filtering an evaporated glycerin bouillon culture of the bacilli, is still used; the purified protein derivative (PPD), prepared from filtrates of cultures in synthetic medium by the method of Seibert, is more stable and probably more uniform. The intracutaneous test, originally due to Mantoux, is probably the most used. In this method, diluted tuberculin is injected into the skin, and a reading is made after 48 hours. Redness, edema, and in very strong reactions, some necrosis, constitute a positive reaction.

A positive reaction indicates that somewhere in the body there is tissue infected with tubercle bacilli. This tissue may be very small in extent, or the lesion may even be completely inactive, and the reaction may still be positive. It used to be found that nearly 90 per cent of adults have small healed or inactive areas of infection, so that a positive reaction of moderate intensity is not of much clinical significance except in very young children. A negative reaction is much more significant, since it shows definitely the absence of tuberculosis, except in the cases of patients in the very early stages, or the last stages, of infection, or with acute fulminating types of tuberculosis ("galloping consumption").

2. Allergy of Infection in Other Bacterial Diseases

The delayed tuberculin type of allergy is not confined to tuberculosis. Delayed hypersensitivity is demonstrable, for example, in undulant fever, typhoid fever, tularemia, glanders, chancroid, and whooping cough.

3. Allergy of Infection in Syphilis

Syphilitic infection induces hypersensitivity of the delayed type (76). Earlier investigators noted that after infection with syphilis an animal at first responds to reinfection with an accelerated pathological response, recalling the Koch phenomenon. Later a highly but not absolutely refractory state appears. The tertiary lesions of syphilis tend to become more and more localized as time goes on, first in one part of the body, then in another, and are likely to be more destructive as the interval after infection lengthens. Hinton (43) believed that this suggests a type of allergy growing out of previous sensitization of the tissues by the spirochetes or their products.

4. Allergy of Infection in Virus Diseases: Smallpox

The altered reactivity of the skin which shows itself in the changed course of successive inoculations with vaccinia virus is probably an example of allergy of infection.   In an individual who has never had smallpox and has never been vaccinated, the first inoculation with virus usually causes a reaction which appears after an incubation period of about 3 days and reaches its maximum between the eighth and eleventh days.   In a previously exposed individual with high immunity, the reaction is accelerated, and condensed into a period of a few days.   By the seventh day the site is already entirely healed.   In individuals with less immunity, the reaction may take longer, and response will be intermediate in character.   These types of reaction are characterized as vaccinia, reaction of immunity, and vaccinoid, respectively.

Hooker (46) showed that the hypersensitiveness of infection following smallpox vaccination could be demonstrated by injection of dead virus into the skin. This confirms the idea that the early "reaction of immunity" is allergic in nature, and also affords a method of detecting immunity without the use of living virus, since the degree of reaction correlated well with the degree of immunity, as demonstrated by later response to inoculation of the living virus.

In lymphogranuloma venereum (28) a high degree of hypersensitivity of the delayed type develops and, probably as a result, in its more advanced stages this disease is accompanied by a considerable degree of tissue destruction.   In mumps, also, the delayed type of hypersensitivity develops, and can be used to diagnose past or present infection (24).   A similar allergic response seems to result from infection with influenza, measles, and herpes simplex (79).   It seems likely that some sensitivity of this type may develop in most virus diseases.

5. Fungus Infections

Practically all fungus infections produce the delayed type of hypersensitivity (12), and in many cases the response is specific enough to have diagnostic value.   The systemic infection caused by *Coccidioides immitis* produces pronounced hypersensitivity of the delayed type, and the progress of the disease may well be due to the resulting tissue destruction.

6. Parasitic Infections

Hypersensitive reactions of the delayed type develop, sometimes in addition to the immediate type, in certain parasitic infections, such as infections with helminths, leishmaniasis, and toxoplasmosis (65).

7. Allergy Due to Simple Chemicals

Many drugs and chemicals, including some chemical elements, such as nickel and mercury, may produce a delayed type of hypersensitive reaction.

B. CONTACT ALLERGY

1. Contact Dermatitis

This is an inflammatory disease of the skin, caused by external irritants which are harmless to the individual on first contact (before sensitization). The lesions are localized primarily in the epidermis and are of the vesicular type. The lesions involve also the dermis, with accumulation of lymphocytes, etc. Histopathologists disagree as to which response is primary. In Europe the condition is usually called "eczema," and many American dermatologists call it "eczematous dermatitis." When caused by hypersensitiveness to such plant "poisons" as poison ivy, poison oak, and primrose, it is often called "dermatitis venenata." This name is not so appropriate today, since we know that these agents are not toxic on first contact but affect only individuals who have been sensitized, although nearly all individuals can be sensitized, at least if the contact is sufficiently prolonged.

A very large number of substances can cause contact dermatitis. Many of these are substances with which the individual comes in constant contact in his occupation, and which produce the condition called occupational dermatitis, or trade eczema. This long list includes such substances as dyes, soaps, lacquers, woods, glue, rubber, drugs, metals, and explosives. In addition to the well-recognized poisonous plants, many others, including cotton seed, grasses, and common weeds, may produce dermatitis.

Dermatitis resulting from poison ivy and related plants is well known. Degrees of sensitivity to poison ivy vary widely. There are obviously genetic factors involved in the varying ease of sensitization of different individuals. Some individuals seem absolutely refractory and may pull the plant from fence posts with their bare hands, bruising and crushing the leaves and stems as they do so, without ever getting an attack; others have only to walk through the woods near the plant, without knowingly coming in contact with a single leaf, to develop a bad attack of dermatitis. It is generally believed, however, that dermatitis does not develop without some contact, however slight or indirect, with the sap of the plant.

The active principal, urushiol, is a mixture of three substituted catechols with the average formula $C_6H_3(OH)_2C_{15}H_{27}$, differing in the number and position of double bonds in the side chain (60,18).

There is a good article about poison ivy in the *New Yorker* magazine (78), a magazine that has published a succession of good medical articles.

Allergists, and even botanists, have not always agreed as to the identity and naming of the rather confusing group of poisonous plants in the genus *Rhus*. According to a pamphlet put out by the Clark-West Co., common poison ivy is *Rhus radicans*. It is found in all parts of the U.S. and Canada, except in the extreme southwest of the U.S. It grows as a woody vine, as trailing shrubs mostly on the ground, and as erect woody shrubs, without support. The leaves are always in groups of three leaflets.

Oakleaf poison ivy is called *Rhus diversiloba,* and occurs throughout the southeastern U.S., from New Jersey into eastern Texas. It usually grows as a low-growing shrub. The leaves are in groups of three leaflets, but the center leaflet usually has an oak-leaf look.

Western poison oak is called in the pamphlet *Rhus toxicodendron*. It is found all along the Pacific Coast, from southern California into Canada. It grows most often as an upright shrub, with several woody stems growing from the ground. In open fields it can grow into large spreading clumps, as much as six feet tall. In forests it becomes a vine and grows upward for as much as 30 feet. The leaves are in groups of three leaflets, and the center leaflet is likely to have an oak-leaf appearance. The side leaflets often assume irregular shapes.

Poison sumac is called *Rhus vernix,* is found to some extent in damp areas is nearly every state of the U.S., and is generally prevalent east of the Mississippi. It grows as a coarse woody shrub or as a small tree, never as vine. It has 7 to 13 leaflets, arranged as opposite pairs along a central midrib with a single leaflet at the end.

A curious related condition is lacquer eczema, caused by contact with Japanese lacquer, which is made from the sap of a related plant, *Toxicodendron vernix,* formerly called *Rhus vernix* or *Rhus venenata*. This is a small tree or shrub of the Orient (87).

According to Goldman and Pfose (87), lacquer eczema has been known in the Orient for more than a thousand years. Cases have been observed in this country resulting from contact with the pieces of the Chinese game mahjong, vases, canes, and even telephones and radio headphones.

Vaughan and Black (87) state that in Hawaii, when cans of pineapple were being treated with a hot bath containing one part commercial lacquer and five parts of gasoline, handlers of the cans developed lacquer dermatitis.

The common sumac, which according to Gray's *Manual of Botany* includes three species, *Rhus typhina, R. glabra,* and *R. copallina,* does not cause contact dermatitis, or does so in very few individuals.

Although it is not closely related to *Rhus,* the primrose (*Primula*) causes similar reactions in certain people. Another example is a dermatitis which occurs on the back or back of the neck, in Pakistan and India, known as the dhobi itch. (Dhobi is the Hindi and Urdu word for washerman.) Formerly thought to be an infection, it was found to be a hypersensitivity to the nut of the ral tree, which is used by washermen in making an ink used for marking shirts. The intense reaction which can result from the slight amount of material from the nut which remains in the laundry mark after a garment has been washed and ironed illustrates the exquisite degrees of sensitivity which may occur in contact dermatitis.*

In all of these conditions contact is required for sensitization; first contact does not produce symptoms. Thus it is found that infants and Eskimos (42) do not react when poison ivy is applied as a patch test, since neither has been previously exposed; but American Indians, racially very similar to Eskimos, show about the same incidence of reactors as do Americans of European origin (87).

It is customary to consider contact dermatitis as nonatopic, since almost any individual may be sensitized, although in varying degree. Also the time course and histological changes are completely different; contact dermatitis cannot be transferred by serum but can be transferred by living cells, can be elicited in the cornea, and can be produced by inoculation of an antigen plus adjuvants. The difference might perhaps lie in the mechanism of inheritance; the inheritance of atopy might depend on one or at most a few genes, whereas the hereditary influences in the nonatopic conditions might depend on larger numbers of genes, resulting in more intermediate types and less sharp distinction between the normal and the susceptible individual.

"Desensitization" has been tried, with some success, particularly in the case of poison ivy. In most cases, of course, avoidance of the excitant is easier.

---

* Some American laundries have recently begun using a label of fabric, attached apparently with a low-melting plastic, which does nearly as well.

2. Allergy to Simple Chemical Compounds (Drug Allergy)

Drug allergy is a heterogeneous group, including examples of atopic, contact, tuberculin-type allergies, blood dyscrasias, and various mixtures of these. It is probably not properly a category under contact allergy, but it seems unwise, with the space at our disposal, to devote a separate chapter to the subject.

There are two forms of increased susceptibility to drugs. In one type the patient is abnormally susceptible to the action of the drug, and its administration produces symptoms which are an exaggeration of its ordinary pharmacological action. In the other type the administration of the drug, in an amount nontoxic or perhaps even inactive for the normal individual, produces reactions not characteristic of the drug, but of allergic conditions, such as fever, skin eruption, and pruritus. The second form is what we mean by drug allergy. It is specific in most individuals, in the sense that the sensitivity exists for only one substance or group of chemically related substances. The symptoms show the same independence of the nature of the exciting agent which we have noted in anaphylaxis and other kinds of allergy.

The possible excitants of drug allergy include alkaloids, such as opium products and quinine, essential oils and balsams, such as turpentine and urushiol; metals, such as mercury, nickel, and arsenic (including some forms of sensitivity to arsphenamine); the halogens; various synthetic drugs (formerly "coal tar derivatives"), such as antipyrine, salicylic acid, and arsphenamine; drugs of the barbituric acid series, antibiotics, and endocrine and other glandular products. Some asthmatics are atopically sensitive to aspirin (25). Drugs with a para-amino group in the benzene ring are particularly bad actors (6).

In some cases the patient reacts not to the whole drug molecule but to a portion of it, or to some chemical group contained in it. In allergy to arsphenamine it has been found that some patients are sensitive to the organic part of the molecule, whereas others react to the arsenic. It has been claimed that iodoform sensitivity may be directed towards either the methyl radical or the iodine. It was found by Dawson, Sanders, and Tomlinson (19) that individuals allergic to quinine could be separated into several groups, depending on which part of the molecule was responsible for the sensitivity (see 81).

An interesting feature of drug allergy is that almost none of the incitants are actually antigenic. If we are to suppose that the fundamental mechanism is the same as in the forms of allergy already discussed, the problem arises, how can a nonantigenic agent sensitize? The publication of the work of Landsteiner and his co-workers (see Chapters 2 and 3), which showed that it was possible to render simple chemical compounds antigenic (or haptenic) by attaching them chemically to proteins, provided a possible clue to this mystery. Allergenic drugs probably become haptens by combining with the susceptible individual's own proteins.

There are certain reasons to think that drugs may be able to attach themselves to proteins in the body (see 17). In some cases it is easy for a chemist to see how this might occur; in others it must be supposed that the attachment takes place after chemical alteration of the drug in the body. In fact Mayer (61), studying sensitivity to azo dyes and aniline derivatives, found various group reactions, not based on the complete original substances of exposure, but related to new derivatives formed in the body by oxidation, reduction, etc. An argument in favor of the formation of conjugates came from the work of Landsteiner and Jacobs (57), who studied chlor- and nitro-substitution products of benzene. Treatment with sodium ethylate or sodium methylate was found to remove a chlorine atom or a nitro group much more readily (indicating greater chemical reactivity) from those substances which would sensitize guinea pig skin, than from the nonsensitizers. It was also found that the sensitizing substances alone gave stable substitution compounds with aniline. Later, Landsteiner and Chase (51,55) succeeded in sensitizing the skin of guinea pigs to a simple compound (picryl chloride) by injections of a conjugate of this substance with guinea pig stromata. The experiments of Haxthausen (39,40) on the sensitization of human beings with mixtures of salts of heavy metals and foreign serum also suggest that a substance may become effective through loose attachment to protein.

Eisen and Belman (23) concluded from experiments with guinea pigs and human beings that the allergenic dinitrophenols combine with a protein, propably a keratin, in the epidermis, through —S—S— and —SH groups. Some of these substances would combine *in vitro* with —SH groups only of certain proteins (keratins) at a limited range of pH, suggesting that certain aspects of the complex organization of the keratins are important in the sensitization process.

When sensitivity is produced by contact of the drug with the skin, or when the drug is injected with killed tubercle bacilli as adjuvants, the delayed type of hypersensitivity (contact allergy) results (53). Such sensitivity cannot be passively transferred by serum but can be transferred by living cells. Thus Landsteiner *et al.* (58) found that the delayed type of hypersensitivity could be transferred to rabbits by injecting exudate cells from animals sensitized to picryl chloride (1,2,4 chlordinitrobenzene) and dinitrochlorbenzene, the exudates being prepared by injection of casein.

When conjugates of the drug and protein are injected, the animal responds with antibody production, the immediate type of hypersensitivity, and sensitivity to anaphylaxis (53,9). In contrast to the sensitivity produced by contact of the drug with the skin or by the use of killed tubercle bacilli as adjuvants, this type of sensitivity can be transferred passively by serum.

Drugs differ widely in the ease with which they will sensitize human beings. Landsteiner (53) found that 1,2,4 chlordinitrobenzene would sensitize most people when a single drop of a strong solution was placed once or twice on the skin, whereas allylisothiocyanate (mustard oil) sensitized only one in seven volunteers even after repeated application.

Repeated contact does, however, generally increase the chance that an individual will become sensitized, and it has been shown that whereas only a small porportion of persons who come into contact with primroses become allergic, treatment with the concentrated active principle will eventually sensitize nearly every individual (53).

There are some observations which suggest that sensitization to simple compounds is more likely to result when they are applied to an injured area, as in the sensitization to picric acid which occasionally results from the use of picrate-containing ointments on burns. Also, Landsteiner and DiSomma (56) found that picric acid, which alone did not sensitize guinea pig skin, would do so when painted on after the application of cantharidin.

In man, hypersensitivity of the immediate flare-wheal type has been found to some drugs, including salvarsan, formaldehyde, phthalic anhydride, chloramine-T, sulfathiazole, and sulfadiazine. Chase (8) pointed out that these belong largely in the category of the more reactive compounds.

Since the use of penicillin has become so widespread it has been found that contact dermatitis resulting from its topical application is quite common (5) (p. 431).

A good review of drug reaction was published in 1963 (1).

C. SERUM SICKNESS

Let us begin by stating that serum sickness does not present merely the symptoms of delayed hypersensitivity, but is rather a complex mixture of hypersensitivity reactions. It should perhaps have a chapter to itself, but being opposed to too much fragmentation in classification, we have attempted, perhaps a little like Procrustes, to fit it into the present chapter.

After the introduction of diphtheria antitoxin therapy in 1890, the injection of foreign serum became relatively common. It was soon found that some of those receiving such serum developed unfavorable reactions, often leading to a curious and characteristic condition which was given the name of *serum sickness*. It was natural to suppose at first that the reaction was due to the antitoxin content of the serum, but it was soon observed that the injection of normal serum could produce the same results. Indeed, it is probable that the reaction had been observed a number of years before, following transfusion of animal blood into man, but its nature was not then recognized.

1. Symptoms

The illness is characterized by the occurrence of rashes, especially of an urticarial type, which often commence at the site of the injection, by fever, pains in the joints, and glandular swelling, particularly in the lymph glands near the site of injection. This last may often be the first symptom noticed. There is usually slight edema, and there may be some albuminuria.

In persons not already sensitive to serum there is almost always an incubation period of 8 to 12 days between the injection of the serum and the onset of symptoms. In such persons, serum sickness, although it may produce severe discomfort, is probably not often fatal. It is characteristic of serum sickness that it can result from a single injection, even in individuals who appear to have no previous sensitivity to the proteins of the animal providing the serum. Recurrent reactions have also been observed (references in 11), again after only one injection, with intervals between the eruptions of as little as 3 to 4, or as much as 19 to 21 days.

Focal arteriolar lesions and collagen degeneration may occur. Pathological examination of fatal cases has sometimes shown cardiac damage.

2. Mechanism

Serum sickness is probably a complex made up of all the types of hypersensitivity shown in Table 8-1, but mainly of types *b* and *d*. The symptoms and pathological findings in man certainly, and in animals probably, include those due to several essentially unrelated types of hypersensitivity developing in response to the different antigens in the injected serum, or even to one and the same antigen. Thus an individual may have urticaria (immediate hypersensitivity) followed several days later by morbilliform rashes (delayed hypersensitivity?). The proper study of experimental serum disease has probably been much hampered by the assumption that serum disease is single entity.

A plausible explanation of the etiology of serum sickness was offered by von Pirquet and Schick (68). Their suggestion may be paraphrased thus: following the injection of foreign serum, the patient begins to form antibodies against certain of the serum proteins. After a time, these antibodies appear in amounts sufficient to react with the antigens responsible for their production, traces of which have persisted in the patient's circulation. This reaction is supposed to cause the symptoms. The mechanism would thus be similar to that of anaphylaxis, except that the latter is never observed to follow the primary injection.

Several observations support the idea of von Pirquet and Schick: there is almost always a considerable incubation period before symptoms begin, which could be the time required for antibody production to get under way; the period of incubation may be shortened or be lacking in persons having previously had injections of the serum, or having naturally acquired sensitivity to it; and local edema sometimes occurs at the site of reinjection of serum, suggesting a local antibody–antigen reaction. Furthermore, as would be required by the suggested mechanism, antibodies reacting in various ways (precipitins, anaphylactic antibodies, heterophil antibodies—antisheep hemolysin and agglutinin—and serum reagins; see p. 447) often appear in the blood of the affected individual, more usually after the onset of symptoms. This was thought to be due to a sudden throwing off into the circulation of antibodies which the cells have been gradually elaborating, probably at an increasing rate. The patient's skin is also likely to become specifically reactive.

If these ideas are accepted, the recurrent reactions referred to above could be interpreted as due to the successive appearance of antibodies to various antigenic components of the serum (11,16,44) and, as we now think, to the simultaneous or successive development of hypersensitivity of various types, probably mainly the immediate atopic type and the delayed tuberculin type.

Some doubt has been thrown on this theory, chiefly because precipitin may be found in the absence of serum disease, and serum disease may occur in the absence of circulating antibodies. If some of the symptoms are supposed to be due to the development of hypersensitivity of the delayed type, some of these difficulties disappear.

Some individuals with serum sickness produce antibodies of the non-precipitating reagin type as well as precipitating antibodies (48,80).

Serum disease can result from the parenteral administration of a single highly purified antigen, but there seems to be considerable individual variation in susceptibility to such undesirable reactions. Serum sickness due to purified bovine serum albumin has already been referred to.

It has been shown (38,35) that injection of crystallized bovine albumin into rabbits produces lesions. Hawn and Janeway (38) found mainly arterial lesions, but Germuth (35) found that injection of 0.25 g. crystallized bovine albumin per kilogram of body weight into rabbits produced acute glomerulitis in 80 per cent, endocarditis in 54 per cent and necrotizing arteritis in 28 per cent of the animals.

It is estimated that serum sickness occurs in at least 5 per cent of patients receiving foreign serum (85). Hypersensitivity reactions of the serum sickness type occur in 1 or 2 per cent of all patients receiving penicillin (5).

Serum sickness is not confined to human beings. It may be produced in rabbits and guinea pigs by a single large injection of foreign serum (51,27). Some of the symptoms, unsurprisingly, are somewhat different; the edema which is so characteristic in man is less striking, although horses are reported to develop hives (34).

Patients who have been previously treated with serum often exhibit a considerable degree of sensitivity. Even small amounts of serum may be sufficient to produce sensitization. Hooker (45) and Tuft (86) found that, following the three injections at weekly intervals of the very small amount of horse serum (about 0.01 ml.) contained in diphtheria toxin–antitoxin mixtures then in use in diphtheria immunization, more than 25 per cent of normal individuals became sensitive. If such individuals, or persons having naturally acquired sensitivity to proteins of the species from which the serum originated (e.g., asthmatics whose sensitivity is to horses), are injected with serum, they may experience a reaction which sets in sooner than in ordinary serum sickness (in some cases immediately), and which may be correspondingly more severe. In very severe cases the symptoms resemble those of anaphylaxis. This is called by clinicians "serum shock." Fatal cases are fortunately rare (86,72). The pathological findings in such cases usually suggest those of guinea pig anaphylaxis, but at least one case has been reported where they resembled more those in the dog.

The symptoms and post-mortem findings of serum sickness are discussed by Parish and Pepys (67). For a recent discussion of serum sickness see Gell (33).

It is difficult to escape the impression that death in such human cases is due essentially to the same mechanism as that of anaphylactic death in animals. If we accept the idea that serum sickness is an example of the immunological mechanism gone wrong, we may assume that the more rapid appearance of symptoms is a sign of a better development of antibodies. Therefore, the earlier the symptoms, the more severe they tend to be, particularly since the amount of foreign antigen remaining to react with the induced antibodies is greater, the more recent the injection.

Some believe that polyarteritis nodosa (see Chapter 13) is essentially the same as serum sickness, although the causative agent may not be foreign serum. Indeed, the cause of polyarteritis nodosa is still uncertain (67).

3. Prophylaxis

Serum sickness and serum shock are best avoided by not giving foreign serum to persons who are sensitive to it. Skin tests should be made on all patients who are to receive serum. If no reaction is obtained, the physician has provided himself with pretty good (but not infallible) insurance that no fatal accident will follow administration of the serum.

In addition, the patient should be carefully questioned concerning any previous administration of serum, whether for prophylactic or therapeutic purposes and about immunization with diphtheria toxin–antitoxin mixture. (Note that immunization with toxoid, which contains no serum, will of course not sensitize to serum.) The patient should be questioned also about any previous allergic symptoms in himself or in his family, and particularly (if horse serum is to be used) about asthmatic sensitivity to horses.

4. Desensitization

It will be remembered that the repeated administration of doses of antigen too small to shock will make an animal temporarily insusceptible to anaphylaxis with this antigen. A similar technic has frequently been tried with human patients who are sensitive to serum, by giving small, gradually increasing doses at intervals of about half an hour. However, there is no convincing clinical proof that such procedures are of definite value in preventing serious serum reactions. Particularly if a natural serum sensitivity exists, such methods are likely to be without value.

5. Treatment of Symptoms

The only treatment of any value consists in the administration of adrenaline subcutaneously or, if required, intravenously. A syringe containing this solution should always be on hand. If the serum has been give subcutaneously or intramuscularly in a region where a tourniquet can be applied above the site of injection, such application may be helpful in delaying the entrance of further serum into the circulation.

D. CHARACTER OF DELAYED HYPERSENSITIVITY REACTIONS

The reactions of the delayed type may occur locally, systematically, or both. At the site of entrance of the antigen into the skin, or in a local lesion where bacteria are aggregated, cells are damaged to various degrees, depending upon the level of sensitivity and the local concentration of antigen. Inflammation, often quite marked, develops. In certain diseases, such as tuberculosis, lymphogranuloma venereum, and coccidioides infection, the reactions damage the tissues to such an extent as to constitute a main factor in the pathogenesis of the disease (75). In a local pluminary tubercular lesion the tissues may undergo allergic necrosis, which may even result in cavity formation.

In contact allergies the antigen ordinarily comes in contact with the skin. The resulting lesion is usually a papular indurated one which becomes vesicular, or it may be vesicular at first. If the antigen responsible is injected intracutaneously, a lesion similar to the tuberculin reaction may result.

E. ADJUVANTS AND TUBERCLE BACILLI IN HYPERSENSITIVITY

An observation of considerable significance was made by Dienes and Schoenheit (21,22). They found that reactions indistinguishable from the tuberculin type could be obtained even with ordinary antigens such as egg white or horse serum, if the proper method of sensitization were used. This method consisted in the injection of the antigen *into the lesions* of a tuberculous animal. Freund and McDermott (30) were able to obtain, in guinea pigs, reactions to horse serum similar to the tuberculin reaction. This was accomplished by injecting horse serum combined with the Freund adjuvants (p. 125). Dienes and Mallory (20) suggested that the tuberculin type of hypersensitiveness represents the first stage of every immune response to injected protein. This was also suggested by some observations of Hooker (45), who found that many untreated individuals who gave "delayed" reactions to horse serum on primary test usually gave, after a course of toxin-(horse) antitoxin injections, the immediate wheal type of reaction when tested with horse serum. Pappenheimer, Scharff, and Uhr (66) suggested that the production of the hypersensitive cell is merely the first stage in the process that in many cases eventually results in antibody formation.

Some have supposed that the Dienes effect is due to modification of the injected antigen in the tubercular focus, in such a way that it produces the tuberculin type of sensitization. However, Hanks (37), attempting to test this idea, found it possible to obtain the tuberculin type of response to ordinary antigens without having to inject the sensitizing dose directly into a well-developed focus.   He did this by inoculating one testicle of a guinea pig with tubercle bacilli, removing the testicle the following day, and injecting the antigen (horse serum) into the opposite testicle.   Ten days later an injection of horse serum produced a skin reaction of the delayed tuberculin type.   Hanks concluded that the tuberculin type of hypersensitiveness could be produced without the antigen's being modified by the inflammatory tubercular reaction.   It seems not improbable that this conclusion is justified, although it has been pointed out (93) that there might have been even in 24 hours a considerable distribution of the tubercle bacilli through the body with the consequent formation of small foci.   Whether it may be supposed that these small and undeveloped foci could alter much of the injected antigen is another question.   It seems equally probable that the essential modification is in the mode of response of the tissues themselves.

In the discussion of adjuvants (p. 125), it was pointed out that their effect was much increased if killed tubercle bacilli were added.   This striking effect has been shown to be due to a lipopolysaccharide extractable from the bacillus (71).   Raffel and his associates and Choucroun (69,10) demonstrated that this same substance had a marked effect in the induction of hypersensitivity of the delayed type.   They found that if tubercle bacilli were thoroughly extracted with ether, alcohol, and chloroform, they would no longer, when injected into guinea pigs, produce tuberculin sensitivity, even if given in very large doses over long periods of time.   But if these defatted bacteria, or even purified tuberculoprotein, were mixed with the lipopolysaccharide and injected, they would again be able to induce tuberculin sensitivity.   If any other protein antigen, such as egg albumin, were substituted for the tuberculoprotein, hypersensitivity of the delayed type was induced for the new protein.   It is apparent that the induction of the delayed type of hypersensitivity is made much easier by the presence of this lipopolysaccharide, and that contact hypersensitivity of the delayed type must apparently in general be mediated through the skin.   Raffel (70) speculated that the reason may be that the skin may contain a lipide similar in its effects to the lipide from tubercle bacilli.

F. MECHANISM OF DELAYED HYPERSENSITIVITY REACTIONS

Waksman (89) concluded that the primary event in hypersensitivity reactions of the delayed type is a reaction of sensitized cells, probably coming from the circulation, with antigen.   This reaction appeared to consist of local accumulation and proliferation of these cells. Waksman recognized three distinct types of damage: an active destruction of antigen-containing parenchyma by the invading mononuclear cells, fibroid necrosis of vessel walls in association with intense perivascular mononuclear infiltration, and massive ischemic necrosis resulting from arrest of vascular flow.

That circulating antibody plays no role in the delayed type of hypersensitivity is suggested by several lines of evidence: (1) The sensitivity has never been transferred to normal recipients by the serum of sensitive individuals. (2) The delayed type of sensitivity can be transferred by cells (3,7,59) not only in the case of tuberculin sensitivity but also in the case of sensitivity to simple chemicals. Of course it might be argued that antibodies are transferred inside the sensitive cells, or at least that each cell is an antibody factory (32), but at present this is entirely speculative.

It was found that macrophages or fibroblasts in tissue culture from tuberculous animals were injured by tuberculin (77,2,41). The growth of such leukocytes from tuberculous animals is inhibited in vitro by tuberculin (88,83), and this inhibition is correlated with the skin sensitivity of the animals from which the leukocytes were taken. Favour thought the same thing operated with polymorphonuclears and lymphocytes, but found that if the leukocytes are thoroughly washed and suspended in normal plasma, tuberculin exerts no effect (63,648,8). The lytic action has been shown to require a factor present in the plasma of tuberculous animals (66,64,88), which is not correlated with the characteristic skin sensitivity to tuberculin, nor associated with precipitating or complement-fixing antibody (91). It therefore has nothing to do with tuberculin sensitivity.

Slavin and Garven (82) found that preparations of circulating lymphocytes from patients with sensitivity of the delayed type to timothy and ragweed antigens would transfer such sensitivity to nonsensitive volunteers, and that the transfer was specific.

In spite of the fact that circulating antibodies have not been demonstrated in the delayed type of hypersensitivity, many authors continue to believe that some sort of antibodies, perhaps not in circulation but fixed to the susceptible cells, must be involved. Rich (73) maintained this, and Cooke (13) said flatly of the two types of hypersensitivity that "both have been proved to be due to a transferable antibody," although he adds "in the delayed . . . strictly . . . cellular." Chase (8) pointed out some reasons for believing at least that the process of sensitization of the delayed type involves in some way the antibody-forming mechanism: (1) After transfer of cells from a sensitive animal to a normal to produce the delayed type of hypersensitivity, circulating antibodies are sometimes produced, indicating that the two types of immunological mechanism at least run in parallel. (2) Feeding certain allergenic chemicals to nonsensitized animals may produce a state of specifically depressed receptivity involving both the acquisition of delayed-type sensitivity and the production of antibody. The animal is made resistant to sensitization by skin contact with the chemical and also fails to respond with the production of circulating antibodies or anaphylactic sensitivity to injection of protein conjugates of the chemical. Chase suggested this may be due to the retention of the specific determinant in the tissues in such a way as to hinder the antibody-producing mechanism (cf. Chapter 12).

Karush and Eisen (49) suggested that hypersensitivity of the delayed type must be due to small amounts of antibody of high avidity, but this suggestion seems to have been received with mixed feelings by other immunologists (15,84) .

References

1. Ackroyd, J. F., and A. J. Rook, in *Clinical Aspects of Immunology*, P. G. H. Gell, and R. R. A. Coombs, eds., F. A. Davis, Philadelphia, 1963, pp. 448–496.
2. Aronson, J. D., *J. Exptl. Med.*, **64**, 339 (1933).
3. Bail, O., *Z. Immunitätsforsch.*, **4**, 470 (1910).
4. Baldwin, E. R., *J. Med. Res.*, **22**, 189 (1910).
5. Boger, W. P., *et al.*, *J. Allergy*, **24**, 383 (1953).
6. Calnan, C. D., in *Clinical Aspects of Immunology*, P. G. H. Gell and R. R. A. Coombs, eds., F. A. Davis, Philadelphia, 1963, pp. 514–534.
7. Chase, M. W., *Proc. Soc. Exptl. Biol. Med.*, **59**, 134 (1945).
8. Chase, M. W., "The allergic state," in *Bacterial and Mycotic Infections of Man*, R. J. Dubos and J. G. Hirsch, eds., Lippincott, Philadelphia, 1965.
9. Chase, M. W., *Intern. Arch. Allergy Appl. Immunol.*, **5**, 163 (1954).
10. Choucroun, N., *Compt. rend.*, **226**, 1477 (1948).
11. Coca, A. F., *Practice of Medicine*, F. Tice, ed., Price, New York, 1920.
12. Conant, N. F., in *Bacterial and Mycotic Infections of Man*, R. J. Dubos, ed., Lippincott, Philadelphia, 1952.
13. Cooke, R. A., *Ann. N. Y. Acad. Sci.*, **59**, 304 (1955).
14. Corper, H. J., M. L. Cohn, and A. P. Damerow, *Am. J. Clin. Pathol.*, **10**, 361 (1940).
15. Crowle, A. J., *Science*, **138**, 1189–1192 (1962).
16. Dale, H. H., and P. Hartley, *Biochem. J. (London)*, **10**, 408 (1916).
17. Davis, B. D., *J. Clin. Invest.*, **22**, 753 (1943).
18. Dawson, C. R., *Trans. N. Y. Acad. Sci.*, **18**, 425 (1956).
19. Dawson, W. T., J. P. Sanders, and L. M. Tomlinson, *J. Immunol.*, **24**, 173 (1933).
20. Dienes, L., and T. B. Mallory, *Am. J. Pathol.*, **8**, 689 (1932).
21. Dienes, L., and E. W. Schoenheit, *Am. Rev. Tuberc.*, **20**, 92 (1929).
22. Dienes, L., and E. W. Schoenheit, *J. Immunol.*, **19**, 41 (1930).
23. Eisen, H. N., and S. Belman, *J. Exptl. Med.*, **98**, 533 (1953).
24. Enders, J. F., S. Cohen, and L. W. Kane, *J. Exptl. Med.* **81**, 119 (1945).

25. Feinberg, A. R., and S. Malkiel, *J. Allergy*, **22**, 74 (1951).
26. Flahiff, E. W., *Am. J. Hyg.*, (Sec B), **30**, 65 (1939).
27. Fleisher, M. S., and L. Jones, *J. Exptl. Med.*, **54**, 597 (1931).
28. Frei, W., *Klin. Wochschr.*, **4**, 2148 (1925).
29. Freund, J., J. Casals-Ariet, and D. S. Genghof, *J. Immunol.*, **38**, 67 (1940).
30. Freund, J., and K. McDermott, *Proc. Soc. Exptl. Biol. Med.*, **49**, 548 (1942).
31. Geiger, W. B., E. M. Hill, and M. Thompson, *Proc. Soc. Exptl. Biol. Med.*, **92**, 793–796 (1956).
32. Gell, P. G. H., *Biochem. Soc. Symposia (Cambridge, Engl.)*, No. **10**, 63 (1953).
33. Gel, P. G. H., in *Clinical Aspects of Immunology*, P. G. H. Gell and R. R. A. Coombs, eds., F. A. Davis, Philadelphia, 1963.
34. Gerlach, W., *Virchow's Arch. pathol. Anat., u. Physiol.*, **247**, 294 (1923).
35. Germuth, F. G., in *Immunity and Hypersensitivity, Relationship to Disease in Man*, report of 9th Radiation Research Conf. of the Ross (M&R) Laboratories, Columbus, Ohio, 1955.
36. Grabar, P., *et al.*, *Compt. rend.*, **234**, 899 (1952).
37. Hanks, J. H., *J. Immunol.*, **28**, 105 (1935).
38. Hawn, C. V. Z., and C. A. Janeway, *J. Exptl. Med.*, **85**, 571 (1947).
39. Haxthausen, H., *Arch. Dermatol. u. Syphilis*, **170**, 378 (1934).
40. Haxthausen, H., *Arch. Dermatol. u. Syphilis*, **174**, 17 (1936).
41. Heilman, D. H., W. H. Feldman, and F. C. Mann, *Am. Rev. Tuberc.*, **50**, 344 (1944).
42. Heinbecker, P., *J. Immunol.*, **15**, 365 (1928).
43. Hinton, W. A., *Syphilis and Its Treatment*, Macmillan, New York, 1936.
44. Hooker, S. B., *J. Immunol.*, **8**, 469 (1923).
45. Hooker, S. B., *J. Immunol.*, **9**, 7 (1924).
46. Hooker, S. B., *J. Infect. Diseases*, **45**, 255 (1929).
47. Janeway, C. A., and J. L. Oncley, in *Advances in Military Medicine*, Vol. I, E. C. Andrus, ed., Little, Brown, Boston, 1948, p. 44.
48. Karelitz, S., and A. Glorig, *J. Immunol.*, **47**, 121 (1943).
49. Karush, F., and H. N. Eisen, *Science*, **136**, 1032–1039 (1962).
50. Keil, H., *et al.*, *J. Exptl. Med.*, **80**, 275 (1944).
51. Kellett, C. G., *J. Pathol. Bacteriol.*, **33**, 981 (1930).
52. Koch, R., *Deut. med. Wochschr.*, **17**, 101, 1189 (1891).
53. Landsteiner, K., *The Specificity of Serological Reactions*, 2nd ed., Harvard University Press, Cambridge, 1945.
54. Landsteiner, K., and M. W. Chase, *Proc. Soc. Exptl. Biol. Med.*, **44**, 559 (1940).
55. Landsteiner, K., and M. W. Chase, *J. Exptl. Med.*, **73**, 431 (1941).
56. Landsteiner, K., and A. H. DiSomma, *J. Exptl. Med.*, **72**, 361 (1940).
57. Landsteiner, K., and J. Jacobs, *J. Exptl. Med.*, **64**, 717 (1936).
58. Landsteiner, K., *et al.*, *Proc. Soc. Exptl. Biol. Med.*, **49**, 688 (1942).
59. Lawrence, H. S., *Proc. Soc. Exptl. Biol. Med.*, **71**, 516 (1949).
60. Mason, H. S., and L. Schwartz, *J. Am. Chem. Soc.*, **64**, 3058 (1942).
61. Mayer, R. L., "Toxicodermien," in *Handbuch d. Haut u. Geschlechtskrankh.*, J. Jadassohn, ed., IV/2, 1933.
62. Middlebrook, G., and R. J. Dubos, *J. Exptl. Med.*, **88**, 521 (1948).
63. Miller, J. M., *et al.*, *Proc. Soc. Exptl. Biol. Med.*, **70**, 738 (1949).
64. Miller, J. H., *et al.*, *Proc. Soc. Exptl. Biol. Med.*, **71**, 287 (1949).
65. Most, H., *Parasitic Infections in Man*, Columbia University Press, New York, 1951.

66. Pappenheimer, A. M., M. Scharff, and J. W. Uhr, in *Mechanisms of Hypersensitivity*, Little, Brown, Boston, 1959.
67. Parish, W. E., and J. Pepys, in *Clinical Aspects of Immunology*, P. G. H. Gell and R. R. A. Coombs, eds., F. A. Davis, Philadelphia, 1963.
68. von Pirquet, C., and B. Schick, *Die Serumkrankheiten*, Leipzig, 1905.
69. Raffel, S., *Experientia*, 6, 410 (1940).
70. Raffel, S., *Immunity*, Appleton-Century-Crofts, New York, 1953.
71. Raffel, S., et al., *J. Exptl. Med.*, 90, 53 (1949).
72. Ratner, B., *Allergy, Anaphylaxis, and Immunotherapy*, Williams and Wilkins, Baltimore, 1943.
73. Rich, A. R., *Physiol. Rev.*, 21, 70 (1941).
74. Rich, A. R., *The Pathogenesis of Tuberculosis*, Charles C Thomas, Springfield, Illinois, 1944.
75. Rich, A. R., *The Pathogenesis of Tuberculosis*, 2nd rev. ed., Charles C Thomas, Springfield, Illinois, 1951.
76. Rich, A. R., A. M. Chesney, and T. B. Turner, *Bull. Johns Hopkins Hosp.*, 52, 179 (1933).
77. Rich, A. R., and M. R. Lewis, *Bull. Johns Hopkins Hosp.*, 50, 115 (1932).
78. Roneché, B., *New Yorker*, Sept. 12, 1964.
79. Rose, H. M., and E. Molloy, *Federation Proc.*, 6, 432 (1947).
80. Sherman, W. D., et al., *J. Allergy*, 19, 160 (1948).
81. Simon, F. A., *J. Exptl.*, 75, 315 (1942).
82. Slavin, R. G., and J. E. Garvin, *Science*, 145, 52–53 (1964).
83. Stinebring, W. R., and J. A. Flick, *Federation Proc.*, 13, 513 (1954).
84. Talmage, D. W., H. N. Claman, and E. P. Cohen, *Science*, 138, 1192–1193 (1962).
85. Toogood, J. H., *Canad. Med. Assoc. J.*, 82, 907 (1960).
86. Tuft, L., *Clinical Allergy*, 2nd ed., Lea and Febiger, Philadelphia, 1949.
87. Vaughan, W. T., and J. H. Black, *Practice of Allergy*, 3rd ed., Mosby, St. Louis, 1954.
88. Waksman, B. H., *Am. Rev. Tuberc.*, 68, 746 (1953).
89. Waksman, B. H., in *Mechanism of Cell and Tissue Damage Produced by Immune Reactions*, Benno Schwabe, Basel, Switzerland, 1962.
90. Waksman, B. H., and D. Bocking, *Am. Rev. Tuberc.*, 69, 1002 (1954).
92. Zinsser, H., *J. Exptl. Med.*, 34, 495 (1921).
93. Zinsser, H., J. F. Enders, and L. D. Fothergill, *Immunity: Principles and Application in Medicine and Public Health*, Macmillan, New York, 1939.

CHAPTER 10

Non-Immunological Equivalents of Hypersensitivity Reactions

Certain phenomena closely resemble the symptoms of hypersensitivity reactions, but differ in that they have no immunological basis; that is, they are not produced by exposure to an antigen, and they are not immunologically specific. The reason for the superficially close similarity is probably that these non-immunological phenomena are caused by events which are the same as the end-mechanisms which act to produce the symptoms of hypersensitivity reactions, such as release of histamine, acetyl choline, heparin, and possibly other substances, mobilization of leukocytes, etc.

1. Injection of Histamine

Intravenous injection of histamine reproduces most of the symptoms of anaphylactic shock, and indeed it is the similarity between the two phenomena which led Dale and Laidlaw (5) and Abel and Kubota (1) to suggest that histamine or some similar substance might be released by the antibody–antigen reaction. Dragstedt (6) has reviewed the pharmacology of histamine and its role in anaphylaxis. The main actions of histamine are as follows:

In most animals, intravenous injection of histamine in minute doses causes a marked fall in blood pressure. There is a sharp initial fall which is due to temporary constriction of the pulmonary arterioles. Following this there is a further steady prolonged fall which may even lead to a state of circulatory failure.

In the dog, monkey, and man, histamine produces arteriolar dilatation in addition to capillary paralysis. A subcutaneous injection of 0.3 mg. histamine in man causes general flushing of the skin, a rise in temperature of 1° or 2°C., a small decline of systolic, and a great fall of diastolic, blood pressure.

487

There is dilatation of the vessels of the brain and a rise of cerebrospinal fluid pressure. This leads to stretching of the dura mater and consequent stimulation of the local sensory endings of the fifth nerve. These changes may account for the headache which often follows the injection of histamine in man. The coronary vessels may be constricted or dilated, depending on the species. In the dog, histamine contracts the ring of muscle at the point of entrance of the hepatic vein into the inferior vena cava with resulting intense engorgement of the liver and other viscera.

Histamine increases the permeability of the capillaries, so that fluid and protein escape into the tissue spaces, still further reducing the circulating volume and thus aggravating circulatory collapse. The red count and hemoglobin consequently rise, and the blood becomes more viscous.

Smooth muscle, including that of the bronchioles, intestine, spleen, and uterus, is contacted. In the guinea pig the bronchial spasm may cause death from asphyxia.

There is stimulation of the glands, resulting in increased secretion of saliva and a marked flow of gastric juice.

In the cat, an intense leukocytosis is seen, owing to an increase in the number of neutrophils. Histamine has a stimulating effect on the reticuloendothelial system (24). By merely rubbing the skin of a rat with an alcoholic solution of histamine, the endothelial cells of the capillaries around the treated area are induced to engulf solid particles such as the carbon of India ink injected intravenously.

According to the theory of Mautner and Pick (24), histamine shock is due to the stimulation of smooth muscle, and the characteristics of histamine shock in different animals can be explained by the localization of "strategic points" in the circulatory apparatus. In the dog the main bulk of smooth muscle is in the suprahepatic veins; consequently histamine in the dog produces increased pressure in the portal region with stagnation in the splanchnic area. In the cat and rabbit, there are thick layers of smooth muscle in the pulmonary artery bed, and in these species histamine produces dilatation of the right heart and stagnation of blood in the venous part of the circulation.

Injection of histamine into the skin produces the now classic "triple response," consisting of initial erythema, the formation of a central wheal (a raised delimited area of edema), and flare (spread of erythema from the injection site). This sequence of events follows local injury to the skin also, and is observed in the immediate cutaneous reaction of hypersensitivity. This similarity led Lewis (17) to suggest that the release of "H-substance" accounted for the inflammatory allergic reaction.

The toxicity of histamine for animals varies with the species. Guinea pigs may be killed by doses as low as 0.3 to 0.4 mg./kg. of body weight (24). For the rabbit the LD50 is about 0.6 to 0.7 mg./kg. The mouse and rat are much more resistant, doses as high as 250 mg./kg. being required.

2. Histamine Releasers

The symptoms of anaphylaxis can also be produced by administration of a group of substances which have the property, when injected, of causing the release of histamine into the blood stream. The first substance of the group, the alkaloid *d*-tubocurarine, was found by Alam, Anrep, Barsoum, Talaat, and Weininger in 1939 (*3*), and a large number of such substances are now known. A report of an extensive study was published by MacIntosh and Paton in 1949 (18). One of the most potent of these compounds is 48/80, a condensation product of *p*-methoxyphenylethyl-methylamine (21,9), which has a structure of the general type

Compound 48/80 has also another interesting property, that of causing the release, in addition to histamine, of a "slow-reacting substance" (*cf.* p. 436), which increases still further the similarity of the effects to anaphylaxis (21). Not only this, but it has considerable power of acting antagonistically to the slow-reacting substance. Paton (21) suggested that this may indicate that the slow-reacting substance is itself concerned in some way with histamine release, but that it is still too early to speculate on the nature of this connection.

This remarkable compound also releases histamine from the skin, on being injected into the skin of the intact animal, or when skin preparations *in vitro* are perfused with it. The substance is so potent that one molecule is able to release 10 to 30 molecules of histamine. When injected into the skin in a concentration of 1:1,000,000 it produces the characteristic "triple response." It does not release histamine from human blood (20).

Further study of these histamine-liberating substances may throw new light on the symptoms of hypersensitivity. For instance, Feldberg (10) suggested that possibly histamine is the agent responsible for itching (originating in the skin). He pointed out that "itching powder" consists of the hairs of a plant, cowhage, containing very fine spikes which make minute mechanical wounds. Studies of Broadbent (10) suggest that these spikes contain a histamine liberator, and Feldberg stated that fragmented glass wool can also be converted into an effective itching powder by treating it with a histamine liberator.

It was discovered by Parfentjev and Goodline (cf. 19) that the sensitivity to histamine of the white mouse could be increased about 50-fold by a preliminary inoculation with Hemophilus pertussus vaccine. The reason for this remarkable effect is not known. According to Malkiel (19) it is not due to a toxic action of the vaccine on the adrenals.

3. Acetylcholine

Acetylcholine has a peripheral dilator action on certain blood vessels, and stimulates the entire autonomic system, as do small doses of nicotine. In small doses acetylcholine lowers the blood pressure by a direct dilator action on the walls of certain peripheral blood vessels. In larger doses there is a considerable fall in blood pressure which is associated with, and largely due to, a vagus effect on the heart.

Acetylcholine is the chemical released at the nerve terminal when the parasympathetic (preganglionic and postganglionic) fibers are stimulated. It is also produced by preganglionic sympathetic nerves. Acetylcholine is present in the tissues in an inactive bound form, probably in loose combination with protein or lipoprotein.

The actions of acetylcholine on the viscera accurately repeat the effects of parasympathetic stimulation; secretion of tears, saliva, and gastric and pancreatic juice occurs, and there are increased movements of the esophagus, stomach, small and large intestine, and bladder. There is pelvic vasodilation and, in the male, erection of the penis. In the female, the uterus, though not inervated by the sympathetic system, is stimulated by a direct action on its smooth muscle.

Respiration is strikingly increased by acetylcholine.

The similarity of these symptoms to those of hypersensitivity reactions (Chapters 8, 9) is evident. It is believed by some workers that many types of non-immunological disease which resemble atopy are due to abnormalities in acetylcholine release or to excessive acetylcholine release from excessive nerve stimuli.

4. Anaphylactoid Shock

There are a number of substances which, when injected intravenously, produce symptoms of acute shock which resemble the syndrome of anaphylactic shock. This phenomenon is called anaphylactoid shock. It differs from true anaphylactic shock in at least two ways: (*1*) the symptoms are produced by the *first* injection of the material, and (*2*) many of the materials are not antigens, or even, so far as we know, haptens.

Among the substances which have been observed to produce anaphylactoid shock are: peptone, agar solution, aqueous suspensions of $BaSO_4$, typhoid vaccine, starch, gum acacia solutions, arsphenamine, acetic acid, India ink, snake and bee venoms, colloidal iron, cow and horse lung extracts, sodium citrate (13,7).

Doerr (7) pointed out that intravenous injection of a foreign substance might lead to the production of shock (*1*) by some alteration of the blood stream, which in itself leads to shock, (*2*) by stimulation of the endothelium of the blood vessels in some unspecified way (*3*) by liberation from the endothelium of the vessels or the neighboring tissues of histamine or histamine-like substances. There is little doubt that snake and bee venoms act by the third of these hypothetical mechanisms, liberating histamine by virtue of the lecithinase which they contain (Chapter 7). Evidence also exists that histamine is probably liberated in anaphylactoid shock produced by peptone (7,24). Crystalline trypsin injected intravenously into the intact animal or used for organ perfusion liberates histamine and thereby causes shock (23). In many cases, however, it is difficult to see how the substance injected could operate in this way, and we are inclined to believe that a direct toxic action of the injected material is responsible. Some of the substances on the list, such as acetic acid, India ink, colloidal iron, lung extract, sodium citrate, and tragacanth, seem to operate by causing profound alterations in the lung and perhaps in other tissues. The shock resulting from injection of these substances is usually somewhat different from typical anaphylactic shock, the emphysema being absent; instead we observe peribronchial edema, thrombosis, embolism, and hemorrhage. The extent of these different processes varies with the agent injected.

5. Shwartzman-Sanarelli Phenomenon

One of the most amazing imitations of hypersensitivity reactions is the Shwartzman-Sanarelli phenomenon. Although it does not depend upon an antibody–antigen reaction, it may nevertheless be involved in certain acute disease mechanisms (4).

In 1924 Sanarelli (27) reported that if he injected rabbits with a sub-lethal dose of cholera vibrios, and later injected them with a small dose of colon bacilli, the animals died, although neither of these injections alone would have killed them. Autopsy revealed necrosis of the intestinal mucosa, where the vibrios had localized, and Sanarelli called the condition hemorrhagic allergy.   In 1928 Shwartzman (29) and Hanger (12) rediscovered this reaction, and the extensive investigations of Shwartzman (30) showed that, although Sanarelli's observations were correct, his interpretation was wrong, for the reaction is immunologically nonspecific.

Shwartzman found that if he injected rabbits intracutaneously with the filtrate of a young agar culture washing of *Salmonella typhosa,* or of any one of a variety of other organisms, nothing much happened.   But if 24 hours later he injected intravenously a small amount of the filtrate, *or of some other filtrate such as one from Meningococcus,* the injected skin site changed markedly within 2 to 4 hours.   The area took on a purplish, congested appearance, then quickly underwent hemorrhagic necrosis. The reaction reached its maximum about 5 hours after the intravenous injection, and the histological findings included thrombosis, disruption of the blood vessels, and hemorrhage.

The Shwartzman reaction can be provoked by amounts of materials that are quite nontoxic in themselves.   It has been shown that the local inflammation provoked by the initial intracutaneous injection is not the complete explanation of the essential preparation, for the skin cannot be "prepared" by other substances, such as xylene, although they also provoke inflammation (30).   The prepared area does not show increased permeability to intravenously injected dyes, as do ordinary inflamed areas (11).

The essential conditions for the production of the Shwartzman-Sanarelli phenomenon are (22):   (*1*) The provocative injection must be given intravenously.   (*2*) The provocative injection must follow within a limited interval (generally 8 to 32 hours) after the preparatory injection.   Bacterial and other substances may induce reactivity, and bacterial and even nonantigenic substances such as starch and agar solutions may be used for the intravenous provocative dose.

The Shwartzman-Sanarelli phenomenon differs from a local hypersensitive reaction of either the immediate or the delayed type in several ways (22):   (*1*) Reinjection of material into the same site as that employed for the preparatory dose is not effective.   (*2*) The time range between the injections differs from that of any known immunological response.   Sensitization is effected too soon and does not last long enough.   (*3*) There is no specificity.

The Shwartzman-Sanarelli phenomenon has long baffled immunologists, who were distinctly disconcerted at the discovery of this powerful reaction, reminiscent in many ways of reactions of hypersensitivity, which apparently depends upon no immunological mechanism. Studies of Thomas and Stetson (31), extending and reinterpreting many earlier observations, partially cleared up the problem. These workers found that as a consequence of the preparatory injection, polymorphonuclear leukocytes accumulate locally in the tissue around the smaller veins, as "cuffs"; and probably chiefly because of the metabolic character of "exudate" polymorphonuclear leukocytes, abnormal quantities of lactic acid are produced in these areas through anaerobic glycosis. The essential role of the polymorphonuclear leukocytes is shown by the fact that the Shwartzman reaction can be inhibited by pretreatment with nitrogen mustard, X-rays, or benzene, which are all known to produce a leukopenia (II). Histologically inapparent changes proceed to occur in the adjacent vascular endothelium, perhaps of a sort to render this tissue susceptible to the action of tissue protease. After the intravenous eliciting injection white cells and blood platelets clump together, forming masses which are removed from the circulation and become sequestered in the lung and perhaps also in the liver and spleen, especially along the damaged endothelium. In the latter areas, the aggregates from leukocyte-platelet thrombi and actually occlude the small veins and capillaries. Death and disintegration of the cells and vessels involved occurs within 2 to 3 hours; the activated tissue proteases and interruption of the blood supply probably play a role. As a consequence of the necrosis of the blood vessels, the characteristic and prominent hemorrhage follows in the prepared site.

Thrombus formation seems to be essential as a stage in the development of the Shwartzman reaction, as shown by the fact that heparin, dicumarol, and other anticoagulants, given in quantities sufficient to make the blood incoagulable, completely block the development of the reaction (11).

Organs other than the skin, particularly the kidney, can be "prepared" by Shwartzman-active substances, and a similar hemorrhagic reaction, but different in that it is general instead of localized, can be produced in rabbits by an intravenous preparation followed by an intravenous provocative dose.

6. "Physical Allergy"

The term "physical allergy" is due to Duke (8). It has been applied to a group of conditions which simulate the reactions of hypersensitivity. Here the incitant is not an antigen nor even a chemical, but cold, sunlight, or mechanical irritation. A common manifestation is urticaria of the exposed part, or angioedema, but this may be accompanied by systemic effects such as headache, fever, tachycardia, fall in blood pressure, and collapse.

In some cases of "physical allergy" there seems to be some evidence that some sort of immunological mechanism is involved, as for instance in a case of cold sensitivity studied by Sherman and Seebohm (28), where the sensitivity could be transferred passively by serum.   Such an immunological mechanism might be based upon the production of autoantibodies by the patient (see Chapter 13), but this possibility does not seem to have been investigated (22).   In most cases, however, no such mechanism can be demonstrated, and it seems more likely that the physical agent which brings on the attack does so by causing the liberation from the skin of histamine or other substances of cells concerned in the end effects of hypersensitive reactions (32).   This idea is supported by the finding of Horton, Brown, and Roth (15) that exposure of cold-sensitive individuals to the cold produced effects on the blood vessels, gastric secretion, and blood pressure which were characteristic of histamine.   Rose (25) studied the histamine content of the blood in 15 cases of reactivity to cold, heat, light, and mechanical stimulation (dermatographism), and in 7 of these found levels above the normal.

Nevertheless, it cannot be regarded as conclusively established that the manifestations of "physical allergy" are always due to the release of histamine. For one thing, not all cutaneous reactions to cold are of the immediate urticarial type which histamine produces.   In some cold-sensitive patients application of minute pieces of ice to the skin results in delayed reactions of the tuberculin type.   This also occurs in about 10 per cent of normal individuals, and in over 50 per cent of patients with asthma, tuberculosis, or diabetes, being especially severe in tuberculous subjects (26).

Also, unsurprisingly, sensitivity to light can be induced by the deposition in the skin of photosensitive substances, such as porphyrins.   Sulfanilamide has also been reported to cause sensitivity to light.   The subject of light sensitivity is discussed in reference (13a).

7. Psychogenic Factors

Since the allergic reaction consists primarily of vasomotor reactions, with edema and infiltration of the tissues by leukocytes and eosinophils, it seems evident that these changes can also result from emotional disturbances. As Vaughan and Black (32) point out, if an emotion can cause blushing, there is no reason it cannot cause a similar change in the nasal or bronchial mucosa.

The problem is, to what extent can emotional disturbances bring on the manifestations of allergic disease in nonallergic individuals, and to what extent will correction of the emotional disturbance in an allergic individual alleviate his allergic symptoms? Upon these questions workers in the field of allergy are by no means agreed at the present time. The literature on the subject is extensive, and we cannot attempt to summarize it here. Further references will be found in current issues of the *Quarterly Review of Allergy and Applied Immunology,* the *Annals of Allergy,* the *Journal of Allergy, Acta Allergologica,* and the *Archives of Dermatology and Syphilology.*

The psychogenic element in allergy was discussed in four chapters of the book edited by Abramson (2). Ross and Wilson, in one of the chapters, conclude that "asthma is a symptom in which personality disturbances play a highly significant role, whether in a merely contributory or as yet obscurely etiological way."

A typical example of the influence of emotional factors on an allergic condition is provided by a case described by Woodhead (33). A girl of 21 had severe eczema with eosinophilia, and the eczema was clearly traceable to family disputes and emotional upsets. In this case the influence of the emotions is quite evident. The history does not, however, establish that the eczema was entirely of psychogenic origin and had no basis in allergy, and it is doubtful if this was the case. Henderson (14), discussing the role of psychogenic factors in asthma, stated that he believes that most of the cases of bronchial asthma investigated by psychiatrists occur in "psychoneurotics with bronchial asthma." He thinks that only in rare instances would the disease appear to be originally psychogenic, and even then he thinks careful search would usually reveal that a state of "allergic equilibrium" had been upset by the psychic trauma.

Our appreciation of the possible role of emotional factors in allergy has increased to such an extent that not all workers, probably, would be prepared to deny that this may have been a contributing factor in the allergic condition of the baby walrus (Fig. 8-3), which, being bottle fed, was doubtless starved for mother love.

References

1. Abel, J. J., and S. Kubota, *J. Pharmacol. Exptl. Therap.,* **13,** 243 (1919).
2. Abramson, H. A., ed., *Treatment of Asthma,* Williams and Wilkins, Baltimore, 1951.
3. Alam, M., *et al., J. Physiol. (London),* **95,** 148 (1939).

4. Chase, M. W., in *Bacterial and Mycotic Infections of Man*, R. J. Dubos, ed., Lippincott, Philadelphia, 1952.

4a. Dacie, J. V., *The Haemolytic Anaemias: Congenital and Acquired*, Churchill, London, 1954.

5. Dale, H. H., and P. P. Laidlaw, *J. Physiol. (London)*, **41**, 318 (1910).

6. Dragstedt, C. A., *J. Allergy*, **26**, 287 (1955).

7. Doerr, R., *Die Immunitätsforsch. VI, Die Onaphylaxie*, Springer-Verlag, Vienna, 1950.

8. Duke, W. W., *J. Am. Med. Assoc.*, **84**, 736 (1925).

9. Feinberg, S. M., et al., *Quarterly Bull. Northwestern Univ. Med. School*, **28**, 246 (1954).

10. Feldberg, W., *J. Pharmacol.*, **6**, 281 (1954).

11. Good, R. A., in *Immunity and Hypersensitivity, Relationship to Disease in Man*, Report of 9th Radiation Research Conf. of the Ross (M&R) Laboratories, Columbus, Ohio, 1955.

12. Hanger, F. M., *Proc. Exptl. Biol.*, **25**, 775 (1928).

13. Hanzlik, P. J., and H. T. Karsner, *J. Pharmacol. Exptl. Therap.*, **23**, 173 (1924).

13a. Harkavy, J., Chapter 30 in *Allergy in Theory and Practice*, R. A. Cooke, ed., Saunders, Philadelphia, 1947.

14. Henderson, A. T., *Can. Med. Assoc. J.*, **55**, 106 (1945).

15. Horton, B. T., G. E. Brown, and G. M. Roth, *J. Am. Med. Assoc.*, **107**, 1263 (1936).

16. Kohn, C. M., *Ann. Allergy*, **13**, 228 (1955).

17. Lewis, T., *The Blood Vessels of the Human Skin and Their Responses*, Shaw and Sons, London, 1927.

18. MacIntosh, F. C., and W. D. M. Paton, *J. Physiol. (London)*, **109**, 190 (1949).

19. Malkiel, S., *Atti del VI Congresso Internanazionale di Microbiologia*, Rome, **2**, 265 (1953).

20. Noah, J. W., and A. Brand, in *Mechanisms of Hypersensitivity*, J. H. Shaffer, G. A. LoGrippo, and M. W. Chase, eds., Little, Brown, Boston, 1959.

21. Paton, W. D. M., *Brit. J. Pharmacol.*, **6**, 499 (1951).

22. Raffel, S., *Immunity*, Appleton-Century-Crofts, New York, 1953.

23. Rocha e Silva, M., *J. Immunol.*, **40**, 399 (1941).

24. Rocha e Silva, M., *Histamine: Its Role in Anaphylaxis and Allergy*, Charles C Thomas, Springfield, Illinois, 1955.

25. Rose, B., *J. Allergy*, **12**, 357 (1941).

26. Saier, M. H., W. C. van Deventer, and G. D. Barnett, *Proc. Soc. Exptl. Biol. Med.*, **29**, 936 (1931–1932).

27. Sanarelli, G., *Ann. inst. Pasteur*, **38**, 11 (1924).

28. Sherman, W. B., and P. M. Seebohm, *J. Allergy*, **21**, 414 (1950).

29. Shwartzman, G., *J. Exptl. Med.*, **48**, 247 (1928).

30. Shwartzman, G., *Phenomenon of Local Tissue Reactivity*, Hoeber, New York, 1937.

31. Thomas, L., and C. A. Stetson, *J. Exptl. Med.*, **89**, 461 (1949).

32. Vaughan, W. T., and J. H. Black, *Practice of Allergy*, Mosby, St. Louis, 1954.

33. Woodhead, B., *Arch. Disease Childhood*, **21**, 98 (1946).

For the Sensitive Plant has no bright flower;
Radiance and odour are not its dower;
It loves, even like Love, its deep heart full,
It desires what it has not, the Beautiful!
—Shelley, "The Sensitive Plant," lines 74–77

CHAPTER 11

Hypersensitivity and Immunity

We now come to an important and difficult problem. It is obvious that hypersensitivity reactions all too often do the patient no good; indeed, they may lead to serious illness or even death. The question is: do they ever do any good? Do reactions of hypersensitivity represent a kind of miscarriage of effort on the part of the body, always detrimental to the patient? Or are the detrimental effects merely side effects of a mechanism which has positive value as a defense mechanism? What is the relationship between hypersensitivity and immunity?

If we look at the subject purely speculatively at first, there seem to be two ways in which hypersensitivity could be of advantage to the patient in infection, or at any rate in which hypersensitivity might be correlated with resistance to infection: (*1*) The same (beneficial) antibody which tends to immobilize or kill the invading organism, or which neutralizes some of its toxic antigens, might sensitize the tissues of the host, resulting in the (undesirable) reactions of hypersensitivity. (*2*) The hypersensitive reaction, especially the delayed type, is followed by considerable local inflammation, and the inflammatory process might effectively localize, and promote the destruction of, the foreign pathogenic agent.

It is even quite conceivable that the hypersensitivity which develops during an infection, far from enhancing immunity, may actually diminish it. These are questions that cannot be answered by speculation; they must be investigated experimentally.

During infection the host is exposed to the action of a large number of antigens elaborated by the invading organism. Any or all of these may cause the production of antibodies, and any or all may induce hypersensitivity. Some of the antibodies, particularly those against the antigens mainly responsible for virulence, may have protective value. There does not seem to be any way of predicting *a priori* whether the antigens against which they are directed will at the time induce a hypersensitive state in the host. The infection may indeed produce hypersensitivity, but to antigens unimportant for virulence or invasiveness. Such hypersensitivity would appear then more or less simultaneously with the development of protective antibodies, yet play no role in protection. We must be careful to distinguish between such a parallelism and a real causal connection between hypersensitivity and immunity.

Since we have seen that there is a fundamental difference in mechanism between the two types of hypersensitivity, immediate and delayed, it seems advisable to consider separately the relation of each type of hypersensitivity to immunity.

A. IMMEDIATE HYPERSENSITIVITY AND IMMUNITY

1. Parasitic Infections

Many parasitic infections produce hypersensitivity of the immediate type. Anaphylaxis can often be induced in parasitized animals by injection of extracts of the parasite (21). Most parasitic infections result in a greater or lesser degree of immunity, which we shall discuss in Chapter 13. Are the two phenomena unrelated, or is the production of the immediate hypersensitive state itself part of the immune process in parasitic infections?

It is not easy to answer these questions, for a number of reasons. (1) Parasitologists have not always looked for antibodies in the sera of infected animals, even when the sera were shown to confer immunity passively. (2) When parasitologists have looked for antibodies in such sera, they have generally looked for precipitating or complement-fixing antibodies. But we have already seen that reagins, the type of antibodies which are responsible for immediate hypersensitivity, typically do not precipitate or fix complement (Chapter 8). (3) Allergists who have observed skin-sensitizing antibodies in parasitic infections have generally not looked for possible beneficial effects.

Kuhns and Pappenheimer (11,12) showed that reagin-type antitoxin, produced by atopic individuals, effectively neutralizes diphtheria toxin. There is therefore no doubt that this antibody, which confers hypersensitivity of the immediate type, is of real service to its possessors, since it protects them against diphtheria. If parasites typically produced toxins, we might well suppose that reagins found in infected individuals were capable, in some instances at least, of neutralizing these toxic products.

Unfortunately, it is by no means established that parasites regularly produce toxins. Toxic reactions are of course often seen in infected individuals, but it is possible, indeed probable, that in many cases at any rate these are due rather to the very hypersensitivity we are discussing, and that normal individuals would not find these materials toxic. The evidence that parasites may produce true toxins was summarized in 1929 by Taliaferro (23) and was on the whole not very convincing. In Culbertson's later review (6) the subject was discussed much more briefly, and the verdict of the author seemed on the whole against the idea that toxins are produced.

Study of the sera of animals infected with parasites has, on the other hand, shown that in many cases antibodies of the ordinary kind, which precipitate with the antigen and fix complement, are present. They have been observed to form precipitates on and in the body of the parasite in a manner which leaves little doubt that these antibodies play a role in resistance to the infection (Chapter 14). So in many parasitic infections, perhaps in most, antibodies of the ordinary sort are concerned in resistance.

However, not all the precipitating antibodies found in parasitic infection contribute to resistance, as shown by Campbell's (2) experiments with a carbohydrate antigen isolated from *Taenia taeniaeformis*. This antigen, which was a polysaccharide, stimulated the production of good precipitating antibodies but did not contribute to immunity, as shown by the facts that it would not immunize animals against infection, antibody to it would not protect passively, and it would not absorb out the protective agent of immune sera. Furthermore, it has sometimes been observed that immune sera which gave a negative precipitin reaction *in vitro* would protect animals against infection (3). Altogether, it is hard to escape the impression that the question of a possible protective value of reagin-type antibodies in parasitic infections has not been properly examined, and that when it is, these antibodies *may* be found to be of considerable importance in resistance.

If this should prove to be the case, it would support the suggestion of L. Dienes, referred to in Chapter 8, that the immediate type of hypersensitivity may be the characteristic response of the animal host to metazoon infections. It is certainly a common consequence of such infections. *Ascaris lumbricoides*, in particular, will produce this type of hypersensitivity in nearly all, perhaps all, individuals, irrespective of their atopic status (23). It has been observed that people may become sensitized to *Ascaris* merely by contact with the fresh worms or even with the preserved worms (17), and Brunner (1) states that extracts of *Ascaris* appear to have some characteristic which makes them unusually potent atopens.

In any case, it is evident that many parasites easily provoke formation of reagin-type antibodies, and it has been suggested by several authors that such antibodies might under some circumstances have a protective function. Whether such a function will eventually be *demonstrated* in the case of some or all parasite infections remains to be seen.

2. Bacterial Infections

The evidence that a relation exists between immunity and the immediate type of hypersensitivity in bacterial infections is not extensive, partly because bacterial infections are more likely to produce the delayed type of hypersensitivity (see p. 465). It has been shown, to be sure, that bacteria or their products may produce anaphylactic sensitization in animals (20), but it remains a question whether this anaphylactic sensitization increases the resistance of an animal.

One example is known, however, in which a reaction of hypersensitivity of the immediate type is definitely correlated with immunity. This is the skin test in pneumonia described by Francis (7), in which 0.1 mg. of homologous specific capsular polysaccharide, dissolved in 0.1 ml. of saline, is injected intracutaneously. If circulating antibody is present, a wheal and erythema reaction appear at the site of injection within 15 or 30 minutes. Since it is known that resistance to pneumococci depends upon the presence of circulating antibody to the capsular polysaccharide, this immediate reaction is evidently closely related to immunity. In fact it used to be recommended (13) that as early as possible in the course of the disease, antibody be administered intravenously in amounts sufficient to make the Francis test positive.

The Francis reaction is not typical of the atopic type of immediate skin reaction, since it is due to antibody of the precipitating type. Actually, there does not seem to be any well-documented example of a reaction of the atopic type which has been shown to contribute to resistance in a bacterial infection.

Another skin reaction observed in pneumonia (and in certain other diseases, for it is not specific) is elicited by the somatic "C" polysaccharide common to all pneumococci. This reaction is biphasic, exhibiting an immediate wheal and erythema followed by an edematous but flattened reaction which reaches its height in 6 to 12 hours (8). This reaction is not due to an antibody, but to an abnormal albumin which has the property of precipitating "C" substance. This albumin appears in the course of the disease and disappears with recovery.

3. Virus Infections

There do not seem to be any authenticated examples of a relation between hypersensitivity of the immediate type and immunity in virus diseases.

4. Fungus Diseases

In fungus infections, hypersensitivity is usually of the delayed type, but some subjects respond to some fungus antigens with reactions of the immediate type. Marcussen (4), by the Prausnitz-Küstner passive transfer technic, demonstrated circulating antibodies of the reagin type in individuals infected with *Trichophyton*, but there seems to be no proof that these antibodies contribute to resistance.

B. DELAYED HYPERSENSITIVITY AND IMMUNITY

1. Parasitic Infections

Some parasitic infections produce both the immediate and the delayed type of hypersensitivity in man. It is generally stated that they produce mainly the delayed type in animals. There does not seem to be any persuasive evidence that hypersensitivity of the delayed type contributes to resistance in parasitic infections, either in animals or in man.

2. Bacterial Infections

Delayed hypersensitivity is a characteristic feature of bacterial infections, and has been called "bacterial allergy" by some writers.

The debate concerning the possible role of hypersensitivity in immunity has been carried on chiefly in connection with bacterial disease, particularly tuberculosis.

It has long been believed that delayed hypersensitivity, which is such a typical feature of tuberculosis, contributes to resistance. The Koch phenomenon (p. 465) was regarded as a "local sacrifice of tissue" made for the purpose of walling off and expelling a new infection, and it was considered that the success of this process was attributable to the hypersensitivity rather than to any immune mechanism depending upon antibodies. A number of immunologists and pathologists have in fact maintained that hypersensitivity is the essential mechanism of resistance in tuberculosis, basing their position upon the following arguments: (*1*) Since there is little or no evidence in tuberculosis of protective antibodies, some other mechanism must be operating. (*2*) Hypersensitivity and acquired resistance closely parallel each other, suggesting that resistance depends upon hypersensitivity. (3) It is known that an established infection can inhibit the spread of bacteria from a local site; therefore inhibition of the spread of tubercle bacilli in the body with acquired resistance is brought about by the accelerated hypersensitive inflammation. (4) Since inflammation is a protective device, the more rapid and abundant inflammation which hypersensitivity causes provides an enhanced degree of protection against the tubercle bacillus. (5) It seems only reasonable that a phenomenon such as hypersensitivity, which appears during infection of all types, should have some function.

These arguments are indeed impressive, and they have their adherents today, but they have been almost completely demolished by workers such as Rich (18) and Raffel (16), who have quite well established that the connection between hypersensitivity and immunity is at best one of parallelism and not of causal connection. Rich (18) stated that there has "never been placed on record one single experiment or clinical observation that demonstrated that hypersensitivity is *necessary* for protection in any stage of tuberculosis or any other infection. . . ."

Rich proceeds to examine one by one the arguments just given in favor of the role of hypersensitivity in immunity in tuberculosis.

1. Antibodies, including opsonins, precipitins, and complement-fixing antibodies, *do* appear in the circulation of animals infected or immunized with tubercle bacilli. It is true that there is a lack of parallelism between the titer of these antibodies and the degree of resistance, but this is also observed in diseases such as pneumonia, where it is known that antibodies are of great importance. Even in these diseases, phagocytosis is essential. Rich also points out that our *in vitro* technics for the detection and quantitative estimation of antibody are by no means infallible, and that we are not always able to test for the most important effect of antibodies, namely, their injurious effect on the bacteria. Furthermore, Rich points out, in chronic diseases such as tuberculosis the level of protective antibodies is generally low, as shown by the very fact that the body is unable to get rid of the invading bacteria promptly. Rich also presents considerable evidence that antibodies are operative in tuberculosis: facts such as increased ability of the body to immobilize tubercle bacilli, increased ability to clear the blood of bacilli, and increased bactericidal power.

It seems likely that antibodies are indeed operating in tuberculosis, as in other infections, but proof of this is not essential to the argument that hypersensitivity is not the essential mechanism. Rich goes on to show:

2. Hypersensitivity does not always parallel resistance. Animals immunized by intravenous injection of tubercle bacilli often acquire as high a degree of resistance as those injected intracutaneously. The latter become hypersensitive, but the former may not, possibly because of the desensitizing effect of the repeated intravenous injections. Also, hypersensitivity decreases after a tuberculous infection has become arrested, but the acquired resistance remains. The lack of parallelism between hypersensitivity and immunity is further shown by the fact that Negroes tend to develop a higher degree of hypersensitivity as a result of tuberculous infection than do whites, but their acquired resistance tends to be lower.

Convincing evidence that hypersensitivity does not necessarily parallel resistance is provided by experiments in which animals are desensitized (in tuberculosis this can be accomplished by injections of tuberculin). The desensitized animals continued to have just as high a degree of resistance as the sensitive control animals. This result applies to other infections.

Raffel (16) and Choucroun have both shown that animals can be made hypersensitive by the injection of purified products of the tubercle bacillus, but that such sensitized animals develop no resistance to infection.

Humphrey and White (10) state ". . . the concept of the Mantoux test as an indicator of immunity is highly questionable."

3. Although it is true that some bacteria injected into an inflamed locus are prevented from spreading, bacteria injected along with an inflammatory agent are not, and may actually spread more readily.

4. Inflammation alone does not destroy the tubercle bacillus.

5. Rich does not deny that hypersensitivity may be basically a beneficial mechanism. He merely states that this has not been demonstrated, and that even if it had been, it is possible for a useful mechanism to be forced into action in situations and under conditions quite different from those under which it has a good effect. As we have previously remarked. it is possible for homeostatic mechanisms to begin to function in a non-homeostatic manner, and for the "wisdom of the body" to become stupidity. Rich mentions the pathological states produced by hypersensitivity, such as hay fever, asthma, food sensitivity, and serum sickness. He might well have added the diseases now thought to be the result of autoimmunization, which we shall discuss in Chapter 13.

If hypersensitivity of the delayed type has any beneficial effect, it must be admitted that we do not know what it is. And the beneficial effects of hypersensitivity of the immediate type are still largely problematical. Consequently we must agree with Rich in thinking that the existence of the phenomenon of delayed hypersensitivity does not of itself show that the process is beneficial.

In the book by Rich will also be found evidence that hypersensitivity is not important for immunity in a number of other bacterial diseases, including infection by *Treponema pallidum, Pneumococcus,* and *Pasteurella aviseptica.*

It has apparently been found that human beings with strongly positive skin reactions to tuberculin run a greater risk of developing clinical tuberculosis later on than do those with only moderate skin sensitivity (10). A high degree of allergy, it would therefore seem, may not only not protect, but may be a positive disadvantage.

Raffel (16) states, "At the present time . . . there exists little basis for regarding the hypersensitivity reaction as part of the mechanism of resistance to infectious disease."

Many workers have believed that hypersensitivity plays a significant role in immunity to syphilis. A number of earlier investigators noted that after infection with syphilis an animal at first responds to reinfection with an accelerated pathological response, although later a highly but not absolutely refractory state appears. Other workers (references in 25) noted that resistance was likely to be less following an infection which arouses little or no tissue reaction, than after one when the response was violent with rather extensive lesions. The tertiary lesions of syphilis tend to become more and more localized as time goes on, first in one part of the body, then in another, and are likely to be more destructive, as the interval after the infection lengthens. According to Hinton (9), this suggests a type of allergy growing out of previous sensitization of the tissues by the spirochetes or their products. Sulzberger (22) goes so far as to say that allergy plays the significant role in the basic mechanism of both human and experimental (animal) syphilis.

Rich, Chesney, and Turner (19) made a detailed examination of the question. They immunized rabbits to *Treponema pallidum* and infected them, along with normal controls, with virulent spirochetes. There was no evidence that the immunized animals made a greater or more prompt hypersensitive response than did the controls. On the contrary, after a slight initial inflammatory reaction at the site of infection, which was never more prominent than in the controls, the sites of infection in the immunized animals promptly became normal and remained so, except for occasional minute infiltrations of mononuclear cells, whereas the lesions in the controls progressed steadily to destructive chancre formation.

3. Virus Infections

There seems to be no evidence that delayed hypersensitivity aids resistance in virus infections. McKee (14) observed the appearance of hypersensitivity to one virus (infectious myxomatosis) in the absence of acquired resistance. In fact in animals having this hypersensitivity the progress of experimental infection was even more rapid than in normal controls.

4. Fungus Diseases

Infections with fungi and with the actinomycetes, which are considered intermediate between the true bacteria and the true fungi, have been discussed by Conant and Rosebury (5) and Conant (4). Hypersensitivity of the delayed type is often reported, but there seems to be no evidence that it is connected with immunity, and indeed Sulzberger (22) believed that many fungus diseases, at least, are largely the result of the allergic reaction of the host to allergenic products of the fungus. According to him the hypersensitivity is "unequivocally and obviously harmful." Sulzberger believes that these diseases could be best treated by desensitization measures like those used in hay fever.

Allergy to *fungi* is discussed by Vaughan and Black (24).

C. SUMMARY

We are obliged to conclude that the available evidence, with the possible exception of the (still hypothetical) role of antibodies of the reagin type in parasitic infections (p. 501), evidence at present available provides no basis for regarding the hypersensitive reaction as part of the mechanism of resistance. On the contrary, in view of the damage to the tissues of the host which it often causes, it must be regarded as a liability, and interpreted as another example of a miscarriage of the generally beneficial immune process.

References

1. Brunner, M., *J. Allergy*, **5**, 257 (1934).
2. Campbell, D. H., *J. Infect. Diseases*, **65**, 12 (1939).
3. Chen, H. T., *J. Infect. Diseases*, **86**, 205 (1950).
4. Conant, N. F., in *Bacterial and Mycotic Infections of Man*, R. J. Dubos, ed., Lippincott, Philadelphia, 1952.
5. Conant, N. F., and T. Rosebury, in *Bacterial and Mycotic Infections of Man*, R. J. Dubos, ed., Lippincott, Philadelphia, 1952.
6. Culbertson, J. T., *Immunity Against Animal Parasites*, Columbia University Press, New York, 1941.
7. Francis, T., *J. Exptl. Med.*, **57**, 617 (1933).
8. Francis, T., in *Bacterial and Mycotic Infections of Man*, R. J. Dubos, ed., Lippincott, Philadelphia, 1952.
9. Hinton, W. A., *Syphilis and Its Treatment*, Macmillan, New York, 1936.

10. Humphrey, J. H., and R. G. White, *Immunology for Students of Medicine,* 2nd ed., Davis, Philadelphia, 1964.
11. Kuhns, W. J., *Federation Proc.,* **13,** part 1, 501 (1954).
12. Kuhns, W. J., and A. M. Pappenheimer, *J. Exptl. Med.,* **95,** 375 (1952).
13. MacLeod, C. M., in *Bacterial and Mycotic Infections of Man,* R. J. Dubos, ed., Lippincott, Philadelphia, 1952.
14. McKee, C. M., *Am. J. Hyg.,* **12,** 178 (1939).
16. Raffel, S., *Immunity,* 2nd ed., Appleton-Century-Crofts, New York, 1961.
17. Ransom, B. H., W. T. Harrison, and J. F. Couch, *J. Agr. Res.,* **28,** 577 (1924).
18. Rich, A. R., *The Pathogenesis of Tuberculosis,* 2nd ed., Charles C Thomas, Springfield, Illinois, 1951.
19. Rich, A. R., A. M. Chesney, and T. B. Turner, *Bull. Johns Hopkins Hosp.,* **52,** 179 (1933).
20. Seegal, B. C., *Ann. N. Y. Acad. Sci.,* **50,** 758 (1949).
21. Sprent, J. F. A., *J. Infect. Diseases,* **88,** 168 (1951).
22. Sulzberger, M. B., *Dermatologic Allergy,* Charles C Thomas, Springfield, Illinois, 1940.
23. Taliaferro, W. H., *The Immunology of Parasitic Infections,* Century, New York, 1929.
24. Vaughan, W. T., and J. H. Black, *Practice of Allergy,* Moxby, St. Louis, 1954.
25. Zinsser, H., J. F. Enders, and L. D. Fothergill, *Immunity: Principles and Application in Medicine and Public Health,* Macmillan, New York, 1939.

Y yo les digo: "Si, yo soy eso, cuando eso es yo y
todo es mio y mia la totalidad de las cosas"
—Miguel de Unamuno, *Del Sentimiento Trágico*
de la Vida, part III

CHAPTER 12

Immunological Tolerance and Intolerance: Fate of Tissue Transplants

1. Historical

The earliest workers in the science of immunology realized that there existed an interesting and challenging problem which we may state as follows: All higher vertebrates are capable of making antibodies, or producing some other immune response, to a wide assortment of antigens. At the same time, each such individual is himself full of a variety of antigens (his own proteins, carbohydrates, etc.) to which he as a rule does not produce antibodies or make any immune response (there are exceptions, see Chapter 13). Paul Ehrlich, one of the great pioneers in immunology, formulated the fact that such response is not made in his famous principle of *horror autotoxicus* (fear of poisoning one's self). This name implied that the formation of antibodies to your own antigens would be bad for you [and, as we now know, this is quite true (Chapter 13)] and consequently that Nature, in her infinite wisdom, had somehow arranged that this could never happen. As Ehrlich himself probably realized, however, though this was a formulation, it was hardly an explanation.

It is now realized that this immunological unresponsiveness is not necessarily restricted to one's own antigens. Under certain conditions, the body becomes unresponsive to, or tolerant of, antigens that are foreign to it.

Such tolerance is often, probably usually, established when the fetus or unhatched bird comes in contact with a foreign antigen. Owen (37,38) found that fraternal twins in cattle, which almost invariably exchange blood early in embryonic life through anastomosis of the blood vessels of the placenta, generally possess a mixture of two types of erythrocytes, each type containing the blood group antigens correspond-

507

ing to the phenotype of one of the individuals. Owen concluded that red cell mosaics or "chimeras" had been established in the calves by fetal exchange of "embryonal cells ancestral to the erythrocytes of the adult animal." This mixture of genetically different tissue evidently persisted even after the animals became adult and immunological maturity had occurred.

Further investigation has shown that the fetus generally cannot produce antibodies of its own, and consequently will accept foreign tissue without making an immune response, which is exactly what the calves studied by Owen had done. It is not fully understood why the fetus is so poor at making lymphoid tissue (29). There is some evidence that the fetus can, under some conditions, make some sort of immune response (40). In any case, whatever the reason, the fetus seldom produces antibodies, and in general even the adult animal will not produce antibodies to antigens with which it came in contact as a fetus. Theories that might possibly account for this will be considered below.

Medawar and a talented group of colleagues (10,5) found that fraternal cattle twins not only shared each other's erythrocyte types, but would accept skin transplants from each other, even many sets in succession, but rejected grafts from other siblings or from their parents. Since the number of tissue compatibility antigens is probably greater than the number of erythrocyte isoantigens (see below), it thus became clear that the tolerance induced in the animals by the embryonic sharing of tissue went much deeper than the blood.

Knowing these facts, when Dunsford et al. (21) found a patient whose circulation contained erythrocytes of two different serological types, they accordingly asked, to the patient's great surprise, whether she was a twin. She was, although the co-twin had died and was not available for testing. Beyond any doubt, the patient and her co-twin, due to some placental anastomosis, had shared certain erythropoietic tissue, and the patient, at least, had become a chimera. Also beyond any doubt, if the co-twin had survived, the patient could have accepted tissue grafts from him.

Although, in contrast to the situation in cattle, such chimerism is rare in man, other such twin pairs have since been found (27).

Billingham, Brent and Medawar (7) showed that the long-term vascular anastomosis that exists in the case of fetal calves is not essential to establish tolerance. Tolerance could be established in mice by injecting into the embryo in utero living cell suspensions from an animal of an antigenically different strain. When the injected embryos were born, they would, then or later, accept grafts from the otherwise incompatible strain.

The length of time such grafts would last varied considerably, as would have been expected.

Rejection of Homografts

Aside from grafts to animals rendered tolerant to the tissue antigens of the donor, tissue transplants into vascularized tissue are, as a rule, successful only when the donor and recipient are of identical genetic constitutions. This is ordinarily only true of identical twins and strains of animals that have been intensively inbred (usually by many generations of brother–sister mating) to make them homozygous. Grafts between such animals, and between identical twins, may be as successful as grafts of skin from one part of an individual's body to another part. (Grafts of an individual's own tissues are called autografts, grafts from other individuals of the same species are called homografts.)

A homograft from another individual of the same species may at first seem to "take." The graft heals in, forms vascular and lymphatic anastomoses, and looks just like an autograft. But after some time, usually several days, round cell infiltration begins, vascular disturbances and necrosis begin, and finally the graft sloughs off. The total series of events may take 8 to 12 days.

If a second graft is made in the same recipient from the same donor, the response is more rapid. This second-set graft never gives the appearance of a real take. Vascularization is incomplete, round cell infiltration of the bed and the bottom layers of the graft occurs immediately, and the graft is rejected, usually in less than six days.

Antibodies may be, and often are, stimulated by the presence in an organism of such an incompatible graft. Hemagglutinins have been found, as have antibodies that lessen the growth capacity of the foreign cells (30). However, there is ample evidence that the rejection of homografts is not primarily due to circulating antibodies, but to cell-carried sensitivity of the delayed type (see Chapter 9) (15,30). This is indicated by experiments in which tissue cells have been implanted in the host, surrounded by a membrane permeable to protein (antibody) molecules, but impermeable to cells. Such implanted cells are not destroyed (2,3).

3. Tolerance

Once immunological tolerance became an object of investigation, it was realized that tolerance could be, and indeed had been, induced in ways other than placental anastoinosis or grafting. Sulzberger (15) had observed in 1929 that an intradermal injection of neoarsphenamine that would sensitize guinea pigs, producing the delayed type of skin sensitivity (see Chapter 9), would not elicit this response in animals previously injected intravenously with a larger dose of the same antigen. Before this, Wells and Osborne (15) had discovered (because the breeder who supplied their guinea pigs had changed the animals' rations) that inclusion of corn (maize) in a guinea pig's diet would make it refractory to anaphylactic sensitization to the corn protein zein. Chase (15) found in 1946 that guinea pigs could be rendered tolerant to the sensitizing action of other types of chemical allergens by feeding the chemicals before the sensitizing treatment.

Also, Felton had noted (23) in 1949 that whereas the injection of 0.5 μg. of pneumococcus polysaccharide would immunize a mouse, *i.e.* cause it to produce specific antibodies and make it resistant to the injection of live pneumococci of that type, the injection of larger doses (0.5 mg. to 5.0 mg.) not only did not immunize, but rendered the animal impossible to immunize (to this type of pneumococcus) for many months. Felton and Ottinger (25) called this phenomenon "immunological paralysis."

Later, Dixon and Maurer (20) found that even adult rabbits could be made unresponsive by injecting very high doses of soluble protein antigens. Tolerance of nonliving antigens has been reviewed by Smith (42).

There is a growing feeling that all these forms of tolerance or unresponsiveness are basically similar, and are the result of overloading the antibody-forming cells with antigen (29).

4. Production of Tolerance

The critical time for inducing tolerance varies with the species of animal (15). In the early work of the Billingham-Medawar group, mouse embryos were injected with living cell suspensions *in utero* through the body wall of the mother. A colored photograph displaying this technique is shown in a paper by Billingham, Brent, and Medawar (8,9). The time during which tolerance can be induced lasts longer than originally supposed. In rats it persists for some days after birth (15), and even in mice, dogs, chickens, and turkeys, in which the potentially tolerant phase is just ending at birth or hatching, tolerance can often be induced by injecting the foreign cells intravenously.

The induction of tolerance for tissue transplants requires the use of living nucleated cells; heat-killed or lyophilized cells will not work.

In newborn rabbits Cinader and Dubert (17) found that about 600 mg. of human serum albumin would induce tolerance. Much larger doses

(0.5 g./kg. of body weight daily) were required in adult rabbits (20). The dose of pneumococcal polysaccharide required to "paralyze" mice for 15–18 months was given above.

Unresponsiveness of a somewhat different origin is produced by exposure of an animal to very high doses of ionizing radiation (20). The lethal effects of such radiation can be avoided in some cases by injecting spleen cells and bone marrow from nonirradiated animals of the same species, or a closely related species. The foreign marrow cells become established and multiply, and the animal becomes a virtually permanent chimera. Because of the destruction of its own immunological apparatus by the radiation, the animal accepts and retains the foreign cells it would otherwise have rejected.

Induction of "tolerance" in adult animals may be facilitated to some extent by treatment with certain purine and pyrimidine antagonists, such as 6-mercaptopurine or methotrexate (11).

It is easier to induce tolerance to an antigen somewhat related to an antigen possessed by the experimental animal than to a taxonomically very foreign antigen.

5. Duration of Tolerance

The tolerance produced by living cells seems to be virtually permanent (8,9), probably because the cells multiply and continue to produce a continuing antigenic stimulus. "Mrs. McK," the human erythrocyte chimera described by Dunsford et al. (21) was 28 years old in 1956, and still had two types of erythrocytes, and chimeras have been found to persist for 3 or 4 years in birds, and even longer in cattle (8,9). Tolerance produced by overloading with protein antigens, on the other hand, is of much shorter duration, unless it is kept up by repeated injections. This is partly a function of the age at which the first injection is made. Dixon and Maurer (20) found that the tolerance induced in adult rabbits by very large doses (see above) of bovine serum albumin lasted only a matter of weeks; Cinader and Dubert (17) found that injection of human serum albumin into new-born rabbits immediately after birth induced a refractory state that lasted at least four months.

All the evidence indicates however that tolerance to nonreproducing antigens, although it may persist for a long time, is always transient unless reinforced by further injections of antigen (31,30). For example, if rabbits are given a single injection of 50 mg. of human serum albumin at birth, they will all be unresponsive to this antigen at any time up to 4 months later. If they are not tested until they are 12 months old, however, a portion of them will give an immune response (32).

In many, perhaps all, cases of tolerance to nonliving antigens, the unresponsiveness, if not reinforced by further injections of antigen, gives way to antibody production as it disappears (22). Tolerance to living antigens, if not complete, may gradually disappear and give way to an immune response leading to graft rejection (8,9). Such a process may take 20 to 30 days. The graft becomes pink, showing the existence of a chronic state of mild vascular dilatation and congestion. "Small superficial scabs or other blemishes appear on the epithelial surface, patches of hair are lost, and the graft as a whole contracts. Normally the process ends with the scabbing of the entire epithelial surface, but in borderline cases . . . a mildly eczematous state may persist indefinitely, and may even from time to time improve" (8,9).

6. Specificity of Tolerance

Since tolerance is an immunological phenomenon, it shows the same sort of specificity that other immunological reactions do. Dixon and Maurer (20) found that rabbits made unresponsive to human plasma proteins or bovine serum albumin still responded normally to other unrelated antigens. Cinader and Dubert (17) found that rabbits made unresponsive to human serum albumin responded normally to injections of tobacco mosaic virus, and produced antibody. Furthermore, of six such rabbits injected with human albumin coupled with diazotized sulfanilic acid, two responded by producing antibodies to the benzene-p-sulfonic acid group. These antibodies were essentially directed solely to the hapten, and had little or no avidity for human serum albumin.

Felton et al. (25) found that immunological paralysis of mice to pneumococcus polysaccharide of one type did not reduce the ability to form antibodies to a polysaccharide of another type.

A tolerant animal will accept a graft from another individual of the same species or strain, other than the donor whose tissues were used to produce the tolerant state in the first place, only if the second donor possesses no tissue compatibility antigens not present in the first donor. In non-inbred animals these conditions are seldom fulfilled, and grafts from such second donors are rejected (8,9).

7. Histocompatibility Antigens

It has not been possible to show that the antigenic differences seen in tissue transplants are identical with the blood group antigens, although these may play a role. The number of blood group antigens is large, and new ones are still being discovered, so that at least 30,000 different combinations of the human blood group factors so far discovered are possible (39). This number will undoubtedly increase, but it does not seem likely that it will ever be large enough to account for the fact that no two human beings, except identical twins, seem to be genetically identical, and thus capable of accepting homografts from each other.* It would seem, therefore, that other kinds of hereditary antigenic differences must exist, in addition to those that manifest themselves by variations in the agglutinability of the erythrocytes, analogous to those demonstrated in lower animals such as mice (see below).

The genetics of transplantation in lower organisms have been studied by a number of workers (see references in 4,43,44). Snell and co-workers, in a series of brilliant investigations (1,43,44) found that the compatibility of transplants in the mouse is controlled by genes at a number of loci, but chiefly by genes at a locus called H-2. At least 20 alleles are known to occur at this locus, and there are at least 15 different histocompatibility loci. Histocompatibility antigens determined by different genes, and antigens determined by genes at different loci, vary in the strength of their effect on the fate of a transplant (11).

Billingham, Brent, and Medawar (8,9) found that the histocompatibility antigens in mice reside wholly in the nuclei of the cells, and are developed well before birth. They are inactivated by lyophilization, freezing and thawing, or heating to 48.5°C. They are inactivated by digestion with deoxyribonuclease but not by ribonuclease. Billingham, Brent, and Medawar thought these antigens were deoxyribonucleoproteins.

The apparent individual specificity of tissues from different individuals is due, not usually to the presence of any antigen that is truly unique, but to the rarity of identical combinations of the various antigens (which may individually be fairly common) which affect "histocompatibility." The problem of finding compatible transplant donors may be treated mathematically (12) somewhat along the lines suggested by Good (28,34).

Since most of the blood group loci may be occupied by one of at least two antigen-producing alleles, we may logically suppose this is true of histocompatibility loci in general. If there are just two alleles, we may represent the frequency of one of them by p and of the other by $1 - p$. Then if donors for transplants are selected at random, we shall have the following situations (see p. 514):

---

* The acceptance of grafts from one chimera by the other, referred to above, is a matter of tolerance rather than genetical identity.

Combination	Antigens in donor	Antigens in recipient	Probability of combination
1	AA	AA	p^4
2	AA	BB	$p^2(1 - p)^2$
3	AA	AB	$2p^3(1 - p)$
4	BB	AA	$p^2(1 - p)^2$
5	BB	BB	$(1 - p)^4$
6	BB	AB	$2p(1 - p)^3$
7	AB	AA	$2p^3(1 - p)$
8	AB	BB	$2p(1 - p)^3$
9	AB	AB	$4p^2(1 - p)^2$

Now presumably the recipient will react immunologically to a transplant, and as a result reject it, only in situations 2, 4, 7, and 8, where the donor has an antigen not possessed by the recipient. The other situations, 1, 3, 5, 6, and 9, will be favorable and the transplant will take and become permanent. The combined probabilities of these situations are

$$p^4 + 2p^3(1 - p) + (1 - p)^4 + 2p(1 - p)^3 + 4p^2(1 - p)^2 =$$
$$2p^4 - 4p^3 + 4p^2 - 2p + 1.$$

This expression has a minimum value of 0.625 when $p = 1 - p = 1/2$

When more than 2 alleles are present, and if some of the genes are dominant over others, the formulas become more complicated. For instance, if we assume that transplants from donors of blood group O are compatible with recipients of any group, but that otherwise the above rule applies, we find the probability that a transplant made at random will be compatible with respect to the ABO blood group system is

$$P = r^2 + (p^2 + 2pr)^2 + (q^2 + 2qr)^2 + 2pq(1 - r^2)$$

where p, q, and r are the frequencies of the genes A, B, and O. For the population of the U.S.A. this gives $P = 0.63$ approximately.

If n alleles can occupy a locus, we may simplify the calculations by assuming that their frequencies are equal, which is often not too far from the truth. We easily obtain the formula for the chances of a compatible transplant

$$P = (4n - 3)/n^3.$$

If the alleles are not equally frequent, the true probability will be greater than the minimum value given by the formula. For instance, for the Kell system, where $k = 0.955$, the true probability is about 0.91, whereas the assumption that the alleles are equally frequent ($k = 0.5$)

gives $P = 0.625$, as did the previous formula. When a gene (or chromosome) can cause the production of more than one antigen, as in the MNS and Rh systems, the above formulas do not strictly apply, but results which are not too much in error may be obtained by applying the first formula to the individual antigen pairs MN and Ss and Cc, Dd and Ee and multiplying the results together. For the MNS system we thus obtain $P = 0.41$ and for the Rh system $P = 0.31$.

The chance of getting a transplant compatible with respect to all 9 of the well-studied blood group loci simultaneously is the product of the separate probabilities, since they are inherited independently (unless Lutheran and Lewis are loosely linked), and turns out to be 0.011, or about 1/90.

It is clear however that there are other histocompatibility loci in man in addition to the blood group loci. The exact number is unknown and we can only guess. It hardly seems likely that fewer than 20 loci are involved altogether, so we may assume 11 additional loci. If we assume only 2 equally frequent alleles at each of these, the probability of a compatible transplant for any one locus is 0.625, and the probability for all is $(0.625)^{11}$ or 0.0057. The probability of getting a transplant compatible with respect to the blood groups and the 11 hypothetical histocompatibility loci simultaneously is

$$0.011 \times 0.0057 = 0.000062$$

or about 1/16,000. The true probability may be much less than this.

It is thus quite understandable that there seems to be almost complete individuality of human tissues, and that the chances of finding a compatible transplant donor, other than an identical twin (or a fellow chimera), are negligible.

8. Abolition of Tolerance

Not only may tolerance disappear spontaneously, it may be abolished deliberately by certain measures. One of the most interesting of these is the injection of an antigen closely related to the tolerated antigen. For instance, Cinader and Dubert (18) interrupted tolerance to human serum albumin by injection an azobenzene derivative of albumin. At first the antibodies were merely to the hapten, but the specificity of the antibodies gradually broadened, as it often does (p. 54), and came to include enough receptors nearby the hapten so that antibody to unaltered human serum albumin was produced. Cinader (16) has shown diagramatically how breakdown of tolerance might be brought about in this way (Fig. 12-1).

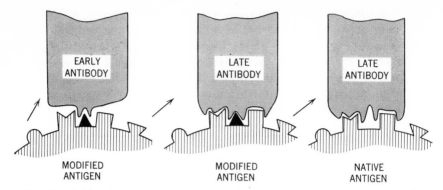

Fig. 12-1. Schematic representation of possible changes in the adaptation of antibody in animals tolerant to native albumin of another species, in the course of immunization with a chemically modified antigen. The black triangular area on the antigen represents the introduced synthetic determinant. [Modified from (16).]

Weigle terminated tolerance to bovine serum albumin by the administration of serum albumins from a variety of phylogenetically related species (46), Newton (36) reversed tolerance to DNP-human serum albumin by injecting DNP-bovine gamma globulin. Curtin (19) abolished tolerance to Bence-Jones protein by injecting myeloma proteins from the same individuals, and Bussard (14) reported that the injection of sheep erythrocytes into rabbits induced the formation, by isolated lymphoid cells, of antibodies that reacted with rabbit erythrocytes.

It is apparent that observations such as those of Bussard may have a bearing on the mechanism by which the formation of antibodies in autoimmune disease (Chapter 13) may be initiated.

Tolerance can also be abolished by the transfer of immunologically active cells (lymph node cells in this case) from a donor immunized to the antigen or antigens to which the recipient animal is tolerant. This was reported by Billingham, Brent, and Medawar (8,9). Tolerance of skin homografts (8,9) and of serum proteins (15) can also be abolished by transfer to the tolerant animal of lymph node cells from normal, non-immune, animals. It would seem that the introduction of these foreign cells not only introduces antibody against the antigens of which the recipient is tolerant (or initiates such antibody production) from the introduced cells, but enables the lymphoid tissues of the tolerant animal itself to begin antibody production.

9. Mechanism of Tolerance

Medawar (35) has given a thoughtful discussion of possible theories to account for immunological tolerance. He makes two preliminary assumptions: (A) *The maintainance of the tolerant state depends on the persistence of the antigen, and tolerance disappears when antigen disappears, or shortly thereafter.* (B) *Any one antibody-forming cell, and its direct descendants, responds to only one antigen at a time.* Medawar knows that there is some evidence that some cells can make two antibodies, but he prefers to make assumption (B) nevertheless.

He now finds three sets of alternative possibilities that might apply to assumption (B) (*Each antibody-forming cell, and its direct descendants, responds to only one antigen at a time*): (C1) *... and this is the only antigen to which it could have responded* ("predestination" theory), or (C2) *... but it could have responded to a different antigen if that other antigen had reached it first* ("pre-emption" theory. He does not find it possible at present to make a firm choice between C1 and C2.

The next pair of alternatives is: (D1) *Potential antibody-forming cells at a stage at which they are capable of being made tolerant occur only in embryos or very young animals,* or (D2) *Cells capable of being made tolerant occur in adults as well as in embryos.*

The last pair of alternatives bears on the change we suppose to occur in the cell when it becomes tolerant: (EI) *The production of tolerance involves the killing of an antibody-forming cell and a consequent lack of any descendants of that cell.* No good reason for the death of the cell can be offered, though Medawar suggests it might be due to hypersensitivity of the cell to antigen at some stage in its (the cell's) development. Burnet (13,13a) and Lederberg (33) have both suggested alternative (E1). (E2) *The production of tolerance involves some change in the immature antibody-forming cell other than its death and elimination.*

According to hypothesis (E1) there is no such thing as a tolerant *cell,* tolerance is a state of the whole organism due to the elimination of cells with certain potentialities. It is true that nobody has yet demonstrated the existence of a tolerant cell (47).

Medawar points out that the number of logically acceptable combinations of these alternatives is limited. If (E1) is accepted, we must also accept (C1), for otherwise the first exposure of the fetus to an antigen would kill all its future antibody-forming cells. If we accept (E1), (C1), and (A), it is virtually necessary to accept (D2), for why would antigen have to persist except to put out of commission the newly-differentiating stem cells envisaged by alternative (D2)? The choice (A)-(C1)-(E1)-(D1) seems in fact to be the one Lederberg makes.

The two self-consistent theories of tolerance that result from combinations of these alternatives are (A)-(C1)-(D2)-(E1), which is the Burnet-Lederberg theory, and (A)-(C2)-(D2)-(E2). Medawar points out that the second theory is much vaguer than the first.

If alternative (E1) were true, it would explain why the body does not (usually) form antibodies to its own antigens (*horror autotoxicus*). Any antibody-forming cells of the fetus that are able to make antibodies to any of the antigens of the fetus, being exposed to these antigens, are killed and there is no derived lineage. It has to be admitted that this is a neat explanation of a mysterious fact, but the present writer must confess that it leaves him less than entirely happy. The forces of evolution, over thousands and millions of years, have ruthlessly eliminated nearly all structures and mechanisms that have no survival value, and eliminated all the wasteful ways of doing biological things in favor of efficient ways. It hardly seems that the production in early embryonic life of a lot of potential antibody-forming cells that are just going to get killed off is an efficient mechanism.

Eisen and Karush (22), in an ingenious and provocative paper, have proposed a theory of immunological tolerance that emphasizes the bivalence of antibody (see Chapter 2). They postulate: (*a*) Bimolecular antibody–antigen complexes, Ag-Ab, are able to enter the antibody-forming cells and stimulate the formation of further antibody, (*b*) trimolecular complexes, Ag-Ab-Ag, cannot do this, nor can antigen (Ag) alone. They realize there is no particular evidence at present in favor of assumption (*b*); it is essentially an *ad hoc* hypothesis. The first Ag-Ab complexes would be formed with the "natural" antibody supposed always to be present, as in Jerne's theory of antibody formation (Chapter 2).

If the postulates of Eisen and Karush are granted, then tolerance would be due to persistence of the antigen, in amounts sufficient to make Ab-Ag complexes impossible, by turning them all into Ab-Ag-Ab. Eisen and Karush are able to account for the other phenomena described above also. As the authors point out, their theory may at least stimulate further experimental work.

10. The Fetus as a Homograft

The fetus, usually different antigenically in a number of ways from the mother, present us with an example of a generally well-tolerated homograft, and immunologists have concerned themselves with the problem of how this happens. The explanation favored by Billingham and Silvers (11) is a "barrier" hypothesis. They believe this barrier is the trophoblast cells which always constitute an unbroken, uninterrupted boundary of fetal tissue in immediate contact with the maternal tissue. It seems that histocompatibility antigens are either lacking in, or ineffectively expressed by, the trophoblast.

11. Reaction of Graft Against the Host

Tissue transplants contain some immunologically competent cells, and the host usually possesses antigens the donor does not. It would therefore not be surprising if the graft made an immune response to the host, and there is abundant evidence that this may happen. This GvH reaction, as Woodruff (48) calls it, was first recognized by Billingham and Brent (6) and Simonsen (44). In mice injected at birth with spleen cells from other mice, Billingham and Brent observed symptoms of wasting, diarrhea, and hypoplasia of lymphoid tissue. Since the animals were below normal size as a result of this syndrome, Billingham and Brent called the condition *runt disease*. It is sometimes fatal. Simonsen observed, in chickens that had been injected similarly, severe hemolytic anemia associated with the appearance of numerous plasma cells in the spleen, bone marrow, and thymus. Death usually occurred within 2 weeks after hatching (15).

Another condition that seems to be mainly due to a GvH reaction is the so-called *secondary disease*, which sometimes develops in heavily irradiated animals that have recovered temporarily following the injection of spleen or bone marrow cells from other individuals of the same species (48).

The literature on immunological tolerance is already enormous, and no attempt has been made to cover the subject exhaustively here. Reviews will be found in refs. 30,42,35,15,45,11. The last reference contains references to numerous other reviews and symposia.

References

1. Agner, K., *J. Exptl. Med.*, **92**, 337 (1950).
2. Algire, G. H., *J. Natl. Cancer Inst.*, **15**, 483–491 (1954).
3. Algire, G. H., J. M. Weaver, and R. T. Prehn, *J. Natl. Cancer Inst.*, **15**, 493–507 (1954).
4. Allen, S. L., *Cancer Res.*, **15**, 315 (1955).
5. Amos, D. B., P. A. Gorer, B. M. Mikulska, R. E. Billingham, and E. M. Sparrow, *Brit. J. Exptl. Pathol.*, **35**, 203–208 (1954).
6. Billingham, R. E., and L. Brent, *Transplant. Bull.*, **4**, 167 (1957).
7. Billingham, R. E., L. Brent, P. B. Medawar, *Nature*, **172**, 603–606 (1953).
8. Billingham, R. E., L. Brent, and P. B. Medawar, *Nature*, **178**, 514–519 (1956).
9. Billingham, R. E., L. Brent, and P. B. Medawar, *Phil. Trans. Royal Soc. London*, **B239**, 357–414 (1956).
10. Billingham, R. E., G. H. Lampkin, P. B. Medawar, and H. L. Williams, *Heredity*, **6**, 201–212 (1952).
11. Billingham, R. E., and W. K. Silvers, *Ann. Rev. Microbiol.*, **17**, 531–564 (1963).
12. Boyd, W. C., *Surgery*, **40**, 1007–1009 (Dec.) (1956).
13. Burnet, F. M., *Australian J. Sci.*, **20**, 67 (1957).

520   FUNDAMENTALS OF IMMUNOLOGY

13a. Burnet, F. M., *The Clonal Selection Theory of Acquired Immunity*, Vanderbilt University Press, Nashville, 1959.
14. Bussard, A., and C. Hannoun, *Nature*, **194**, 881 (1962).
15. Chase, M. W., *Ann. Rev. Microbiol.*, **13**, 349–376 (1959).
16. Cinader, B., *Brit. Med. Bull.*, **19**, 219–224 (1963); *Canadian Cancer Conf.*, **5**, 279, Academic Press, New York, 1963.
17. Cinader, B., and J. M. Dubert, *Brit. J. Exptl. Pathol.*, **36**, 515–529 (1955).
18. Cinader, B., and J. M. Dubert, *Proc. Roy. Soc.*, **B146**, 18 (1956).
19. Curtin, C. C., *Brit. J. Exptl. Pathol.*, **40**, 225 (1958).
20. Dixon, F. J., and P. H. Maurer, *J. Exptl. Med.*, **101**, 245 (1955).
21. Dunsford, I., C. C. Bowley, A. M. Hutchison, J. S. Thompson, R. Sanger, and R. R. Race, *Brit. Med. J.*, **2**, 81 (1953).
22. Eisen, H. N., and F. Karush, *Nature*, **202**, 677–682 (1964).
23. Felton, L. D., *J. Immunol.*, **61**, 107 (1949).
25. Felton, L. D., G. Kauffmann, B. Prescott, and B. Ottinger, *J. Immunol.*, **74**, 17 (1955).
25a. Felton, L. D., and B. Ottinger, *J. Bact.*, **43**, 94 (1942).
26. Felton, L. D., B. Prescott, G. Kauffmann, and B. Ottinger, *J. Immunol.*, **74**, 205–213 (1955).
27. Glynn, L. E., in *Modern Trends in Immunology*, Butterworth, Washington, D. C., 1963, pp. 206–225.
28. Good, I. J., *Lancet*, **II**, 289 (1952).
29. Good, R. A., and B. W. Papermaster, in *Adv. Immunol.*, **4**, 1–115 (1964).
30. Hašek, M., A. Lengerová, and T. Hrava, *Adv. Immunol.*, **1**, 1–66 (1961).
31. Humphrey, J. H., *Immunology*, **4**, 380–387 (1961).
32. Humphrey, J. H., and R. G. White, *Immunology for Students of Medicine*, F. A. Davis, Philadelphia, 1963.
33. Lederberg, J., *Science*, **129**, 1649–1653 (1959).
34. Medawar, P. B., *J. Natl. Cancer Inst.*, **14**, 691 (1953).
35. Medawar, P. B., in *Cellular Aspects of Immunity*, G. E. W. Wolstenholme, and M. O'Connor, eds., Little, Brown and Co., New York, 1960, pp. 134–156.
36. Newton, W. T., *Fed. Proc.*, **22**, 440 (1963).
37. Owen, R. D., *Science*, **102**, 400–401 (1945).
38. Owen, R. D., H. P. Davis, and R. F. Morgan, *J. Heredity*, **37**, 291–297 (1946).
39. Race, R. R., and R. Sanger, *Blood Groups in Man*, Blackwell Scientific, Oxford, 1954.
40. Silverstein, A. M., *Science*, **144**, 1423–1428 (1964).
41. Simonsen, M., *Acta Pathol. Microbiol. Scand.*, **40**, 480 (1957).
42. Smith, R. T., *Adv. Immunol.*, **1**, 67–129 (1961).
43. Snell, G. D., *J. Natl. Cancer Inst.*, **14**, 691 (1953).
44. Snell, G. D., P. Smith, and F. Gabrielson, *J. Natl. Cancer Inst.*, **14**, 457 (1953).
45. Stetson, C. A., *Adv. Immunol.*, **3**, 97–130 (1963).
46. Weigle, W. O., *J. Exptl. Med.*, **114**, 111 (1961).
47. Woodruff, M. F. A., in *Biological Problems of Grafting, a Symposium*, F. Albert and P. B. Medawar, eds., Blackwell, Oxford, 1959, p. 258.
48. Woodruff, M. F. A., in *Clinical Aspects of Immunology*, P. G. H. Gell and R. R. A. Coombs, eds., F. A. Davis, Philadelphia, 1963.

ipsam seque retro partem petere ore priorem
vulneris ardenti, ut morsu premat, icta dolore.
—Lucretius, *De Rerum Natura III*, 662, 663

CHAPTER 13

Autoimmunization and Disease

1. Introduction

The immune process is clearly one of the body's defense mechanisms against infection. Ideally, therefore, the body should respond immunologically only to the antigens of pathogenic microorganisms, viruses, and parasites. However, this is not so; animals, including man, will respond to injection of harmless antigens such as foreign serum proteins. We have seen in Chapters 8 and 9 that some persons also respond, often to their ultimate disadvantage, to otherwise harmless antigens of pollens, house dust, and animal danders. It is likely that such individuals have inherited a greater than normal tendency to respond allergically, for the rest of us are generally not affected in this way, although to some allergens, such as those of *Ascaris,* virtually every human being will respond. It is true that in this case it is possible that the response is on the whole a beneficial one (p. 500).

However, even though the antigens of allergic incitants are in themselves harmless, they are nevertheless foreign, and it seems but a small indiscretion on the part of the body to be unable to distinguish, occasionally, between antigens of harmful pathogens and those of harmless animals and plants. It used to be taken for granted that the body would at any rate never make the much graver mistake of responding immunologically to its own antigens. Ehrlich formulated this in his famous rule of *horror autotoxicus,* and Burnet (12) believed that each cell contains a warning "self-marker component" established during embryonic life, which prevents the body from making an immunological response to constituents of one of its own cells.

But the body can, and in many cases does, produce an immunological response to its own antigens. Mackay and Burnet (77) believe that the "immunological tolerance" to the organism's own antigens, which normally develops, is destroyed, probably by the development, presumably

521

by mutation, of a new clone of immunologically competent cells, which are uninstructed not to respond to the organism's own antigens, and begin to elaborate antibodies to these antigens.

We have mentioned above (Chapter 4) that the organism can respond by antibody production to those of its antigens that ordinarily do not enter the circulation. According to Ammann, von Muralt, and Hässig (6), in about 20 per cent of nursing mothers, rapid cessation of lactation causes the production of passively agglutinating and complement-fixing autoantibodies against the antigens in human milk.

Ordinarily, Burnet believes (77) the homeostatic mechanisms of the body prevent the emergence of clones of immunologically competent cells that can produce antibodies (or other immune response) to the antigens of the organism itself. But in some cases this homeostatic mechanism breaks down, and such cells are produced, and such unwelcome anti-bodies are produced. This Burnet believes, may be either the result of mutation or of some "triggering mechanism." The triggering mechanism may be an infection, in which perhaps a toxin combines with some of the patients' erythrocytes so as to make them "foreign" to his antibody-form-ing cells, or the combination of some drug with some of his cells, which apparently can make them "foreign" to these antibody-forming cells.

The antibodies an individual produces to his own antigens are called *autoantibodies,* that is, antibodies to "self." We thus distinguish them from *isoantibodies,* which are produced by an individual of a species in response to the antigens of another individual of the same species; and *heteroantibodies,* which are produced against the antigens of a member of another species.

There seem to be at least three ways in which autoantibodies can be produced (133):

First of all, autoantibodies for red cells may be of heterogenetic origin, formed in response to infections, possibly inapparent, by microorganisms which possess antigens related chemically to antigens present in human red cells. If this is the case, these antibodies do not represent the result of a true autoimmunization, and Wiener (133) compared their reactions with human red cells to the opening of a lock by a skeleton key.

Secondly, Wiener (129,133) suggested that individuals exist who have a remarkable propensity to form antibodies. Such individuals are oc-casionally encountered, for example, in blood transfusion practice, where they present difficult problems in the selection of donors because they have developed so many immune isoantibodies. Some of these indi-viduals have formed antibodies against antigens which are generally found to be extremely weak. Such individuals may form true autoantibodies. It may be significant that Callender and Race (13) found in a patient with lupus erythematosus, a disease thought to be due to autoimmunization, antibodies to the weak antigens c and N and three previously undescribed—and therefore probably weak—blood antigens.

Finally, Wiener (133) mentioned the hypothesis that bacteria, or viruses, toxins, and other hemagglutinating or hemolytic agents may alter red cells and thus render them autoantigenic. Wiener points to the analogy with the enhancing effect of adjuvants, and we should also mention the effect of certain drugs, such as Sedormid (p. 525).

The first disease for which an antoimmune origin was established is paroxysmal cold hemoglobinuria, the mechanism of which was explained by Donath and Landsteiner (32,33). The serum of individuals with this disease contains a hemolysin capable of uniting with, and hemolyzing (in the presence of complement), their own erythrocytes. The autohemolysin unites with erythrocytes only at low temperatures, and causes hemolysis only at body temperature. If an affected person has even a part of his body exposed to cold, he later suffers intravascular hemolysis. Donath and Landsteiner found that nearly all affected individuals were syphilitic. Nonsyphilitic cases certainly exist (23).

The lysin was found to be unrelated to the Wassermann antibody, but it is clearly suggestive that the autoimmunization had taken place mainly in infected individuals, and this observation colors our thinking about other diseases.

Autoantibodies against red cells are also produced in other circumstances. These antibodies are of two types: warm autoantibodies which sensitize the red cell to the action of antiglobulin (see p. 374) but which do not agglutinate in saline, and cold agglutinins which do agglutinate in saline and which act much more strongly at lower temperatures. Antibodies of the former kind were demonstrated in 1945 by Wiener (126a) in a case of acquired hemolytic anemia, by the "conglutinin" test.

Such antibodies are found in many patients with atypical pneumonia, and less regularly in certain acute bacterial infections, trypanosomiasis, Raynaud's disease, cirrhosis of the liver, and lupus erythematosus (q.v.). Autoantibodies of the "warm" class almost invariably cause trouble, according to Dameshek, as do high concentrations of "cold" antibodies.

Autoantibodies against platelets have been shown to be operating in some cases of idiopathic thrombocytopenic purpura.

The recognition of the possible role of autoantibodies in disease was also facilitated by the discovery of the cytotoxic effects of antiorgan sera. Lindemann (74) demonstrated an injurious activity of antikidney serum in 1900, but it was not until 1934, when Masugi (80) showed that anti-rat-kidney serum produced in the rabbit would induce nephritis in rats, that interest in the subject was aroused, and the question seriously debated, whether nephritis as seen in man could be in some cases the result of the action of antikidney antibodies produced by autoimmunization.

Another line of thought concerned the similarity of the disseminated demyelinating encephalomyelitis which sometimes follows vaccination against rabies, in which a vaccine made of rabbit spinal cord or brain is employed, to demyelinating diseases of unknown etiology, such as multiple sclerosis. It was shown that injection of heterologous brain substance into various animals would produce striking brain damage. Then it was found that injection of homologous brain substance would produce the same effect, if the brain were autolyzed or infected with vaccinia (70,53). Rivers and Schwentker (98) found that injections of brain tissue extract into monkeys, continued over a long period of time, resulted in a demyelinating encephalopathy bearing certain resemblances in pathology to multiple sclerosis. Since then various workers have shown that if the brain extract were mixed with the adjuvant mixture of oil and killed tubercle bacilli devised by Freund (see p. 125), the time required to produce symptoms was cut to three weeks or so (113,59).

Still other procedures will cause an animal to produce antibodies to his own tissues when these, or an extract of them, are injected. Mixing with streptococcus or staphylococcus toxin has been found to make rabbit kidney antigenic for rabbits (14), and it has been reported that human beings with scarlet fever may develop antibodies reactive upon rabbit kidney. It is true that none of these findings have been confirmed by all workers, but they are all compatible with the idea that an animal's own tissues may in themselves induce an antibody response, especially when they are slightly modified or mixed with certain stimulating agents.

Such evidence has led to the search for autoantibodies or other evidence of autoimmunization in a number of diseases of man, with positive results in a number of cases.

It is probably no accident that many of the diseases now suspected of being the result of autoimmunization follow infections, or the development of drug allergy, or something of the sort. It seems likely that the pathogenic agent (e.g., hemolytic streptococcus in rheumatic fever—this is one of the possibilities, at least) or the drug (e.g., sulfonamides) acts in some way so as to make certain constituents of the individual's own tissues antigenic for him. The mechanism involved is not yet known: it may be that some of the products of the microorganism, or the drug, combine with certain tissue constituents, and thus function like haptens, or the bacteria or some of their products may have an adjuvant action; or the bacterial products or the drug may induce sensitization which results in stepped-up antibody production; or they may act in some way as yet not elucidated.

There is a proprietary sedative, Sedormid (allylisopropylacetylurea), which has been observed to cause thrombocytopenic purpura. It has been suggested that this occurs when the drug after ingestion combines with the platelets, and forms a Sedormid-platelet conjugate which is antigenic for the patient (1,2). It has in fact been observed that the serum of individuals sensitive to Sedormid will lyse platelets *in vitro* only in the presence of Sedormid. Other drugs, notably quinidine, may cause thrombocytopenia (109).

Another suggestion which has encouraged belief in the existence of autoimmune diseases is that of Klemperer (63,64) that certain apparently unrelated diseases could be grouped together as "collagen diseases." According to Mackay and Burnet (77) this term has only anatomical validity. It seems best to quote the author's own words. In the original paper Klemperer and his associates stated:

"It must become quite clear that one may regard the connective tissues of the body . . . as a well-defined, widely dispersed system liable to a variety of injuries. We are concerned here only with those processes which affect the system in its entirety. . . . However, to identify this system as a seat of certain diseases is by no means to identify these diseases with one another or even to relate them; this would be an unjustifiable oversimplification."

Among the diseases which have been classed as collagen diseases we may list thrombohemolytic thrombocytopenic purpura, periarteritis nodosa, disseminated lupus erythematosus, rheumatoid arthritis, rheumatic fever, generalized scleroderma, dermatomyositis, atypical verrucose endocarditis, and serum sickness. Serum sickness is of course a disease of hypersensitivity (p. 475), and a fair number of the others have been suspected of being autoimmune in etiology (129).

Further progress resulted from the study of acquired hemolytic anemia, leukopenias, and purpuras.

Evans (38) pointed out that the dividing line between immunohemolytic and immunothrombocytopenic disease is difficult to define, for some patients display both processes simultaneously. Some cases of predominantly autoimmune hemolytic disease show also thrombocytopenia and leucopenia. The disorder idiopathic thrombocytopenic purpura perhaps represents at least a triple immunological disturbance in which the platelets are involved and, in acute cases, the small blood vessels may also be affected. Another disease, thrombotic thrombocytopenic purpura, presents a triad as defined by Singer: (1) hemolytic anemia, (2) thrombocytopenia, and (3) transitory cerebral symptoms due to thrombi in the brain. Dameshek and Stefanini (26) suggest that a better name for the condition might be "thrombohemolytic thrombocytopenic purpura." Wiener (129) suggested it was autoimmune in origin. The impression is gaining ground (71) that this disorder may be related to periarteritis nodosa (which we saw in Chapter 8 is also thought to be a disease due to hypersensitivity), and that these two diseases and a number of the other collagen diseases are the direct result of autosensitization. According to Dameshek, we ought to consider including in this class also acquired hemolytic anemia, thrombocytopenia, and even the occasional coagulation disorder based on the development of an anticoagulant. Klinge (65) included, with the diseases due to hypersensitivity, malignant nephrosclerosis, thromboangiitis obliterans, certain nephritides, and subacute bacterial endocarditis.

The concept of autoimmunization as a cause of the diseases discussed here is not accepted by all (37). Even if an autoimmune origin were established for all these diseases, however, there would still remain much to be learned about the actual pathological processes involved. Kissmeyer-Nielsen, Bichel, and Hansen (62) have proposed the hypothesis that autoimmunization, rather than being the cause of diseases such as immunohemolytic anemia, is a *consequence* of the increased blood destruction, of unknown etiology, which characterizes the disease.

Dameshek and Stefanini (26) believe that the unifying concept of autoimmune disease is so important that in every instance of autoimmune hemolytic anemia and of idiopathic thrombocytopenic purpura it is essential to search for a possible underlying disorder. They liken the situation to an iceberg floating nine-tenths submerged, with only certain peaks above the water level (Fig. 13-1). Thrombocytopenic purpura or hemolytic anemia or arthritis or nephritis may be at the surface and readily recognizable, but the great mass of the iceberg—disseminated lupus, periarteritis nodosa—may be out of sight below the water level and thus not recognized until it is perhaps too late for either proper diagnosis or proper therapy.

The development of more sensitive methods of detecting antibodies, and particularly methods of detecting nonprecipitating and nonagglutinating antibodies, such as the so-called conglutinin reaction (31,127), the "Coombs test" (development with antiglobulin) (19–21), and enzyme treatment of erythrocytes (89), has a good deal to do with the recent advances in these investigations.

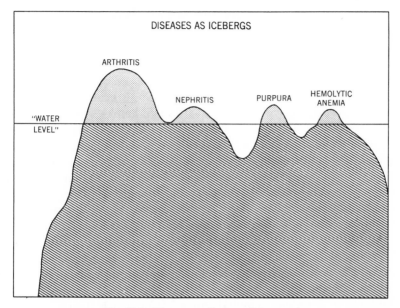

Fig. 13-1. Diseases as "icebergs" (see text).

In support of the concept of the autoimmune origin of the collagen diseases, it has been pointed out that collogen is definitely antigenic (124), and that antibodies for gelatin are often found in normal blood (82,83, 40). Rabbits can be immunized to gelatin if it is first coupled with a hapten such as diazotized arsanilic acid (51) or mixed with adjuvants (82–84). It seems entirely possible that antibodies to collagen or other basic constituents of the body might be produced as a consequence of enhancement of the antigenic activity by infection, induced allergic state, or other alterations of normal physiology.

All or nearly all the diseases to be discussed here have certain things in common: they often follow an infectious disease, they are often familial, suggesting that the patient has inherited a tendency to produce antibodies readily and perhaps unnecessarily, they often produce "biologically false-positive" tests for syphilis, and they are often relieved or improved by ACTH and cortisone.

The general concept of autoimmunization in relation to disease has been reviewed by Dameshek (25), Vorlaender (115), Dausset (27), Wiener (135), and Cavelti (15).

2. Conditions Affecting the Blood

Acquired Hemolytic Anemia

It is now firmly established that one variety, at least, of acquired hemolytic anemia depends upon the mechanism of autoimmunization (54). The antibodies formed are not specific for the cells of the individual but seem to act on the red cells of nearly all human beings. Free antibody is difficult to detect in the circulation of patients with this disease, but the use of technics derived from Rh studies (see p. 374) has been uniformly successful in demonstrating the presence of antibodies combined with the erythrocytes (8,22). It has also been possible to elute the antibody from the erythrocytes and verify its specificity for human cells (67).

The term "acquired hemolytic anemia" is descriptive of a number of disorders of probably different etiology and pathogenesis. In many instances, certainly, the excessive hemolysis seems to be due, at least in part, to the action of antibodies directed against the patient's own erythrocytes, but in other cases the pathogenesis is less obvious, and in some patients it is quite unknown.

The types of acquired hemolytic anemias for which definite evidence exists of the formation of autoantibodies, the "autoimmune" type, have been classified by Dacie (23) as follows:

1. "Idiopathic" acquired hemolytic anemia.

2. Hemolytic anemia following virus pneumonia or certain other infections. Here the antibodies are heterogenetic (131).

3. Paroxysmal cold hemoglobinuria.

4. Hemolytic anemia associated with chronic lymphatic leukemia, reticulosarcoma, or disseminated lupus erythematosis, etc.

For a detailed treatment of each of these various types the reader is referred to Dacie (23). Only a brief general discussion of the conditions as a group will be possible here.

In "immunohemolytic anemia" the patient is observed to have formed antibodies against his own erythrocytes. These antibodies may vary somewhat from patient to patient, and the serum of one patient may contain more than one kind of antibody. The autoantibodies produced seem to be of two main kinds: warm antibodies active at 37°C. and cold antibodies active only at lower temperatures.

At first these antibodies were thought to be "nonspecific," that is, to be directed against some hypothetical antigen possessed by all human cells, but in recent years evidence has been accumulating that in some cases, at least, the antibodies are directed against definite blood group antigens (references in 94).

A significant step forward in our knowledge of autoantibodies was taken by Weiner *et al.* in 1953 (125). They examined the red cells of a man who had acquired hemolytic anemia. These cells were agglutinated by antihuman globulin serum, showing that antibody was combined with them. When this antibody was eluted from the washed cells, it was found to be the Rh antibody anti-e. The patient's Rh genotype, however, was CDe/CDe, so that his own red cells possessed the antigen against which he had formed an autoantibody. Without thorough investigation this antibody would have been reported as "nonspecific," for anti-e agglutinates the bloods of 98 per cent of English and European (and white American) populations.

The findings of Weiner *et al.* were confirmed by Dacie and Cutbush (24) in England, and Holländer (50) in Switzerland. Dacie and Cutbush found anti-e in five out of ten patients, all five of whom were of genotype ee. (In one case the anti-e was accompanied by anti-C.) Holländer (50) found anti-c in a patient who was CDe/cde.

Van Loghem and van der Hart (75) reported studies of a number of cases of acquired hemolytic anemia in which specific autoantibodies, usually directed against the Rh system, were demonstrable. Kissmeyer-Nielsen, Bichel, and Hansen (62) report two cases of autoimmune anti-D.

Race and Sanger went so far as to say "It looks as if most auto-antibodies will, in the end, be found to have some blood group specificity." Wiener believes, on the contrary, that autoantibodies are specific for antigens present in *every* human blood (132). No convincing evidence has been obtained that any of these autoantibodies are strictly "autospecific," that is, capable of reacting only with the patient's cells.

From the reactions of the autoantibodies of acquired hemolytic anemia at different temperatures, with cells of other species, with enzyme-treated cells, and with antiglobulin serum, Wiener, Gordon, and Gallop (134) deduced that some are directed against the "nucleus" (that part of the antigenic structure common to all human beings) of the ABO antigenic system, some against the nucleus of the MNS system, and some against the nucleus of the Rh system.

Wiener (132) believed that cold autoantibodies are naturally present, to some extent, in serum of all normal persons, but are not observed to act unless they are tested for at low temperatures, or with especially sensitive antigens such as enzyme-treated cells. A second type of antibody, which Wiener believes is the result of true autosensitization, in contrast to the cold antibodies, which he believes are of heterogenetic origin, acts preferentially at body temperature. Using Ehrlich's old analogy of the lock and key, Wiener likens the autoantibodies which act preferentially at body temperature to the specific key for a specific lock and likens the cold autoantibodies to a skeleton key.

Zoutendyk and Gear (137), using the Coombs antiglobulin test, have reported evidence of autoantibodies in a variety of conditions in addition to acquired hemolytic anemia and acute disseminated lupus erythematosus. They obtained positive Coombs reactions in some patients with aplastic anemia, glandular fever, myeloid leukemia, acute rheumatic fever, acute glomerular nephritis, atypical and subacute pneumonitis, infectious hepatitis, syphilis, trypanosomiasis, and malaria.   Marshall, Zoutendyk, and Gear (78) found positive Coombs tests in 3 cases of acute disseminated lupus erythematosus, 2 out of 14 cases of chronic discoid lupus erythematosus, 2 out of 3 of the Stevens-Johnson syndrome, 2 out of 3 cases of dermatomyositis, 1 case each of scleroderma and Raynaud's disease, and 1 case of erythema multiforme which developed acute hemolytic anemia.   Selwyn and Alexander (102) found a positive Coombs test in a case of pernicious anemia.

It has not been established that these patients produce autoantibodies as the result of enhanced antigenicity due to infection, allergic response to drugs, or any other such factor, though this is one hypothesis.   Rosenthal, Komninos, and Dameshek (99) believed that the important factor is some inherent character of the individual which makes him particularly likely to respond to an antigenic stimulus by an outpouring of antibodies. Stats and Wasserman (107) suggested that alteration of red cells by combination with viruses, proteins, polysaccharides, etc., may modify them sufficiently to convert them into autoantigens.

Wallace, Dodd, and Wright (122) reported that treatment of chicken erythrocytes with trypsin, Newcastle disease virus, or influenza virus created or exposed new antigenic material, and that normal erythrocytes would not absorb these antibodies from an antiserum against the treated cells.   They suggest that virus or possibly enzyme alteration of red cells may perhaps be trigger mechanisms in certain of the autoimmune diseases.

It is not known just how the antibodies which are produced exert their damaging effects on the cell.   In some cases hemolysins can be demonstrated, and the mechanism of their action is of course plain, but such antibodies are much less common than agglutinating or coating antibodies demonstrable by the Coombs test, use of albumin, or the use of trypsinized cells (99).   However, Evans and Duane (38) believed that even slight agglutination in the blood stream may cause stasis resulting in increased fragility of erythrocytes and possibly increased susceptibility to phagocytosis.   It has been demonstrated that a dose of immune antiserum for erythrocytes regularly destroys many more corpuscles when administered *in vivo* than it seems capable of hemolyzing *in vitro* (23). Wiener (129) believed that "autoconglutination" *in vivo* produces vascular damage and disseminated lesions.

Wasastjerna (123) believed that the main mechanisms of red cell destruction are probably (1) intravascular hemolysis, (2) intervascular agglutination with mechanical trauma acting on the red cell clumps, and sequestration followed by hemolysis of agglutinated cells in the spleen and other organs, and (3) phagocytosis of red cells coated with globulin, *i.e.,* antibody. The spleen is probably always enlarged in human acquired hemolytic anemia, and splenectomy often has a favorable influence on the course of the disease. This suggests that much of the blood destruction occurs in the spleen (23).

It has been reported (99) that the administration of ACTH and cortisone may bring about reduction and eventual disappearance of the hemolysin and agglutinin and the antibodies against lipide antigens. The nonagglutinating coating antibodies may be only partially suppressed. Residual tissue damage is not repaired (77).

Idiopathic Thrombocytopenic Purpura

Purpura means abnormal bleeding, which can be due to abnormalities in the vessels (purpura simplex, Henoch's and Schoenlein's purpura), to low platelet count (thrombocytopenic purpura), or to deficiencies in particular substances in the plasma. Thrombocytopenia can be due to drug allergy or can be idiopathic (cause unknown).

Idiopathic thrombocytopenic purpura refers to a disease entity characterized by low platelet count of undetermined origin with extravasations of blood into the skin and mucous membranes, frequently responding to splenectomy. The permeability of the small blood vessels is altered, and mechanical factors probably influence the distribution of the lesions. According to Dameshek and Stefanini (26) idiopathic thrombocytopenic purpura has three features which are all-important for differential diagnosis and definition:

1. The platelet count is low but there is no apparent abnormality of the red cells or leukocytes.

2. The spleen is not ordinarily palpable, or if so, just slightly.

3. The bone marrow contains abundant megakaryocytes.

Evans (38a) suggested in 1951 that this disease might be due to autoimmunization. In confirmation, he frequently found a positive Coombs test and platelet agglutinins. By the very direct method of injecting blood plasma from patients suffering from idiopathic thrombocytopenic purpura into healthy persons, Harrington and his associates (43) proved that a platelet-destroying factor was present. Miescher and Vannotti (88) demonstrated that the plasma of patients would lower the platelet count of rabbits. Observations of Stefanini and co-workers and of Hirsch and Gardner (26) showed that the platelet survival time in patients with the disease was considerably less than normal, particularly in acute cases. Stefanini and others developed methods for the accurate determination of platelet agglutinins, and showed that such agglutinins were present in about 50 per cent of the chronic cases, sometimes in very high concentration (26). The mechanism of platelet destruction in autoimmune thrombocytopenia is undoubtedly related to splenic function (44).

Tullis and Surgenor (114), using an *in vitro* test for platelet antibody, found a positive reaction in 24 out of 40 sera from patients with idiopathic thrombocytopenic purpura. In a series of 2000 normal sera, no positive reactions were found, nor were any found in the sera from 9 patients with active nonthrombocytopenic purpura.

Stefanini *et al.* (108a) reported that there are two natural isoagglutinins for platelets in human serum, and that their reactions with platelets of different individuals suffice to determine four types, analogous to, but entirely independent of, the blood groups of the erythrocytes. Gurevitch and Nelkin (41), on the other hand, reported that platelets are agglutinated by anti-A and anti-B sera just like erythrocytes, and that their groups correspond to the erythrocyte group of the individual. Moureau and André (90) also concluded that platelets contain the antigens A and B in correspondence with the blood group of the individual, but that these antigens are located inside the protoplasm of the platelets. Using "isoimmune" plasmas (from patients who had received repeated platelet transfusion), Stefanini *et al.* thought they could distinguish six serologically different platelet types. They pointed out that occasionally the anti-platelet agglutinins found in the plasma of persons who have received repeated transfusions react with the individual's own platelets, and are thus autoantibodies.

Dameshek (25) summarized the persuasive evidence that vascular purpura is an autoimmune disease.

According to Dameshek and Stefanini (26) ACTH and cortisone appear to have definite value in reducing the bleeding symptoms in idiopathic thrombocytopenic purpura, probably by decreasing the capillary permeability rather than by any effect on the platelet level. With adequate hormone therapy, the bleeding time, the tourniquet test, and other indications of increased capillary permeability are usually diminished within a few hours.

Chronic Leukopenia

This disease, formerly thought to be due to a hyperplasia of the reticulo-endothelial system of the spleen, is now believed by a number of workers (86,27) to be due in some cases at least to autoimmunization to antigens contained in the leukocytes. Miescher (86) supported this theory by the following observations: injection of the serum of a patient with chronic leukopenia into rabbits was fatal in doses of 3 ml. per kilogram of body weight; at autopsy aggregates of agglutinated leukocytes were in the arteries, especially in the lungs and kidneys; the addition of normal leukocytes to such a serum neutralized this toxic property, and after this absorption the β_2- and γ-globulins were found to be diminished.

Dausset (27) summarized the findings of antileukocytic antibodies in cases of agranulocytosis, neutropenia, and leukopenia, and showed that in very many cases lysins for leukocytes, or toxic action on leukocytes in man or animals, have been demonstrated in the serum of the patient. He pointed out that these antileukocytic substances have all the properties we commonly associate with antibodies.

The technic of detecting leukoagglutinins was described by Dausset, Nenna, and Brecy (28). These authors believe the phenomenon to be immunological, since leukocytes are known to be antigenic, and they point out that antigenic specificity has been demonstrated for neutrophils and lymphocytes. They feel that the antibody they find by this technic may be an autoantibody, although they do not regard this as demonstrated.

Miescher and Fauconnet (87) found that the antileukocyte antibody in the serum of certain patients agglutinates the leukocytes of certain individuals only. Absorption experiments showed that this agglutinin could be absorbed by leukocytes that gave positive agglutination reactions, but not by leukocytes that were negative. This suggests that leukocyte groups exist in man. These groups seem to be quite independent of the blood groups.

Treatment with cortisone has sometimes given spectacular but temporary improvement (28).

Physiologic Icterus

The icterus index of the serum of newborn infants is higher than the values considered normal for adults. Moreover, in most infants the icterus index rises during the first few days of life, not infrequently with resulting noticeable jaundice of the skin and mucous membranes. It has generally been considered that this is due to functional immaturity of the liver at birth, but Wiener (130,126) suggested that one of the contributing fatcors may be the presence in the mother's circulation of auto-antibodies which diffuse into the circulation of the fetus. These antibodies are believed to be of the cold variety, and the cooling of the baby's skin after birth is thought to bring about clumping of the cooled red cells and to act as the trigger mechanism which sets off the mild explosion which is physiologic icterus.

3. Diseases Affecting Connective Tissue

Periarteritis Nodosa

Periarteritis (polyarteritis) nodosa is a form of inflammatory panarteritis affecting any of the medium-sized and small arteries, with added regional symptoms depending upon the organs specifically involved. The disease is rather rare, and attacks primarily middle-aged males. The occurrence of the disease in patients who have suffered from asthma, serum sickness, or sulfonamide reactions has been thought for some time to argue in favor of a hypersensitivity reaction as the basis. The possible autoimmune origin is suggested by the frequent association of the disease with rheumatic endocarditis, scarlet fever, and tonsillitis; this might suggest that infections may alter normal tissue constituents so as to render them auto-antigenic (42). It has been found possible to produce the characteristic lesions in rabbits by the repeated injections of horse serum (96a).

These observations are compatible with the long-recognized fact that the blood vessels are susceptible to injuries by reactions of hypersensitiveness. The damage to the media in periarteritis nodosa may be a consequence of endothelial injury of the intima just as in local anaphylactic reactions. The focal injury and localized edema in the arteries could be interpreted as "hives" of the blood vessels (18). Collins and Wilensky state that the weight of evidence available at the present time suggests that periarteritis nodosa may be fundamentally an antibody–antigen reaction occurring in the blood vessels of various tissues and organs.

A case of periarteritis nodosa with LE cells (see p. 539) has been reported (73), further strengthening the notion that we are dealing with a disease which in some way involves hypersensitivity.

Administration of cortisone in cases of periarteritis nodosa was found to give prompt subjective relief; subsidence of fever took place within 24 to 72 hours, with gradual decrease of elevated sedimentation rates to normal or nearly normal. Partial relapse occurred when the cortisone was discontinued, followed by further improvement after the administration of cortisone was resumed. Histologically, the most remarkable finding was complete healing of all arterial lesions.

Rheumatic Fever

Rheumatic fever is a disease, long supposed to be infectious, closely associated with the invasion of the body by Group A hemolytic streptococci. It is characterized by febrile and toxic states and by the presence of multiple disseminated focal inflammatory lesions in various parts of the cardiovascular system and joints, and, at times, of serofibrinous inflammation of some of the great mesothelial-lined body cavities and joints. It is particularly interesting in connection with the present chapter that the earliest evidence of injury, pathologically speaking, is a fibrinoid swelling of the "ground substance" of the connective tissue. It has long been remarked that the lesions seen in the heart and other tissues in rheumatic fever are similar to those of periarteritis nodosa.

The disease is not rare; it has been estimated that there are about 60,000 deaths from rheumatic heart disease per year in the United States.

Evidence that the hemolytic streptococcus is in some way related to this disease was summarized by Aikawa (4):

1. Rheumatic fever has been found to follow known hemolytic streptococcal infections, particularly of the respiratory tract.

2. Epidemics of rheumatic fever are known to follow outbreaks of scarlet fever or streptococcus sore throat.

3. Recrudescences of activity frequently occur when infections by beta hemolytic streptococci occur in persons who have previously had attacks of rheumatic fever.

4. High titers of various antistreptococcus antibodies and cutaneous sensitivity to products or fractions of the streptococcus are usually demonstrable in persons suffering from acute rheumatic fever or from recurrences of this disease.

It has been shown (85) that prompt and intensive treatment of streptococcus infections with penicillin greatly reduce the risk of subsequent rheumatic fever. Such intensive therapy often inhibits the formation of antibodies (111), and it is tempting to think there might be some connection.

Although there is little doubt about the role of streptococcus infection in triggering the disease, there is a body of evidence which suggests that the basic mechanism involves some sort of hypersensitivity reaction. Many histological and clinical similarities exist between acute rheumatic fever and serum sickness (3). Repeated sensitization of rabbits with group A streptococci may produce histological lesions closely resembling those of rheumatic fever. It seems possible that the streptococcus or its toxins might in some way act as adjuvants to other antigens, possibly the patient's own tissues, and thus bring about sensitization.

The etiology of rheumatic fever was reviewed in 1949 by Waksman (116). At that time he pointed out the considerable body of evidence that the disease was due to autoimmunization, a view which was then comparatively new. According to this view, due apparently to Kerr, rheumatic patients form antibodies against what are essentially artificial antigens, consisting of denatured proteins of their own tissues or of tissue proteins combined with some streptococcal or other material as hapten. The antibodies are capable of combining with the original undenatured or uncombined tissue protein, and clinical symptoms result when their concentration is high enough to permit their combining with, and damaging, the tissues in question.

In support of this view it was pointed out that Cavelti (14) had been able to produce autoantibodies in rabbits and rats by injecting mixtures of the animals' own heart muscle, skeletal muscle, or connective tissue, mixed with streptococci or other products. Subsequent investigators, however, have been unable to confirm this work (4). Furthermore, Dr. Waksman (120) informed me that he later changed his views on this subject. In his opinion, the best experiments did not then suggest that autoimmunization plays much of a role in the etiology of rheumatic fever.

In rats, though not in rabbits, injection of homologous tissue has resulted in the appearance of lesions in the endocardium and myocardium, and Cavelti described these lesions as grossly comparable to those observed in human rheumatic fever. Similar lesions were reported to result from injections of connective tissue, but not of skeletal muscle, spleen, or kidney. This has been confirmed by Jaffe and Holz (57), but Humphrey (52) reported a failure to confirm. Other workers have reported the presence of precipitins not absorbed by streptococci which appeared in the blood of rheumatic patients during phase III (the rheumatic attack). Points which favor the immunological theory were summarized by Waksman: absence of immunity, sudden onset, and relation to a precipitating illness. The frequency of multiple cases in a family suggests a hereditary or constitutional factor (or possibly some peculiarity of diet), and hypersensitivity is known to be strongly influenced by heredity.

Rantz, Cregor, and Choy (96) have presented evidence in favor of the autoimmunization hypothesis of rheumatic fever. The opinion of many, perhaps the majority of workers, is that conclusive evidence is not yet available to allow us definitely to accept or reject the autoimmunization hypothesis in rheumatic fever.   The experimental evidence is suggestive, but the lesions do not imitate those of the disease in human beings completely, and in other respects the evidence is still incomplete.   It is to be hoped that future investigations will clear up this fascinating and important problem.

Massell (79) reviewed the use of ACTH and cortisone in rheumatic fever and rheumatic carditis.   He concluded that many clinical data suggest that cortisone and ACTH produce a favorable response in many important manifestations of rheumatic fever, and the data strongly suggest that ACTH or cortisone may be effective in preventing heart damage, especially if treatment is started early in the course of the disease.

Rheumatoid Arthritis

Rheumatoid arthritis is a fairly prevalent chronic disease of the joints, characterized by inflammatory changes in the synovial membrane and periarticular structures and by atrophy and rarefaction of the bones.   It is similar to the diseases we are considering here, in that it tends to run in families and to be precipitated by some such factor as shock, fatigue, trauma, infection, or exposure.   The incidence of cardiac lesions similar to those of rheumatic fever is high (97), and focal degeneration of collagen is a characteristic occurrence.   Inflammatory changes in arteries also occur.   The coexistence of other collagen disorders in patients with rheumatoid arthritis has been described (7).

Heller et al. (46,47) and Jacobson et al. (56) found that 70 to 75 per cent of patients with active peripheral rheumatoid arthritis possess specific agglutinating factors (apparently associated with the β-lipoproteins of the serum (48)) which are found much less frequently (2 to 4 per cent) in the sera of nonrheumatoid individuals.   These factors can be detected by agglutination of sheep erythrocytes which have been sensitized by low concentrations of rabbit antisheep agglutinins or by the agglutination of tannic-acid-treated sheep erythrocytes sensitized with human plasma fraction II (gamma globulin).

In spite of these somewhat suggestive findings, the view that rheumatoid arthritis is an autoimmune disease has not gained general acceptance. Mackay and Burnet (77) do not regard the autoimmune origin of the disease, though possible, as yet established.   Rich (16) suggested that the inflammatory reactions in the disease are an expression of tissue sensitivity to some protein of bacterial or other origin.   The serum of about 70 per cent of cases of rheumatoid arthritis will agglutinate group A hemolytic streptococci.

Cortisone and ACTH produce remarkable effects in rheumatoid arthritis (49).   Levin *et al.* (72), however, doubted the advisability of long-continued administration of cortisone or ACTH except in patients who demonstrate progressive disease despite adequate trial of more conservative therapy.   It is of interest that during remissions, no matter what the therapeutic agent, an increased excretion of histidine in the urine is observed, suggesting that less of this amino acid is being used for histamine production (36).   (The connection between hypersensitivity and histamine production was discussed in Chapter 8.)

Systemic Lupus Erythematosus (SLE)

Disseminated lupus erythematosus is one of the heterogeneous rheumatoid diseases.   It is distinguished by a prolonged clinical course which usually terminates fatally, a striking predilection for young females, and characteristic pathological changes in the vascular system.   In many cases an erythematous rash is apt to appear on the face and other parts of the body; this led to the name by which the disease is known (see Fig. 13-2). More recently it has been recognized that the skin rash is not invariably

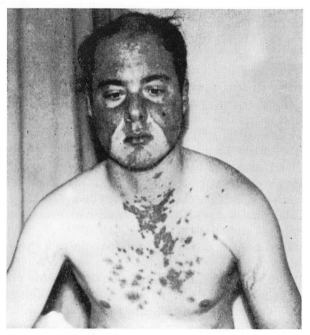

Fig. 13-2. Patient with typical lupur erythematosis lesions.
(Courtesy of Dr. William Damdshek and the patient.)

present and that when it appears it is a superficial manifestation of a wide-spread injury to the collagen which serves as a matrix and binding substance for the capillaries and other small blood vessels in various parts of the body. The morphological changes involve the skin, mucosal membranes, heart, blood vessels, and kidneys.

Wiener (129) suggested in 1950 that this disease was of autoimmune origin, and Dameshek and Stefanini (26) consider lupus erythematosus to be the autoimmune disease *par excellence,* and believe that it provides particularly strong evidence for the autoimmunization theory.

In 1948 Hargraves described a nuclear phagocytosis in bone marrow of patients with acute disseminated lupus erythematosus. It was later shown that this phenomenon (so-called LE cells) was produced by a factor present in the gamma globulin of patients who have the disease. LE cells are polymorphonuclear leukocytes containing chromatic inclusion bodies which may represent depolymerized nuclei of damaged cells.

Now it is known that patients with lupus erythematosus may exhibit thrombopenia or hemolytic anemia, which we have seen to be probably autoimmune in nature. Miescher (86) therefore reasoned that the LE cell might be the result of autoantibody action on the nucleus of the lymphocytes. He suggests that there would be three degrees of this effect, depending upon the concentration of antibody. These are illustrated in Fig. 13-3.

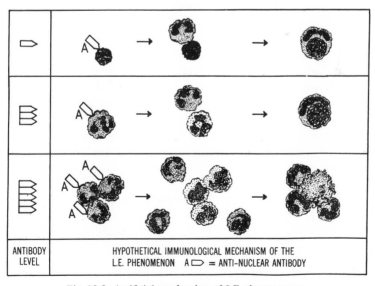

Fig. 13-3. Artificial production of LE phenomenon.

Making use of antinuclei sera, obtained by sensitizing guinea pigs with nuclei isolated from human and rabbit cells, Miescher (86,87) was able to produce the first two stages of this hypothetical scheme.

Waksman (120) pointed out that the hexatoxylin-staining bodies which are found show that the LE phenomenon occurs throughout the body, and that the best experimental duplication of the LE phenomenon is non-immunological (Inderbitzin), and is an excellent example of why we should be cautious about accepting certain kinds of serum behavior as manifestations of antibody.

In about 70 per cent of the cases of SLE there is involvement of the kidneys (77). This is a serious manifestation, for the glomular lesions, once started, tend to progress relentlessly. It has been stated that the majority of patients who have SLE will die of renal failure (103).

4. Diseases of the Kidneys

Glomerulonephritis

The patient with chronic glomerular nephritis is likely to come for medical attention because (*1*) he has noted the gradual onset of edema, (*2*) he complains of recurrent headaches, (*3*) he has developed dyspnea which may be exertional or paroxysmal in nature, (*4*) he has been discovered, on routine examination, to have albuminuria. It was reported that 25 per cent of the patients dying of acute nephritis at the Presbyterian Hospital were shown at autopsy to have associated active rheumatic disease.

Cases of acute glomerular nephritis are often observed to follow infections of the upper respiratory tract, especially with hemolytic streptococcus Group A. Chronic glomerular nephritis has no such clear-cut antecedents. In 1912 Escherich and Schick expressed the view that glomerulonephritis was due, not to infection per se, but to the immune reactions resulting from the infection. This point of view was strengthened when Masugi (81,80) produced the disease in experimental animals by the intravenous injection of sera containing antibodies against the animal's kidneys.

Not all workers agree that a direct cytotoxic action of antibody against kidney elements accounts for their injury. Kay (61) suggested that what really happens is that the antikidney antibody combines with the kidneys but is in itself harmless. According to Kay, it is only when the subject develops antibodies to the attached antibody that a hypersensitive reaction involving the glomerulus takes place.

We must now deal with the crucial missing link in the argument that glomerulonephritis is in fact due to autoimmunization of the patient to his own kidney substance. Several workers have reported that injection of rabbit kidney mixed with streptococcus or staphylococcus toxin, or of kidney which had undergone ischemic necrosis *in vivo,* produced *kidney* antikidney autoantibodies (101,91). It has even been reported that human beings with scarlet fever may develop antibodies which react with rabbit kidney antigen (101). But not all workers have been able to confirm these findings (95).

Even if it were known definitely that autoimmune antikidney antibodies do sometimes develop, not all workers in the field are prepared to admit that this would lead to renal lesions. The Caveltis have done much work to indicate that they would. In rats regularly, although in rabbits infrequently, they found that glomerular lesions developed after repeated injections of homologous kidney mixed with killed hemolytic streptococci (14a). In view of the commonly accepted role of hemolytic streptococci in the etiology of the disease, this is certainly suggestive. Some workers have confirmed these findings (106,35), but others have failed to do so (52).

5. Diseases of the Eye

For some years there has been evidence in the literature that certain diseases of the eye are due to autoimmunization. No attempt will be made here to review the extensive literature; instead a few illustrative examples will be described.

In the condition known as sympathetic ophthalmia, an injury to one eye involving the uveal tissue often results in a later granulatomous lesion in the uveal tract of the other eye. This is thought to result from the development by the patient of hypersensitivity to uveal pigment, for antibody and skin reactivity to this substance are detectable in such persons. It has apparently not been firmly established that such antibody or sensitivity can cause the damage seen in such cases, but Collins (17) injected 25 guinea pigs with guinea pig uveas plus adjuvants and found in 12 of the animals focal areas of lymphocytes and epithelioid cell infiltration in the choroid of both eyes. Woods (136), however, suggested that some further injury, such as the localization of bacteria in the eye in addition to the damaging effect of a hypersensitive reaction, may be required to bring about the characteristic lesions of this disease.

A second condition in which autoimmune mechanisms may be involved is one which follows damage to the lens of the eye. Occasionally the removal of a cataract is followed by a postoperative intraocular inflammation. It has been suggested that this is due to sensitization of the patient by remaining lens substance, which is known to be antigenic, even in the same species (p. 124), followed by a reaction between lens substance and ocular tissues sensitized to it. Skin tests indicate a hypersensitive reaction to lens extract on the part of many of the affected individuals. Because of the possibility of this hypersensitive etiology, the disease has been given the name of "endophthalmitis phacoanaphylactica." Attempts to produce the syndrome in animals failed until Burkey (9–11) injected rabbits with cow lens substance mixed with staphylococcus toxin. When he inserted a needle into the anterior chamber, withdrew 0.2 ml. of the aqueous humor, and injected it into the lens, the sensitized animals developed marked intraocular inflammation, conjunctival and pericorneal injection, steamy cornea with vascularization and plastic iritis.

There is no doubt that lens protein can easily escape from the lens during operations (100). In removing cataracts, particularly the more Morgagnian type, some of the mature cataract is easily squeezed out, and when the capsule ruptures during extraction, as it not infrequently does, you have lens protein right in the chamber.

The source of the staphylococcus, if this is indeed always required, is only a little more problematical. The field of operation, in the case of eye operations, is after all never sterile, and staphylococci and other microorganisms which might act as adjuvants are frequently present. It must be admitted that the evidence is strongly suggestive that an autoimmune mechanism may be involved in this disease.

6. Diseases Affecting the Nervous System

Multiple Sclerosis

Multiple sclerosis is an acute or chronic, remittent or progressive, disease, affecting mainly the white matter of the central nervous system. The lesions consist of demyelinated glial patches ("plaques"), mainly in the white matter, representing the end results of a series of changes. The peripheral nerves (cranial and spinal) are rarely if ever involved (30).

Frequently the first symptoms are onset of sudden diminution of vision, usually of one, but some times of both, eyes, with no other signs (100). These symptoms generally clear up, and the characteristic signs of multiple sclerosis may not develop until two or three years later.

The estimated prevalence of the disease varies from 40 per 100,000 population in Boston and Winnepeg to 13 per 100,000 in New Orleans, showing considerable geographical variation.

Destruction of myelin, demyelinization, is a primary characteristic of such diseases of the nervous system as multiple sclerosis, diffuse sclerosis, neuromyelitis optica, the encephalomyelitides that sometimes follow infectious diseases, and the neuroparalytic accidents sometimes following the use of antirabies vaccine made from nervous tissue. The cause of the demyelinization has been obscure. It is now beginning to be thought that it is a distinct possibility, at least, that this process may be the result of some allergic or autoimmune process (66).

According to Stevenson and Alvord (110), Glantzman in 1947 was the first to suggest that "allergy" might be a factor in causing demyelination of the nervous system. It should be noted that the word "allergy," as used by many writers, would include autoimmunization as well as hypersensitivity.

For a role of allergy in its strict sense in multiple sclerosis there is little evidence (60):

1. The incidence of atopic hypersensitivity is little higher in patients with multiple sclerosis than in any equivalent unselected group.

2. Antihistamines fail to produce improvement in patients with multiple sclerosis.

3. ACTH and cortisone *may* improve some cases, but they make others worse.

Sachs and Steiner reported serological studies on multiple sclerosis in 1934, using as an antigen an alcoholic extract from the brain of patients who had died of multiple sclerosis. They performed complement fixation tests on 289 cases and obtained positive reactions in 41 per cent (38b). They assumed these reactions were due to some pathological organism, or other infectious agent in the central nervous system, but Frick (38b) found that antigen prepared from normal brain tissue produced identical results. He believes that the antigen is a lipide or a lipoprotein of normal brain.

This clear suggestion that multiple sclerosis may be due to autoimmunization to brain or other nervous tissue receives support from experiments such as those of Kabat (59,76), and Thomas, Paterson, and Smithwick (113) showing that injection of homologous brain mixed with Freund's adjuvants will produce acute disseminated encephalomyelitis in animals. Attempts to produce the condition by injecting emulsions of other tissues have been uniformly unsuccessful, indicating the etiological specificity of nervous tissue. Also, it should be noted that this experimental disease resembles postinfectious encephalomyelitis much more than multiple sclerosis.

If multiple sclerosis were due to autoimmunization, this would make much more intelligible the observations that experimental malarial infection and "protein shock" (injection of typhoid vaccine), which were tried at one time in treatment, are generally deleterious rather than beneficial (29). Obviously a condition due to the manufacture by the patient of unwanted antibodies would not be benefited by treatment which stimulated his antibody production, as either of these treatments might possibly do.

The mechanism by which the actual disease is produced is still obscure, but it seems reasonable to assume that it is the result of some process which enhances the antigenicity of the patient's nervous tissue for his own antibody-forming organs (76).

By injecting nerve tissue mixed with the Freund adjuvants, Waksman and Adams (119) produced a condition which they called experimental allergic neuritis. Rabbits receiving homologous spinal cord may show extensive lesions both of peripheral nerves and of spinal ganglia, in addition to the usual lesions of the central nervous system. The use of optic nerve as antigen also produces this pathological picture. In contrast, injection of homologous sciatic nerve or ganglion produces lesions merely of nerves and ganglia, while the cord, brain stem, optic nerves, cerebellum, and cerebrum remain entirely normal.

Waksman and Adams reported that the antigenic activity of the nerve tissue used in their experiments was unaffected by autoclaving, suggesting that the antigen might not be a protein. It was suggested by Tal and Olitsky (112) that the activity resides in one of the proteolipides (lipide-protein compounds with the physical–chemical properties of lipides, which make up less than 10 per cent of all the proteolipides in myelin). This was confirmed by Waksman et al. (121).

In spite of the evidence just summarized, it is far from established that multiple sclerosis is an autoimmune phenomenon. The evidence for its autoimmune origin depends largely upon the claim that some of the histological changes observed are characteristic of the allergic response, and Hurst (54) did not believe that, taken alone, the histological evidence offers a very secure basis for regarding "allergy" as the etiologic factor of the morbid process.

Waksman and Morrison (118) found skin reactions to homologous white matter, which exhibited both gross and histological characteristics of the delayed tuberculin reaction of hypersensitivity, in animals with experimental allergic encephalomyelitis, but Stauffer and Waksman (108) did not find such reactions in patients with multiple sclerosis.

Hurst (54) did not believe there can be a common basis for all the naturally occurring demyelinating diseases of man and animals, and thinks that demyelination is merely the response of the white matter to noxious stimuli of a certain intensity. Consequently he does not think there is adequate evidence for believing that all demyelinating diseases are "allergic" in origin.   Hurst and others (60) did consider the "allergic" basis a reasonable assumption in some, such as acute hemorrhagic leuko-encephalitis, which appears to be the naturally occurring counterpart of the experimentally induced Arthus phenomenon.   They also believe that the acute epizootic leukoencephalitis of horses may fall into the same category, and think the balance of evidence favors an "allergic" basis for the postvaccinial type of encephalitis and some of the paralytic accidents following antirabies prophylaxis in man and in the dog.

It is perhaps not yet excluded that multiple sclerosis may be caused by a virus (55).

7. Thyroid Disease

There are a number of diseases of the thyroid known as "thyroiditis" (77), hitherto of uncertain etiology and pathogenesis.   The best known is Hashimoto's disease (45).   This characteristically occurs in middle-aged or elderly women and causes goiter and (mild) thyroid insufficiency.   Microscopically the thyroid in such cases shows dense invasion of lymphocytes and plasma cells.

Antithyroid antibody, demonstrable *in vitro* (34), is generally present in such patients, and Hashimoto's disease is recognized as a typical autoimmune disease, indeed as the prototype of autoimmune diseases.

8. Diseases of the Skin

Wiener (128) reported a case of Ritter's disease (a rare exfoliating skin disease of newborn infants) which he thought might have an autoimmune etiology.   The disease was seen in fraternal premature boy twins.   Near the end of the pregnancy, the mother acquired a case of poison ivy dermatitis which was unusual in its severity and in the extensive distribution of the lesions.   Wiener suggested that the allergenic principle of the plant combined with the mother's skin proteins, altering them sufficiently to make them autoantigenic.   The autoantibodies produced as a result would then combine with the skin on other parts of the body, thus accounting for the extensive lesions.   Such antibody, passing through the placenta and reacting with the fetal skin, could account for the exfoliative dermatitis seen in the twins.

9. Mechanism of Damage by Autoantibodies

According to Raffel (95) there would seem to be four conceivable mechanisms by which tissue damage could be brought about by autoantibodies, and Wiener (129) suggested a fifth: (*1*) direct cytotoxic effect of the anti-bodies upon the cells; (*2*) an Arthus reaction (p. 416) in which the anti-bodies react with antigen to produce vascular damage which in turn injures the organ in which this takes place; (*3*) the development of hy-persensitivity of the delayed type to a tissue antigen, leading to injury or death of cells exposed to it; (*4*) a direct toxic action of injected substances, entirely apart from their immunological characteristics; (*5*) intravascular "conglutination" by red cell autoantibodies, resulting in disseminated vascular damage due to obstruction of circulation to tissues and organs (129).   Of course it is entirely possible, even probable, that two or more of these mechanisms may operate simultaneously in certain cases.

1. Cytotoxicity.   In the case of the autohemolysins of paroxysmal hemoglobinuria, and almost certainly in the case of acquired hemolytic anemia, the autoantibodies definitely bring about the destruction of the cells against which they are directed.   In other cases evidence for direct cytotoxic action is much less satisfactory.   Although encephalomyelitis has been repeatedly produced experimentally by the injection of brain tissue mixed with adjuvants, it has not been possible to demonstrate a correlation between the occurrence or extent of the lesions and the titer of such antibodies as can be detected and titrated (76,118,68,69).   Indeed, in guinea pigs circulating antibodies seem to be present rarely if at all (118).

Also, in the case of nephritis produced by injection of antikidney anti-bodies there is but a poor correlation between antibody titer and nephro-toxic effect (105,61).   Even in Cavelti's work, in which nephritic lesions were produced by injection of kidney tissue plus streptococci, the corre-lation between the presence of antibodies and the occurrence of kidney damage was not complete.   In the case of the lens of the eye, Burkey (10,11) found it necessary to damage the lens of animals possessing anti-lens antibodies in order to bring about intraocular inflammation, sug-gesting that antibodies by themselves do not injure the lens.

2. Arthus reaction.   In experimental encephalomyelitis small lesions occurring in the blood vessels have been described, but they are not so apparent when the damage has become more extensive (98,58).   It has been pointed out (95) that if an Arthus reaction does account for demyeli-nating encephalomyelitis, it is difficult to see why the damage should be limited to the brain.

Pressman's work (92,93) shows that heterologous antikidney antibody localizes in the renal vascular bed, and in fact he suggests that antiorgan antibodies are generally directed against the cells of the vascular system. This observation might tie in with Kay's suggestion (p. 540) that it is not the localized antibody which causes damage, but the subject's counter-response to the antibody. This would be a sort of Arthus reaction.

In the case of damage by antilens antibody there is some suggestion that the Arthus reaction may be responsible for the ocular inflammation which follows injury to the lens.

Evidence from tissue grafts also bears on the question. As has been mentioned (p. 509) skin transplants from one individual to another fail as a rule, and there is no doubt that an immunological mechanism is involved, although circulating antibodies have not usually been found. As pointed out earlier (p. 509) the fact that transplants will grow in the (unvascularized) anterior chamber of the eye suggests that Arthus reactivity may be a factor. The importance of the immunological response in causing the rejection of skin transplants is confirmed by the recent report of Good and Varco (39) of a successful skin transplant to a child with agammaglobulinemia (see p. 513).

3. *Delayed sensitivity.* The evidence, such as it is, for the operation of delayed hypersensitivity is all indirect. First of all, there is the lack of correspondence between antibody titers and the occurrence and extent of the lesions, mentioned above. Second, there is the failure of passive transfer of serum to cause lesions (118). But neither of these facts really excludes the supposition that some sort of antibody may be involved.

Waksman and Morrison (118) found a parallelism between delayed-type skin responses to nerve tissue and the occurrence of encephalomyelitis in rabbits injected with nerve tissue, although occasionally an animal with slight or no sensitivity had marked symptoms of brain damage, and vice versa.

Even if the evidence that hypersensitivity operates to cause tissue damage in autoimmunization were conclusive, the problem would remain, just what cells have become hypersensitive? How does injection of myelin sensitize the myelin of the subject? It might perhaps be suggested that the injection stimulates the production of some sort of antibody, in-detectable by present technics, which settles down in the myelin and makes it sensitive, but there is no evidence for this. Waksman and Morrison (118) suggested that it is other cells, perhaps those responsible for the maintenance of the myelin, which become sensitized, and that their destruction results in turn in the failure of *production* of the myelin.

4. *Toxicity of injected material.* There seems to be no positive evidence for a direct toxic action of homologous tissue materials, and the available evidence suggests more strongly an immunological mechanism, but Alvord (5) suggested that in the case of encephalomyelitis some metabolic defect is engendered by the injections of brain substance. This

is a possibility which should perhaps be kept in mind, if the evidence for immunological mechanisms does not continue to become stronger.

For reviews of the subject of this chapter, the reader is referred to Waksman (117), and Mackay and Burnet (77).

References

1. Ackroyd, J. F., *Clin. Sci.*, **7**, 231; *ibid.*, **8**, 235 (1949).
2. Ackroyd, J. F., *Clin. Sci.*, **10**, 1851 (1951).
3. Aikawa, J. K., *Ann. Internal Med.*, **23**, 969 (1945).
4. Aikawa, J. K., *Ann. Internal Med.*, **41**, 576 (1954).
5. Alvord, C. E., *J. Immunol.*, **61**, 355 (1949).
6. Ammann, P., G. von Muralt, and A. Hässig, *Schweitz. Med. Woch.*, **93**, 818–822 (1963).
7. Bauer, W. J., E. Giansiracusa, and J. P. Kulka, *The Protean Nature of the Connective Tissue Diseases*, Saunders, Philadelphia, 1952.
8. Boorman, W. J., B. E. Dodd, and J. F. Loutit, *Lancet*, **I**, 812 (1946).
9. Burkey, E. L., *Proc. Soc. Exptl. Biol. Med.*, **31**, 445 (1933–1934).
10. Burkey, E. L., *J. Allergy*, **5**, 466 (1934).
11. Burkey, E. L., *Arch. Ophthalmol. (Chicago)*, **12**, 536 (1934).
12. Burnet, F. M., and F. Fenner, *The Production of Antibodies*, 2nd ed., Macmillan, Melbourne, 1949.
13. Callender, S. T., and R. R. Race, *Ann. Eugenics*, **13**, 102 (1946).
14. Cavelti, P. A., *Schwiez med. Wochschr.*, **78**, 83 (1948).
15. Cavelti, P. A., *J. Allergy*, **26**, 95 (1955).
16. Cecil, R. L., in *Textbook of Medicine*, R. L. Cecil and R. F. Loeb, eds., Saunders, Philadelphia, 1951.
17. Collins, R. C., *Am. J. Ophthalmol.*, **32**, 1687 (1949).
18. Collins, W. S., and N. D. Wilensky, *Peripheral and Vascular Diseases*, Charles C Thomas, Springfield, Illinois, 1953.
19. Coombs, R. R. A., A. E. Mourant, and R. R. Race, *Lancet*, **II**, 15 (1945).
20. Coombs, R. R. A., A. E. Mourant, and R. R. Race, *Brit. J. Exptl. Pathol.*, **26**, 225 (1945).
21. Coombs, R. R. A., A. E. Mourant, and R. R. Race, *Lancet*, **I**, 264 (1946).
22. Dacie, J. V., *Blood*, **8**, 813 (1953).
23. Dacie, J. V., *The Haemolytic Anaemias*, Grune and Stratton, New York, 1954.
24. Dacie, J. V., and M. Cutbush, *J. Clin. Pathol.*, **7**, 18 (1954).
25. Dameshek, W., *Blood*, **8**, 382 (1953).
26. Dameshek, W., and M. Stefanini, *Med. Clin. N. Amer.*, **37**, 1395 (1953).
27. Dausset, J., *Le Sang*, **25**, 683 (1954).
28. Dausset, J., A. Nenna, and H. Brecy, *Blood*, **9**, 606 (1954).
29. Denny-Brown, D. E., *Am. J. Med.*, **12**, 501 (1952).
30. Denny-Brown, D. E., in *Textbook of Medicine*, R. L. Cecil and R. F. Loeb, eds., Saunders, Philadelphia, 1955.
31. Diamond, L. K., and R. L. Denton, *J. Lab. Clin. Med.*, **30**, 821 (1945).
32. Donath, J., and K. Landsteiner, *Munch. med. Wochschr.*, **51**, 1590 (1904).
33. Donath, J., and K. Landsteiner, *Ergebn. Hyg.*, **7**, 184 (1925).
34. Doniach, D., and I. M. Roitt, *J. Clin. Endocrinol. Metabol.*, **17**, 1293–1304 (1957).

35. Donoso, J., H. Rodriguez, and A. Steiner, *Rev. méd. Chile,* **77,** 498 (1949).
36. Duncan, G. G., *Diseases of Metabolism,* 3rd ed., Saunders, Philadelphia, 1952.
37. Ehrich, W. E., *Am. Heart J.,* **43,** 121 (1952).
38. Evans, R. S., and S. T. Duane, *Blood,* **4,** 1196 (1951).
39. Good, R. A., and R. L. Varco, *J. Am. Med. Assoc.,* **157,** 713 (1955).
40. Grabar, P., *Proc. VI Intern. Congr. Microbiol. Rome, Sept. 6–12,* **1,** 475 (1953).
41. Gurevitch, J., and D. Nelkin, *Nature,* **173,** 356 (1954).
42. Harkavy, J., *Progr. Allergy,* **3,** 335 (1952).
43. Harrington, W. J., *et al., J. Lab. Clin. Med.,* **38,** 1 (1951).
44. Harrington, W. J., V. Minnich, and G. Arimura, "Autoimmune thrombocytopene-ias," Ch. 8, *Progress in Hematology,* Vol. 1, L. M. Tocantins, ed., Grune and Stratton, New York, 1956.
45. Hashimoto, H., *Arch. klin. Chir.,* **97,** 219 (1912).
46. Heller, G., *et al., J. Immunol.,* **69,** 27 (1952).
47. Heller, G., *et al., J. Immunol.,* **72,** 66 (1954).
48. Heller, G., *et al., J. Immunol.,* **74,** 340 (1955).
49. Hench, P. S., *et al., Arch. Internal Med.,* **85,** 545 (1950).
50. Holländer, L., *Experientia,* **9,** 468 (1953).
51. Hooker, S. B., and W. C. Boyd, *J. Immunol.,* **24,** 141 (1933).
52. Humphrey, J. H., *J. Pathol. Bacteriol.,* **60,** 211 (1948).
53. Hurst, E. W., *J. Hyg.,* **32,** 33 (1932).
54. Hurst, E. W., *Am. J. Med.,* **12,** 547 (1952).
55. Innes, J. R. M., *Am. J. Med.,* **12,** 574 (1952).
56. Jacobson, A. S., *et al., Ann. Rheumatic Diseases,* **12,** 321 (1953).
57. Jaffe, R., and E. Holz., *Exptl. Med. Surg.,* **6,** 189 (1948).
58. Jervis, G. A., and H. Koprowski, *J. Neuropathol. Exptl. Neurol.,* **7,** 309 (1948).
59. Kabat, E. A., A. Wolf, and A. E. Bezer, *J. Exptl. Med.,* **88,** 417 (1948).
60. Kane, C. A., personal communication, 1955.
61. Kay, C. F., *J. Exptl. Med.,* **72,** 559 (1940).
62. Kissmeyer-Nielsen, F., J. Bichel, and P. B. Hansen, *Acta Haematol.,* **15** (1956).
63. Klemperer, P., A. D. Pollack, and G. Baehr, *Arch. Pathol.,* **32,** 569 (1941).
64. Klemperer, P., *Am. J. Pathol.,* **26,** 505 (1950).
65. Klinge, F., *Ergeb. allgem. Pathol. u. pathol. Anat.,* **27,** 1 (1933).
66. Kolb, L. C., *Medicine,* **29,** 99 (1950).
67. Komninos, Z. D., and M. C. Rosenthal, *J. Lab. Clin. Med.,* **41,** 887 (1953).
68. Kopeloff, L. M., and N. Kopeloff, *J. Immunol.,* **48,** 297 (1944).
69. Koprowski, H., and G. A. Jervis, *Proc. Soc. Exptl. Biol. Med.,* **69,** 472 (1948).
70. Koritschoner, R., and F. Schweinburg, *Z. Immunitätsforsch.,* **42,** 217 (1925).
71. Lecutier, M. A., *J. Clin. Pathol.,* **5,** 336 (1952).
72. Levin, M. H., *et al., Am. J. Med.,* **14,** 265 (1953).
73. Lincoln, M., and W. A. Ricker, *Ann. Internal Med.,* **41,** 639 (1954).
74. Lindemann, W., *Ann. inst. Pasteur,* **14,** 49 (1900).
75. Van Loghem, J. J., and M. van der Hart, *Vox. Sang.,* **4,** 129 (1954).
76. Lumsden, C. E., *et. al., J. Exptl. Med.,* **92,** 253 (1950).
77. Mackay, I. R., and F. M. Burnet, *Autoimmune Diseases,* Charles C Thomas, Springfield, Illinois, 1963.
78. Marchall, J., A. Zoutendyk, and J. Gear, *S. African Med. J.,* **25,** 764 (1951).
79. Massell, B. F., *New Engl. J. Med.,* **251,** 183, 221, 263 (1954).
80. Masugi, M., *Beitr. pathol. Anat. u. allgem. Pathol.,* **92,** 429 (1934).

81. Masugi, M., and T. Isibasi, *Beitr. pathol. Anat. u. allgem. Pathol.*, **96**, 391 (1936).
82. Maurer, P. H., *Federation Proc.*, **13**, 504 (1954).
83. Maurer, P. H., *J. Exptl. Med.*, **100**, 497 (1954).
84. Maurer, P. H., *J. Exptl. Med.*, **100**, 515 (1954).
85. McCarty, M., in *Textbook of Medicine*, R. L. Cecil and R. F. Loeb, eds., Saunders, Philadelphia, 1955.
86. Miescher, P., *J. suisse med.*, **83**, 1042 (1953).
87. Miescher, P., and M. Fauconnet, *J. suisse med.*, **84**, 597 (1954).
88. Miescher, P., and A. Vannotti, *Bull. acad. suisse sci. med.*, **10**, 85 (1954).
89. Morton, J. A., and M. M. Pickles, *Nature*, **159**, 779 (1947).
90. Moureau, P., and A. André, *Nature*, **174**, 88 (1954).
91. Parks, A. E., and G. Shanks, *J. Lab. Clin. Med.*, **26**, 950 (1941).
92. Pressman, D., *et al.*, *J. Immunol.*, **65**, 559 (1950).
93. Pressman, D., *Federation Proc.*, **10**, 568 (1951).
94. Race, R. R., and R. Sanger, *Blood Groups in Man*, Blackwell Scientific, Oxford, 1962.
95. Raffel, S., *Immunity*, Appleton-Century-Crofts, New York, 1953.
96. Rantz, L., W. P. Cregor, and S. H. Choy, *Am. J. Med.*, **12**, 115 (1952).
97. Rich, A. R., *Harvey Lectures*, Ser. **42**, 106 (1947).
98. Rivers, T. M., and F. F. Schwentker, *J. Exptl. Med.*, **61**, 689 (1935).
99. Rosenthal, M. C., Z. D. Komninos, and W. Dameshek, *New Engl. J. Med.*, **248**, 537 (1953).
100. Runge, P. M., personal communication, 1955.
101. Schwentker, F. F., and F. C. Comploier, *J. Exptl. Med.*, **70**, 233 (1939).
102. Selwyn, J. G., and S. S. Alexander, *Brit. Med. J.*, **I**, 564 (1951).
103. Shulman, L. E., and A. M. Harvey, "Systematic lupuserythematosus," Ch. 44, *Arthritis*, J. L. Hollander, ed., Lea and Febiger, Philadelphia, 1960.
104. Smadel, J. E., *J. Exptl. Med.*, **64**, 921 (1936).
106. Sprunt, E., W. R. Rogers, and A. D. Dulaney, *Federation Proc.*, **9**, 344 (1950).
107. Stats, D., and L. R. Wasserman, *Trans. N. Y. Acad. Sci.*, **14**, 238 (1952).
108. Stauffer, R. E., and B. H. Waksman, *Ann. N. Y. Acad. Sci.*, **58**, 570 (1954).
109. Stefanini, M., and W. Dameshek, *Ann. Rev. Med.*, **5**, 87 (1954).
110. Stevenson, L. D., and E. C. Alvord, *Am. J. Med.*, **3**, 614 (1947).
111. Swift, H. F., in *Bacterial and Mycotic Infections of Man*, R. J. Dubos, ed., Lippincott, Philadelphia, 1952.
112. Tal, C., and P. K. Olitsky, *Science*, **116**, 420 (1952).
113. Thomas, L., P. Y. Paterson, and B. Smithwick, *J. Exptl. Med.*, **92**, 133 (1950).
114. Tullis, J. L., and D. M. Surgenor, paper presented at V Intern. Congr. Hematol., Paris, Sept., 1954.
115. Vorlaender, K. O., *Acta Allergol.*, **7**, 224 (1954).
116. Waksman, B. H., *Medicine*, **28**, 143 (1949).
117. Waksman, B. H., *Progr. Allergy*, **5**, 349–458 (1958).
118. Waksman, B. H., and L. R. Morrison, *J. Immunol.*, **66**, 421 (1951).
119. Waksman, B. H., and R. D. Adams, *Federation Proc.*, **13**, 516 (1954); *J. Exptl. Med.*, **102**, 213 (1955).
120. Waksman, B. H., personal communication, 1955.
121. Waksman, B. H., *et al.*, *J. Exptl. Med.*, in press.
122. Wallace, J. H., M. C. Dodd, and C. S. Wright, *J. Immunol.*, **74**, 89 (1955).
123. Wasastjerna, C., *Blood*, **8**, 1042 (1953).

124. Watson, R. F., S. Rothbard, and P. Vanamee, *J. Exptl. Med.*, **99**, 535 (1954).
125. Weiner, W., *et al.*, *Brit. Med. J.*, **II**, 125 (1953).
126. Wexler, I. B., and A. S. Wiener, *Brit. Med. J.*, **I**, 128 (1951).
126a. Wiener, A. S., *J. Lab. Clin. Med.*, **30**, 662 (1936).
127. Wiener, A. S., and J. G. Hurst, *Exptl. Med. Surg.*, **5**, 285 (1947).
128. Wiener, A. S., *N. Y. State J. Med.*, **47**, 1796 (1947).
129. Wiener, A. S., *Brit. Med. J.*, **II**, 163 (1950).
130. Wiener, A. S., *Brit. Med. J.*, **I**, 435 (1951).
131. Wiener, A. S., *J. Immunol.*, **66**, 679 (1951).
132. Wiener, A. S., *et al.*, *Am. J. Clin. Pathol.*, **22**, 301 (1952).
133. Wiener, A. S., *Ann. Allergy*, **10**, 535 (1952).
134. Wiener, A. S., *et al.*, *J. Immunol.*, **71**, 58 (1953).
135. Wiener, A. S., *Rh-Hr Blood Types*, Grune and Stratton, New York, 1954.
136. Woods, A. C., *N. Y. State J. Med.*, **36**, 67 (1936).
137. Zoutendyk, A., and J. Gear, *S. African Med. J.*, **25**, 665 (1951).

CHAPTER 14

Immunity in Action: Some Examples

1. Introduction

We have considered in some detail the principal lines of defense against infection, as well as some of the ways in which these mechanisms can go wrong. We may now attempt some sort of synthesis and examine the relative roles played by these various mechanisms in resistance to infection under "natural" conditions.

The body's first line of defense is the relative impermeability of its natural coverings; most of the countless pathogens with which our environment teems never get into the body. In addition to this mechanical factor, there is the entrapment of foreign particles by the epithelium of the respiratory and urogenital passages, and the motion of the cilia of the former to sweep trapped particles outwards. Skin and mucosa have bactericidal and virucidal powers, as do fluids such as tears.

Any injury to cells, by liberation of histamine, calls forth an increased local supply of blood and a passage of blood fluids into the damaged tissues. If some of the cells are killed, inflammatory changes, probably resulting from the diffusion of the products of the self-digestion of the cells, cause a slower but more lasting dilatation of the capillaries, and phagocytes pass through the capillary walls and surround the necrotic tissue.

If the tissues are infected with a microorganism, the damaged cells produce histamine and, if seriously enough damaged, other products of cell destruction; inflammation results, and phagocytes move in. Many microorganisms encountered by the phagocytes are engulfed. If the invader is an organism such as *Staphylococcus,* at first many of the phagocytes will be killed by poisonous substances produced by the *Staphylococcus,* but the area will be surrounded by living phagocytes which prevent the further spread of the bacteria. In most cases the ingested bacteria are killed, and the cells begin the work of cleaning up and repair. If this local defense fails, and bacteria begin to reach the blood, the situation becomes more serious.

Parasites that enter the body through the respiratory or gastrointestinal tract may not meet with so many defense mechanisms. Some parasites possess enzymes which enable them to dissolve the skin and connective tissues and bore directly from the outside surface of the body until they reach the blood stream.

If bacteria succeed in penetrating the barriers of skin or mucous membranes and their antibacterial substances, and reach the blood stream, other mechanisms come into play. Of these the most important is phagocytosis. The various types of phagocytes, discussed in Chapter 1, include the blood leukocytes (polymorphonuclears and monocytes) and the reticuloendothelial system. The largest single collection of macrophages is in the spleen. Even if large numbers of bacteria are deliberately injected intravenously, they are removed in about 20 minutes by phagocytosis, chiefly in the liver, spleen, lungs, lymph nodes, and splanchnic vascular bed. Phagocytosis is the greatest single mechanism contributing to natural resistance.

Wood (98) believed that when acute infections are caused by essentially extracellular bacteria, phagocytosis of the organisms is the decisive factor in the natural resistance of the host. In the case of chronic bacterial infections, on the other hand, which are caused by microorganisms capable of surviving and multiplying in the cells of the host, phagocytosis is less decisive. The cytoplasmic factors responsible for the destruction of such intracellular parasites are unknown.

The mechanism of inflammation next comes into play. It consists essentially of dilatation and increased permeability of the capillaries with emigration of cells and plasma into the tissues. As fibrinogen of the plasma clots, a fibrous network forms and mechanically traps invading microorganisms. The phenomenon of surface phagocytosis (Chapter 1) takes place more readily in such a network.

Other changes which favor the body's defense, such as alteration of the body temperature (fever), may take place. Maintenance of proper pH and oxygen tension in the tissues is also protective.

Antibodies, discussed in Chapter 2, constitute one of the most important of the immune mechanisms. If antibodies for the invading organism are present, as the result of a previous infection or of an infection by a related organism, or from artificial immunization, they greatly aid phagocytosis by opsonizing the microorganisms which reach the circulation and tissues. More antibodies of the same sort will begin to be produced and, acting together with complement, may kill the invading micro-organisms. If no antibodies were present to begin with, they will begin to form within a day or two, and after 7 or 8 days will be detectable in the circulation.

2. Typical Course of an Infection

Topley and Wilson (95) attempted to reconstruct what happens when bacteria enter the tissues of a host and succeed in gaining access to the blood stream, but are finally vanquished by the defensive mechanisms.

During the initial phase, the bacteria enter through a mucous surface and pass to a regional lymph gland, where they proceed to proliferate. Then they begin to collect in the reticuloendothelial system, for example, in the liver and spleen, brought there by the circulation of the blood. They continue to proliferate there and in the lymphatic glands where they entered. This phase corresponds to the incubation period. Then, if the disease is serious, the bacteria reinvade the blood stream, bacteremia results, and the organisms are carried to other, previously uninfected tissues. This is the phase of clinical illness, and if the host's immune mechanisms are not equal to the battle, death will soon occur. If the host is going to recover, antibodies usually make their appearance during this phase. As a consequence the clearing mechanisms are speeded up, bacteremia disappears, and only a few scattered foci of infection are left, for example, in the spleen, liver, and lymph nodes. This stage may persist for a long time in some cases. Finally, the remaining foci of infection may be eliminated, and the host is once more completely free from the infection.

In mild infections the stage of clinical illness may never be reached, and the infection is said to be abortive, inapparent, or subclinical. Such infections may nevertheless produce effective immunity, especially if re-peated, and protective antibodies to a variety of infections may be found in individuals who so far as is known have never had a clinically recogniz-able case of the disease in question.

Let us now take a look at the operation of the various immune mecha-nisms in some representative diseases: bacterial, mycotic, viral, rickettsial, and parasitic.

3. Bacterial and Mycotic Diseases

Diphtheria

The mechanism of resistance to diphtheria is fairly well understood. When a virulent diphtheria bacillus reaches the throat of a susceptible person, its growth begins in a superficial layer of mucous and desquamated epithelial cells. The bacilli do not reach the circulation but begin elaborating toxin *in situ;* this toxin has a necrotizing action on the adjacent living cells and destroys them in a few hours. The necrotic tissue provides a favorable medium for further growth of the organisms, more toxin is formed, and the process extends in area and depth.

In the meantime, the body responds with an inflammatory reaction. Capillaries engorge, leukocytes enter, red cells become extravasated, and a layer of exudate composed of these elements begins to form. It becomes thicker and tough, forming the dull white "pseudomembrane" which was so much dreaded before the discovery of antitoxin. Later the membrane becomes a dirty gray, and later still brown or even black as the result of hemorrhage. If the membrane develops in or reaches the larynx, death may result from mechanical stoppage of breath.

Before artificially produced antitoxin was available the disease would run its course, and if the patient did not die of suffocation, he might die later from cardiac damage by the toxin, or recover with the help of antitoxin produced by his own antibody-forming mechanism.

Treatment with antitoxin, if adequate amounts are given promptly (without waiting for the report on a throat culture), will probably save the patient's life, and result in a recovery very similar to a spontaneous one, but earlier.

Immunity to diphtheria is basically simple: it depends upon the development by the individual of an adequate concentration of antitoxin in his circulation.

However, there are complications. A single infection with diphtheria bacilli of low virulence may be overcome before the body has come in contact with much toxin; then, although the body is perhaps "conditioned" to respond more rapidly the next time, it may not produce an effective level of antitoxin at the time (61). It is therefore possible for an individual who has recovered from diphtheria not to be immune.

On the other hand, repeated encounters with organisms of low virulence, without the production of evident disease, may result in fairly solid immunity, even to a virulent strain, by virtue of the repeated stimulation of the antibody-forming mechanism. Before the introduction of antitoxin, this was probably the process by which the population acquired the immunity which was generally seen in adults.

Widespread artificial immunization of populations, by reducing the prevalence of diphtheria bacilli, has tended to interfere with this process, perhaps aided by a natural downward trend of the disease (34). This means that persons immunized in infancy are not so likely to be exposed to the organisms in later life, and their immunity does not get a natural stimulus. Therefore "recall" or "booster" injections are needed in later years to make sure the individual will not contract diphtheria.

Some workers believe that in addition to antitoxic immunity, anti-bacterial antibodies, perhaps opsonins, are important in resistance to diphtheria (references in 69). Ipsen (50), however, observed that patients who have been vaccinated with toxoid but who nevertheless contract diphtheria, do better on the whole than similar patients who have acquired partial immunity as the result of natural exposure to diphtheria bacilli.

Pneumonia

Wood (98) outlined the course of events in infection with pneumococci. The body defends itself against the invading microbes by three more or less separate lines of defense. The first is located in the pneumonic lesion itself, the second in the regional lymph nodes draining the lesion, and the third in the blood stream.

The pneumonic lesion may be regarded as consisting of four zones. From outside inwards they are: an edematous zone, a zone of early consolidation, a zone of advanced consolidation, and a zone of early resolution. In the outer zone the edematous alveoli contain many pneumococci, which apparently multiply freely in the serous fluid. In the second zone (of early consolidation) the leukocytes, when present in sufficient numbers, can be seen to have phagocyted many of the bacteria. In the zone of advanced consolidation each alveolus is filled with polymorphonuclear leukocytes. The bacteria are either extremely scarce or completely absent, having apparently been phagocyted and digested by the leukocytes. The packing of leukocytes in the alveolar cavities has literally converted each alveolus into a tiny bag of pus. In the fourth zone, in the extreme center of the lesion, there may be found a zone of resolution, in which macrophages predominate and the exudate shows signs of clearing. Evidently all stages of the inflammatory process may be present in a single pneumonic lesion.

Since all these phenomena can be seen in sections of the lungs of animals in the first 24 hours of infection, when antibody cannot be demonstrated either in the blood stream or in the lesion, Wood believed the phagocytosis must have taken place in the absence of antibody, by the mechanism of "surface phagocytosis."

If specific therapy is introduced, the agent must act on the bacteria in the outer zone of edema. Type-specific antiserum, which is no longer used, causes the pneumococci in this zone to agglutinate and stick to the alveolar walls. They are thus immobilized and their phagocytosis is accelerated. Sulfonamides and antibiotics, on the other hand, have no effect upon phagocytosis. They stop the multiplication of the bacteria in the outer edematous zone and prevent further spread of the lesion. Wood believed that in this case final destruction of the bacteria depends upon the same nonantibody mechanism of phagocytosis which operates in the untreated host. Certain antibiotics, such as penicillin, may exert a direct bactericidal effect upon susceptible microorganisms.

The second line of defense in acute bacterial pneumonia is provided by the tracheobronchial lymph nodes. The extensive system of lymphatic channels from the parenchyma of the lungs brings to these nodes such bacteria as escape the destructive action of the alveolar phagocytes. Organisms caught in the node may ultimately be phagocyted by macrophages contained in the nodal sinuses. This filtering action of the nodes is greatly increased by the explosive inflammatory process which results from infection of the sinuses.

The third line of defense operates in the blood stream. As already pointed out, bacteria which reach the blood stream are ordinarily removed by phagocytosis in the spleen, liver, and lungs. Wood showed that the polymorphonuclear leukocytes in the blood also played an important part in this phagocytosis.

Before specific antisera, sulfa drugs, and antibiotics were available, spontaneous recovery from pneumonia depended upon the patient's forming sufficient antibody to combine with the capsules of the bacteria and render them susceptible to phagocytosis. Today antibiotics are probably more important than antibodies in this and a number of other diseases. In mice treated with penicillin, antibody apparently plays no role at all, but in man it evidently does. Tillett found that single large doses of penicillin were not effective in curing human infections, and that it is unwise to treat in this way. After a single dose the temperature comes down, but very commonly goes up again after 12 to 18 hours, so that therapy must be continued. In the case of patients treated with sulfa drugs, Wood believed that antibody plays no role, or a slight one, but other authors believe that the sulfa acts mainly to restrain the growth of the bacteria until sufficient antibody has been formed (54).

The "crisis," which in the days before specific therapy was developed, occurred on the sixth or seventh day in patients who were going to recover, was a sign that antibody had begun to appear in adequate amounts, as is shown by the fact that the serum of a patient after the crisis would opsonize the phagocytosis of pneumococci, whereas the serum of a patient before the crisis would not (17).

Tuberculosis

Human beings do not have a high degree of resistance to the tubercle bacillus. However, most of the population survive the first infection, and develop some immunity as a result. There are evidently racial differences in susceptibility.

For many years it was thought that the allergic inflammatory reaction was the essential mechanism of immunity to tuberculosis. In Chapter 11, however, we summarized the arguments of Rich (71) that in fact tuberculin hypersensitivity does not aid the body in its struggle with tuberculous infection, and that such hypersensitivity can be abolished without decreasing the degree of immunity, and immunity can persist after the hypersensitivity has disappeared. According to Rich sensitivity not only does not contribute to resistance, but, because of the tissue destruction it causes, is actually a bad thing. He believed that desensitization, if done skillfully and carefully, aids resistance instead of diminishing it.

Although it is generally stated that the antibodies found in tuberculosis play little or no role in acquired resistance, Rich (71) (see Chapter 11) believed that antibodies do in fact play an important role. According to him they immobilize tubercle bacilli (see Fig. 14-1), aid in clearing the blood of bacteria, and possibly have other effects.

Lurie (53) believed that the essential mechanism of resistance in tuberculosis is an increased capacity of the mononuclear phagocytes to destroy tubercle bacilli. This he attributed to an increase in the physiological activities of the leukocyte, resulting in accelerated division and increase in phagocytic and digestive capacities. What accounts for the specific orientation of these processes to the destruction of tubercle bacilli is unknown; specific antibodies may be involved, directed towards other constituents of the tubercle bacilli than are the antibodies thus far demonstrated, but this is pure speculation at present.

Dubos, however, pointed out (32) that there is definite evidence that the multiplication of tubercle bacilli *in vivo* can be, and often is, inhibited by factors having nothing to do with phagocytes, thus indicating that phagocytosis is not the whole story. He describes experiments in which virulent tubercle bacilli are injected into normal rabbits. The microbial population of the spleen at first increases, then becomes stabilized at a fairly low level. Transplants of the infected spleen tissue, however,

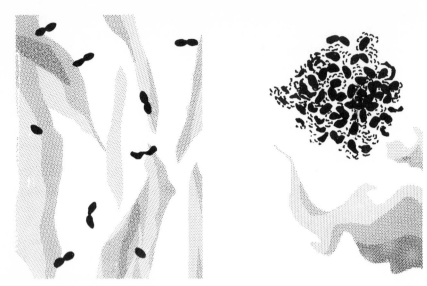

Fig. 14-1. Immobilization by antibody of bacteria in tissues of immune host. Left, site 4 hours after intracutaneous injection of culture of pneumococci into a non-immune rabbit. Right, site 4 hours after injection of the same culture into an immune rabbit. Modified from *The Pathogenesis of Tuberculosis* by A. R. Rich, by permission of the author and Charles C Thomas, publisher.

taken at this point, when cultivated *in vitro* soon allow the bacteria to multiply again and overgrow the tissue. Evidently the inhibition of the growth in the spleen *in situ* required something not possessed by the phagocytes present in tissue cultures.

Another experiment referred to by Dubos involved the implantation of tubercle bacilli enclosed in collodion-impregnated silk bags, into normal and tuberculous guinea pigs. The bacilli multiplied inside the bags in the normal animals, but chiefly decreased in numbers in the tuberculous animals. Since phagocytes could not penetrate the bags, the antimicrobial action must have been accomplished by an antibody or some other humoral factor. Dubos thought it may have been due, at least in part, to chemical changes in the local environment resulting from the more intense inflammatory reaction produced in the tuberculous animals.

The primary tubercular infection differs in a number of ways from the postprimary type (58). The primary type of tuberculosis is an acute disease, which either heals or progresses in a relatively short time, whereas the postprimary type is more stable, and more chronic. There are many other differences between the two.

The question arises, how much immunity does recovery from, or arrest of, a primary tubercular infection confer upon the patient? This is a difficult problem. In the first place, it does not seem ever to have been definitely settled whether, after the primary infection, reinfection can take place (71). Some workers have maintained that any postprimary process represents merely the spread of bacilli from the arrested primary infection; others maintain that the adult type of tuberculosis is nearly always the result of exogenous infection. Rich (71) concluded, after an exhaustive survey of the situation, that the available evidence was insufficient to settle the question.

It is certainly true that infection with the tubercle bacillus does not produce a solid and permanent immunity. Some individuals, after having successfully resisted a primary tuberculous infection, succumb to a subsequent infection, or a recrudescence of the first.

Rich believed (71) that the primary tuberculous infection does confer an appreciable degree of resistance, arguing as follows: (1) In animals, infection or vaccination confers a striking degree of increased resistance, which is readily demonstrated experimentally. (2) The human body, after infection, exhibits an increased power to restrain the multiplication in it of tubercle bacilli, and an increased power to inhibit their spread in the tissues, and to destroy them. (3) The characteristics of the postprimary infection in man—slow progress, reparative fibrosis, and inconspicuous involvement of the regional lymph nodes—are known to characterize the resistance that can be conferred experimentally on animals. (4) Distant organs only infrequently develop progressive lesions from the episodes of bacteremia that occur during local tuberculosis.

Syphilis

This disease, due to *Treponema pallidum,* is generally spread by sexual contact. The degree of immunity following an infection (which today is easily cured by penicillin), is not high, and reinfections are common.

The infection causes the body to produce reagin (p. 629), which fixes complement in the presence of suitable lipide "antigens" which, however, do not derive from the spirochete. The presence of this reagin forms the basis of the Wassermann and other serological tests for syphilis.

4. Resistance in Virus and Rickettsial Diseases

In most virus diseases lasting immunity follows an attack, but some virus diseases may attack repeatedly. Some workers believe that when there is lasting immunity, virus remains in the body of the apparently fully recovered animal, as has been demonstrated in the case of some virus diseases of plants.   If the living virus does so persist, it seems possible that in some cases, as when the host is weakened by some other agency, his immunity might be lowered to the point where the virus could again grow rapidly and produce a new infection or a relapse.   This explanation has been advanced for the recurrence of fever blisters (15a,17), and may be one of the possibilities in the interesting case of the common cold.   See also Brill's disease (p. 638).

Mechanisms of Antivirus Immunity

Age, sex, climate, and genetic background undoubtedly influence susceptibility to virus infection in many instances, but the relative importance of these factors is not easy to assess.   The role of genetic factors has been established for certain virus diseases in experimental animals; they may operate by determining the level of virus multiplication in the host, as well as by determining the vulnerability of the tissues.   Sabin (74) found that the mechanism of resistance to at least one mammalian virus (yellow fever 17D) is Mendelian in character (Chapter 1).   The special susceptibility of some mice (PRI) to the French yellow fever neurotropic virus was found also to be genetically determined, and is due to a gene which makes for high cellular vulnerability.   These two sets of genes are inherited independently.

Variants of a virus can sometimes overcome inherited resistance of a host, either by possessing or developing the capacity to kill at lower levels of multiplication or by overwhelming the innate barrier to higher levels of multiplication.   Hormones, such as cortisone, and changes produced in the tissues by age, also alter the response of the host to certain virus infections.

We have seen above that two factors may be involved in active immunity. The tissue cells of an animal may develop an intrinsic resistance, or circulating antibodies may be produced.   Some workers believe that in antivirus immunity cell immunity is the important thing, and the role of the circulating antibodies is a minor one.   This is supported by the observation that animals may have antibodies that produce agglutination, precipitation, and complement fixation, without being immune or resistant to vaccinia infection (68).   Also, in some diseases, such as lymphocytic choriomeningitis in mice (96), recovered animals are refractory to reinfection.   Also, in patients with hypogammaglobulinemia (Chapter 2), who seem nearly incapable of forming antibody, recovery from virus infections, with the usual degree of immunity, seems to take place.

Antivirus antibodies capable of protecting against measles and infectious hepatitis have been found in the gamma globulin separated from plasma (65,83,84). Circulating antibody for mumps virus has been demonstrated by Enders (37). The serum of most adult city-dwellers contains antibodies capable of neutralizing considerable amounts of influenza virus A (18).

Antivirus antibodies in an animal's circulation may be tested for by inhibition of hemagglutination, precipitation, complement fixation, or neutralizing power. All of these forms of antivirus activity have been observed. For some viruses it is probable that not all of these antibodies are identical. Certainly, there is evidence that the neutralizing antibodies are different from the others. In the case of vaccinia, complement-fixing antibodies, agglutinins, and precipitins can be obtained by injecting the purified substance S (66), or completely inactivated elementary bodies (68), although practically no neutralizing antibodies are formed as a result of this treatment. The neutralizing antibodies are absorbed by washed elementary bodies, but not by the soluble specific substance (76).

At one time it was supposed that the neutralizing antibodies killed the virus, but this belief is no longer held (78). Todd (93), Andrewes (5), and others have shown that in some cases neutral mixtures can be made active again by simple dilution or centrifugation. Such observations were at first thought to show that no combination took place between the neutralizing antibodies and the virus, but Andrewes (5) and Salaman (75) later showed that the mixtures did not become active when diluted or centrifuged, if they were first allowed to stand for sufficient periods of time. Salaman (76) pointed out that the fact that neutralizing antibody can be absorbed by elementary bodies is evidence for real union.

The interesting observation has been made that the neutrality or lack of neutrality of a mixture of virus and serum depends to some extent upon the organ into which it is injected for test. Certain virus–serum mixtures are neutral when injected into the skin, but still somewhat active when injected into the brain (5,73) or the testicles. Also (see 103), when vaccinia cultures are made with normal serum, the virus promptly attaches itself to the tissues and multiplies, but in cultures made with immune serum, although the virus similarly becomes attached to the tissues, it does not multiply. Inapparent infection seems to be a much commoner phenomenon in virus diseases than in bacterial and mycotic infections. Such tissue–virus mixtures can be washed until no neutralizing antibodies are detectable in the washings, but the tissue will still not become infected, even though the tissue–virus mixture is infectious for other unprotected tissues. Extended washing will render even protected tissue susceptible. Salaman (76) with Robinow found that in tissue cultures of rabbit's cornea, if virus is applied first and then antiserum, infection is not prevented. They also found that, when elementary bodies are mixed with antiserum, centrifuged, washed, and resuspended, their infectivity is much reduced.

Once virus has reached the interior of the cell, antiserum can probably do nothing to prevent its survival and multiplication there, for the walls of living cells do not seem to be permeable to antibody.

Influenza

Influenza is an acute, self-limited, infectious disease caused by a virus of the influenza group. The symptoms are mainly constitutional, although the *infection* seems to be limited to the respiratory tract. Influenza tends to occur in epidemics. Of these the greatest on record was the great epidemic of 1918–1919, which is believed to have resulted in the death of some 20 million human beings.

Some authorities believe that the constitutional symptoms are a consequence of primary toxicity of the influenza virus, and it has in fact been shown that the virus in sufficient amount is toxic, even after being heated or otherwise modified (85,86). Some workers (23) have described hepatic, splenic, cerebral, and possibly cardiac damage as resulting from the toxic action of the virus, but others (67) have described autopsies of fatal cases in which no destructive lesions were found.

Like a number of other viruses, influenza virus can agglutinate the erythrocytes of chickens, man, and other animals. It will combine in the same way with cells of the respiratory epithelium. The virus spontaneously elutes from erythrocytes and from cell preparations from excised lung, but not from preparations of living lung. Burnet (16) believed that after combining with cells of the respiratory epithelium, the virus sinks into the susceptible cell, thus initiating an infection. This sounds inherently plausible, but there has been one report (46) of infective virus particles that would not cause hemagglutination, which if confirmed would be hard to reconcile with this hypothesis.

It is probable that recovery from influenza is associated with the production of antibodies, and there is good evidence that antibodies are an important part of the mechanism of resistance to reinfection which is possessed for a time by patients who have recovered.

Influenza vaccines are highly efficient in preventing infection (41a), their efficiency amounting to 75 to 80 per cent. The degree of resistance conferred has been shown to be quite consistently related to the antibody level induced by the inocculation.

The duration of the vaccine-induced immunity remains uncertain. Annual vaccination is currently practiced, not so much because it is known that the induced immunity will have fallen to a nonprotective level in a year, but because we cannot yet make an informed guess as to the degree of strain variation in the viruses the next season will bring (41a).

Variola (Smallpox)

Downie and McCarthy (31) pointed out that smallpox might be regarded as the classical type of the exanthematous infections.

The variola virus probably enters the human body through the mucosa of the respiratory tract, and a period of 10 to 14 days, usually 12, elapses before the onset of illness. It is not known where the virus is multiplying during this period. Virus appears in the blood in all cases at or just before the onset of illness. In the more severe cases virus is found in the blood for a longer time and in larger amounts.

The viremia at the onset of illness leads to infection, in the first place, of the capillary endothelium of the subepithelial vessels. The appearance of the characteristic lesions of the disease are too familiar to demand a description here. Excellent pictures are to be found in the article by Smadel (80) and the book by Top (94). Histological studies are shown by Downie and McCarthy (31).

About the fourth or fifth day of illness, if the patient is going to recover, the temperature falls and the clinical condition of the patient improves. This coincides with the appearance of antibody, which may be demonstrated by virus neutralization, complement fixation, and the antihemagglutination test (cf. ref. 3).

Some patients may contract smallpox in spite of previous vaccination; in such patients antibody appears earlier and in larger amounts (31), especially if the previous vaccination was not too many years before. In some such cases antibody may be detectable from the third day onwards.

The progress of the lesions through the stage of pustulation and crusting is thought to be the inflammatory response to the products of cell destruction (31) and in moderately severe and severe infections may be associated with return of fever and deterioration in the clinical condition of the patient. In some cases death may occur towards the end of the second week. Usually, however, according to Downie and McCarthy, the spread of the virus has been halted earlier, at about the fifth or sixth day of illness, by the action of the antibody, and after that further infection of cells does not take place. The virus already inside the cells, however, protected from the action of the antibody, continues to grow and produce cell necrosis.

If infection of epithelial and other cells has become too widespread before antibody appears, the resulting cell necrosis may have very serious effects, and may even result in a fatal termination of the disease.

The antibody produced inhibits infectivity of the virus and is capable of conferring passive protection. It seems likely that it is one of the main factors in acquired immunity to smallpox.

Not all workers, however, are convinced that antibody is of prime importance in acquired resistance to smallpox. Several investigators have reported that although the injection of killed vaccinia virus into animals may give rise to neutralizing antibodies, these animals show only slight and temporary resistance to infection, and the presence of even a considerable titer of neutralizing antibody is not necessarily proof of a state of protection against the virus (68,57).

Poliomyelitis

Poliomyelitis is actually a rather common virus disease, but since it usually runs a mild course, characterized by upper respiratory or gastrointestinal symptoms, many victims never know they have had it. Sometimes, however, the picture is complicated by invasion of the central nervous system. In this case the virus may become widely disseminated through the neuraxis: the clinical picture that results is dominated by flaccid paralysis of voluntary muscles, resulting from destruction of motor neurons in the spinal cord (49). It is then that the disease is generally recognized and called infantile paralysis, although in this country paralytic poliomyelitis is no longer primarily a disease of infants.

The commonness of the infection is part of our newer knowledge. Bodian (12) estimated that 99 per cent of adults in this country have experienced the primary infection in the alimentary tract, without being harmed. By the age of 20, about 1 per cent have also experienced the paralytic effects of the subsequent infection of the central nervous system (CNS).

Landsteiner and Popper (51) demonstrated that poliomyelitis was a virus disease when they showed that the spinal cord of a child dead of infantile paralysis could be inoculated into the brain of monkeys to provide a similar, often fatal, disease. The virus multiplied in the monkey, and by inoculation of suitable extracts of nervous tissue could be passed indefinitely from animal to animal. Enders, Weller, and Robbins (38, 35,36) succeeded in growing the three types of poliomyelitis virus in tissue cultures of skin and in intestines of human embryo. Later it was shown that it could be grown in cultures of certain monkey's tissues.

Three immunologically distinct strains of poliomyelitis virus are currently recognized (49), and infection with one of these protects against that strain but not against either of the other two. The strains, familiarly known as Brunhilde, Lansing, and Leon, are now generally designated as type I, II, and III.

Poliomyelitis has a world-wide distribution, although in some areas it is of little importance as an epidemic disease (49). In countries such as Cuba, Ecuador, Egypt, Japan, Malta, Mauritius, Puerto Rico, and Venezuela, epidemics are relatively small and infrequent, and 80 to 90 per cent of the reported paralytic cases occur in children less than five years of age. It is generally agreed that there can be only one explanation of these facts, which is that in these countries the virus is so omnipresent that virtually everyone comes in contact with it before the age of five. The discrepancies in the age incidence of the paralytic disease in different countries therefore appear to be based upon differences in degrees of exposure and immunization, brought about by differences in cultures, climates, and possibly genetic differences.

It has been clear for a long time that poliomyelitis is spread by human contact, although there is still not a complete agreement as to the nature of this contact. There is even no complete agreement as to the portal of entry of the virus; Bedson (7) thought the available facts suggest that the virus can be spread either by the infectious secretions of the throat or nasopharynx, or by intestinal excreta (4,41a).

The evidence clearly suggests that the reservoir of the virus is the human being, and that symptomless carriers must be extremely numerous during epidemics.

Bodian was inclined to consider the pathogenesis of poliomyelitis as proceeding in three steps (36). (1) Virus multiplication in the alimentary tract, (2) multiplication in organs such as lymph nodes and spleen, and finally (3) in the nervous system. The virus may reach the nervous system either along nerve pathways or from the blood stream at certain points.

Immunity to poliomyelitis definitely follows infection, and it is generally supposed that this resistance is permanent, although Raffel (69) pointed out the difficulties of proving this. The presence of immunity is shown by observations such as the Malta outbreak reported by Seddon et al. (49).

The mechanism of resistance depends to a large extent, at least, upon antibodies. Lenette and Hudson (52) were able to infect monkeys by injecting the virus intravenously, by giving starch intracerebrally to break the barrier between the blood stream and the central nervous system (CNS). But if circulating antibodies were first established by immunization, the injected virus did not usually infect under these conditions, indicating that the intravenously injected virus had been neutralized in the blood stream before it reached the CNS. Of course this mode of infection is somewhat artificial, but Bodian (13) has described feeding experiments which show that even very low levels of antibody are capable of preventing CNS infection even by this natural route. He points out, however, that his demonstration does not reveal precisely at what site the antibody prevents access of the virus to the CNS.

Since considerable antibody rise occurs in infections in which the CNS is not involved, it is apparent that the sharp early rise which is observed is not the result of virus multiplication in the CNS (13).

Yet there are some reasons for doubting that antibody is the only factor involved in resistance to poliomyelitis. After paralytic infection of animals due to intracerebral inoculation a high degree of type-specific immunity is observed, although the serum antibody level may be low (13). Bodian (13) reported that after paralytic infection experimental animals display a considerable degree of cross immunity (*i.e.,* immunity to other types of polio virus), although it is not so solid as the homotypic immunity. But animals with high titer of antibodies may exhibit little heterotypic immunity.

Bodian (13) therefore believed that the local immunity of the central nervous system is unrelated to the circulating antibody. If this is so, the mechanism of this immunity is as yet unexplained. Bodian does not believe it is due to local formation of antibody in the CNS. There have been reports of antivirus substances in the spinal cord, but the other workers have not confirmed them (13,69).

The course of a paralytic poliomyelitis infection has been diagrammed by Bodian (12) and is shown in Fig. 14-2.

After an attack of poliomyelitis, antibody persists in the circulation for a considerable time. Winsser and Sabin (97) examined the virus-neutralizing antibody in the sera of seven patients at intervals of three months and three years after the attack, and found that very high levels of neutralizing antibodies were still present after three years. In fact, since they did not succeed in establishing the maximum titers, it is not certain that the antibody levels had fallen at all in three years. This persistence of antibodies after infection suggests that it may account for the prolonged immunity which is observed, and encouraged those who

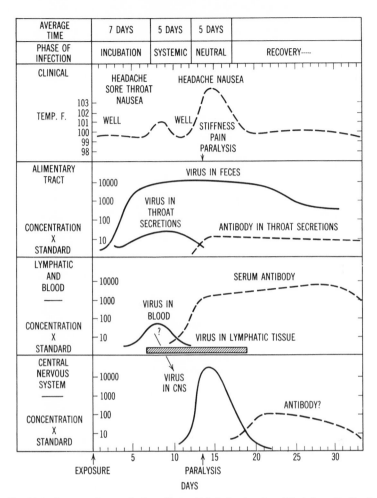

Fig. 14-2. Course of a paralytic poliomyelitis infection (modified from Bodian).

went on to develop practical methods of artificial immunization (see Chapter 15).

When the first epidemic of any size appeared, in 1890, poliomyelitis was truly a disease of infants. Since that time the age at which individuals are generally attacked has been steadily increasing in those countries in which the disease is of importance as an epidemic. The shift in age of selection in the United States is shown in Fig. 14-3, taken from Howe (49). It will be seen that 30 years ago the highest attack rates were recorded

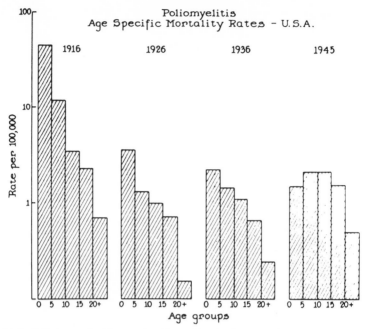

Fig. 14-3. Shift in age incidence of poliomyelitis in the United States. From *Bacterial and Mycotic Infections of Man*, edited by R. J. Dubos. Courtesy of the editor, R. J. Dubos, the author, H. A. Howe, the publishers, J. B. Lippincott Co., and the National Foundation for Infantile Paralysis.

in the 0 to 4 years age group, but in 1945 the highest were in the 5 to 9 and 10 to 14 years age group.

The same tendency appears if we compare an area where there is little epidemic poliomyelitis with, successively, the New York–Chicago area, 1916–1940; and four northern agricultural states, 1930–1940, as shown in Figure 14-4.

It is generally agreed that these observations can all be interpreted on the basis of one hypothesis, namely, that exposure to poliomyelitis is postponed longer in rural communities than in cities, and that it is postponed in the United States longer at the present time than it was in the past. It is also generally agreed (17) that the postponement in the average age at which infection occurs is due to the development of Western twentieth-century civilization, with its emphasis on cleanliness, sanitary disposal of feces, sterilization of eating utensils, and general improvement in the standard of living.

This improvement in "civilized" living carries with it a lower exposure to poliomyelitis in the early years, and consequent lower degree of im-

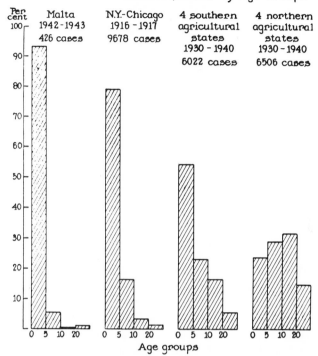

Poliomyelitis
Per Cent Distribution of Cases by Age Groups

Fig. 14-4. Shift in age incidence of poliomyelitis when different communities are compared. From *Bacterial and Mycotic Infections of Man,* edited by R. J. Dubos. Courtesy of the editor, R. J. Dubos, the author, H. A. Howe, the publishers, J. B. Lippincott Co., and the National Foundation for Infantile Paralysis.

munization. The reason more persons in the older age groups are being attacked in current epidemics is that there are more people in these age groups who have never had polio. The reason persons in these age groups do not get polio in Malta is that they have all had it, and are immune as a result. Burnet (17) believed that even the 1942–1943 epidemic in Malta became possible only when a new and more virulent strain of virus was introduced. In this outbreak there were 57 cases among the British troops, and 397 among Maltese children, but none in the Maltese soldiers, although they were equally exposed. Clearly more of the Maltese soldiers than the British had acquired immunity in childhood. Hammon's (47) analysis of the evidence suggests that immunity is eventually acquired by the majority of urban residents as a result of repeated exposures to the virus. Restimulation may take place at intervals, but such infections may often be limited to the intestinal tract.

Tumors

There are two main theories of the cause of cancer, the virus theory (70) and the somatic mutation theory (39,11,2). If the virus theory is right, one would expect immunity to play some role.

Without attempting a survey of the literature on this subject, we may summarize a few of the arguments of those who believe that viruses are involved in cancer production. In the first place, it has been noted that the most typical symptoms of neoplastic growth, proliferation, and degeneration, recall the characteristics of cells infected with virus.

Stanley (82) summarized the position of those who believe in the probable virus origin of cancer. He pointed out in the first place that some cancers in animals and plants are known to be caused by viruses; for example, the fowl sarcoma discovered by Rous (72) and the rabbit papilloma of Shope (79). If one cancer can be caused by a virus, it is therefore *possible* that all, or nearly all, cancers are caused by viruses.

Stanley next discussed the latency phenomenon. Readers of this book will already be aware of examples of latency in virus infections, as in the case of herpes simplex, where the virus is continually present, yet the disease manifests itself only under the stimulus of irritation, loss of sleep, infection with the virus of the common cold, etc. Stanley pointed to the latent potato virus, present in all or almost all of the potato plants grown in the United States. It does not cause any obvious disease, and our plants appear healthy. If one had as material only the potato plants grown in this country, it would be difficult if not impossible to prove the existence of this virus. Extracts of one potato plant would have no effect on another plant because the second plant would always already contain the virus. The virus has been demonstrated only because we have access to plants which do not already contain it, namely, certain potato plants from parts of Europe. Stanley raised the question, how many such viruses exist without our knowing about them? We might ask further, could it be that all of us carry one or more such viruses, and it is only when the virus mutates, or is aided by irritation, that cancer results?

Another interesting fact is the masked condition of viruses at certain times, for instance, in the insect vectors which transmit them. There is also the example of the swine influenza virus in the hog lung worm.

Also possibly pertinent is the phenomenon of virus interference, described on page 32. Stanley raised the question whether the regression of certain tumors following virus infection can be connected with the interference phenomenon.

Finally there is the observation that in some cases cells which seemed to be irreversibly changed can, under suitable conditions, literally outgrow a virus infection of a virus-like agent. Various workers (Braun, Kidd, Sonneborn, and Spiegelman) have reported work of this sort with crown gall disease of plants, the V_2 carcinoma, paramecium, and bacteria, respectively. The interesting thing about these observations is that the infective agent (SDE) was reproducing itself as fast as, or faster than, the host cell, so that the phenomenon seemed to duplicate exactly the multiplication of a permanently altered cell. But when the cell was stimulated to grow faster than the self-duplicating entity (SDE), it freed itself of the alteration by outgrowing it. It is true that in the V_2 varcinoma a somatic change persists in spite of the apparent loss of the virus.

If cancer were due to virus infection, antibodies should appear in the blood of cancer patients. The finding of such antibodies would, however, not prove the virus origin of cancer, for if cancer cells merely represent mutated normal tissue cells they might contain new antigens against which the host could form antibodies. The question of antibodies to cancer, long a moot question, is apparently being resolved by current work.

Graham and Graham (45) tested the sera of 48 patients for antibodies to their own tumors by the complement-fixation technic. The antigen was prepared by extracting a water-soluble, saline-insoluble fraction from the tumor. Twelve patients were found to have titers of 1:16 to 1:128. It is of interest that these were patients who seemed to be resisting the progress of the neoplasm better than the others. The majority of the patients who failed to show circulating antibodies had far advanced lesions.

However, it is likely that not all immunity depends upon antibodies, and some antitumor immunity may be predominantly of this other type. This idea is supported by observations such as those of Mitchison (59), who observed that a tumor (a lymphosarcoma) which regressed with a median survival time of 9.9 ± 0.8 days in untreated mice, had a median survival time of only 2.1 ± 0.3 days in mice which had been immunized by previous transplants. This immunity could not be transferred to susceptible mice by injection of serum, but could be transferred by lymph node grafts.

Fink (41) was also able to demonstrate acquired immunity to tumors in experimental animals.

The immunological aspects of cancer are discussed by Woodruff (99) and by a series of Russian authors (57a).

Typhus

Epidemic louse-borne typhus is an acute infectious disease caused by *Rickettsia prowazekii*. It is characterized by severe headache, sustained high fever, generalized macular or maculopapular rash. The rash persists until the second week when, in severe cases, the macules become purpuric in character and fresh petechiae may appear. During this second week the patient is drowsy, confused, or even stuporous, and a fall in blood pressure with diminution of urinary output indicates severe involvement of the vascular system. About the fourteenth day, if the patient is going to recover, the temperature falls, the rash begins to fade, and the patient's mental condition improves. Convalescence is soon established.

The typhus rickettsiae invade the endothelial cells of the small arteries, capillaries, and venules. The affected cells tend to proliferate, and as a result of the injury thrombus occurs, with small areas of necrosis and perivascular accumulations of phagocytes.

Although endemic in many areas, typhus fevers have always been particularly associated with wars, famines, and other mass misfortunes of mankind. Their effect on the outcome of battles has in the past often been decisive (101). Epidemics occurred during both World Wars. Typhus has in fact been one of the major epidemic diseases of all time, and Snyder (81) believed that the widespread human suffering caused by this disease has been exceeded only by that caused by malaria.

Epidemic louse-borne typhus is spread by the human head louse and the human body louse, chiefly by the latter; the rickettsiae appear in the feces of the louse. Each louse takes from four to six meals a day from its host (81). According to Top (94), whenever a louse bites, it makes a small puncture in the skin and defecates at the same time. The scratching which the bite causes may rub the feces into the puncture and thus initiate the infection.

Whereas the insect vectors of some diseases do not seem to be much discommoded by the presence in their bodies of the pathogen which they transmit (this seems to be the case with the ticks which transmit spotted fever, see following section), this is not true of the louse which transmits *Rickettsia prowazekii*. As Zinsser (101) described it:

"The louse shares with us the misfortune of being prey to the typhus virus. If lice can dread, the nightmare of their lives is the fear of some day inhabiting an infected rat or human being. For the host may survive; but the ill starred louse that sticks his haustellum through an infected skin, and imbibes the loathsome virus with his nourishment, is doomed beyond succor. In eight days he sickens, in ten days he is *in extremis*, on the eleventh or twelfth his tiny body turns red with blood extravasated from his bowel, and he gives up his little ghost. . . To the louse, *we* are the dreaded emissaries of death. He leads a relatively harmless life— the result of centuries of adaptions; then, out of the blue, an epidemic occurs; his host sickens, and the only world he has ever known becomes pestilential and deadly; and if, as a result of circumstances not under his control, his stricken body is transferred to another host whom he, in turn, infects, he does so without guile, from an uncontrollable need for nourishment, with death already in his own entrails."*

A human being who has recovered from an attack of epidemic typhus possesses immunity which lasts for many years. Living rickettsiae may however, persist in the body for long periods of time, and may cause a mild secondary attack as much as 40 to 50 years later (Brill's disease).

A milder form of typhus, transmitted to man by the rat flea, is caused by *Rickettsia mooseri*, and is known as murine typhus. It is world-wide in distribution, and cases have been reported from more than three-fourths of the states of the United States. A person who has recovered from murine typhus is immune to epidemic typhus, and vice versa. The vaccines used for immunization to the two diseases, however, do not confer this cross-protection.

It is probable that immunity to typhus depends largely upon antibodies; certainly antibodies can be detected by several methods in typhus patients and in those who have recovered.

The antibodies which form the basis of the classical Weil-Felix test have the property of agglutinating certain strains of the bacillus *Proteus vulgaris* (OX 19), owing to the accidental occurrence of an antigenic component which is common to this bacillus and to the rickettsiae. These agglutinins appear in the sera of most patients between the fifth and eighth days of illness. In most cases the titer rises to 1:160 or higher, and often goes as high as 1:1000 at the peak of the response, which is usually in the third week of illness or the first two weeks of convalescence. A few weeks later the titer is again below 1:160. This agglutinin is produced in murine typhus and in some members of the Rocky Mountain spotted fever group, so it does not distinguish between these different

* From *Rats, Lice, and History*, by Hans Zinsser. Courtesy of Little, Brown and Co. and the Atlantic Monthly Press.

diseases. An infection with *Proteus vulgaris* also gives rise to agglutinins against OX 19.

Agglutinating antibodies for rickettsial suspensions are also produced, appearing in the sera of patients as early as the seventh or eighth day of illness. Suspensions of homologous organisms are agglutinated to a higher titer than are those of the heterologous species, but a considerable degree of cross-reaction occurs. The species-specific agglutinins can be detected by absorbing the sera with heterologous rickettsiae.

Complement-fixing antibodies also appear, about the same time as the agglutinins. They increase in concentration, reaching a maximum by the twelfth to the sixteenth day after onset. Subsequently the titer falls slowly; low values may persist for years.

Zinsser and Castaneda (102) showed that neutralizing antibodies for rickettsiae were present in hyperimmune serum. Precipitins and opsonizing antibodies are also found (81).

It does not seem to be known which of these antibodies is responsible for immunity (42,62). That the antibodies are not all identical is suggested by the observations of Murray, Ofstrock, and Snyder (62) which show that changes in the titers of complement fixing, agglutinating, and neutralizing antibodies which follow a recall injection do not always run parallel.

Rocky Mountain Spotted Fever

The causative agent of this disease is *Rickettsia rickettsii*. It is transmitted to man by the bite of a tick. In the United States, six species of ticks have been found to be infected, and others have been shown capable of transmitting the infection. The disease has been reported from 44 states.

The main vector, *Dermacentor andersoni*, is found throughout the Rocky Mountain region and adjacent areas. This insect does not seem to suffer from the presence of the rickettsiae, which may be found in all stages, and so far as is known they survive the winter only by persistence in infected nymphs and adult ticks.

The disease is essentially a specific intracellular infection of small peripheral blood vessels. The rickettsiae can be recovered from the circulating blood during the first and part of the second week of infection. The organisms first invade the nuclei of endothelial cells in the capillaries, where they multiply in great numbers and destroy the cells. From there the lesion extends centripetally along the intima into slightly larger vessels (arterioles), where smooth muscle cells of the media are also invaded and destroyed. This destruction of muscle cells is a distinctive feature of the disease.

After the death of the cells, necrosis occurs in the intima and media of the vessels, resulting in thrombosis and extravasation of blood. As a result of the thrombosis, microinfarcts are formed, chiefly in the skin, subcutaneous tissues, and central nervous system. As the disease progresses, perivascular accumulations of mononuclear macrophages develop, and the vascular lesions assume a proliferative character, as indicated by the pressure of numerous mitoses in cells.

In nonvaccinated adults, the incubation period ranges from 2 to 12 days, averaging 6 or 7 days. The actual onset, as in typhus, may be preceded by a few days of ill-defined symptoms, such as listlessness, loss of appetite, and headache. The onset of illness is commonly abrupt, with chills, prostration, and a rapidly rising fever. A distinctive rash usually appears on the third or fourth day.

The mortality rate has varied from 19 to 36 per cent (48). In the absence of therapy, recovery takes place, if it is going to, through the development of immunity. When clinical improvement begins, the rickettsiae disappear from the blood, and circulating antibodies appear. Harrell (48) believed that cellular immunity must be an even greater factor in recovery than humoral immunity. Whether this is so or not, it is generally considered that persons having recovered from spotted fever are more or less permanently immune. The probable role of antibodies in acquired resistance is shown by the definite protective value of the vaccines which have been developed.

5. Immunity to Parasites

Animal parasites, as well as bacteria and viruses, contain antigenic substances (see Chapter 4), and it is to be expected that immunization, in the broad sense of the word, will occur whenever these antigens reach the circulation of the host. Sometimes a hypersensitivity of infection also results (Chapters 9, 11), and the disease can often be diagnosed by skin tests, as in the case of infection with echinococcus or trichina.

There is no doubt that acquired resistance plays an important role in protozoan and metazoan infections, just as in bacterial infection. It is well known that protozoan infections, after an acute attack, usually go into a chronic state in which the parasites are few and difficult to demonstrate. This state may be interrupted by relapses. During the chronic state there is usually marked resistance to reinfection. Thus adults native to highly malarial countries do not develop acute malaria, and chronic carriers of amoebic dysentery do not seem to develop amoebic dysentery.

It is not always easy to demonstrate antibodies in such cases, partly because of technical difficulties, but Coggeshall and Kumm (28) showed that the serum of rhesus monkeys with *Plasmodium knowlesi* malaria conferred a passive immunity on normal monkeys, and Coggeshall (25) found that protective and complement-fixing antibodies were produced in human beings following experimental infection with *Plasmodium knowlesi.*

In trypanosome infections it has been possible to demonstrate another aspect of the defense mechanism of the host, inhibition of reproduction of the invading organism. This cannot be shown in bacterial infections because it cannot be differentiated from the result of a partially effective bactericidal activity. In the case of *Trypanosoma lewisi,* definite morphological features characteristic of various stages of growth can be observed, and after the infection has been under way for a few days, young forms of the parasite are not present, although the total number of parasites is at its height. This reproduction-inhibiting substance was called *ablastin* by Taliaferro (89). It can be passively transferred to other animals and appears in the globulin fraction of the serum, being in these respects like an antibody. Unlike a typical antibody, however, it is not absorbed out of a serum by the organisms against which it is directed. It might be wondered if this substance is related in any way to the treponema-immobilizing antibody found in syphilis (p. 630).

Leishmania Infections

There are three human diseases recognized as caused by infection with parasites of the protozoan genus *Leishmania.* *Kala-azar* is a chronic infection caused by *L. donovani,* with its principal seat in the reticuloendothelial system. It may affect all parts of the body, however, and should be considered as a general disease. The main characteristics are fever, enlargement of the spleen and liver, leukopenia, anemia, and hyperglobulinemia. It occurs widely, in China, India, Asiatic Russia, etc. The *oriental sore,* also known as the Baghdad boil, Aleppo button, etc., is a cutaneous infection with *L. tropica* which is characterized by cutaneous granulomas with a strong tendency to ulceration. The lesion persists for a year or so. The disease is focal but widespread, being found in western India, Mesopotamia, Africa, etc. It used to be stated in Baghdad that no person who lives there more than a month escaped infection, which is transmitted by the sand fly, *Phlebotomus papatasii* (1) and possibly by the stable fly, *Stomoxys calcitrans* (8). The use of insecticides in malaria eradication schemes has, by controlling sand flies, caused the almost complete disappearance of cutaneous leishmaniasis in the Middle East (42a).

American *mucocutaneous leishmaniasis,* attributed to *L. brasiliensis,* is similar to the oriental sore, but in addition many cases show further involvement of nose, mouth, and pharynx. The disease is endemic in much, perhaps all, of Central and South America.

Leishmania infection produces good immunity. Persons who have recovered from either kala-azar or oriental sore are seldom reinfected, and deliberate inoculation with *L. tropica* on parts of the body hidden by clothing has been recommended to protect against later possible facial lesions, with the resultant conspicuous scars (9).

Antibody production does not seem to be good in *Leishmania* infections, although enough is generally formed for a complement fixation test. The immunity apparently depends partly upon the antibody and partly upon the histiocyte response, which is very characteristic of kala-azar (30).

Malaria

Malaria is the most important parasitic disease of man, and in fact probably the most important human infection. It is caused by a protozoon, of which there are various species causing the disease in lizards, birds, monkeys, and man: in man *Plasmodium vivax* causes tertian malaria, *P. malariae* causes quartan malaria, *P. falciparum* causes falciparum malaria, and *P. ovale* causes ovale malaria. None of these parasites are infectious for lower animals.

The only means of transmission in nature is by female anopheline mosquitoes; different species act as vectors in different parts of the world. The mosquito is not a mere mechanical carrier, but a true (final) host. Following the bite of an infected mosquito, the parasites undergo 6 to 8 days development in some of the fixed tissue cells of man, probably in the liver (40), before they appear in the blood stream. On about the eighth or tenth day they can be detected in the erythrocytes, where they develop rapidly.

The mature asexual form ruptures the red cell and releases daughter cells (*merozoites*) which then attack unaffected red cells. This process is repeated for a period of about 10 days. At the end of this time some of the parasites have developed into sexual forms (male and female *gametocytes*). They cannot fertilize themselves in the human body, but when the gametocytes are taken up by an *Anopheles* mosquito fertilization takes place and the fertilized parasite forms cysts on the outer stomach wall of the mosquito. These cysts rupture and release *sporozoites* which make their way to the salivary glands of the mosquito, where they mature and await introduction into man when the mosquito again bites a human being.

The symptoms of malaria vary with the type of parasite. Each of the four human types has a characteristic behavior and time of sporulation, which determines the intervals between successive segmentations of the mature parasite, which produce the characteristic paroxysm ("chill"). *Falciparum* malaria is a more severe disease than the others, and varied localization of the parasites may produce different alarming symptoms. It is *falciparum* that causes most of the deaths. If the process occurs in the brain, the onset is rapid, with delirium or coma; edema and necrosis of the blockaded capillaries will be found. Or the disease may present a gastrointestinal syndrome with abdominal cramps, diarrhea, and vomiting. If localization is in the lungs, the picture is that of early pneumonia.

A malaria infection confers a low-grade immunity of short duration. In experimental animals it is found that immunity outlasts complete cure of the infection only a few weeks. Many workers believe that a host is immune to malaria only in the presence of an infection, and Coggeshall (26) stated that the immunity to malarial infections is better described as an acquired tolerance.

This tolerance (or immunity to superinfection) persists for as long as a year and may last seven years (90). Successive reinfections with the same strain, whether by sporozoites or blood stages, result in progressively milder infections, showing that the degree of immunity becomes progressively higher (90).

Such immunity as there is is species-specific. In areas where all three of the major species of *Plasmodium* are present, individuals can have an acute attack of each disease, all within a single year. It is likely (26) that there are immunologically different strains within each species which cannot be differentiated morphologically. It has been shown (27) that a person immune to a strain of *Vivax* malaria in his own locality is nevertheless susceptible to infection with a *Vivax* strain from another locality.

Although infection with one strain apparently confers no immunity to another, experimental studies show that simultaneous infection with two species influences the development of each parasite (30). When *P. vivax* and *P. malariae* are inoculated simultaneously, *P. vivax* is the dominant species, *P. malariae* sometimes failing to develop at all. When *P. vivax* and *P. falciparum* are inoculated together, *P. falciparum* is at first the more prominent, but *P. vivax* eventually becomes the dominant species.

Antibodies of the complement-fixing, agglutinating, and protective type have been demonstrated in malaria, and it is likely that these antibodies are of great importance in immunity. Freund (42,92) was able to confer good immunity upon ducks and monkeys by injection of killed parasites mixed with adjuvants. Complement-fixing antibody was found in immunized monkeys, and in general the groups of monkeys with higher titers showed higher protection, but there was not a strict correlation in individual monkeys between antibody titer and protection. Eaton (90) reported that complement-fixing antibodies, produced in monkeys by the injection of a soluble malaria antigen, conferred little or no protection. Modern work has supported the idea that antimalarial antibodies, though generally weak, are effective (42a).

Marked racial differences in susceptibility to malaria have been reported. Negroes are said to be almost wholly insusceptible to *P. vivax* and *P. ovale* (15,14). Notably also, the disease produced in Negroes by *P. falciparum*, at least in adults, is much milder than that produced by this parasite in Europeans, and it is stated that Negroes practically never develop the serious complication of *P. falciparum* infection, blackwater fever (44,14). In fact it has been suggested that it was the presence of entrenched endemic Falciparum malaria in Africa which prevented the continent from being colonized, and its natives from being exterminated or displaced into the less desirable lands, as happened, for example, in North America and Australia.

Part of the greater resistance of the African to *P. falciparum* has apparently been elucidated. In the most malarious parts of Africa sickle-cell anemia (a hereditary disorder of the blood), caused by a recessive gene, is a prevalent disease. People who are homozygous for this gene are at a considerable disadvantage, but Allison (3,4) has shown that those who are heterozygous, who do not have the anemia but do exhibit the sickle-cell trait, possess an advantage, which he estimates to be about 25 per cent, over those homozygous for the normal gene, because they are much more resistant to infection with *P. falciparum*. Allison demonstrated this greater resistance by an actual experiment, in which heterozygotes for the sickle-cell gene and normal controls were deliberately exposed, by bite of infected mosquitoes or by injection, to *P. falciparum*. Only 2 of the 15 sickle-cell carriers were infected (lightly), whereas 14 of the 15 controls developed severe infections, many of which required chemotherapy for management.

It seems likely that this selective advantage of the heterozygote explains the high frequencies of this otherwise disadvantageous gene in various parts of the world, especially in Africa. The reader will be reminded of the selective advantage of certain blood groups with regard to disease, which we discussed in Chapter 5.

Metazoan Infections

In the case of worms, increased resistance seems to take two forms: interference with maturing of the parasites after their entry, and resistance to injurious effects of the parasite.   Natural immunity appears to depend partly on differences in the action of the gastric juices.   There is evidence that antibody production is concerned in acquired immunity.

Taliaferro (88) believed that the chief mechanism of immunity is the formation of specific antibodies.   These may have three main effects: they may form specific precipitate around the parasite, thus immobilizing it, and perhaps also stunting its growth; they may be specific for enzymes of the worm which are instrumental in digesting and attacking host tissues; and the antibodies may have some part in increasing cellular response, leading to walling off of the immobilized parasite and mobilization of macrophages to remove the dead parasite.

Passive transfer of immunity to parasitic infection has been demonstrated (21,77,78), and all the manifestations of active immunity, with the possible exception of the death of the worms, can thus be duplicated.

We discussed in Chapter 11 the speculation that nonprecipitating antibody of the reagin type may play a role in acquired immunity to animal parasites, in particular to *Ascaris*.

Circulating antibodies may also be produced and may be detected by precipitation or by complement fixation.   In the case of worms living in the alimentary canal such tests seem to be less reliable, perhaps because less unchanged protein or other antigen from the parasite ever reaches the host's circulation, so that the degree of immunization remains less.

Immunity due to antibodies has been demonstrated for *Cysticercus fasciolaris, Taenia taeniaeformis, Nippostrongylus muris, Ancylostoma canium, Trichinella spiralis, Trichosomoides crassicauda, Schistosoma,* and *Ascaridia galli* (24).

Wright and Oliver-Gonzalez (100) found in rabbits injected with *Trichinella spiralis* that as immunity developed, the proportion of gamma globulin in the serum increased.

There is probably a considerable diversity of antigens in a single worm. and Canning (20) found comparatively sharp tissue specificity in *Ascaris*. Oliver-Gonzáles (64) has also made observations on the parts of this parasite to which antibody is directed.   Probably not all of the antigens are concerned in the actual development of resistance. Campbell (19) obtained a purified polysaccharide antigen from the larvel form of *Taenia taeniaeformis* which stimulated the formation of precipitins, but did not immunize against infection, and did not absorb the protective antibody from immune serum.

Cordylobia anthropophaga is perhaps less alarming than its name, but still one of the most offensive parasites (22). Man is not the main host of the larvae of this fly, but in Africa he suffers in common with a large number of wild and domesticated animals. The larvae penetrate the skin and burrow beneath it, dissolving the tissues by enzymes as they go. They leave an opening to the surface through which they obtain air.

Blacklock, Gordon, and Fine (10) showed in 1930 that the death of *Cordylobia anthropophaga,* in the skin of immune guinea pigs, is associated with a precipitate in the gut and around the larvae, and that the precipitate is due to the formation of precipitins to the hemocele fluid and excreta of the larvae. They felt that this precipitate prevents assimilation of food and leads to death by mechanically blocking the gut. This was one of the first demonstrations of antiparasitic immunity due to antibodies.

Later Taliaferro and Sarles (91) described the process of resistance of the skin of immune rats to invasion by larvae of *Nippostrongylus muris.* After the larvae penetrate the skin they become somewhat stunted, coiled, and immobilized. Precipitates are observed to be formed in and around them. These precipitates are considered to result from a combination of antibodies produced by the host and antigenic constituents of the worm. In addition to immobilizing and sometimes killing the worms, the precipitates increase the intensity of the inflammatory response. A few larvae are retained in the skin and occasionally one dies. Concomitantly, inflammation develops more intensely and involving more hematogenous cells than in the non immune rat, proceeding occasionally to the formation of large diffuse nodules around the larvae. The worms, however, remain alive for long periods in such nodules and many escape. Those that do not escape eventually die, and the macrophages in the nodule remove the debris. In higher degrees of immunity, more worms are retained in nodules and die.

The nodules are formed by the migration of leukocytes from the blood vessels and by their accumulation around an immobilized worm. Edema and hemorrhage are often present. The fully formed nodule consists of a coiled, immobilized worm that contains precipitates and is surrounded by closely packed cells, including macrophages, fibroblasts, etc.

Rats infected with *Trichinella spiralis* develop a considerable immunity to reinfection (6,33,55,63). The immunity was thought by some workers to be localized largely in the intestine. McCoy (56) obtained various degrees of artificial immunization by repeated intraperitoneal injections of living or dead *Trichina larvae*. The resistance of the artificially immunized animals did not affect the initial development of the adult worms in the intestine, but did cause their rapid elimination. In the naturally infected animals both effects were observed. Sarles (77) was even able to observe, after the administration of immune serum, the expulsion of worms already established in the intestine.

Oliver-González (64) found that rabbits, when fed infective eggs of *Ascaris lumbricoides* or injected with powdered *A. lumbricoides,* develop precipitins. Such precipitating sera caused precipitates around the mouth, excretory pore, anus, and cuticle of the larvae. A large per cent of the larvae was immobilized and killed. Microscopic examination suggested that the precipitates were directly involved in the death of the larvae.

Man does not acquire a very solid immunity to reinfection with hookworm as a result of recovery from an initial infection. Reinfection can occur promptly after the worms of the first infection have been eliminated by drugs (30). Dogs and cats, on the other hand, show partial immunity to superimposed infection with *Ancylostoma canium*. The serum of immune dogs contains a specific antibody which acts *in vitro* on the living larval forms. A precipitate can be observed to form at the oral opening and the excretory pore of the larval worm, and later in the esophagus and intestine. In about 5 days the larvae are killed (30).

The reviews of immunity to animal parasites by Taliaferro (87,88) and by Culbertson (29,30), although not recent, are still useful. The subject is also discussed by Chandler (22). There is some additional material in the book edited by Most (60). Immunity to protozoa is discussed in (42a).

References

1. Adler, S., and M. Ber, *Ind. J. Med. Res.,* **29,** 803 (1941).
2. Alexander, J., *Science,* **118,** 198 (1953).
3. Allison, A. C., *Brit. Med. J.,* **I,** 290 (1954).
4. Allison, A. C., *Ann. Human Genetics,* **19,** 39 (1954).
5. Andrewes, C. H., *J. Pathol. Bacteriol.,* **31,** 671 (1928).
6. Bachman, G. W., and J. Oliver-Gonzáles, *Proc. Soc. Exptl. Biol. Med.,* **35,** 215 (1936).
7. Bedson, S. P., *et al., Virus and Rickettsial Diseases,* Williams and Wilkins, Baltimore, 1955.
8. Berberian, D. A., *Proc. Soc. Exptl. Biol. Med.,* **38,** 254 (1938).
9. Berberian, D. A., *Trans. Roy. Soc. Trop. Med. Hyg.,* **33,** 87 (1939).

10. Blacklock, D. B., R. M. Gordon, and J. Fine, *Ann. Trop. Med. Parasitol.*, **24**, 5 (1930).
11. Blum, H. F., *Science*, **118**, 198 (1953).
12. Bodian, D., *Federation Proc.*, **13**, 685 (1954).
13. Bodian, D., in *The Dynamics of Virus and Rickettsial Infections*, F. W. Hartman, F. L. Horsfall, and J. G. Kidd, eds., Blakiston, New York, 1954.
14. Boyd, M. F., *Southern Med. J.*, **27**, 155 (1934).
15. Boyd, M. F., and W. K. Stratman-Thomas, *Am. J. Hyg.*, **18**, 485 (1933).
15a. Burnet, F. M., *Virus as Organism*, Harvard University Press, Cambridge, 1945.
16. Burnet, F. M., *Bull. Johns Hopkins Hosp.*, **88**, 157 (1951).
17. Burnet, F. M., *Natural History of Infectious Disease*, Cambridge University Press, Cambridge, 1953.
18. Burnet, F. M., and E. Clark, *Influenza*, Macmillan, Melbourne, 1942.
19. Campbell, D. H., *J. Infect. Diseases*, **65**, 12 (1939).
20. Canning, G. A., *Am. J. Hyg.*, **9**, 207 (1929).
21. Chandler, A. C., *Am. J. Hyg.*, **28**, 51 (1938).
22. Chandler, A. D., *Introduction to Parasitology, with Special Reference to the Parasites of Man*, Wiley, New York, 1949.
23. Chang, H. T., and J. E. Kempf, *J. Immunol.*, **65**, 75 (1950).
24. Chen, H. T., *J. Infect. Diseases*, **86**, 205 (1950).
25. Coggeshall, L. T., *J. Exptl. Med.*, **72**, 21 (1940).
26. Coggeshall, L. T., in *Communicable Diseases*, F. H. Top, ed., Mosby, St. Louis, 1954.
27. Coggeshall, L. T., in *Textbook of Medicine*, R. L. Cecil and R. H. Loeb, eds., Saunders, Philadelphia, 1955.
28. Coggeshall, L. T., and H. W. Kumm, *J. Exptl. Med.*, **66**, 177 (1937).
29. Culbertson, J. T., *Arch. Pathol.*, **25**, 85, 256 (1938).
30. Culbertson, J. T., *Immunity against Animal Parasites*, Columbia University Press, New York, 1941.
31. Downie, A. W., and K. McCarthy, in *The Dynamics of Virus and Rickettsial Infections*, F. W. Hartman, F. L. Horsfall, and J. G. Kidd, eds., Blakiston, New York, 1954.
32. Dubos, R. J., *Biochemical Determinants of Microbial Diseases*, Harvard University Press, Cambridge, 1954.
33. Ducas, R., *L'Immunité dans la Trichinose*, Paris, 1921.
34. Edsall, G., *Am. J. Pub. Health*, **42**, 393 (1952).
35. Enders, J. F., in *Viral and Rickettsial Infections of Man*, T. M. Rivers, ed., Lippincott, Philadelphia, 1952.
36. Enders, J. F., *Hartford Hosp. Bull.*, **9**, 4 (1954).
37. Enders, J. F., S. Cohen, and L. W. Kane, *J. Exptl. Med.*, **81**, 119 (1945).
38. Enders, J. F., T. H. Weller, and F. C. Robbins, *Science*, **109**, 85 (1949).
39. Fardon, J. C., *Science*, **117**, 441 (1953).
40. Faust, E. C., *Animal Agents and Vectors of Human Disease*, Lea, Philadelphia, 1955.
41. Fink, M. A., G. D. Suell, and D. Kelton, *Cancer Res.*, **13**, 666 (1953).
41a. Francis, T., and H. F. Maassab, in *Viral and Rickettsial Infections in Man*, F. L. Horsfall and I. Tamm, eds., Lippincott, Philadelphia, 1965.
42. Freund, H. J., *et al.*, *Am. J. Trop. Med.*, **28**, 1 (1947).
42a. Garnham, P. C. C., A. E. Pierce, and I. Roitt, eds., *Immunity to Protozoa*, F. A. Davis, Philadelphia, 1963.

43. Gauld, R. L., and K. Goodner, *U.S. Armed Forces Med. J.*, **2**, 1311 (1951).
44. Giglioli, G., *Riv. malariol.*, **11**, 27 (1932).
45. Graham, J. B., and R. M. Graham, *Cancer*, **8**, 409 (1955).
46. Grieff, H. T., H. Pinderton, and R. DeWitt, *J. Exptl. Med.*, **91**, 321 (1950).
47. Hammon, W. McD, *Bacteriol. Rev.*, **13**, 135 (1949).
48. Harrell, G. T., *Ann. N. Y. Acad. Sci.*, **55**, 1027 (1952).
49. Howe, H. A., in *Viral and Rickettsial Infections of Man*, T. M. Rivers, ed., Lippincott, Philadelphia, 1952.
50. Ipsen, J., *J. Immunol.*, **54**, 325 (1946).
51. Landsteiner, K., and E. Popper, Z. *Immunitätsforsch.*, **2**, 377 (1909).
52. Lenette, E. H., and N. P. Hudson, *J. Infect. Diseases*, **65**, 78 (1939).
53. Lurie, M. B., in *Cyclopedia of Medicine, Surgery, Specialties*, F. A. Davis, Philadelphia, 1950.
54. MacLeod, C., in *Bacterial and Mycotic Infections of Man*, R. J. Dubos, ed., Lippincott, Philadelphia, 1952.
55. McCoy, O. R., *Am. J. Hyg.*, **14**, 484 (1931).
56. McCoy, O. R., *Am. J. Hyg.*, **21**, 200 (1935).
57. Magrassi, F., and F. Muratori, *Boll. ist. sieroterap. milan.*, **16**, 505 (1937).
57a. Maiskii, I. N., ed., *Immunologicheskie metody issledovaniya zlokachestvennykh novobrazovannii*, Akademiya Meditsinskikh Naukh USSR, 1959 (Russian).
58. Middlebrook, G., in *Bacterial and Mycotic Infections of Man*, R. J. Dubos and J. G. Hirsch, eds., Lippincott, Philadelphia, 1965.
59. Mitchison, N. A., *Proc. Roy. Soc. (London)*, **B142**, 72 (1954).
60. Most, H., *Parasitic Infections in Man*, Columbia University Press, New York, 1951.
61. Mueller, J. H., in *Bacterial and Mycotic Infections of Man*, R. J. Dubos, ed., Lippincott, Philadelphia, 1952.
62. Murray, E. S., A. Ofstrock, and J. C. Snyder, *J. Immunol.*, **68**, 207 (1952).
63. Oliver-González, J., *J. Infect. Diseases*, **69**, 254 (1941).
64. Oliver-González, J., *J. Infect. Diseases*, **72**, 202 (1943).
65. Ordman, C. W., O. G. Jennings, and C. A. Janeway, *J. Clin. Invest.*, **23**, 541 (1944).
66. Parker, R. F., *J. Exptl. Med.*, **67**, 361 (1938).
67. Parker, R. F., *et al.*, *Am. J. Pathol.*, **22**, 797 (1946).
68. Parker, R. F., and T. M. Rivers, *J. Exptl. Med.*, **63**, 69 (1936).
69. Raffel, S., *Immunity*, Appleton-Century-Crofts, New York, 1953.
70. Rhoads, C. P., ed., *Ann. N. Y. Acad. Sci.*, **54**, 869 (1952).
71. Rich, A. R., *The Pathogenesis of Tuberculosis*, Charles C Thomas, Springfield, Illinois, 1951.
72. Rous, P., *J. Exptl. Med.*, **13**, 397 (1911).
73. Sabin, A. B., *Brit. J. Exptl. Pathol.*, **16**, 70, 84, 158, 169 (1935).
74. Sabin, A. B., *Ann. N. Y. Acad. Sci.*, **54**, 936 (1952).
75. Salaman, M. H., *Brit. J. Exptl. Pathol.*, **19**, 192 (1938).
76. Salaman, M. H., *Proc. III Intern. Congr. Microbiol.*, New York, 1940, p. 356.
77. Sarles, M. P., *J. Infect. Diseases*, **65**, 183 (1939).
78. Sarles, M. P., and W. H. Taliaferro, *J. Infect. Diseases*, **59**, 207 (1936).
79. Shope, R. E., *J. Exptl. Med.*, **58**, 607 (1933).
80. Smadel, J. E., in *Viral and Rickettsial Infections of Man*, T. M. Rivers, ed., Lippincott, Philadelphia, 1952.
81. Snyder, J. C., in *Viral and Rickettsial Infections of Man*, T. M. Rivers, ed., Lippincott, Philadelphia, 1952.

82. Stanley, W. M., *Proc. 2nd Natl. Cancer Conf.*, **1954**, 34.
83. Stokes, J., *J. Am. Med. Assoc.*, **127**, 144 (1945).
84. Stokes, J., *et al.*, *J. Clin. Invest.*, **23**, 531 (1944).
85. Sugg, J. Y., *J. Bacteriol.*, **57**, 399 (1949).
86. Sugg, J. Y., *Proc. Soc. Exptl. Biol. Med.*, **77**, 728 (1951).
87. Taliaferro, W. H., *The Immunology of Parasitic Infection*, Century, New York, 1929.
88. Taliaferro, W. H., *Physiol. Rev.*, **20**, 469 (1940).
89. Taliaferro, W. H., *Bacteriol. Rev.*, **12**, 1 (1948).
90. Taliaferro, W. H., in *Malariology*, M. F. Boyd, ed., Saunders, Philadelphia, 1949.
91. Taliaferro, W. H., and M. P. Sarles, *J. Infect. Diseases*, **64**, 157 (1939).
92. Thomson, K. J., *et al.*, *Am. J. Trop. Med.*, **27**, 79 (1947).
93. Todd, C., *Brit. J. Exptl. Pathol.*, **9**, 244 (1928).
94. Top, F. H., *Communicable and Infectious Diseases*, C. V. Mosby, St. Louis, 1964.
95. Topley, W. W. C., and G. S. Wilson, *The Principles of Bacteriology and Immunity*, 5th ed., G. S. Wilson and A. A. Miles, eds., Baltimore, 1964.
96. Traub, E., *J. Exptl. Med.*, **63**, 847 (1936).
97. Winsser, J., and A. B. Sabin, *J. Exptl. Med.*, **96**, 477 (1952).
98. Wood, W. B., *Harvey Lectures*, Ser. 47, 72 (1953).
99. Woodruff, M. F. A., "Immunological Aspects of Cancer," *Lancet*, Aug. 8, 1964.
100. Wright, G. G., and J. Oliver-González, *J. Infect. Diseases*, **72**, 242 (1943).
101. Zinsser, H., *Rats, Lice, and History*, Little, Brown, Boston, 1935.
102. Zinsser, H., and M. R. Castaneda, *J. Exptl. Med.*, **57**, 391 (1933).
103. Zinsser, H., J. F. Enders, and L. D. Fothergill, *Immunity: Principles and Application in Medicine and Public Health*, Macmillan, New York, 1939.

CHAPTER 15

Practical Use of
Immunity and Hypersensitivity

A. GENERAL PRINCIPLES

1. Preliminary

In the last chapter we investigated some of the mechanisms of natural resistance, and the ways in which this natural resistance is reinforced by immunity which develops during the course of an infection. All this, however, although of the greatest interest, could as well or better be considered a part of the science of pathology, and for this reason no attempt was made to study the process in all human infections.

As we noted in Chapter 1, immunology is a practical science which is concerned, among other things, with methods of artificially increasing the natural resistance of an individual, so that we may provide him with a substitute for the immunity which he would otherwise acquire only by repeated exposure to subclinical infections, or by actually contracting the disease, with the attendant risks and discomforts. In cases where the individual, owing to inadequate resistance, either natural or artificial, has already contracted an infection, we are interested in the possibility of quick means of conferring upon him some of the resistance which will otherwise come only in the course of the infection (if he should recover), which we may perhaps do by administering antibodies produced by some other person or animal. Before proceeding with measures designed to increase the resistance of an individual (immunization), we may wish to test by immunological methods the degree of his immunity, and we may wish to make such tests again after we have taken steps to increase his immunity. In addition to tests for immunity and immunization procedures, active and passive, there is often the possibility of making use of the specificity of serological reactions to establish or confirm the diagnosis of a disease. After the diagnosis is established, it may be possible to treat the disease, partially or wholly, by the administration of antibodies. All these procedures constitute practical applications of immunological principles, and it is to these applications that we shall devote the present chapter.

2. General

It is not easy to say why immunological procedures have been so much more successful in preventing, treating, or diagnosing some diseases than they have with others. The body probably makes some immunological response in its defense effort against any infectious agent. Since in some cases protection of higher or lower degree can be produced by the injection of a dead or attenuated agent, the question may be asked, why can this not be done in all cases? The full answer to this question must await further investigation, but experience suggests certain ideas which may be applicable. For example, some diseases seem intrinsically to produce less immunity in the host than do others. It is understandable that immunization, which probably seldom produces an immunity as lasting and solid as that following a natural attack, should be relatively ineffective in such cases. Adequately controlled experiments, made during World War II, on vaccination against malaria indicated that this procedure, as carried out, was unsuccessful (59).

Sometimes, evidently, the same disease (to all appearances) may be caused by different infectious agents or by different strains of the same agent. Immunity to one of these agents or strains does not necessarily imply any high degree of immunity to another, and attempts at artificial immunization may fail to be fully successful because only one or a few of the antigenic types are represented in the vaccine.

Some individuals seem congenitally incapable of acquiring a high degree of immunity to certain diseases, whereas others rapidly build up a high degree of resistance. It might well be thought that with diseases showing such variation in response on the part of some hosts, artificial methods of immunization would be of less use.

Immunization is probably most successful in diseases in which antibodies play a relatively important role in natural defense. In diseases in which cellular reactions are more important, injection of dead organisms tends to confer less protection. Another factor is the antigenic constitution of the infectious organism, as it exists in the body and as we cultivate it *in vitro*. Often a significant difference has been found between the two forms, and the cultivated organism is seen to lack important or essential antigens for the production of good immunity, or may simply be a different organism. This may be partly responsible for our failure to immunize artifically against syphilis. Another important factor is that we are often limited as to the amount of material we can introduce during immunization. With virus diseases, particularly, this may be an essential factor in our failure to obtain good immunity artificially. Some microorganisms seem to be intrinsically better stimuli to the formation of antibodies than are others, in analogy with what we have observed of antigens in general (see Chapter 3). The immunizing power of an antigen depends upon its possessing a particular chemical configuration, not upon the virulence of the organism in which it occurs (30). Finally, in a number of cases our success has depended upon our being able, by hook or crook, to obtain a modified infectious agent which still has the power to invade the body and produce good immunity, but does not possess the power to produce dangerous disease.

The first successful immunization with such a modified agent was Jenner's smallpox vaccination with the cowpox virus. It is possible that this virus had lost its power to produce a serious disease in man because of its repeated passage through cattle. Jenner's discovery remained an isolated observation for 84 years, until the genius who founded the sciences of bacteriology and immunology, Louis Pasteur, accidentally discovered a modified agent which prevented chicken cholera. Cultures of the chicken cholera bacillus, which regularly produced fatal disease in chickens, had been left in the laboratory over the summer vacation, and then were found to have lost much of their virulence. But when Pasteur inoculated chickens which had received these "attenuated" cultures with fresh virulent cultures, the chickens were not infected. They had become immune. Pasteur showed that the decrease in virulence resulted from prolonged culture under aerobic conditions. He at once saw the similarity between this observation and Jenner's discovery, and in honor of Jenner called his treatment "vaccination," a name that has persisted.

Pasteur's next attenuated vaccine was produced deliberately. He found that by growing anthrax bacilli in shallow layers at 42° to 43°C. he could produce an attenuated bacillus that would not infect cattle or sheep but was a highly effective vaccine.

Finally Pasteur applied his methods to the production of a rabies vaccine. He first shortened the incubation period of the rabies virus, by injecting serially into rabbits an emulsion of infected spinal cords from other rabbits, which reduced the incubation from over a month to seven days. This made it possible to attempt immunization of persons who had been bitten by rabid dogs, with the expectation that the vaccine would take hold before the naturally introduced virus. Pasteur's next step was to attenuate the virulence of the virus, which he eventualy did by drying infected spinal cords of rabbits in air; he found that the virus in them became less and less able to infect as the drying went on. Immunization was produced by injecting emulsions of cord which had been dried for progressively shorer periods of time.

Since the time of Pasteur the principal other bacterial vaccine which has been successfully attenuated by culture methods is the BCG tuberculosis vaccine of Clamette and Guérin. It was also discovered by accident. Calmette and Guérin were growing a virulent bovine strain of the tubercle bacillus on a glycerine–bile–potato medium as a convenient method of obtaining a homogeneous suspension of the organisms in saline, when they found that repeated passage on this medium produced rapid loss of virulence.

Modification by passage through individuals of other species is frequently used (*e.g.*, 119) to produce such an "attenuated" agent, and may have been the mechanism by which vaccinia virus arose from smallpox virus (30). This method has been especially useful for obtaining virus vaccines. The number of passages required for attenuation varies greatly. The two strains of canine distemper virus used to immunize dogs required 26 and 38 passages, respectively, through the chick embryo, hog cholera was passed through the rabbit more than 150 times, the Flury attenuated rabies virus was passed through the chick embryo 40 to 50 times before it became nonpathogenic for dogs, and over 180 times before it became nonpathogenic for cattle. Yellow fever virus was passed through tissue cultures and the chick embryo 220 to 255 times before it become nonpathogenic for man (74). On the other hand, the Blacksburg strain of Newcastle virus has been found attenuated in nature, and is passed through chick embryos only for the purpose of vaccine production.

Poliomyelitis virus has also been successfully attenuated, although a killed preparation is also in use (p. 647).

Following Pasteur's development and use of attenuated vaccines, Theobald Smith, together with Salmon (who gave his name to the *Salmonella*) showed that dead organisms would also immunize in some cases. Their first work was with a vaccine of killed chicken cholera bacilli. Later workers introduced the use of a killed typhoid bacilli in man, and killed vaccines have been tried for all important bacterial and some virus diseases. In some cases good immunity results; in others little or no immunity seems to follow.

No one method of preparing immunizing agents can be expected to be applicable in general. The method will vary with each organism and even with the particular antigen of the organism which it is desired to preserve. The right immunizing agent can be found only by observation and experience (30).

It should also be kept in mind that it may be a positive disadvantage to sensitize, or produce antibodies to an antigen, if the antibodies produced have no protective power. Ideally, it is preferable to produce, when possible, only those antibodies to an infectious agent which aid the body in resisting it.

The use of adjuvants, such as oils from petroleum, lanolin-like substances, and killed microorganisms, to enhance the immunizing power of vaccines and toxins is becoming more common (see p. 125). At the same time their use involves certain additional risks.

The extent to which immunizing procedures, even if successful, will be applied practically, will depend on the prevalence and severity of the disease in the locality in question. If the disease is too rare or seldom dangerous, it will not pay to undertake mass immunization.

Not all immunologists, probably, would concur in this last statement. Some might consider it desirable to immunize routinely, should it eventually prove possible, to certain diseases which are not highly dangerous, such as measles, mumps, and the common cold. Considering the loss in working hours and efficiency which annually results from this last disease, we must admit that a satisfactory method of mass immunization might be of sufficient importance to justify our undertaking it on a national scale. Immunologists in general agree, however, that no procedure thus far tried for producing immunity to colds has proved to have any decided effectiveness (84).

We may classify methods of artificial production of active immunity as follows:

1. Production of infection by living virulent organisms, but an infection which is milder because the infectious agent is introduced by an unnatural route. The immunization of chickens to infectious laryngotracheitis by applying the virus to the mucosa of the cloaca (72) is an example of this, and the ancient practice of variolation (p. 641) in man may be another.

2. Production of an infection by living attenuated or related microorganisms. The resulting infection may be so mild as to be completely inapparent, or may on occasion be a full-fledged disease, but a milder one than would result from the use of unattenuated organisms. This is the classical mode of producing artificial immunity, and the first example known is vaccination to smallpox. Immunization to rabies, yellow fever, and tuberculosis are other examples.

3. Introduction, usually parenterally, of killed microorganisms, which of course produce no infection but do stimulate the production of antibodies. Examples of this are immunization to typhoid fever, whooping cough, and staphylococcal infections.

4. Introduction, usually parenterally, of toxin or detoxified toxin (toxoid) produced by the infective organism, causing the production by the patient of antitoxin. This method is utilized in immunization to diphtheria and tetanus.

5. Introduction, usually parenterally, of a purified antigenic component of the microorganism, causing the production of antibodies. Immunization to pneumonia by the injection of specific capsular polysaccharides of pneumococcus furnishes an example of this method. The same sort of thing has been done experimentally in plague and typhoid.

3. Production of Antibacterial Immunity

From our discussion of the natural course of a typical infection (Chapter 14) it will be seen that during an attack of a bacterial disease the body comes into intimate contact with large numbers of living microorganisms, and doubtless has the opportunity of manufacturing antibodies against a number of the antigens contained in these bacteria. For the artificial production of immunity we shall rarely wish to take the risk of administering living virulent organisms to our patients. It would seem that the next best procedure, from the point of view of the production of an effective antigenic stimulus, consists in the injection either of attenuated organisms, or of killed, washed cultures (called vaccines) of freshly isolated strains of known virulence, or, if the harmful effects of the organism in the body are due mainly or entirely to the action of a soluble exotoxin, injection of the latter substance, or some nontoxic but antigenic modification of it. In some cases, as certainly with *Hemophilus pertussis,* even washing seems to risk removal of constituents of the organisms important for antigenicity.

We are by no means always able to keep to the above prescription in artificial immunization to all bacterial diseases. In a number of cases we are forced, for one reason or another, to make use of preparations which almost certainly lack an important antigen. A good example is the Vi antigen of the typhoid bacillus, which seems to be lost on washing the organisms. Vaccines lacking this antigen, and actually deficient in the "O" antigen also, were in use for many years.

In a number of cases there is evidence that injection of killed organisms has distinct prophylactic value. In pneumonia, there is some evidence that vaccination with killed organisms, or with specific carbohydrate from the organisms, will confer some degree of immunity to the particular type of pneumococci used (21,44,128,148). It seems, however, that this immunity is of short duration, probably not more than a few months (82,132). Heidelberger (57) was able to immunize to a number of pneumococcus types (using the specific polysaccharides) so as to break up epidemics in the armed forces of the U.S.A. during World War II (58). Vaccination with a living avirulent strain of the tubercle bacillus, called BCG (Bacille Calmette-Guérin), was introduced by Calmette (18). Vaccination of tuberculin-negative individulas with BCG definitely confers a certain degree of protection (p. 157).

In the attempt to immunize against some diseases, the high toxicity of the killed organisms presents a difficulty, and attempts must be made to isolate some antigenic component, of less toxicity, from the cell, or to detoxify a toxic component.

A number of fairly successful attempts to accomplish this sort of thing have been reported. Goebel *et al.* (51,103) reported that inoculation with the purified specific antigen of type V *Shigella paradysenteriae* (Flexner) produced agglutinins and mouse-protective antibodies in man. Morgan and Schütze (95) obtained similar results using the O antigen of the Shiga bacillus. Dubos (31) pointed out that in general it is the surface antigens which are needed for effective immunization, but that not all surface antigens will work. Treffers (138) was able to detoxify soluble antigens from *Shigella dysenteriae* (Shiga) and *Salmonella typhosa*. Evans (38) used formaldehyde to detoxify a toxic extract of *H. pertussis*, obtaining an antigenic product.

Even a synthetic antigen, if it possessed the proper specificity, should produce the desired immunity, and an approach to this was made by Goebel (49,50). See page 157.

4. Antitoxic Immunity

When a toxin produced by the invading organism plays the chief role in its harmful effects, we may expect in most cases to be able to immunize with toxin.

Active immunization against diphtheria has been found to be very effective in preventing the disease. Numerous studies have established the value of the procedure beyond question (5).

Immunization with diphtheria toxin directly is not very practical because of its high toxicity. The use of toxin–antitoxin mixtures has been abandoned in favor of toxoid. It has been found as effective as toxin–antitoxin as an immunizing agent. Alum-precipitated toxoid is superior to toxoid in solution (61).

It has been demonstrated by a number of workers that immunization with tetanus toxoid (formalin-detoxified tetanus toxin) will produce in human beings a good titer of antibodies, and in all probability considerable immunity to the disease. See references in Ramon (107) and Janeway (67). The period between injections should be fairly long (six to eight weeks), and it seems advisable to give a "reminder" dose nine months after the first dose. Hall (53) reported that alum-precipitated toxoid seemed superior to plain toxoid. The immunity seems to last for a considerable period of time (one to four years), and can be easily restored by a later single injection, apparently even after a wound or injury has been received which might result in tetanus. Mueller *et al.* (96) showed that satisfactory antitoxin response is obtained by the injection of tetanus toxoid made from toxin from bacteria grown on a purely synthetic medium.

5. Antivirus Immunity

It is an old observation that the immunity resulting from many virus diseases is a lasting one, in many cases apparently good for life. This holds as a general rule in spite of some notable exceptions, such as the recurrence of fever blisters and the very short period of immunity following an attack of the common cold. Three possibilities present themselves to explain the persistence of virus immunity: (*1*) such viruses may be very potent antigens, so that the body forever after retains some antibodies or the ability to make them on short notice; or viruses, being present inside the cells during infection, may possibly afford a more powerful antigenic stimulus; (*2*) the immunity resulting from the infection may be reinforced at intervals, or almost continuously, by new contacts with the active agent; and (*3*) living virus may persist in the apparently fully recovered host, thus providing a continual antigenic stimulus.

The second of these possibilities would hardly explain the persistence of immunity, and of humoral antibodies, for as long in some cases as 50 or 75 years, for example (122), in individuals having once had yellow fever and having resided subsequently in areas where the disease is not found. The trend of evidence today seems to indicate that (3) is the more probable, at least in some cases. The causative agent has been recovered from the immune host in the case of certain plant diseases due to viruses (75), and from animals in the case of various infections, including infectious anemia of horses (73), salivary gland disease of guinea pigs (25), psittacosis (9,90), and lymphocytic choriomeningitis of mice (137).

It would certainly seem easy, *a priori,* for viruses to persist in a host, since they are located inside the cells and, providing they do not by their presence kill the host cells, they might multiply and pass into the new host cells as cellular division takes place, without being acted on by circulating antibodies, which are outside the cell (111,113). This seems to happen in a number of virus diseases, such as in the virus tumors of chickens and rabbits. The presence of the living virus in the recovered host would not necessarily mean that he was capable of infecting others and spreading the disease, as the virus might be restricted to parts of the body not communicating with the outside.

6. Immunization to Viruses

We may obtain active immunity simply by provoking an attack not distinguishable from the natural disease, or by producing an atypical reaction by the introduction of the fully active virus through unnatural portals of entry. The old practice of variolation is presumably an example of the latter. Here virulent smallpox virus was scratched directly into the skin, instead of being allowed to enter the body through its natural route, the upper respiratory tract. This was claimed to produce a comparatively mild disease, recovery from which gave immunity. There was a similar old practice of controlling sheep pox (see 64). Rivers utilized this principle in vaccinating for psittacosis in the laboratory (109).

The use of fully virulent virus for the production of immunity in human beings is not, and is not likely to become, popular. Aside from the possibility, always present, that a typical, perhaps fatal, form of the disease *might* develop, there is the danger that the inoculated individual may be infectious to others and might even start an epidemic.

Therefore, even if routes of inoculation (of virulent virus) which would not produce serious illness were known for all viruses attacking man, it would still be highly desirable to find other methods of producing immunity, if such were possible. This led historically to attempts to produce immunity by use of an "attenuated" virus. The classical example is provided by Jenner's (69) use of the virus of cowpox to produce a mild infection which protects against the much more severe smallpox. We discussed the origin of some of the "attenuated" viruses on page 592. Actually it is not certain that vaccinia is an attenuated smallpox virus or even the same virus Jenner used (p. 654), so that smallpox vaccination may be an example of the use of a related virus rather than an attenuated virus.

Since immunity to various bacterial diseases can be produced by the injection or killed organisms, it was natural to try immunization against virus diseases by injection of killed or inactivated virus. Work in this connection has not been at all uniformly successful. As Rivers (109) pointed out, it is very difficult to determine when a virus has been completely inactivated. Ross and Stanley (112) were able partially to reactivate tobacco mosaic virus which had been inactivated by formalin. Kelser, in Zinsser's laboratory, recovered *virus fixé* from the brain of a dog paralyzed after an injection of supposedly killed rabies virus. Later, infective virus was discovered in some lots of a poliomyelitis vaccine which consisted of formaldehyde-inactivated virus. These facts illustrate how difficult it is to be sure an "inactive" preparation of virus which immunizes is really "dead." In many cases the immunity produced seems to be slight and transitory. In the cases where immunization has apparently been achieved, some workers have doubted if the virus was really inactivated. In other cases (9), the inactivated virus seems to protect against outward evidence of the disease, but not against infection, and virus can be obtained from the vaccinated and experimentally inoculated animals. Several workers (12,143), however, found that the injection of sufficient amounts of inactivated vaccine virus would produce an immune state equal to that resulting from infection. The amounts needed were of the order of milligrams, but Weil and Gall (143) pointed out that they are perhaps no greater than the amounts of living virus produced in an animal during the course of the disease itself.

Mackenzie (79) reported that with large doses of inactive Rift Valley fever virus, administered intraabdominally, he was able to establish a good resistance to the infection. Zinsser *et al.* (148) found that, although it was formerly always supposed that immunity to typhus could be produced only with the living organism, the injection of killed *Rickettsiae* in amounts quantitatively comparable to those injected in typhoid vaccination would produce immunity. Smadel and Wall (127) succeeded in immunizing guinea pigs with suspensions of the formalized, washed virus of lymphocytic choriomeningitis. It could be assumed that the chief reason inoculation with killed virus does not always immunize is that insufficient amounts of the virus substance itself were used, since such preparations usually contain only a small fraction by weight of virus. Also, in inoculation with the active virus, the introduced virus proliferates and thus ultimately a much larger amount of virus substance is available to act as an antigenic stimulus. This clearly puts any method using small amounts of inactive (dead) virus at a disadvantage.

Our most successful virus vaccines (*e.g.*, vaccinia and yellow fever) are living viruses. The yellow fever vaccine is definitely a living attenuated yellow fever virus, which produces an infection, with viremia and sometimes brief fever. The success of these vaccines has caused some workers to wonder if our goal should not be to find and produce attenuated avirulent forms of all the virus agents we wish to protect against.

In opposition to this proposal, advocates of "dead" virus vaccines point out the inconvenience of actually giving the person we desire to protect a virus infection, however mild, and emphasize the possibility of a reversion to original virulence of the attenuated strain. The proponents of the living vaccine, on the other hand, point out that vaccinia and yellow fever vaccines have not regained virulence in practice, and point out the danger of even minute amounts of infective *virulent* virus which might remain in an "inactivated" virus. Some workers even suggest that no "inactivated" virus is really effective unless a little active virus remains!

It seems too early to settle this question; it is obvious that the last word has not yet been said.

7. Precautions in the Use of Egg Vaccines

The majority of the virus vaccines in use today consist of inactivated or attenuated virus grown on embryonated eggs, and in some of them considerable egg and chicken proteins are present. Such vaccines should not be administered to individuals who are allergic to eggs. The patient or his parents and relatives should be questioned about a history of allergy to eggs, and in doubtful cases a skin test should be made.

8. Duration of Artificial Active Immunity

We may probably state as a general rule that artificial active immunization does not give protection for as long a time as does a natural attack of the disease. (It has, however, been claimed by some that smallpox vaccination is more effective in preventing subsequent attacks of smallpox than is an attack of the disease itself.) When immunization has been accomplished by the injection of dead organisms, or nonliving products of the organisms, as is usually the case, this is not very surprising. The amount of material we have introduced is probably very much less than that which the body has to deal with during a natural attack of the disease, and it is introduced suddenly, at intervals, instead of gradually over a period of time, and thus may be thought not to offer as good a stimulus to the immune mechanism of the host.   In addition, there may be anti-genic differences between our artificial antigen and the actual infecting organism.

We have seen that the host may produce antibodies to a number of different constituents of the bacterial cell. Not all of these antibodies have equal protective power.   Thus, in pneumonia it is observed that the antibody directed against the nucleoprotein has little, if any, pro-tective effect (7,8); it is the type-specific anticarbohydrate antibodies which are important.   Of course we cannot conclude from this that no other antibody plays any role in protection against pneumococci, but it has been established that the anticarbohydrate antibody alone is effective.

In the case of the motile bacilli, the results of modern experimental studies have shown that antibodies to the flagellar antigens play little if any role in specific antibacterial immunity; it is the antibodies to the heat-stable somatic antigens, and possibly certain labile antigens impor-tant for virulence, which are all-important (42,43).

Artificial immunity to smallpox can probably be relied on for about five years; we have already discussed possible reasons for greater duration of immunity to many virus diseases.   Even in individuals who lose their artificially induced immunity, however, and eventually contract the dis-ease, it is likely that some residual immunity, perhaps only an ability to "tool up" more rapidly for a new job of antibody production, remains, and in many cases results in the attack's being a relatively mild one.   Our tissues, like the elephant, remember.

9. Passive Immunization and Serum Treatment

It may be supposed that treatment with antisera is likely to be most successful in diseases where the antibodies normally play a particularly important role.   The type of infection, the ease with which the organisms can be reached by antibodies introduced into the blood stream, and the production or nonproduction of a toxin which can be neutralized by anti-body are also deciding factors.   Even if all of these factors are favorable, serum therapy will not ordinarily be practicable unless we are able to produce a potent antibody to the infectious agent (or its toxic products) in some convenient animal.

Progress in chemotherapy has resulted in the discontinuance of the use of serum in the treatment of certain diseases, but it continues to be important in others (see later sections of this chapter).

Treatment of diphtheria with antitoxin was one of the first great triumphs of immunology. It is customary to speak of this as a form of serum therapy, but strictly speaking the action is prophylactic. A patient's life is saved by antitoxin only if enough is introduced to neutralize the toxin not already fixed by the tissues and that which will continue to be formed in the lesion. Diphtheria toxin is a potent tissue poison, and it appears to produce irreversible injuries, so that after it has united with the tissues no amount of antitoxin will cure these effects.

Prophylaxis of certain virus diseases by administration of antibody is successful (see p. 643). Serum treatment of virus diseases has been mainly restricted to the use of convalescent serum and gamma globulin to prevent or lessen the severity of an attack. Because of the difficulties of obtaining and working with pure virus, it has been difficult to prepare suitable sera in animals, and in addition it is doubtful if antibodies artificially introduced into the circulation would have much therapeutic effect, in view of the fact that the virus is located inside the affected cells.

From the fractionation of human plasma, globulin concentrates rich in various antibodies usually present (presumably as the result of previous attack or exposure) in human serum have become available (24).

10. Precautions in Use of Serum

Some of the prophylactic and therapeutic procedures recommended in the following sections involve the use of serum, and it will be well to pause now for a consideration of some of the very definite hazards involved.

We may divide the sera used into two types: homologous and heterologous. Homologous serum is from human beings; heterologous serum is from other species, generally horses, rabbits, cows, or goats. The dangers resulting from the use of the two kinds of serum are rather dissimilar. The main risk involved in the use of heterologous serum is the occurrence of reactions of hypersensitivity, whereas the main risk with homologous serum is the transmission of human disease, principally hepatitis (p. 640), although human serum sometimes causes (relatively mild) urticarial reactions, for reasons which are not well understood.

The risk of transmitting bacterial infection by human serum is avoided by Berkefeld or Seitz filtration before administration. The possibility of transmitting hepatitis cannot be thus eliminated, and the main reliance has been on the selection of donors with no recent history of hepatitis,

FUNDAMENTALS OF IMMUNOLOGY

and on the avoidance of large pools of human serum in the preparation of blood derivatives. If unconcentrated human serum is used, it should be irradiated as a precaution against hepatitis (4). According to Parish (100), however, the value of this procedure is doubtful. It may be noted that although various blood derivatives made from serum can also transmit hepatitis if blood from an infected donor is included in the material from which they are manufactured, this does not seem to be true of gamma globulin, possibly because any virus present is neutralized by the antibody which many normal persons possess.

The hypersensitivity reactions which can result from the administration of heterologous serum may be divided into four types: serum sickness, which is the delayed reaction discussed on page 465; the accelerated reaction; the immediate reaction, which includes serum shock (p. 465), and Arthus phenomenon (p. 438); and the thermal reaction (136). The last of these is merely a sharp rise of 2 to 4°F. following the injection, and is generally not alarming. Its cause is not known. Reactions of the first three types can be very serious or even fatal. The Arthus reaction is not often fatal, it is true, but may produce extensive gangrenous areas followed by sloughing, with slow healing and demanding skin grafting [see illustrations in Top (136)].

Serum in use today has generally been purified and refined, mainly by separating and discarding the serum albumin, and is not so likely to provoke serum reactions as the whole serum formerly used; nevertheless, serum should not be given without observing the precautions mentioned here.

To avoid serious or possibly fatal reactions when heterologous serum is given, eternal vigilance is necessary (136). We may list some of the precautions:

1. Heterologous serum should be used for passive prophylaxis of exposed persons only when absolutely necessary. Consideration should be given to the likelihood of contracting the disease, the age of the exposed persons, their state of health, and the interval which has elapsed since exposure. If convalescent serum or gamma globulin is available, and is known to be effective against the disease in question, it should be used in preference.

2. Heterologous serum must not be given to individuals who are hypersensitive to it. To avoid this the patient or his relatives and friends should be questioned about any history of hay fever, asthma, urticaria, eczema, or food allergy. In addition one should inquire about previous administration of serum, as in diphtheria, tetanus, and scarlet fever, and possible injection of antitoxin to prevent diphtheria (toxin–antitoxin mixtures are no longer used for immunization, so this possible source of sensitization need not be considered). If any history of hypersensitivity is found, careful tests should be made, and serum should be used only when absolutely necessary, and should not be given intravenously, at least not at first.

Hypersensitivity to the serum whose use is contemplated may be detected by the ophthalmic test or the skin test. The ophthalmic test is performed by dropping one or two drops of a 1:10 dilution of the serum on the conjunctiva of the eye. In a positive reaction redness of the conjunctiva occurs within a few minutes. Severe reactions may be controlled by depositing a drop or two of adrenaline into the eye.

The skin test is performed by injecting 0.1 ml. of a 1:100 dilution of the serum intracutaneously. If it is negative, 0.1 ml. of undiluted serum may be given intramuscularly. If no reaction occurs, after half an hour, 1 ml. may be given intramuscularly, and if no reaction occurs after half an hour the entire dose may be given intramuscularly. If the skin test is positive specific desensitization may be attempted.

3. If there is a history of previous administration of horse serum (or if the use of horse serum is not contemplated, administration of serum of the same species as that whose use is contemplated), heterologous serum should be administered intravenously only if the skin test is negative and subcutaneous or intramuscular injection fails to cause a reaction. If the skin test is positive, desensitization must be attempted before the intravenous route is used (136).

4. If the history of allergy and previous use of heterologous serum are both negative, but the skin test is positive, small amounts of serum may be tried subcutaneously or intramuscularly, but intravenous use should be undertaken only with the precautions of section (5) which follows.

5. If the history of allergy, the history of previous administration of heterologous serum, and the skin test are all negative, administration of serum by the subcutaneous or intramuscular route is relatively safe, but before intravenous administration 0.5 ml. should be injected slowly and the patient observed for a period of 20 to 30 minutes. It is preferable to dilute the serum 1:10 both for the test and for the dose desired. According to Parish (100), serum should never be given intravenously unless a preliminary intramuscular injection has been tolerated by the patient.

No serum should be administered, even for a skin test, unless adrenaline (epinephrine) is available, preferably in a syringe ready for instant use.

According to Top (136) the ophthalmic test has been abandoned by most clinicians. The same author, however, records the death from anaphylaxis of a patient following a skin test with serum, and there seems to be no record of death from the ophthalmic test (4). However, it is generally agreed that the skin test offers a number of advantages and that if it is carried out correctly with precautions discussed here the danger of severe reaction is nearly zero.

If serum reactions do occur, they may be controlled with relative ease, if mild, but severe reactions may be very difficult to alleviate. The discomfort of serum sickness (largely due to itching) is relieved by adrenaline (3 to 10 minims depending on age), but the effect lasts only a few minutes to an hour. Ephedrine ($^1/_4$ to $^1/_2$ g.) acts more slowly but the effect lasts longer. In severe cases the two drugs may be used alternately. One of the antihistamines may give marked relief. Accelerated reactions may be controlled by adrenaline. Several doses may be necessary. Too free use should not be made of adrenaline, as large doses may cause reactions more severe than the reaction caused by the serum. Hypertonic glucose is said to be of value in accelerated reactions (136), and antihistamines should be given a trial. The immediate reaction is an emergency and must be treated as such. Artificial respiration or the administration of carbon dioxide + oxygen mixture may be indicated. Edema of the lungs may respond to atropine sulfate. Administration of vasoconstricting agents and plasma should be considered.

11. Diagnosis

Immunological methods often provide considerable assistance in the diagnosis of disease, and in some cases the immunological technics provide the decisive information. We have chosen to exclude isolation and identification of the infecting organism, as belonging more to bacteriology, virology, or parasitology, so we shall here be concerned only with methods of diagnosis which depend upon: (1) Detection of antigens of the infecting organism in material derived from the patient; (2) detection of antibodies to the invading organism in the blood and other fluids of the patient; (3) demonstration of allergic reactions of the patient to antigens of the invading organism.

All of these technics could obviously be of value in diagnosis, but their value varies from one disease to another. In some cases the serological demonstration of antigens derived from the infecting organism is easy, and possible early in the infection; in other cases it is difficult or impossible, or unnecessary because the causative agent can be isolated and identified by microscopic or culture methods. In some diseases antibodies to the infecting organism are regularly produced; in others they are slow to appear or impossible to demonstrate. In some diseases the patient develops a reaction of hypersensitivity, of the immediate or the delayed type, quite regularly; in others this cannot be demonstrated. As pointed out in earlier chapters, demonstration of allergic reactions is of special value in some parasitic infections.

Antibodies produced by the patient may be detected in a number of ways: by the precipitin test, by agglutination, by complement fixation, by neutralization of the infective agent. In the case of virus disease agents they may also be detected by their inhibiting effect on the hemagglutinating activity of the virus, if the virus is one of the group which have this activity (20). Again, one of these procedures may be useful in one disease, but less useful or valueless in another. One of the most consistently useful of these technics is the complement-fixation test.

Some of the antibodies useful in diagnosis of a disease are apparently not specific antibodies valuable in resistance, but heterophil antibodies which react with other antigens or with human erythrocytes at low temperatures. In some cases they nevertheless have their value.

In considering the routine application of these various technics to diagnosis, it is important to consider also that some are more involved and more expensive than others. Lennette (76) listed the following requirements for an acceptable diagnostic test. The test must be: (1) simple; (2) inexpensive; (3) practical; (4) sensitive; (5) specific.

Sensitivity and specificity are of course prime requisites. Lennette pointed out that cost and practicality are not necessarily related to the simplicity of the procedure. He also warned that it is easy for a physician to become convinced from his reading that a diagnostic method is "available," when in fact it is based on a method which is so cumbersome that no large volume of material can be handled.

In the following section of this chapter, we shall mention immunological methods of diagnosis, in so far as they are currently applied, of the main human infections. It will not be possible or even desirable to describe the laboratory procedure for each of these.

12. Skin Tests for Susceptibility and Immunity

The reader may have noted, possibly with some slight confusion, that skin tests are frequently employed in experimental and clinical immunology, but that the results may vary considerably in characteristics and significance. Until we had finished the discussions of allergy of infection in preceding chapters, it was impossible to give an intelligible account of skin tests in general without anticipating much later material. We may now pause to consider the types of skin tests and their significance.

The skin, once thought of as a mere covering, is now known to be an important organ, having a mass twice that of the liver, and many indispensable functions. It is an immunological organ too, and, whether or not it can form antibodies, takes part in many important immune reactions. Some of these seem to be peculiar to the skin, as in eczema and contact dermatitis, and others merely reflect the state of the body tissues in general; the reaction takes place in the skin, which forms the first line of defense against the entry of many foreign substances, because, for convenience, we introduce the material into the skin artificially, or it is naturally deposited there.

Essentially, skin tests are fitted to reveal the presence or absence of two different conditions, immunity and hyersensitiveness. However, it will now be appreciated that hypersensitiveness is itself fundamentally immunological in nature, so the two phenomena are not unrelated. Also, we have seen above that there is some reason to suppose that the hypersensitiveness of infection may in some cases parallel immunity, since it may indicate an infection, past or present, and infections from which the host has recevered have generally produced some immunity.

In the test for immunity, we make use of a toxic product from the disease-producing agent. In normal, nonimmune individuals this will cause damage to the tissues where it is injected, and a reaction, accompanied by redness, itching, and perhaps necrosis, will follow its introduction. This reaction will take time to develop, as the deleterious effects of toxins and similar substances are not immediately apparent. The immune individual, probably because of the presence of free antibody in his skin or circulation, does not react in this way; the toxin, in the concentration used, is neutralized by the antibodies, and either no lesion, or only a mild one, is produced. Tests of this sort are the Schick test for diphtheria and the Dick test for scarlet fever, using diphtherial and scarlatinal toxins, respectively.

In tests for hypersensitiveness, we employ materials which are harmless to the *normal* person, so that a positive reaction is obtained in the susceptible individual. We must remember that there are two types of hypersensitive reactions, in so far as the skin is concerned. In the first, exemplified by atopic hypersensitiveness, the reaction following the introduction of the allergen is almost immediate, developing within a few minutes. This is in line with the known speed of serological reactions, and with the hypothesis that the mechanism of the reaction is the union of antigen and antibody, liberating histamine or a histamine-like substance. Reactions of this kind are characteristic of many allergic conditions where no infection with a living agent is involved, such as hay fever, but they are also observed in a number of diseases, as with the specific polysaccharide in pneumonia, and in a number of parasitic and fungus infestations. Reactions of the immediate type to diphtheria toxin and to tuberculin have also occasionally been observed.

In a number of bacterial infections, such as tuberculosis and brucellosis, the reaction to the introduced material is of the delayed type, developing in about 24 to 48 hours. The reason for this delay is not understood, but the reaction nonetheless denotes the presence of a hypersensitiveness. Enders (37) found that a skin sensitivity to virus develops after recovery from mumps, and on the whole correlates well with a state of resistance.

Since an animal will never be naturally hypersensitive to constituents of an infectious agent without having actually been infected, the presence of such a hypersensitiveness implies a history of infection. Thus the chief value of this test is in diagnosis. In a number of cases it has been found that the more acute the hypersensitiveness, the higher the resistance of the host. Therefore, in such cases the degree of reaction obtained in the skin test is some indication of the degree of immunity.

We may sum up the situation in Table 15-1.

It has been found that the type of skin hypersensitiveness giving the immediate type of reaction can be transferred passively (see p. 421). The procedure is called the Prausnitz-Küstner (104) technic, after the men who first reported it. The delayed type of skin reactivity apparently cannot be transferred by serum.

The significance and mechanism of these various skin tests has also been discussed by Janeway (68).

13. Skin Tests in Allergy

Skin tests for the detection of hypersensitivity are widely, perhaps too widely, used in the practice of allergy. Full discussions will be found in references such as (140,142,55,77). The three most commonly employed methods of testing are the scratch test, the intracutaneous test and the contact or patch test. In addition the ophthalmic or eye test has been employed.

The indirect method of testing, employing the passive transfer (Prausnitz-Küstner) technic, is also used. It is well to remember the danger of transmitting hepatitis by the injection of serum (see p. 601).

14. Serum Treatment of Snake Bite

The therapeutic use of antisera is not restricted to bacterial and other diseases, but has also been applied in cases where the toxic agent comes

TABLE 15-1

Significance of Skin Reactions in Different Conditions

Type	Reagent	Type of reaction	Reason for reaction	Character of reaction	Meaning of a positive reaction (erythema, wheal, itching, etc.)
Schick, Dick	Toxin	Delayed	Damage to tissues by toxin	Inflammatory	Absence of immunity (= absence of antibody)
Atopic (urticarial)	Antigenic extract	Immediate	Antibody–antigen reaction	Wheal, erythema	Antibody (reagin) due to hypersensitiveness, in some cases to infection
Tuberculin	Antigen from microorganism	Delayed	?	Inflammatory	Hypersensitiveness due to infection. Some immunity?
Contact	Various nonantigenic excitants of contact dermatitis	Delayed	?	Eczematous	Hypersensitiveness

from reptiles or venomous insects. Injection of antivenin (serum of horses injected with snake venom) has been found effective in the treatment of bites of poisonous snakes. According to Do Amaral (3) this is particularly true in this country, since the North American snake venoms act slowly. Do Amaral thinks that if antivenin is used within 12 to 24 hours the chances of its being effective are good.

Snake venoms exhibit serologically a good deal of species specificity, so that an antivenin for one species may not be effective against another. However, an antivenin against a related species is usually of some help. The venoms of the various North American rattlesnakes, for example, are almost identical serologically. Antivenins that are at least somewhat effective are now available for most of the commoner species (148) of poisonous snakes.

15. The Control of Communicable Diseases

In the control of some communicable diseases immunological methods play an important role in active or passive prophylaxis, tests for immunity, diagnosis, or treatment, or in some diseases in a number of these procedures. Such applications of immunological methods to the more important human infections will now be discussed.

In so far as any immunological procedures are currently used in connection with the diseases discussed they are arranged under the following categories:

a. Prophylaxis. Under this heading are discussed methods of prevention. This section is divided into subsections:

Active Prophylaxis, which treats of methods of inducing active immunity, and

Passive Prophylaxis, which treats of methods of conferring temporary protection by the administration of immune serum from animals or human beings, hyperimmune serum, or various concentrated antibody preparations made from normal or immune serum, including gamma globulin.

b. Test for Immunity. Under this heading are discussed immunological methods for determining the susceptibility or degree of resistance of an individual.

c. Diagnosis. Under this heading come methods of diagnosis which depend upon antibodies or hypersensitivity reactions.

d. Treatment. Under this heading are discussed any immunological methods employed in the treatment of the disease.

When it happens, as it frequently does, that there are no currently used procedures falling under one or more of these headings for a particular disease, the heading or headings as a rule will simply not be listed in the discussion of that disease.

Only the serological methods relevant to the management of the various diseases are described. Problems of medical diagnosis, treatment with drugs, isolation of infecting organism, etc., will have to be found in the appropriate manuals.

16. Precautions and Contraindications

Precautions

Many of the immunological procedures described in the following sections require injection of vaccines or serum. The particular route of injection is given in each case. We may mention here some precautions to be observed in giving such injections, and some contraindications. These are based on the Report of the Committee on the Control of Infectious Diseases of the American Academy of Pediatrics (4).

1. Needles and syringes must be sterile.

2. The skin should be clean and swabbed *preferably* with 2 per cent tincture of iodine, which is allowed to dry and removed by ethyl alcohol. Before smallpox vaccination, acetone or ether is preferred by many.

3. The rubber stopper of the container of the antigen or serum should be disinfected also.

4. Antigens containing alum or aluminum hydroxide are generally injected intramuscularly.

5. Antigens without adjuvants, such as fluid toxoids and saline suspended vaccines, are generally given subcutaneously. In some instances intracutaneous injection is specified.

6. Immunization of patients receiving steroids should be avoided.

7. Only well persons should be injected for purposes of immunization.

8. Aspirin (acetylsalicylic acid) may be made available to the patient. A dose may be given within an hour or two of injections and may be repeated 4 hours thereafter. The dose for children is one grain (65 mg.) per year of age, up to ten grains (0.65 g.) for older children and adults.

9. Infants with a history of febrile convulsions should be injected with fractional doses of antigens. Phenobarbital in appropriate doses may be useful, in addition to acetylsalicylic acid, in preventing convulsions.

10. Before a second dose of an antigen is given, the patient or the parents, if the patient is a child, should be questioned in regard to the occurrence of fever, somnolence, and severe local reaction following the previous injection. If these are reported, the volume of the next injection should be made correspondingly less. If a convulsion or severe systemic reaction is reported, no further injections should be given for several months. Combined antigens should not be given in such cases, but the injections should begin with fractional doses of single antigens, to test tolerance.

11. Precautions in the use of egg vaccines were discussed in Section 7 (p. 599).

12. Precautions in the use of serum were discussed in Section 10 (p. 601).

Contraindications

1. Injections for the purpose of immunization should be delayed when any respiratory or other acute infection is present. It may be remembered that prolonging the interval between injections, even up to six months, does not generally decrease the final immunity, and in some cases may actually improve it.

2. The presence of cerebral damage in an infant is an indication to delay the start of immunization procedures. In such infants active immunization procedures should not be started until after the age of one year. In such infants also single antigens rather than combined antigens are advised, starting with fractional doses.

3. The presence of an outbreak of poliomyelitis in the community is an indication to defer elective immunization procedures. If other epidemics coincide with the poliomyelitis outbreak, immunization to the diseases involved is of course no longer elective.

4. Infants with eczema, impetigo, or other forms of dermatitis should not be vaccinated against smallpox because of the danger that they may develop generalized vaccina. Siblings of infants with eczema or dermatitis should not be vaccinated against smallpox. According to the American Academy of Pediatrics (4) exceptions may be made to this rule if the siblings can be isolated in separate buildings.

B. BACTERIAL AND MYCOTIC INFECTIONS

Blastomycosis, North American

c. Diagnosis

The complement-fixation test is diagnostic if histoplasmosis can be excluded (5).

Botulism

a. Prophylaxis

Active Prophylaxis. Active immunization against botulism is available, but little used except for laboratory workers (108). It is reported that two injections of alum-precipitated toxoid separated by an interval of two months results in the appearance of the blood of 0.02 unit of antitoxin per milliliter. This is supposed to be a protective level (105).

Passive Prophylaxis. Polyvalent botulinus antitoxin of the appropriate type, if it is available, should be given to all persons who have eaten food suspected of contamination by *Clostridium botulinum* (5). It is possible that some of the disappointing results have been due to the use of inadequate doses of antitoxin (108). The dose is 10,000 to 50,000 units of botulinus antitoxin (136,100).

d. Treatment

The only immunological treatment of botulism is merely passive prophylaxis, mentioned above. Just as in other diseases due to intoxication with bacterial toxins, the value of passive protection falls off very sharply after symptoms have set in.

Brucellosis (Undulant Fever)

c. Diagnosis

Agglutinin Test. This is probably the most valuable serological diagnostic aid, if it is carried out with properly standardized antigens and if the possibility of "blocking" antibodies and other prozone phenomena is kept in mind (35). All but a small fraction (1 or 2 per cent) of cases give a positive test (titer of 1:60 or 1:80 or more) (35,4). Heat-killed, phenolized, agglutinating suspensions of smooth, virulent *Brucella* are available from WHO brucellosis centers in various parts of the world.

According to a committee of the National Research Council, the only absolute proof for diagnosis is isolation of *Brucella,* but if the agglutination test is done with a dependable antigen and the serum–antigen mixture incubated at 37°C. for 48 hours, a presumptive diagnosis can be made if the agglutinin titer is 1:320 or higher, especially if the titer is rising during the course of the illness (136).

Skin Test. This is analogous to the tuberculin test in tuberculosis and by itself gives no information about the current activity of an infection or about the state of immunity. There are available for the test "brucellergen," "melitine," *Brucella* polysaccharide, and suspensions of heat-killed bacilli (35,136).

Immunization to brucellosis, as well as other aspects of the disease, are authoritatively discussed by Dalrymple-Champneys (28a).

Chancroid

c. Diagnosis

The Ito-Reenstierna Reaction (Ducrey Test) is performed by injecting 0.1 ml. of the commercial bacillary vaccine (Lederle) intracutaneously. The reaction is read after 48 hours. A positive reaction consists of an indurated area at least 7 mm. in diameter, surrounded by an area of erythema. In case the induration is slight the area of erythema must measure at least 14 mm. in diameter before being considered positive. The reaction does not become positive until 8 to 25 days after the appearance of the primary lesion. Once sensitivity is established, the test probably remains positive for life. The test is of no value during the first week of the disease. A positive reaction in the presence of typical clinical signs is strongly suggestive, and if the test is at first negative and becomes positive it is probably diagnostic. If the test remains negative over a period of at least three weeks, this presumably rules out chancroid (136).

d. Treatment

Before the introduction of sulfonamides the Ducrey vaccine was used in treatment. It was given intravenously and intramuscularly.

Cholera

a. Prophylaxis

Vaccination against cholera is mandatory for travel to or through many parts of the world, and is recommended by the U. S. Public Health Service for travel to or through a number of other areas (4). Details will be found in the booklet "Immunization Information for International Travel" published by the U. S. Department of Health, Education, and Welfare. The dosage schedule currently recommended by the U. S. Armed Services for dependents of military personnel is as follows:

Basic immunization:

Adults: 0.5 ml. of vaccine subcutaneously followed by a second injection of 1.0 ml. one week later.

Children: Three subcutaneous injections at intervals of 7 to 10 days, in doses varying according to age as follows (Table 15-2).

Recall ("booster") injections may be required as often as every six months in areas where danger of infection currently exists.

Despite the requirement that all travelers to or through many parts of the world be actively immunized against cholera, the value of this pro-

TABLE 15-2

Injection Schedule in Immunization Against Cholera

Adults:　0.5 ml. injected intramuscularly or subcutaneously, followed 1 week later by a second injection of 1.0 ml.

Children: 3 intramuscular or subcutaneous injections at 7 or more days apart in doses varying according to age as follows:

Age	6 mo.–4 yr.	5–9 yr.	10 yr. and over
1st dose	0.1 ml.	0.3 ml.	Adult schedule
2nd dose	0.3 ml.	0.5 ml.	
3rd dose	0.3 ml.	0.5 ml.	

cedure is uncertain (5), for although chlorea vaccine has been in use for over 50 years, it is still impossible to judge its value precisely (145). The most encouraging experiment is probably that carried out in India in 1942–1944 (1). Out of a population of 3,000,000, 1,180,000 were given a single inoculation during an epidemic. The attack rates were considerably lower in the inoculated group, although case mortality rates were not appreciably affected. However, the observations were made under difficult conditions, and as so often happens, the inoculated and control groups were not strictly comparable.

Coccidioidomycosis ("Valley Fever," "Desert Fever")

c. Diagnosis

Skin Test. Injection of *coccidioidin,* which is prepared by growing the fungus on asparagine-synthetic medium, gives a tuberculin-like reaction in persons with an infection or past history of infection. The material for testing is available commercially (4). A 1:100 dilution is used for the usual test: 1:1000 or 1:10,000 is used in cases of "valley fever" with erythema nodosum. The reaction is read at 8 and 48 hours, and is graded by induration as is a Mantoux test (129).

In patients from the Ohio River valley and lower Missouri River valley and adjacent areas, equivocal and even slightly positive coccioidin tests may be due to cross reaction with another agent, possibly the infection which is responsible for the histoplasmin sensitivity which is seen in those patients with pulmonary calcifications which are not due to tuberculosis infections (136). Definite diagnosis is preferably based on the demonstration of the fungus in sputum or exudate directly or by culture (4).

Complement Fixation. This test has proved useful in diagnosis and prognosis. It seems to be specific, except for possible irregular cross reactions with other deep mycotic infections such as histoplasmosis and blastomycosis. The test is positive in 60 per cent of those with coccidioidal pulmonary cavities and in over 99 per cent of those with disseminated infections (136). Antigen for this test is available commercially (4). Rising complement-fixing titer may signify increasing severity of infection (136).

Precipitin Test. This generally parallels the complement-fixation test, but is more useful early, whereas the complement-fixation test is more useful later in the course of the disease (136). In mild infections only precipitins may be present.

Diphtheria

a. Prophylaxis

Active Immunization. It is possible to confer good protection against diphtheria by artificial immunization, and since the mortality caused by this disease is highest in the early years of life, it is desirable to carry out immunization very early. It has been found possible to immunize simultaneously against diphtheria, tetanus, and whooping cough with no more reaction than might be experienced to the inoculation against any one of these separately; there is evidence that the presence of the three antigens in the "triple antigen" makes the action of each somewhat better, so that each antigen acts to some extent as an adjuvant for the others (p. 125).

Infants should be immunized (4) against diphtheria, pertussis, and tetanus with a course of injections of combined alum or aluminum phosphate precipitated, or aluminum hydroxide adsorbed diphtheria and tetanus toxoids containing *H. pertussis* vaccine. These products are considered to be preferable to fluid mixtures for the following reasons: (*1*) They produce more prolonged antitoxic immunity. (*2*) The mixture recommended is more effective in immunizing against pertussis in early infancy. (*3*) Because of their lower protein content and slower absorption, they are less likely to produce systemic reactions.

Immunization against diphtheria, pertussis, and tetanus should be started at the age of one to two months. The initial course should consist of three intramuscular injections of the triple antigen mentioned above, given at intervals of not less than one month and preferably not more than four months. It is recommended that a fourth dose be given about twelve months after the third dose.

The actual amount to be given depends of course upon the concentration of the antigen commercially available. Most products on the market contain a full single dose in 0.5 ml. of suspension.

The injections should be made either into the deltoid or into the gluteus maximus muscles. During the primary course, injection should not be made more than once into the same site.

For children under 4 to 5 years of age who have not been immunized in infancy, the American Academy of Pediatrics (4) recommends three doses of the triple antigen at intervals of four to six weeks. In children over 4 years of age, it is considered advisable by many to use the single antigens, of the diphtheria–tetanus toxoid mixture without pertussis vaccine, in order to avoid the greater frequency of more severe febrile reactions which follow the use of triple antigens in older children.

Recall Injections ("Booster Shots"). Children who have received three doses of the triple antigen, as recommended above, should be given recall doses of 0.5 ml. of this mixture at 12 to 18 months of age and at the age of 3 or 4.

Children of 5 years of age and over who have received a primary course of the triple antigen should be given 0.1 ml. of standard diphtheria-tetanus toxoid mixture (alum or plain) at 3- or 4-year intervals, up to the age of 11 to 12.

Immunization of Older Children and Adults. Older children and adults may have a history of having had whooping cough, and may have been immunized separately to tetanus. In the case of some infants and young children there may be a specific contraindication to the use of the otherwise preferable triple antigen, for instance, if a severe reaction should follow the first injection of triple antigen. For these cases diphtheria toxoid alone may be the preferable antigen to use, although in the case of children who have already had whooping cough combined diphtheria and tetanus toxoids should be used.

A significant number of adults are sufficiently sensitive to diphtheria toxoid (or sometimes merely to the diphtheria bacillus protein contained in toxoid) so that injection of toxoid causes untoward reactions. Disability rates from such inoculations may run as high as 15 per cent (99). Therefore without a preliminary Schick test together with a toxoid sensitivity test diphtheria toxoid should not be administered to individuals over 11 years of age in doses of over 0.02 to 0.05 ml., and preferably not in doses even as small as these, as 0.05 ml. may occasionally cause a sharp reaction.

Children under 10 years of age may be immunized by three intramuscular injections of 0.5 ml. each, given at intervals of at least one month and preferably not over four months.

Individuals of 10 years of age and over:

1. Schick-positive reactors with negative toxoid sensitivity tests may be given the three doses of 0.5 ml. each as just recommended for children less than 10 years of age.

2. Individuals showing positive reactions both to the Schick test and the toxoid sensitivity test should not be given further toxoid.

3. Individuals showing negative reactions to both the Schick and the toxoid sensitivity test require no further toxoid; the small amounts injected in the tests themselves will serve as small recall injections.

4. In some circumstances, as in groups in military service, it may not be feasible to do preliminary Schick and toxoid sensitivity tests. Highly satisfactory levels of immunity to diphtheria may be achieved by the administration of three or four extremely small doses of diphtheria toxoid, either alone or combined with tetanus toxoid, at intervals of four to six weeks. The doses recommended are of the order of 0.01 to 0.02 ml. of standard commercial toxoid for each dose (one to two L_f of toxoid).

Bunch *et al.* (15) recommend the following plan:

1. Do a Schick test on the group to be immunized.

2. Do a Moloney test on the Schick-positive individuals.

3. Give the M− and M+ (see below) reactors the routine 2 ml. of undiluted toxoid in 1 ml. subcutaneous doses with an interval of one month.

4. Give the M++ and M+++ reactors three 0.1 ml. intracutaneous injections of 1:100 dilution of toxoid at weekly intervals.

5. Do Schick tests three to six months after the last injection. (Many now feel this is unnecessary because the percentage of failures is so low.)

6. If any M+++ or M++ subjects remain Schick-positive, inject them with a series of graded subcutaneous injections.

The evidence that diphtheria immunization is effective was reviewed by Edsall (33,34). It appears that adequate immunization against diphtheria may afford 85 to 95 per cent protection, although a few studies have found only about a 50 per cent protection rate. Edsall (34) stated ". . . . toxoid is not a panacea; it does not provide 100 per cent protection, and any health officer who allows his community to believe that it does is simply inviting trouble. On the other hand, it does provide a very high degree of protection—a degree which justifies its use on a large scale among individuals or groups who are likely to be exposed to the disease."

Ipsen (65) compared patients who had been immunized with toxoid but who nevertheless later contracted diphtheria with diphtheria patients who had acquired their partial immunity by natural exposure. Comparison of two such groups of individuals with equivalent blood antitoxin levels indicated that the artificially immunized individuals fared in their illness not merely as well as, but actually better than, those exposed naturally.

Passive Immunization. Since the administration of relatively small amounts of antitoxin (1000 units) may confer protection for a period of two to three weeks, passive immunization is possible, but because of its short duration and the considerable risk of inducing sensitization to foreign protein or actually causing anaphylactic shock in those already sensitized, the use of passive immunization should be confined to persons peculiarly at risk of infection, as, for example, children heavily exposed to virulent diphtheria bacilli. Immunization with toxoid should be carried out at the same time. The exposed persons should be given Schick and toxoid sensitivity tests, and those found to be susceptible should be immunized promptly with toxoid. They should be kept under observation so that antitoxin may be administered at the first signs of suspicious illness. Routine throat cultures do not always yield information of practical value (22).

Under special circumstances the administration of antitoxin prophylactically may be indicated.

In the U. S. A. immunization is started early, and it is likely that all the inoculated children were susceptible to diphtheria and need the immunization. Public health authorities sometimes obtain permission from parents "to do a Schick test and perform any indicated immunization," then proceed to do the immunization immediately (without doing the Schick test), a procedure which may or may not be morally justified. It is certainly preferable that children should be immunized before they reach school age (see above). If desired, susceptibility to diphtheria may be tested by the *Schick test.*

Schick Test. If diphtheria toxin is injected in proper amount into the skin, it will be neutralized in individuals who possess antitoxin, while in susceptible individuals without antitoxin it will produce an inflammatory reaction. This is the basis of the Schick test (91,124). The procedure is described in (123).

The material formerly used consisted of one solution containing 1/50 MLD of aged (*i.e.,* relatively stable) diphtheria toxin in 0.1 ml., and another solution which consisted of toxin which had been heated to abolish toxicity. The latter solution serves as a control on allergic reactions to other components of the toxic filtrate, usually to thermostable proteins of the diphtheria bacillus. Taylor and Moloney (134) proposed a Schick toxin made from "fresh toxin," containing 1/50 to 1/35 MLD in 0.1 ml., with somewhat less antitoxin combining power (1 dose neutralized 1/1250 but not 1/1500 unit of antitoxin). This seems to be better (19). Edsall (34) recommended a highly diluted toxoid as a control.

Cleanse the skin of the flexor surface on both forearms with alcohol or acetone and allow to dry. On the right arm inject intracutaneously 0.1. ml. of the heated toxin dilution (control); on the left arm inject intracutaneously 0.1 ml. of the toxin dilution. The injection technic is the same as that for the tuberculin reaction (p. 634).

Read the reactions on the first or second *and* on the fourth day following the test. If the test has been properly carried out, and the toxin is of the correct potency, absence of a reaction indicates immunity to diphtheria. A positive reaction usually begins to appear in 18 to 24 hours, and present a circumscribed area of redness and slight infiltration 1 to 2 cm. or more in diameter. It reaches its greatest intensity on the fourth day and gradually fades. More or less desquamation follows and an area of brownish pigmentation, more marked in brunettes, may remain for weeks or months. Vesiculation occurs in very intense reactions, indicating virtually complete absence of antitoxin in the subject tested. The degree of reaction is a very roughly quantitative measure of antitoxin. A negative reaction was formerly taken to indicate the presence of at least 0.03 unit of antitoxin per milliliter of serum; more recent estimates have reduced this figure to about 0.004 to 0.01 unit.

In some individuals, especially in adults, an allergic reaction to toxoid or bacterial proteins, called the "pseudo reaction," may develop. It develops and evolves somewhat more rapidly than the true positive reaction, so that by comparing the rate of development and size of the reactions on the two arms, the combined reaction, where susceptibility to toxin and bacterial allergy are both present, can be differentiated from the pseudo reaction. In the latter the reactions on both arms run an equal course, reach their height in about 48 hours, and are of nearly the same size.

In highly sensitive subjects it may be difficult or impossible to distinguish between pseudo and "combined" reactions even at the fourth-day reading. In such cases the final reading may be delayed until the seventh to tenth day, when desquamation and discoloration are more marked on the test site than on the control site.

It is important, when one is dealing with older children and especially with adults, that the early reading be made in order to detect the allergic reactions. Combined reactors are likely to develop severe local and systemic symptoms, when actively immunized with diphtheria antigens, especially toxoid. The occurrence of an allergic reaction is a warning that the usual primary immunizing dose must be greatly reduced. The amount of allergenic material in the Schick control dose is so very small, especially when the extraordinarily potent toxin now obtainable is used, that only the high allergic subjects respond to it, and the more moderately sensitive ones escape detection; they, however, can be made sick by the routine doses used in active immunization, so it is desirable to resort to the toxide sensitivity in order to obtain a better guide to the selection of an appropriate primary immunizing dose.

The negative and pseudo reactions indicate immunity, and the positive and combined reactions indicate susceptibility, as shown in Table 15-3.

References and descriptions of the technic will be found in references (13) and (123).

According to Parish and Cannon (100) the Schick test is not a very reliable indicator of antitoxin level, but the correlation between the Schick reaction and antitoxin titer varies in different persons. Since the antitoxin level is the significant thing in immunity to diphtheria, Parish and Cannon state that examination of blood samples, and not the Schick test, should be relied on in research on methods of immunization.

Toxoid Sensitivity Test. Moloney and Fraser (93) introduced the injection of 0.1 ml. of a 1:20 dilution of toxoid, as a substitute for the control in the Schick test, and an indicator of possible reactors to immuniza-

TABLE 15-3

Interpretation of Reactions to the Schick Test

No.	Left arm (toxin)	Right arm (control)	Reading	Interpretation
1	Positive	Negative	Positive	NOT IMMUNE, not allergic
2	Negative	Negative	Negative	IMMUNE, not allergic
3	*Positive*, larger than (*1*)	(Pseudo-) positive	Combined	NOT IMMUNE, allergic
4	(Pseudo-) positive	(Pseudo-) positive	Pseudo	IMMUNE, allergic

tion; a similar test had previously been proposed by Zoeller (see 148). The test is now widely used, but the dilution of toxoid originally proposed by Moloney seems much too strong; it is possible that its routine use would produce a number of severe or even constitutional reactions.

Underwood (141) recommended 1:200, but it would seem that a 1:100 dilution is most generally used (4).

The test is performed by injecting intracutaneously 0.1 ml. of diphtheria toxoid diluted 1:100. The reactions are read after 24 hours and standardized (86) as follows:

No reaction = M−.
Erythema less than 10 mm. without induration = M+.
Erythema more than 10 mm. without induration = M++.
Erythema with induration = M+++.

d. Treatment

In the treatment of diphtheria, it is important to administer an adequate dose of antitoxin at the earliest possible moment. The action is most rapid if the injection is given intravenously. Since, however, foreign serum given in this way is more likely to cause undesirable reactions, the intramuscular route is preferred where speed is not so urgent. Some workers give half the dose intramuscularly, wait 1 hour, and then, if no untoward symptoms have developed, give the other half intravenously.

The dose of antitoxin is estimated from the site of the diphtherial membrane, the degree of toxicity displayed, and the day of illness. The age and weight of the patient are of less importance (4). The following dosage schedule is recommended for cases seen within 48 hours of onset (Table 15-4):

TABLE 15-4

Lesion	Dosage	Route
Tonsils	20,000 units	Intramuscular
Anterior nose	10–20,000 units	Intramuscular
Pharynx or uvula	20–40,000 units	Intramuscular
Larynx	20–40,000 units	Intramuscular
Nasopharynx	40–75,000 units	Intravenous—$^1/_2$ and Intramuscular—$^1/_2$

The dose should be increased if toxicity is marked or if the patient has been ill for more than 48 hours, and should be given intravenously. Intravenous serum should be given by slow drip in 200 to 300 ml. of isotonic sodium chloride or 5 per cent glucose. Epinephrine 1:1000, in amount suitable for the age of the patient, should be incorporated in the venoclysis.

Penicillin, 300,000 to 2,000,000 units, injected intramuscularly daily, will eradicate 75 per cent or more of the strains of *C. diphtheriae* (4). Chloretetracycline, oxytetracycline, and tetracycline have also been used.

Note that hypersensitivity reactions to penicillin (especially procaine penicillin) are not infrequent, and fatalities have occurred (p. 431). Erythromycin in full therapeutic dose is effective also (4). This and other antibiotics should be given in addition to, not as a substitute for, diphtheria antitoxin (4).

Dysentery (Shiga)

d. Treatment

Antitoxin was formerly used to some extent in the treatment of acute bacillary dysentery when the infection was with Shiga organisms (100). According to Parish (100) there is no evidence that any Flexner or Sonne serum has any specific value. Since the introduction of chemotherapy the use of Shiga antitoxin has been restricted to a few severely toxic or fulminating cases which have gone untreated several days, and to cases which seem to be resistant to the available drugs. The dose has been large; not less than 100,000 units intravenously, repeated in 12 hours if necessary (100).

Food Poisoning (See Botulism)

Gas Gangrene

a. Prophylaxis

In the United States gas-gangrene antitoxin is not much used as a prophylactic agent, but is evidently still in use in England (100).

Parish and Cannon (100) suggest as the therapeutic dose of mixed gas–gangrene antitoxin at least three times the prophylactic dose, *i.e.,* approximately 30,000 units of *Cl. perfringens* antitoxin, 15,000 units of *Cl. septicum* antitoxin, and 30,000 units of *Cl. oedematiens* antitoxin. The dose is given intravenously and repeated at intervals of 4 to 6 hours, according to the signs and the response of the patient.

Histoplasmosis

c. Diagnosis

Skin Test. The histoplasmin test (125) is quite analogous to the tuberculin test. It may be negative in patients with overwhelming infections, and in endemic areas (Central States and some adjacent states) positive reactors without significant active infection are common, making the test of limited diagnostic value (136,4).

Leishmaniasis (Oriental Sore)

a. Prophylaxis

Active Prophylaxis. Immunization by deliberate infection by injecting a pure culture of *L. tropica* [prepared from cultures of infected chick embryo (5)] into the skin will provide lasting immunity (11). In order that the ensuing scar may not be conspicuous, an area of skin not normally exposed is used. The ulcer resulting from the inoculation should not be terminated chemotherapeutically until about 30 days have elapsed after inoculation, as otherwise immunization may not be satisfactory (39).

Leprosy

c. Diagnosis

Complement Fixation. Differential diagnosis of leprosy from syphilis is made difficult by the fact that many cases of leprosy have positive Wassermann (and Kahn) reactions without any evidence of syphilis (136).

Skin Test. According to Top (136) and Manson-Bahr (86a), an intracutaneous test employing a suspension of killed lepromatous nodules is of value in determining what type of leprosy the patient has. In lepromatous leprosy the test is negative; in tuberculoid leprosy (and in many nonleprous adults) the test is positive.

Leptospirosis

c. Diagnosis

The agglutination test is very valuable in the diagnosis of this spirochetal disease (4,136). Specific agglutinins appear in the blood at the end of the first week of the infection.

Meningitis Due to H. influenzae Type b

c. Diagnosis

The bacteria may be identified by *Quellung* with type-specific serum, or a culture of the spinal fluid may be made and the bacteria typed (4). The technic is described by Alexander (2).

Meningitis (Tubercular)

a. Prophylaxis

Active immunization with the BCG vaccine is recommended by the American Academy of Pediatrics (4). See page 632.

Paratyphoid Fever (See Salmonelloses)

Pertussis (Whooping Cough)

a. Prophylaxis

All infants should be immunized to pertussis, using the triple diphtheria, tetanus, and pertussis vaccine, as described under *Diphtheria*.

A local outbreak of whooping cough may be an indication for attempted rapid protection against this disease. For this purpose saline suspended *Bordetella pertussis* should be used. A total of 12 NIH units should be divided into three equal doses of 0.5 ml., and each dose injected subcutaneously at intervals of one week.

Routine Recall. Injections should be given one year after the primary course of vaccine, two years after this, and every three years thereafter up to the age of six or seven.

Whooping cough immunization is hardly worth while for children over 5 years of age, as over 97 per cent of the deaths due to this disease are in children under 5 (100).

b. Test for Immunity

Earlier methods of evaluating the susceptibility of an individual to whooping cough were not satifactory (14). According to Top (136) the skin test described by Flosdorf and associates has been shown to be useful, although there are dissenting opinions.

c. Diagnosis

Test of the patient's serum for anti-pertussis agglutinins is of value only late in the disease. It is necessary to test two specimens taken at intervals in order to demonstrate a rising titer.

d. Treatment

Serum treatment of pertussis is possible with pertussis immune serum (85) intramuscularly, or in critically ill patients, intravenously. The dose is 20 ml. daily, or every second day, up to a total of 60 to 100 ml. Hyper-immune gamma globulin may be given intramuscularly, in doses of 2.5 ml. daily or every second day, up to a total of 7.5 to 12.5 ml. In serious cases antibiotics are used also (4). Not everyone agrees that serum therapy is of value.

Plague

a. Prophylaxis

Immunization alone is not the ideal method of eradicating plague, but widespread active immunization of native populations with a single dose of living avirulent plague vaccine has proved valuable (5). Killed vaccines are less useful under such conditions because of the practical difficulties of getting the repeated injections into all the members of the exposed population.

The United States Armed Services recommended the following dosage schedule of killed vaccine for dependents of military personnel (4):

Basic Immunization:

Adults: 0.5 ml. subcutaneously, followed by a second injection 7 to 28 days later.

Children: Three subcutaneous injections at intervals of 7 to 10 days, in doses varying according to age as follows (Table 15-5):

TABLE 15-5

Age	6 months–4 years	5–9 years	10 years and over
1st dose	0.1 ml.	0.3 ml.	Adult schedule
2nd dose	0.3 ml.	0.5 ml.	
3rd dose	0.3 ml.	0.5 ml.	

Recall ("booster") injections are given any time within four years after the basic series or the last recall dose. The doses are 1.0 ml., 0.12 ml., 0.25 ml., or 0.5 ml. according to age, as above. Reimmunization may be required, not oftener than every four to six months, in areas where plague is a current hazard.

Pneumonia

a. Prophylaxis

Active Immunization. Immunization with killed pneumococci probably has some prophylactic value in pneumococcus pneumonia, but most of the studies undertaken have been deficient as critical evidence (80). Immunization with type-specific polysaccharide is apparently successful (81). Immunization was carried out in an Army camp during World War II where types I, II, III, V, VII, and XII pneumococcal pneumonia had been epidemic for two years. Half of the population received 0.06 mg. of each of the capsular polysaccharides I, II, V, and VII subcutaneously; the other half of the population served as controls. Pneumococcus pneumonia of types I, II, V, and VII ceased to occur in the immunized group within two weeks but continued to occur in the controls. The incidence of pneumonia caused by pneumococci of the other types was not significantly affected in either group (33,80). It was further observed that although pneumococcal pneumonia caused by pneumococci of types I, II, V, and VII continued to occur in the control half of the camp population, the incidence was less than excepted, suggesting that the protection afforded the immunized group reduced the dissemination of these particular organisms.

Immunization of civilians by means of specific polysaccharides has not yet been carried out on a large scale. The Massachusetts Department of Public Health has recommended that multiple-antigen immunization against pneumococcal pneumonia be considered for the elderly, the very young, special occupational groups with a high natural incidence of pneumonia, and patients about to undergo major surgical operations (33). Two mixed polysaccharide preparations have been put on the market: a mixture of types I, II, III, V, VII, and VIII, primarily for use in adults and adolescents, and mixture of types I, IV, VI, XIV, XVIII, and XIX, for protection of infants and young children against the types to which members of this age group are most subject (33).

b. Test for Immunity

Although not a test for immunity, the Francis test should be mentioned at this point. It consists in the intracutaneous injection of 0.1 mg. of homologous specific capsular polysaccharide dissolved in 0.1 ml. of saline. If circulating antibody is present, a wheal and erythema reaction appear within 15 to 30 minutes at the injected site. This reaction is an indication that sufficient antibody is present in the pneumonia patient. If such an amount is not present, it should be administered (80).

d. Treatment

Before the days of sulfa drugs and antibiotics, specific antibody therapy had been developed for pneumococcal pneumonia. It was shown that the antibody must be type-specific, must be given in adequate amounts, and was most effective when given early in the course of the disease (80).

The first sera were produced by immunizing horses with killed pneumococci, and were given to the patient intravenously in unconcentrated form. Later the antibodies, or rather the serum globulins, of such sera were separated and concentrated. Rabbit sera later displaced horse sera, because higher titers could be obtained, the antibody had a lower molecular weight and possibly therefore greater diffusibility, and there were other advantages. The dose was controlled by the Francis test (see above, p. 626).

According to Top (136), in mild to moderately severe pneumonia type-specific serum may act to produce a "crisis," but is not necessary, since the response to antibiotics is uniformly good, while in severe to overwhelming pneumonias the usual doses of serum are insufficient to neutralize the circulating capsular polysaccharide and are clinically ineffective. Therefore Top believed that antiserum has no place in the modern management of pneumonia.

Rheumatic Fever

c. Diagnosis

Diagnosis of acute rheumatic fever may be made tentatively but not definitely by demonstration of high or steadily increasing concentrations of antistreptolysin in the patient's serum (133,136,5); these results merely demonstrate recent experience with group A hemolytic streptococci.

Salmonelloses, Including Paratyphoid Fever

The bacteriology of *Salmonella* infection is complex. More than 600 serotypes of Salmonellae have been identified (4) (see Chapter 4). Among the commoner strains are *S. typhimurium, S. enteritidis, S. choleraesuis,* and the paratyphoid types A, B, and C (*S. paratyphi, S. schottmuelleri,* and *S. hirschfeldii*).

Salmonellae may cause (*a*) gastroenteritis and food poisoning, (*b*) septicemia and localized infection, such as endocarditis, pneumonia, osteomyelitis, meningitis, pyelonephritis, etc., (*c*) paratyphoid salmonella fever, (*d*) typhoid fever.

a. Prophylaxis

Active immunization against paratyphoid fever is probably as effective as that against typhoid (which see), but the disease has become so rare in this country that para A and B organisms, once always included in typhoid vaccine (so-called triple vaccine), were omitted, because the para A and B organisms increased the incidence of unfavorable reactions. Later the A and B components were reintroduced into the vaccine put out by some manufacturers.

c. Diagnosis

Tests for agglutinins aid in the diagnosis of paratyphoid fever, and the specificity of the agglutinins aids in the differentiation of these infections from typhoid fever (136). In the United States *S. typhosa, S. schottmuelleri,* and *S. choleraesuis* cultures are commonly used for screening agglutinin tests (94). Pooled sera for identification of the major "O" types are available commercially and are useful. Final serological identification is done in only a few laboratories.

Scarlet Fever

a. Prophylaxis

The Committee on the Control of Infectious Diseases of the American Academy of Pediatrics (4) does not believe immunization against scarlet fever with the toxin is of any value.

b. Test for Immunity

Dick Test. This is an intracutaneous test for immunity or susceptibility to scarlet fever, quite analogous to the Schick test. The scarlatinal toxin used has been standardized by tests in the skin of susceptible persons so that one skin test dose (STD) is contained in a volume of 0.1 ml. As in the Schick test, heated toxin (100°C. for 2 hours) is used as a control on possible allergic reactions. Pseudo and combined reactions may occur but are very rare following primary tests and uncommon even in retests after active immunization. This allergic reaction usually lasts longer than the simple reaction toxin.

The reactions are read after 18 to 24 hours. Differences in size and intensity (redness) of the reaction indicate degrees of susceptibility. A reaction is considered positive if there is an area of redness at least 1 cm. in diameter with a negative control (29).

The reliability of the Dick test does not seem to be quite so high as that of the Schick test, for Dick-negative individuals may sometimes contract scarlet fever, although only about one-twentieth as often as Dick-positive individuals (6). Top (136) reported seeing a number of individuals who just a few days previously showed a negative Dick test develop scarlet fever with a rash.

c. Diagnosis

Skin Test. Potent antitoxic sera have the ability to blanch a scarlatinal rash by neutralizing the toxin in the skin (Schultz-Charlton phenomenon). This is demonstrable only during the first few days of scarlet fever. It is occasionally useful in differentiating scarlet fever from other cutaneous erythemas (133).

Syphilis

Two distinctive forms of syphilis are recognized. The venereally spread form is of world-wide occurrence. The non-venereal form, called *bejel* in the Middle East (63a), is confined to parts of the world where economic, social, and climatic conditions favor its development. It is not seen in the United States.

c. Diagnosis

Two distinct types of serological procedures are currently in use in the diagnosis of syphilis. The first of these depends upon the development by the patient of an antibody which combines with mammalian lipides to give positive complement-fixation (Wassermann) and flocculation (Kahn, Eagle, Hinton, etc.) reactions. Such tests are not necessarily diagnostic unless confirmed by a history or clinical findings of syphilis. False positives may occur in as many as 7 per cent of normal individuals, and false negatives in as many as 50 per cent of cases of latent syphilis (136).

The complement-fixation and flocculation tests for syphilis usually become positive between the third and the sixth weeks after contraction of the infection, but the exact time depends upon the individual patient and the sensitivity of the test used. In some patients the tests do not become positive until about three months after acquisition of the infection (83).

Diagnosis of syphilis should not be based solely upon a positive serological report from the laboratory, but a thorough physical examination should be made. The serological test should be made in a first-class, well-equipped laboratory, and a positive test should be repeated. In interpreting positive tests attention should be given to the possible presence of jaundice, infectious mononucleosis, vaccinia, undulant fever, malaria, leprosy, upper respiratory infections including pneumonia, infectious hepatitis, lupus erythematosis, measles, mumps, chickenpox, scarlet fever, subacute bacterial endocarditis, rheumatoid arthritis, pregnancy, cachetic stages of tuberculosis, cancer, and acute febrile reactions.

A strongly positive reaction which persists for three months may be considered as diagnostic.

The treponema-immobilizing test developed by Nelson (97) is considerably more specific than the complement-fixation and flocculation tests, and may become the test of choice for syphilis (32,136). In the absence of a method of cultivation of *T. pallidum in vitro,* however, only certain laboratories are in a position to carry out the test.

In Germany a "Pallida-antigen," prepared from a cultivated strain of the spirochete, has seen considerable application (48,114).

Tetanus

a. Prophylaxis

Active Immunization. All children should be immunized to tetanus, with the use of the triple vaccine containing diphtheria toxoid, tetanus toxoid, and pertussis vaccine, as described under diphtheria. All adults frequently subjected to abrasions and minor trauma should also be immunized, using alum-precipitated toxoid.

It is recommended that adults receive two injections of 0.5 ml. each of alum-precipitated toxoid, at an interval of not less than one month and not more than four months.

British usage still favors toxoid solution (100); American ideas are discussed by Edsall (34a) and Stafford (131a).

Routine recall injections are advised one year after completion of the primary course of injections and every three years thereafter. (In the case of children inoculated with the triple vaccine recall injections should be given as recommended under Diphtheria.) It is important to give the routine recall injections, for they maintain high titers of circulating antitoxin. However, recall injections given at the time of an injury ("wound boosters") are of considerable value. The dose for the recall injection is 0.5 ml. of alum-precipitated or aluminum hydroxide adsorbed tetanus toxoid. For children who have had one or more recall injections already, this dose may be divided in half. The dose for "wound boosters" is the same, but use of fluid or aluminum hydroxide adsorbed toxoid results in somewhat more rapid antitoxin response (about 24 hours) than does the use of alum-precipitated toxoid (4).

It has recently been shown that a recall injection is still effective even if as much as nine years has elapsed since the patient's last injection of tetanus toxoid.

The value of active immunization to tetanus is convincingly shown by the experience of the American Army in World War II. Soldiers were given three doses of toxoid at intervals of three weeks, followed by a fourth dose one year later or before military operations (108), with emergency "booster" injections when indicated (34). Only 15 cases of tetanus occurred among over 2,000,000 wounded men in the U. S. Armed Forces during World War II, and in only 6 of these had the scheduled full immunization been administered (34). The British experience was similar. The efficacy of the immunization was illustrated by the contrast —to pick but one example—of the several hundred cases of tetanus which occurred among injured Filipinos in and about Manila during the liberation of that city.

Passive Immunization. Tetanus is a relatively rare disease in this part of the world, and according to Edsall (34) there is no doubt that its incidence is kept low in large part by the assiduous use of prophylactic antitoxin following injuries. Such prophylaxis is of course no substitute for active immunization, since its effect is transitory, since it has sometimes failed to protect, and since the injection of horse serum invites a variety of untoward reactions. On the other hand, administration of antitoxin is the only means of attempting protection of injured persons who have not been actively immunized.

It is sometimes difficult to decide whether or not to give prophylactic tetanus antitoxin. It is clearly impossible to give antitoxin after every slight injury or scratch contracted at work or play. It is necessary to consider the locality and the circumstances under which the injury was contracted. If it is decided that antitoxin should be used, then:

A dose of 1,500 International Units (1950) should be injected subcutaneously or intramuscularly into all non-immune or incompletely immune persons as soon as possible after injury (100). Some U. S. authorities recommend 5,000 to 10,000 units, and follow this six to eight weeks later with active immunization with tetanus toxoid. In cases with heavily contaminated wounds 10,000 units may offer some advantage.

In cases considered to be at greater risk (dead tissue or foreign material in the wound or delay between injury and efficient surgical treatment), it is usual to give two further doses of antitoxin, of 1,500 units each, after the first (100,136).

For puncture wounds treated more than 24 hours after accident and for all other wounds and burns, the recommended dose of antitoxin is 5,000 units. This should be repeated in one week if the wound is not then clean and healing.

Antitetanus human gamma globulin is used in patients who are allergic to horse serum (100).

d. Treatment

The serological treatment of tetanus consists in the intramuscular injection of 50,000 to 100,000 units of tetanus antitoxin. Parish and Cannon (100) recommend 100,000 to 200,000 International Units (1950), mainly intravenously, with all necessary precautions. Intrathecal antitoxin is definitely contraindicated (4). It is not necessary to give antitoxin locally around the wound.

Tuberculosis

a. Prophylaxis

The American Academy of Pediatrics (4) recommends vaccination with BCG of tuberculin-negative children who will necessarily be exposed to tuberculosis. The vaccination should be performed as soon as possible after completing the tuberculin test. If it is at all possible, the child should be kept isolated, after vaccination, from known sources of tuberculous infection for six to eight weeks, until the tuberculin reaction has become positive.

Newborn infants who may be exposed to manifest cases of tuberculosis at home can be vaccinated 24 to 48 hours after birth, without preliminary tuberculin test, provided they have not been exposed to a tuberculous person. If this is not done, it is best to wait for about six weeks, carry out a tuberculin test, and vaccinate if the test is negative (4). If at all possible these infants should be kept from contact with known cases of tuberculosis for about two months, after which time the great majority will have become tuberculin-positive. If after six to eight weeks they are still tuberculin-negative, the BCG vaccination should be repeated.

Of course BCG vaccination of infants or children should not take the place of hospitalization of adults with open cases of tuberculosis. However, BCG vaccination is advised for those areas where there is a high infection rate and where there are inadequate facilities for the hospitalization of patients or where the patient refuses to be hospitalized.

BCG should not be administered to premature infants or to those who are markedly underweight at birth. The vaccine should not be given to a person suffering from impetigo or other infectious skin disease, nor should it be given simultaneously with smallpox vaccination. It may be given with other types of antigens, however.

The intracutaneous method of administering the vaccine is preferred by most investigators (4). The dose is 0.1 ml. of material equivalent to 0.1 mg. BCG vaccine, injected intracutaneously, as superficially as possible, over the deltoid muscle.

The BCG vaccine has been in use for more than 30 years in some parts of the world, but opposition to it in certain quarters continued to be very stiff in English-speaking countries until recently, and the American Public Health Association, in their 1955 Report on the Control of Communicable Diseases in Man, stated that "The role of BCG vaccination of uninfected persons is still unsettled." However, Middlebrook and Freund (92) stated that "There is convincing evidence that vaccination with . . . (BCG) can confer some protection against naturally acquired tuberculous disease in man. . . ."

TABLE 15-6

Results of BCG Vaccination of Tuberculin-Negative Swedish Soldiers (28)

Type of disease	Time of detection of disease (days after vaccination)	Incidence, cases per 1000		Ratio of incidence, non-vaccinated to vaccinated
		Nonvac-cinated (25,239)	Vacci-nated (36,235)	
Primary tuberculosis	0–120	2.22	1.13	1.96
Primary tuberculosis	>120	3.33	0.47	7.07
Postprimary tuberculosis (rein-fection type)	0–180	0.32	0.39	0.82
	>180	1.47	0.42	3.54
Pulmonary tuberculosis, de-structive on discovery	0–180	0.08	0.11	0.72
	>180	0.68	0.14	4.85
Fatal tuberculosis		1.51	0.50[a]	3.03
Nontuberculous pneumonia		2.62	2.54	1.03

[a] It was stated that no less than 11 of the 18 cases of fatal tuberculosis among the BCG vaccinated had, in all probability, been infected prior to six weeks after vaccination.

The evidence bearing on the efficacy of BCG is far too extensive to summarize here. The findings up to 1949 were summarized by Irvine (66) and by Edsall (33). Irvine quoted one study by Hyge which was almost an ideal experiment, although accidental. In a school where the pupils were exposed much more intensively than is usual to infection by a tuberculous teacher, of 94 tuberculin-negative pupils exposed 70 became tuberculin-positive and of these 41 had pulmonary tuberculosis, 36 with roentgenological changes, and 37 with tubercle bacilli shown by gastric lavage. Among 106 exposed pupils who had been vaccinated with BCG, there were two cases of pulmonary tuberculosis, both showing tubercle bacilli in the gastric lavage. This incident could be construed as showing that 96 per cent of those vaccinated developed resistance to infection with tuberculosis (66).

Another convincing study is that reported by Dahlstrom and Difs (28) on Swedish soldiers vaccinated with BCG. The results, shown in Table 15-6, are highly significant statistically, and strongly indicate a protective action of the vaccine, at any rate after two or three months have elapsed.

According to the Report of the Committee on the Control of Infectious Diseases of the American Academy of Pediatrics (4), there is reasonable evidence that even those individuals who, following administration of BCG, do not become tuberculin-positive, nevertheless have their resistance enhanced.

c. Diagnosis

Skin hypersensitivity to products of the tubercle bacillus is responsible for the positive tuberculin reaction, which is the paradigm of skin tests for the delayed type of hypersensitivity resulting from infection. Either the Vollmer patch test or the Mantoux intracutaneous test may be used (4). For the Mantoux test either old tuberculin (OT) or purified protein derivative (PPD) may be used (100). In the United Kingdom the Heaf multiple puncture is rapidly becoming the test of choice (100).

A positive tuberculin test indicates that the patient is or has been infected with tubercle bacilli; the lesion may be extensive or small, active or healed. The reaction can be positive in the absence of roentgenological evidence of lesions. A negative reaction indicates the absence of infection, *except that* the person may be in the preallergic stage of first infection (a period lasting not over a month) or may have lost his allergy due to an overwhelming infection (this is uncommon). The intensity of a positive reaction may in some cases parallel the intensity of exposure or the activity of the infection, but is on the whole of little significance in individual cases (92).

The tuberculin test is of great value in excluding tuberculosis in individuals being examined, and in epidemiological surveys to indicate the prevalence of infection. In recent years it has been repeatedly observed that tuberculin sensitivity may be lost by persons with healed tuberculosis of first infection, suggesting that perhaps repeated contacts are necessary to maintain sensitivity (92).

Tularemia

a. Prophylaxis

Apparently useful immunity can be produced by vaccination with phenolized or acetone-extracted microorganisms (87,136). It is recommended only for laboratory workers, persons engaged in handling wild rabbits, etc. (4). Subjects should be skin tested before vaccination, using a 1:1000 dilution of the vaccine in saline. Those showing a positive skin test should not be vaccinated, as they may develop severe reactions. The following doses are used in immunization: 0.1 ml. subcutaneously, 0.5 ml. subcutaneously, 0.5 ml. subcutaneously. The injections are given at intervals of 2 days. Longer intervals may result insensitization and severe reactions (4).

c. Diagnosis

Agglutination Test. Specific antibodies do not appear before the first 10 or 12 days of the disease, but almost always appear during the second week, rise sharply during the third week, and reach a maximum titer during the fourth and fifth weeks. A rising titer is almost conclusive proof of tularemia (87). Cross reactions with *Brucella abortus* and *Proteus* OX19 are common (4).

Skin Test. Foshay's test (45) is a valuable diagnostic aid. It consists in the intracutaneous injection of 0.01 ml. of a specially prepared detoxified suspension of killed *B. tularense*. A tuberculin type reaction appears within 48 hours in positive cases. The test almost always becomes positive during the first week, when agglutinins are still absent. The skin sensitivity persists for many years, and its disappearance cannot be used as an index of recovery.

Intracutaneous injection of a very small amount of antitularense serum into the skin of a patient causes an immediate erythematous-edematous reaction, which is specific. It is useful as a quick confirmatory test (46).

Typhoid Fever

a. Prophylaxis

Active immunization with suspensions of killed typhoid bacilli seems to reduce the incidence and fatality of infections with *S. typhosa*, but there is no evidence that it alone can stamp out the disease, and it should be regarded as a poor substitute for sanitary measures (94). Immunization should be performed in cases of persons intensively exposed, as the staffs of contagious disease hospitals, soldiers or travelers in countries where the disease is still endemic, residents of rural areas of the United States and Canada where typhoid fever is prevalent, and in some cases campers (94,4).

The commercial vaccine is a saline suspension of killed organisms standardized to contain 1000 million *S. typhosa* per milliliter. The recommended total dose for adults is 1.5 ml. (1500 million organisms.). This should be divided into three equal doses given one to four weeks apart, preferably subcutaneously (4). In the case of infants less than one year of age, the recommended total dose is 1.0 ml. (1000 million organisms). Since sharp febrile reactions are not uncommon, it is better to make the first dose 0.2 ml., and make the subsequent doses depend upon the presence or absence of reactions. Usually it is possible to complete the immunization with two injections of 0.4 ml. each, but in some cases it is advisable to give more and smaller doses to make up the total of 1.0 ml. Children over one year of age should receive the same total dose as for adults (1.5 ml.), but it is advisable to give only 0.3 ml. for the first injection (4).

Where the danger of infection is great, as, for example, in Central Europe, persons should be revaccinated annually.

For a long time typhoid vaccine always included also para A (*Salmonella paratyphi*) and para B (*S. schottmuelleri*). The incidence of infections with these organisms eventually fell to such a low level that inclusion of para A and B in the vaccine was discontinued, especially as their presence tended to make the reactions which often follow the injections more severe. It is recommended, however, that the mixed vaccine (so-called TAB vaccine) be employed for individuals who plan to travel outside the continental United States and Canada (4). Where paratyphoid fever is prevalent, as in southwestern Texas, the vaccine should include para A and B.

Protection by typhoid inoculation is not complete, but a study of vaccinated groups in the United States military indicates that the incidence of the disease in vaccinated groups was approximately 25 per cent of that in comparable nonvaccinated groups (139,17). Edsall (34) has summarized the evidence that immunization with a good vaccine gives good protection against typhoid, but at the same time this author points out that this immunity, probably like all artificial and even natural immunity, is not 100 per cent. According to Marmion, Naylor, and Stewart (100) even an attack of typhoid confers no more than a moderate degree of immunity, at least if the attack is treated with chloramphenicol.

Recall injections are recommended every two years unless the probability of exposure is great, in which case they should be given yearly.

A dose of 0.5 ml. subcutaneously (146), or 0.1 ml. intracutaneously, is adequate. The intracutaneous injection is to be preferred as less likely to cause severe reactions, but is not recommended for primary immunization (4).

Commercial TAB vaccine is a saline suspension containing 1000 million S. typhosa, 250 million S. paratyphi, and 250 million S. schottmuelleri per milliliter. In Great Britain more para A and para B are included (500–750 million) (100). The dosage is the same as for the straight typhoid vaccine, namely 1.5 ml. divided into not less than three doses. Since febrile reactions are more common with the polyvalent vaccine, injections after the first are governed by the degree of reaction produced, and some immunologists begin with an initial dose of 0.2 ml. The course of inoculations can usually be completed with three subsequent injections of 0.25 ml., 0.25 ml., and 0.3 ml. Children over one year of age should receive the adult dose of 1.5 ml. unless they exhibit marked febrile reactions (4).

c. Diagnosis

A positive Widal test indicates the presence of typhoid "O" or "H" antibodies. This gives strong support to a diagnosis of typhoid, but two sources of error should be recognized. Persons who have been vaccinated for typhoid within the previous six to twelve months may have such agglutinins as a result. Persons vaccinated at a more remote time, and persons who have had typhoid, may show an anamnestic reaction during some other febrile illness, especially typhus or brucellosis. These errors in interpretation may be guarded against by checking the history for vaccination and noting that in the anamnestic reaction the titer rises and falls early and antibodies for the agent responsible for the current disease will appear and rise to even higher titers, and persist longer, than the antityphoid antibodies. The Widal is seldom positive to a diagnostic titer in less than 10 days in persons with typhoid.

O agglutinins are more significant than H agglutinins, but both should be tested for. It is not possible to set any arbitrary titer as diagnostic; some patients never develop titers higher than 1:40 or 1:80. The demonstration of a rising titer is more significant than any single level, although titers of the order of 1:160 are strongly suggestive (10).

d. Treatment

Treatment of typhoid fever is generally with chloramphenicol at the present time (94,136). According to Top (136), whole blood from a recently recovered patient or from a typhoid bacillus carrier has been found to be of value.

Undulant Fever (See Brucellosis)

Whooping Cough (See Pertussis)

Yaws

c. Diagnosis

Serological reactions for syphilis are positive in yaws as frequently as in actual syphilis. (5). They become positive during the primary stage, remain positive during the secondary stage, and tend to become negative after many years of latency (5).

C. VIRUS AND RICKETTSIAL INFECTIONS

African Tick-Borne Fever, Rickettsial

a. Prophylaxis

Vaccines are not commercially available (5).

c. Diagnosis

Antibodies may be demonstrated using the specific rickettsial antigen. The Weil-Felix reaction, with Proteus OX 19, is often positive, but the titer of the agglutinins is lower than in other rickettsial diseases (5).

Brill's Disease (Recrudescent Typhus)

c. Diagnosis

The diagnosis of Brill's disease can be confirmed by the demonstration of a rising titer of complement-fixing antibodies or antibodies which agglutinate suspensions of washed *R. prowazekii*. The serology of Brill's disease differs in two important respects from that of epidemic louse-borne typhus: (*1*) in Brill's disease the rise in specific antibodies begins early, from the fourth to the sixth day after onset of illness, with a peak response generally about the tenth day, whereas in a primary attack of epidemic typhus the antibody rise begins about the eighth to the twelfth day, with a maximum between the twelfth and sixteenth days. (*2*) The

Weil-Felix reaction (agglutination of *Proteus* OX 19) is usually negative in Brill's disease (130).

Cat-Scratch Fever

This disease, only recently recognized, is often contracted as a result of a bite, lick, or scratch of a cat. It is probably caused by a virus and is characterized by the frequent occurrence of a small pustular lesion at the site of inoculation, followed by malaise, fever, and involvement of regional lymph nodes.

c. Diagnosis

Skin Test. This is carried out with an antigen prepared similarly to that used for the Frei test [heat-inactivated pus diluted 1:15 with sterile saline and heated to 56°C. for an hour on 2 successive days (136); or it may be heated to 58°C. for 1 hour and 0.5 per cent phenol added (4)]. After test for sterility, 0.1 ml. of the antigen is injected intracutaneously, and the reaction read at 24 and 48 hours. A positive test shows an indurated papule 5 to 10 mm. in diameter, surrounded by an area of redness 15 to 60 mm. in diameter. This reaction is said to be free from false positive reactions (136). The material is not available commercially.

Chickenpox (Varicella)

a. Prophylaxis

Passive Prophylaxis. When convalescent serum is available, contacts who for some special reason need protection from the disease may be given a dose of from 10 ml. to 15 ml., preferably within the first 7 days after exposure. This measure may prevent or modify the disease (136).

It has been reported that gamma globulin is of no value in the prevention of chickenpox (136).

Common Cold

a. Prophylaxis

Active Prophylaxis. Although there has been much experimentation with vaccines against the common cold, there is no convincing evidence of any significant degree of protection from their use (63,136).

Dengue

c. Diagnosis

Serological tests which are of assistance in the diagnosis of dengue include hemagglutination, complement-fixation, and neutralization tests, using a specific type of virus (115,5).

Encephalitis

The encephalitides are a group, difficult to classify, of inflammatory virus diseases of short duration, involving parts of the brain, spinal cord, and meninges. The Report of the Committte on the Control of Infectious Diseases of the American Academy of Pediatrics discusses only three types, western equine encephalitis, eastern equine encephalitis, and St. Louis type encephalitis. Olitsky and Casals (98) discussed a large number. For those types for which serological diagnostic tests are available, the procedures are very similar, and it is sufficient to describe those for St. Louis type encephalitis.

c. Diagnosis

Paired specimens of serum from the patient are required for the tests. The first specimen should be taken as soon as feasible after the beginning of illness, and the second taken late in convalescence. The paired specimens are then tested simultaneously for both neutralizing and complement-fixing antibodies. If the second specimen contains antibodies for St. Louis virus and the first does not, the patient has had St. Louis encephalitis. If neither specimen contains antibodies for the virus, the patient probably did not have St. Louis encephalitis, although this is not certain, as some patients do not produce antibodies against this virus within the period involved. If both specimens contain antibodies to the same titer (and the first specimen was taken early enough), the current illness is not St. Louis encephalitis, but the patient had the disease in the past (98).

German Measles (See Rubella)

Hepatitis, Viral

Two forms of virus hepatitis were formerly distinguished, infectious hepatitis and serum hepatitis. They are probably different forms of the same disease (63). At least two different viruses seem to be involved;

virus A, with a relatively short incubation period (2–6 weeks), and virus B, with a longer incubation period of $1^1/_2$ to 6 months (136). Virus A is probably transmitted through human feces; either virus can be transmitted by infected human blood or blood products (except gamma globulin). Extremely small amounts of blood can infect (1 ml. of a 1:1,000,000 dilution), and it seems established that transmission can be through improperly sterilized syringes, needles, lancets, or other instruments that have been in contact with human blood, including dental instruments and tattooing apparatus (63).

a. Prophylaxis

Gamma globulin seems to have some value in preventing or mitigating infection by hepatitis virus of either type (63). Protection conferred by gamma globulin against hepatitis of the endemic type may last from 3 to 6 months (63).

Infectious Mononucleosis (See Mononucleosis, Infectious)

Herpes Zoster

This disease (shingles) is a local manifestation of recurrent infection with chickenpox virus (5).

Influenza

a. Prophylaxis

Active Prophylaxis. There is convincing evidence that subcutaneous vaccination with inactivated influenza virus exerts a significant effect upon susceptibility to the epidemic disease (4,136). The immunity is quite specific for each type of virus and fairly specific for different strains within types A and B, and the resistance conferred is not 100 per cent effective. Because the immunity is strain-specific, immunization even of a whole population might fail to prevent an epidemic, if a different strain of virus should come along. Polyvalent vaccines containing virus strains responsible for epidemics of the last three decades or so are used in the U. S. A.; British virologists favor single-strain vaccines (100).

The protective effects probably do not last more than a year (136).

Influenza vaccines are available commercially. They are made from virus which has been grown on chick embryos, inactivated by formaldehyde, purified, and concentrated. In view of their origin, they should not be given to individuals with known egg hypersensitivity, and should be used with caution in any individual known to be highly allergic (136). Influenza vaccines are not recommended for routine use in children (4).

Lymphocytic Choriomeningitis

c. Diagnosis

Serological tests are of assistance in the diagnosis of this disease. Two or three specimens of serum are required in order to demonstrate a rising titer. Complement-fixing antibodies appear in one to three weeks; neutralizing antibodies not until four to ten weeks. The neutralizing antibodies usually persist for years (4).

Lymphogranuloma Venereum

c. Diagnosis

Skin Sensitivity Test. The Frei test (88,136) depends upon the skin hypersensitivity of the delayed type which results from infection with the virus of lymphogranuloma venereum. The antigen used for injection into the skin of the patient can be made with bubo pus obtained from human lesions, from infected mouse brains, or from infected yolk sacs. The last source is now used almost exclusively (89). The virus is inactivated by heat. The inactivated virus and a control made from normal yolk sacs are injected intracutaneously into separate sites on the forearm, using a dose of 0.1 ml. Readings are taken at 48 and 72 hours. A positive reaction consists of central induration with surrounding edema, when the control shows slight induration of an area less than 5 mm. in diameter. Erythema, regardless of its extent, is of no significance.

The Frei test usually becomes positive 7 to 40 days after the onset of the adenitis. The test may rarely be negative in definitely positive cases, owing to concomitant infections, menstruation, etc. The Frei test should be repeated if the patient is in an early stage of infection. The Frei test is believed to be highly specific (88).

Complement-Fixation Test. According to Meyer (89) the attempts to use the complement-fixation test in lymphogranuloma venereum have given equivocal results. However, Meyer believes that with the standardized antigenic procedures used by many workers, a titer of 1:32 or 1:40 or higher in a patient with symptoms of the infection is beyond the range of nonspecific effect, and indicates active infection. According to Top (136) this test is available in only a few centers.

Once the Frei test has become positive in a patient, it apparently remains positive for life, except sometimes in the presence of other profound systemic diseases (136).

Measles (Rubeola, Morbilli)

a. Prophylaxis

Although measles is not generally considered a serious disease, complications can develop, and immunization is recommended (4). Children should be given the vaccine at the age of nine months or as soon after that as possible. This is particularly recommended for children likely to develop complications, such as institutionalized children, and children with cystic fibrosis, tuberculosis, heart disease, asthma, and other chronic pulmonary diseases.

Live attenuated measles virus plus measles immune gamma globulin, is recommended (4). In the majority of children the symptoms resulting from the vaccine are very mild, but 30 to 40 per cent develop a temperature of 103°F. or more, and in 30 to 60 per cent a modified measles rash is seen.

Prevention of measles in exposed non-immunized children should be attempted in the case of infants less than 12 months of age, children ill with other diseases, particularly tuberculosis and rheumatic fever, healthy children whose siblings are ill with other diseases, particularly tuberculosis, pertussis, and rheumatic fever, or when the disease breaks out in an institution and it is considered necessary to abort the epidemic.

Prevention may be accomplished by giving children three years of age or younger 5 ml. of convalescent serum or 10 ml. of adult serum within 6 days after exposure (106). For older children the dose is multiplied by two for convalescent serum and by four for adult serum. Gamma globulin, 0.25 ml. per kilogram of body weight (0.1 ml. per pound) prior to the sixth day after exposure, may be used for prevention (4,5). Such protection is of course temporary only.

Successful prevention means that no active immunity results in the protected child, and consequently, except in the special cases mentioned above, the attempt should be to modify rather than prevent. In this way a mild attack of measles is allowed to develop, the child produces antibodies, and active immunity results. To accomplish this, the dose of serum or other preparation is adjusted in accordance with the size of the child and the estimated length of time after exposure. If the preparation is given later than 6 days after exposure, the attempt will probably fail; the same amounts should be used as prescribed for prevention before this time. Within 6 days after exposure, preferably on the third day, 0.05 ml. per kg. is given (106). If the ideal dosage is given, the disease is so modified that there is no real malaise, but solid immunity results. Frequently the symptoms are so mild that without careful examination they would never be noticed (106).

Active immunization with a live attenuated measles virus mixed with immune gamma globulin is now possible (4).

Mononucleosis, Infectious

c. Diagnosis

Diagnosis of this disease is facilitated by finding heterophile antibody (= an increased agglutinin titer for sheep erythrocytes) in the serum (102)). Since this test is positive in only about 95 per cent of the cases, a negative test does not exclude infectious mononucleosis (110), especially since as long as seven weeks may elapse before the patient's serum becomes positive.

The test is carried out with a specimen of serum which has been heated to 56°C. for 15 minutes. It is then mixed with a 2 per cent suspension of washed sheep erythrocytes in saline. The mixture is incubated at 37°C. for an hour and then in the refrigerator overnight. The reaction is considered positive if dilutions of the serum of 1:80 or higher agglutinate the sheep cells. A titer of 1:60 is considered normal. Since the heterophile antibody in the blood is increased after the injection of horse serum, this may cause errors. However, the heterophile antibody resulting from horse serum, and the antibody normally present, can be removed by absorption with guinea pig kidney. The heterophile antibody resulting from horse serum is also removable by absorption with boiled sheep cells. The antibody resulting from infectious mononucleosis is removable only by boiled sheep cells. Use may be made of these facts to show that the heterophile antibody found is actually that due to infectious mononucleosis (Paul-Bunnell antibody) (110).

The serological test for syphilis may become temporarily positive in infectious mononucleosis (5).

Mumps

a. Prophylaxis

Active Prophylaxis. There is experimental evidence that a considerable degree of resistance to mumps can be produced by the administration of a formaldehyde-inactivated virus grown on embryonated eggs, or by living mumps virus which has been attenuated by repeated passage through chick embryos (36). The number of injections required and the intervals between them remain to be determined (4). Not all susceptible individuals are protected by such vaccines, and the duration of the resulting immunity is still not definitely known, but probably does not exceed 2 years (4,5,136).

Active immunization to mumps is not advised for children except under unusual circumstances.

Passive Prophylaxis. Serum from those who have recently had the disease may be of value as a prophylactic measure. The immunity conferred by such serum, if any, is of short duration, probably two or three weeks. The indicated dose is 5 to 20 ml., given within the first few days after exposure. However, Enders points out (36) that even very large (200 ml.) doses of convalescent serum have failed to prevent the disease.

b. Test for Immunity

In most patients hypersensitivity of the delayed type develops several weeks following the onset of mumps. A positive reaction is generally considered to be associated with immunity (36,4,100). Henle *et al.* (60) found the incidence of mumps in the area studied by them was 1 to 2 per cent in the positive reactors, and 18 to 49 per cent in the negative reactors.

c. Diagnosis

In cases where involvement is minimal and the disease has attacked other organs, it is frequently impossible to make a diagnosis of mumps on the basis of the clinical findings alone (36). In such cases serological tests can be of considerable value.

The Complement-Fixation test is used. Ideally two different mumps antigens are employed, the S or "soluble" antigen, and the V or "virus" antigen. As with most other serological tests, a definite diagnosis can usually be made only if test of two samples of blood taken at different times from the patient shows a significant rise in titer as the disease progresses. Antibodies to the S antigen rise rapidly early in the course of the infection and fall off rapidly after the first week. Antibodies to the V antigen appear later, often toward the end of the first week, reaching a maximum about the third week, then falling off. Anti-V antibodies may persist at detectable levels for many years (36,4).

A single serum specimen taken early in the disease which shows considerable anti-S antibodies but little or no anti-V antibodies provides sufficient evidence for a presumptive diagnosis of mumps (36).

Neutralizing Antibody for the hemagglutinating activity of mumps virus can also be used in the serological diagnosis of mumps (36).

d. Treatment

The American Academy of Pediatrics (4) does not recommend any specific treatment in infants and children. It may be attempted to reduce the incidence of complications in adults (especially orchitis) by the use of large doses (200 ml.) of serum from convalescents or vaccinated donors, or gamma globulin prepared from convalescent serum (36). Gamma globulin (from pooled normal blood) is of no value in the treatment of mumps (36).

Murine Typhus (See Typhus, Flea-Borne)

Phlebotomus Fever (Sandfly Fever)

c. Diagnosis

A diagnosis of phlebotomus fever may be confirmed by testing the patient's serum for virus-neutralizing antibodies, using mouse adapted virus (5).

Pleurodynia

c. Diagnosis

Coxsackie group B viruses have been repeatedly implicated as causative agents, and diagnosis may be aided by the demonstration of a rise in titer of type-specific neutralizing antibodies in serum specimens taken early and late in the illness (5).

Pneumonia, Primary Atypical (Virus Pneumonia, Acute Pneumonitis)

c. Diagnosis

The presence of cold hemagglutinins for blood group O erythrocytes or of agglutinins for streptococcus MG aids in the diagnosis of primary atypical pneumonia, especially if there is a significant increase in either antibody some weeks after onset.

Cold hemagglutinins develop in the sera of about 50 per cent of the patients, and titers of 1:64 or more, or fourfold increases in titer, or more, strongly support a diagnosis of primary atypical pneumonia (63,136).

The test is not specific, for elevated cold agglutinin titers have been found in trypanosomiasis, liver disease, hemolytic anemias, and certain blood dyscrasias (136).

Agglutinins for streptococcus MG develop in about 30 per cent of patients. They are not identical with the cold agglutinins, and it is possible for the streptococcal agglutinins to increase without corresponding increase of the cold agglutinins. Both antibodies usually appear between the seventh and twentieth days of the disease. In about 20 per cent of the cases, the titer for streptococcal MG agglutinins does not rise until one or two weeks after the titer of the cold agglutinins has gone up (136). The rise in titer of both antibodies and the extent of the rise are related to the severity of the illness.

Test for these agglutinins during convalescence confirms diagnosis in one-half to two-thirds of cases (5).

Since there is no specific diagnostic test for atypical pneumonia, it is important to exclude other similar diseases produced by known agents by testing for them by the specific serological tests which are available. For example, it would be well to exclude psittacosis and "Q" fever by complement-fixation tests (p. 648).

Poliomyelitis

a. Prophylaxis

Active Prophylaxis. In spite of the fact that paralytic poliomyelitis is a rare disease, the tragic spectacle of those who are crippled by it has caused an enormous amount of effort to be put into the problem of prophylaxis.

Two vaccines are available for poliomyelitis, the formalin-inactivated Salk vaccine, and the attenuated live virus of Sabin. Both are licensed by the Division of Biologic Standards of the U. S. Public Health Service, and both have been shown to be effective. On the whole the attenuated virus has advantages in ease of administration (oral), antigenic effect, protective capacity, and potential for the eradication of poliomyelitis from the community (4). The Sabin vaccine has been given extensive trials in the Soviet Union (23).

According to Salk, the third dose of the formaldehyde-inactivated vaccine produces a "hyper-reactive" state (leading to more rapid response to further immunization) lasting more than two years. A fourth dose is thought to establish long-lasting immunity in most persons. It is probable, but not yet certain, that the oral vaccine confers a life-long immunity (100).

Passive Prophylaxis. Gamma globulin has received rather extensive trial as a preventive of poliomyelitis, but there has been dispute over its effectiveness (54,116,117,5).

b. Test for Immunity

Neutralizing antibodies for any or all of the three strains of poliomyelitis virus can be tested for in serum specimens taken from the individuals in question. Unfortunately it is not known how high a level of antibody is necessary for immunity in man, or even if antibodies are the sole or the chief mechanism of resistance in this disease; Salk (121) assumed they are. The only available evidence is the accumulated data on the relationship between antibody levels and resistance in monkeys. Salk (121) reported that of 92 unvaccinated monkeys 81 per cent were infected by intravenous injection of virus, whereas of 106 vaccinated monkeys with an antibody titer of less than 1:4, 68 per cent became infected, and of 92 vaccinated monkeys with an antibody titer of 1:4 or greater none were infected.

Psittacosis

c. Diagnosis

At the present time the complement-fixation test is the only quick and simple means available of making an early diagnosis of psittacosis (88,89). Complement-fixing antibodies may appear in the serum of untreated patients from 4 to 5 days after the onset of symptoms, but under vigorous chemotherapy the appearance of such antibodies may be delayed for 20 to 30 days. A single complement-fixing titer of 1:64 or above is suggestive that the patient is or has been infected with a member of the psittacosis-lymphogranuloma group of viruses, but is not diagnostic in itself (89). Additional serum specimens should be examined; if the titer rises within the next 4 or 5 days, a tentative diagnosis of psittacosis may be given.

The possibility of cross reactions of viruses of the psittacosis-lymphogranuloma venereum group should be kept in mind in interpreting the results of complement-fixation tests (89).

Skin tests in psittacosis have not yet been successful for diagnosis (89).

Q Fever

a. Prophylaxis

Vaccine has been prepared for active immunization but is not generally available. It is used only for laboratory workers who have a high risk of infection (4).

c. Diagnosis

Serological diagnosis of Q fever is highly satisfactory. Either the agglutination or the complement-fixation technic will provide, under proper conditions, a technic which involves very few false positives or false negatives (126). It is practically essential to test both early and late samples of serum to detect the appearance of antibodies, or an increase in their titer, during convalescence.

Agglutinins seldom appear before the ninth day of illness, and even by the end of the second week only about 25 per cent of patients show positive tests; by the end of the fourth week 90 per cent show agglutinins. Complement-fixing antibodies are nearly always detectable between the seventh and thirteenth day, reaching a maximum titer of the order of 1:160 about the twenty-first day. The reactions are highly specific (126).

Rabies

a. Prophylaxis

Active Immunization. Owing to the long incubation period of rabies, active immunization can be started after exposure. Only a few laboratories outside of France and the French colonies continue the original Pasteur technic of preparation of vaccine from the desiccated spinal cords of infected rabbits. Rabbits brain is a much better source of the virus, and the Semple vaccine, which has been much used in the United States, is a saline suspension of rabbit brain containing 0.25 per cent phenol. The usual treatment consists of the subcutaneous injection of 14 daily doses into the subcutaneous tissue of the abdominal wall. A different site should be used for each injection.

A preparation of virus inactivated by ultraviolet radiation is also available. It is packaged in seven doses of 2 ml. of 5 per cent or 1 ml. of 10 per cent rabbit brain suspension in saline, containing "merthiolate" as a preservative.

Fox (47) employed the HEP Flury strain of live rabies virus for the immunization of human beings, in a clinical trial involving 90 patients. Some of the patients received amounts of the virus equivalent to 12 dog doses, or 20 ml. of 40 per cent suspension. No untoward reactions were observed, and Koprowski (74) considered that the safety of this immunization procedure is beyond any doubt. See (100).

The use of this vaccine has the advantage that it would probably eliminate the risk of postvaccinal sequelae, but it might cause untoward reactions in individuals sensitive to hen's eggs.

There has been considerable controversy over the efficacy of antirabies inoculation. According to Johnson (70) the clinical evidence indicates beyond doubt that rabies vaccine is effective in preventing the disease in the majority of instances in which there is an expected incubation period of more than one month. Vaccine treatment should not be given unless there is good evidence of exposure to rabies, but should be started, according to Johnson (70), immediately when (*1*) the biting animal is caught and shows clinical evidence of rabies, (*2*) the animal is killed and the brain is found positive on microscopic examination, (*3*) the animal is killed, and the microscopic examination is negative, but nevertheless there is good reason to suspect the animal was rabid, (*4*) the animal escapes or cannot be identified.

The post-exposure "prophylatic" dosage of rabies vaccine depends on the circumstances. For mild or moderate exposures 14 daily doses of avian or brain tissue should be given. In severe exposures antirabies serum (Lederle) may also be used. In general the procedure is governed by the symptoms of the animal responsible for the bite. If it shows signs of rabies when captured, vaccine is started in the person attacked. If the animal is normal, vaccine is deferred until the first symptoms of rabies develop in the animal. In the case of severe exposures from an apparently healthy animal, serum is given, but vaccine is begun only if the animal develops rabies. In the case of bites from animals that escape, or bites by wolves, jackals, foxes, bats, etc., vaccine is started immediately.

Severe reactions resulting from sensitization to rabbit brain have sometimes followed immunization (144). Acute reactions, including syncope, generalized urticaria or angioneurotic edema, may occur soon after injection of later doses, and encephalitis and paralysis may occur. Acute encephalitis caused by the vaccine is characterized by high fever, delirium convulsions, and coma, and may terminate fatally. For some of the possible consequences of sensitization to brain material, see Chapter 13.

The incidence of posttreatment encephalitic changes is hard to estimate exactly. Reports have ranged from 1 case in 600 to 1 case in 7000 treated persons (136). Considering that the chances of actual rabies following a known dog bite may be of the order of 1 in 1400 to 1 in 2100, it is apparent that rabies vaccine should not be used indiscriminately.

Other Measures. The availability of effective antirabies vaccines for dogs is one of the most important elements in the structure of rabies prevention. Vaccines made of infected brain tissue and the attenuated Flury strain of virus are available, and the evidence seems quite conclusive that such measures are very effective (70).

Rickettsialpox

c. Diagnosis

Specific diagnosis can be made by complement-fixation tests. The test becomes positive between the second and third week of the disease (5). Two samples, one taken during the acute stage of the disease and one during convalescence, should be examined (4). Patients with rickettsialpox show no agglutinins (26) or quite low titers (5) for *Proteus* organisms (Weil-Felix reaction).

Rift Valley Fever

Naturally acquired Rift Valley fever has been reported only from Africa. It is caused by a specific virus.

c. Diagnosis

During convalescence the diagnosis can be made by the demonstration of specific virus-neutralizing antibodies. Serum from the patient is mixed with an equal amount of a virus preparation known to be lethal for mice, and 0.2 ml. of the mixture is injected intraperitoneally into mice. Control mice are inoculated with a mixture of normal serum and virus. Survival of the mice receiving the mixture with the patient's serum, and death within 2 or 3 days of the controls, indicate that the patient's serum contains protective antibodies. Such neutralizing antibodies have been detected as early as 4 days after onset and as long as twelve years after recovery (135).

Rocky Mountain Spotted Fever

a. Prophylaxis

Vaccination reduces the chance of becoming infected, lessens the severity of the attack if infection occurs, and lowers the fatality rate. The protection lasts one or two years. Yearly vaccination is, however, recommended for persons who expect to enter areas infested with infected ticks (136).

c. Diagnosis

The Weil-Felix reaction generally becomes positive in Rocky Mountain Spotted Fever, and aids in the diagnosis of a disease of the rickettsial group. It does not distinguish spotted fever from typhus. It is desirable to perform the test on two blood samples, one taken as soon as spotted fever is suspected, the other about 12 to 15 days after the onset. Generally the titers against OX are highest, but in some cases those for OX 2 are highest. The agglutinins for *Proteus* generally appear toward the end of the second week of illness, but sometimes only in early convalescence. Some patients do not produce them.

Protective virus-neutralizing antibodies are apparently of diagnostic value (130). See description of the technic in Snyder (130).

The *complement-fixation reaction* has the advantage over the Weil-Felix reaction of being highly specific. It will differentiate spotted fever from epidemic typhus, murine typhus, Q fever, scrub typhus, and boutonneuse fever. References to the technic are given by Snyder (130).

d. Treatment

Hyperimmune serum from rabbits has been used in treatment with some success, especially if it is administered before the third day of rash (130). It may be doubted if it is needed, however, as antibiotics are quite effective.

Rubella (German Measles)

a. Prophylaxis

Passive Prophylaxis. Gamma globulin has been used empirically to prevent German measles in women exposed during the first trimester of pregnancy. It is doubtful if this procedure is of much value. Gamma globulin made from immune serum, given in a dose of 0.1 ml. per pound of body weight, has been used, and may be of value.

Sandfly Fever (See Phlebotomus Fever)

Serum Hepatitis (See Infectious Hepatitis)

Smallpox (See Variola)

Typhus (Epidemic Louse-Borne)

a. Prophylaxis

Active immunization with the Cox-type vaccine (prepared from the yolk sac of infected developing chick embryos) has been found to reduce the mortality from typhus practically to zero (130,131). Vaccination probably also lowers the incidence of the disease in exposed persons, but this has not been established. The course of the disease in immunized persons is milder and shorter than in nonimmunized persons, and the incidence of serious complications is sharply reduced.

The vaccine is administered in two doses not less than one week apart. Further doses should be given every four months in areas where danger of infection persists (5).

Children should receive three subcutaneous injections at intervals of one to three weeks, with doses varying according to age as follows, according to the U. S. Armed Services recommendations for dependents of military personnel (Table 15-7):

TABLE 15-7

Age 6 mo.–2 yrs.	3–6 yrs.	7–10 yrs.	11 yrs. and over
0.12 ml.	0.25 ml.	0.5 ml.	Adult schedule

c. Diagnosis

As indicated in Chapter 14, various antibodies appear in the blood of patients suffering from typhus. Agglutinins for *Proteus* OX 19 appear in the sera of most patients between the fifth and eighth days of illness. In a large percentage of cases the titer rises to 1:160 or higher, even exceeding 1:1000 at the peak of the response during the third week of illness or the first two weeks of convalescence. An infection with *Proteus vulgaris* also causes a rise in titer of agglutinins to *Proteus* OX 19. As in other diseases, a rising titer is more important for diagnosis than a considerable but stationary titer.

Complement-Fixing Antibodies. These may be detected in the sera of patients as early as the seventh or eighth day of illness. They reach a maximum titer between the twelfth and sixteenth days after onset. Low titers may persist for years. It may be very difficult, perhaps impossible, to differentiate epidemic typhus from murine typhus by complement fixation in the case of persons who have been immunized (130).

Specific Agglutinins for rickettsiae appear in the sera of typhus patients about the same time as do complement-fixing antibodies (130). Castaneda (20a) developed a rapid slide test for use at the bedside.

Opsonins, precipitins, and neutralizing antibodies also appear, and are valuable diagnostic aids, but the tests can be carried out only in laboratories in which extensive work with rickettsial diseases is being done (130).

Typhus, Flea-Borne (Murine Typhus)

a. Prophylaxis

Vaccines of killed rickettsiae are available for murine typhus and give good protection, but the efficacy of specific therapy leads to the recommendation of immunization only of persons exposed to unusual risk, such as laboratory workers and rat control operators (130,131,5).

Varicella (See Chickenpox)

Variola (Smallpox)

Smallpox is an ancient disease, caused by the variola virus and characterized by chills, prostration, headache, severe backache, vomiting, and fever, followed by a papular eruption which becomes vesicular and then pustular. Smallpox is generally classified into variola minor (mild) and variola major (severe). The mortality in variola major may run to 40 to 50 per cent.

a. Prophylaxis

Vaccination to smallpox is the oldest form of artificial immunization, and still one of the most successful. It is carried out by introducing into the skin living vaccinia virus which has been grown on the skin of a calf. Vaccination was introduced by Jenner in 1798; the virus used by Jenner was one which caused a disease of cattle called cowpox, and the virus used today was long supposed to be the lineal descendant of Jenner's original cowpox virus. It has been shown, however (16), that the three viruses, smallpox, vaccinia, cowpox, are distinguishable when grown on the membranes of the chick embryo, although any one of them will produce immunity, of a sort, to any of the others. According to Burnet·(16), vaccinia virus is considerably more like smallpox than it is like cowpox virus, and is probably a modified smallpox virus that has lost its power to spread through the body.

Dried smallpox vaccine has important advantages over the relatively unstable lymph, especially in tropical countries and for reserves for use in emergencies (100).

Children should be vaccinated during the first year of life, for undesirable complications are less likely to follow at that time. This should be followed by revaccination when the child is ready to start to school (56,136).

Infants with eczema or other forms of severe dermatitis should not be vaccinated against smallpox because of the danger of producing generalized vaccinia, which has a high fatality rate (4). Siblings of infants with severe eczema or severe dermatitis should either not be vaccinated, or if vaccinated, should be separated from the affected child for a 10-day period. This separation must actually be in different households.

Revaccination is recommended every five years, before going abroad, and in the presence of an epidemic of smallpox (4). In parts of the world where smallpox is epidemic, yearly vaccinations are required to give solid protection (4). The U. S. Military Services require yearly revaccination of all personnel stationed overseas and revaccination at intervals of three years of those stationed on the North American Continent.

Vaccination failures in very young infants have been shown to be due to placentally transmitted maternal antibodies. Vaccination should be repeated at the age of eight to ten months (4). Repeated failures in attempts at primary vaccination should lead to the employment of a fresh lot of vaccine. Repeated failures in revaccination may possibly be due to local hypersensitivity, and attempts should be made at another site, such as the opposite arm, away from the previous scar. When protection is imperative, revaccination on the flexor surface of the forearm will result in a vaccinoid reaction in nearly everyone (4).

The failure to get a "take" is not proof that the the individual is immune. It simply indicates an unsuccessful effort (4). The vaccination should in such cases always be repeated.

There is little doubt that smallpox vaccination, if a "take" is obtained, produces good immunity to smallpox, and it is hardly necessary to discuss the matter in great detail. As an example of the available evidence we may consider the results obtained in an epidemic of (mild) smallpox in Fitchburg, Massachusetts, in 1932. See Table 15-8.

TABLE 15-8

Incidence of Smallpox in Relation to Previous Vaccination Experience. Fitchburg, Mass. (40)

Vaccination status	No. of persons	No. of cases of smallpox	Case rate per 100,000 population
Unvaccinated	5,457	57	1,048
Vaccinated over 40 years previous	4,926	3	60
Vaccinated during past 40 years	29,558	None	None

TABLE 15-9

Relation of Smallpox Morbidity to Vaccination Laws in the United States, 1919–1928
(147)

Vaccination laws	Cases per 100,000 population
Compulsory vaccination	6.6
Local option	51.3
No vaccination laws	66.7
Compulsory vaccination prohibited	115.2

In the United States some states require vaccination against smallpox as a prerequisite to school attendance, some allow the local community to decide this question, some have no regulations on the subject, and four states (Arizona, Minnesota, North Dakota, and Utah), under the influence of the "antivaccinationists," have laws forbidding compulsory vaccination. A study of the increase of smallpox in these various communities powerfully supports the belief that vaccination is effective. (See Table 15-9.

There are a number of possible reactions to an attempt at vaccination, ranging from a typical "take" to no reaction at all. The interpretation of these is very important in estimating the degree of immunity probably possessed by the individual or probably conferred. See (136).

Complications following vaccination have occasionally been observed (33). One of these is eczema vaccinatum, which may occur in eczematous children. It is very rare, 36 cases with 2 deaths being observed in conjunction with the mass vaccination of 6,000,000 people in New York City in 1947. Another complication, postvaccinal encephalitis, is also very rare; 2 cases were reported in Paris among over 1,000,000 vaccinations. In view of the seriousness of the malignant forms of smallpox, it is clear that taking the risk of these extremely rare complications is amply justified.

b. Test for Immunity

The standard test for immunity in smallpox is revaccination. This has the advantage that if the individual is not immune, he will develop a primary take reaction and become immune; if he is partially immune he will develop the accelerated or vaccinoid reaction and become fully immune; and if he is fully immune he will develop the immediate reaction and suffer virtually no inconvenience.

The immediate reaction following vaccination is an allergic response to vaccinal materials, and it has been shown that it can be obtained with inactive virus as well as with infectious material (62,126). It apparently indicates immunity (62). This would make it possible, if it were considered desirable, to test for immunity without at the same time exposing the individual to the chance of developing vaccina.

It must be kept in mind that inactive virus, although it may be used to test for immunity, is of no use in conferring immunity upon susceptible persons.

c. Diagnosis

Although diagnosis of smallpox on clinical evidence alone is generally possible (4), sporadic cases and the mild alastrim type are sometimes missed (126,136). Certain immunological procedures may therefore be of assistance.

Flocculation Test. A suspension of ground-up material from the lesions is mixed and incubated with a rabbit antivaccinia serum. In a positive reaction a fine flocculant precipitate is produced (27). By this method a rapid diagnosis of smallpox can be made in doubtful cases (136).

Hemagglutination Inhibition Test. This is a test for antibodies in the patient's serum which inhibit the hemagglutinating action of vaccinia virus on red cells. It becomes positive after the fourth or fifth day of the disease. The results can be available in 2 hours (4). This test may be especially useful in differentiating variola from varicella (126).

Complement Fixation. Immune rabbit serum may be employed to detect variola antigens in the patient's serum, scrapings of macules or papules, vesicle fluid, pustule fluid, tops of vesicles, pustules, scabs, crusts, and seeds (78). Or a variola antigen from man or a vaccinia antigen from rabbits may be used to detect antibodies in the patient's serum (if the patient has not been vaccinated for six to nine months), or to detect a rising titer (in patients vaccinated less than six months previously). The former method is evidently more common. Descriptions of the technics are given by MacCallum (78).

The complement-fixation test will not distinguish variola, vaccinia, and cowpox, but will distinguish these from varicella (chickenpox), herpes, etc. (78). The results can be available in 24 hours.

Yellow Fever

a. Prophylaxis

Vaccination against yellow fever is mandatory for travel to or through many parts of the world, and is strongly recommended for travel to or through a number of other areas.   Details may be found in the booklet published by the United States Public Health Service (USPHS).   Yellow fever vaccine cannot be obtained from the usual commercial sources, and individuals requiring this vaccine must go *in person* to one of the several Public Health Service stations located throughout the country or to a military hospital or dispensary which has the vaccine.

The dosage schedule recommended by the U. S. Armed Services for immunization of dependents of military personnel is the same for all age groups; *viz.,* a single subcutaneous injection of 0.5 ml. of a 1:10 dilution of concentrated yellow fever vaccine may be required every six years.

The yellow fever vaccine used in this country is a suspension of pulped chicken embryos which were infected with the attenuated 17D strain of virus developed by Theiler.   The French employ a dried mouse brain which has been infected with the French neurotropic strain of yellow fever virus.   This is suspended in a gum arabic solution and applied to the scarified skin.

This is good evidence that vaccination against yellow fever is one of our most successful immunization procedures.   The most conclusive evidence is perhaps that furnished by laboratory workers with the virus (135).   Before the development of the vaccine, laboratory infections were extremely common, and in several instances were fatal.   Since the introduction of the vaccine, no accidental infections of laboratory workers have occurred.   Also convincing is the experience of workers who have investigated jungle yellow fever using themselves as mosquito bait.   In spite of the fact that on numerous occasions such workers were able to isolate the yellow fever virus from the mosquitoes (*Haemagogus*) which they caught in this way, none of them contracted yellow fever.

c. Diagnosis

When facilities for isolation of the virus by animal inoculation are not available, as is often the case, a diagnosis can often be established by the examination of two specimens of serum for protective antibodies for mice (135).   The first specimen of blood is taken as early as possible in the disease, and the second during convalescence.   If there are no protective antibodies in the first specimen, where specific antibodies are present in the second, the patient was infected with yellow fever.   Antibodies are rapidly produced during the infection, however, and it may happen that the first specimen also protects.   In this case a diagnosis may often be made by titrating the two specimens for protective antibodies.   If the second has a higher titer than the first, this is good evidence that the disease was yellow fever, but if the two titers are the same, the disease is probably not yellow fever, and the antibodies are a consequence of a past infection (135).

D. PARASITIC INFECTIONS

Ascariasis

c. Diagnosis

Skin Test. This consists in placing a few drops of the body fluid of *Ascaris lumbricoides* on a scarified area of the skin. In sensitive individuals there is a reaction of the immediate type. The symptoms can be rather alarming, including extensive lymphatic and systemic involvement. The more alarming symptoms disappear in the course of an hour or so, but generalized edema may persist for several days (39).

A positive reaction does not necessarily mean active infection, for sensitivity to *Ascaris,* once acquired, persists long after the end of the infection, and may be acquired by laboratory workers merely by contact with fresh or even preserved worms.

Complement Fixation. This may be carried out with an antigen consisting of a saline extract of macerated worms. A positive reaction is of little practical interest in diagnosis, except in infections with male worms only (39).

Cysticercosis (See Taeniasis)

Echinococcosis

c. Diagnosis

Skin Test. This may be performed with antigens prepared in a number of ways. According to Faust (39), the most potent antigen is that prepared by Dennis' technic (39). The test consists in injecting 0.2 ml. of a 1:10,000 solution of the antigen intracutaneously. An injection of saline is used as a control. The reaction is of the immediate type. The test is particularly useful preoperatively (39). After removal of the cyst the reaction remains positive for many months.

Complement Fixation. The antigen consists of hydatid fluid from human cases or domestic animals. The antigen must not be contaminated (39). The Dennis antigen can be used in a concentration of 1 : 5000. Apparently the test is quite specific (39).

Filariasis

c. Diagnosis

Skin tests and complement-fixation tests are described by Faust (39), but according to the American Public Health Association (5) the skin test is nonspecific and experimental.

Schistosomiasis

S. mansoni occurs in the West Indies, northeastern and eastern South America, the Arabian peninsula, and Africa. *S. hematobium* occurs in Africa and parts of the Middle East. *S. japonicum* occurs in Japan, China, Formosa, the Philippines, and Celebes. The measures discussed below apply to infections with any of the three species.

c. Diagnosis

Skin Test. This is a schistosome group reaction. Preparation of the antigen is described by Katzin and Most (71) and Faust (39). Some workers have reported that the skin test provides a higher degree of accuracy in diagnosis than does routine microscopic examination of stools. Katzin and Most (71) suggested that the test may be valuable in evaluating the success of therapy, as it becomes negative, in 60 to 80 per cent of patients, three to six months after completion of therapy.

Complement Fixation. With an antigen prepared from the livers of infected snails (preparation described in Faust (39), positive complement-fixation tests are obtained with the serum of infected individuals, with apparently no false positives (39).

Strongyloidiasis

c. Diagnosis

Skin Test. The application of powdered *Strongyloides* to a scarified area of the skin produces an immediate urticarial wheal in animals infected, even lightly, with this worm. The technic is described by Faust (39).

Precipitin Test. This has been used as a check on the intracutaneous test (39).

Taeniasis and Cysticercosis

Infection with the adult tapeworm (taeniasis) is a benign intestinal infection; infection with the larvae (cysticercosis) is a severe somatic disease of many different tissues (5).

c. Diagnosis

In testing for *cysticercus cellulosae* (the larval form of the pork tape-worm, *Taenia solium*), there has been employed:

Skin Test. Antigen may be obtained from the fluid of various species of cysticerci in domestic animals (39).

Precipitin Test. The test is made as in testing for hydatid infection. Antigen may be obtained from cysticerci from human cases or more simply from the bladder worms of *Taenia* in hogs, rabbits, and other intermediate hosts (39).

Tapeworm (See Taeniasis)

Toxoplasmosis

c. Diagnosis

The preferred serological test is the dye test of Sabin and Feldman (118,41,120) for thermostable cytoplasm-modifying antibody. This test depends upon the discovery that the cytoplasm of *Toxoplasma*, acted on by a specific antibody and a complement-like accessory factor, loses its affinity for methylene blue at pH 11. The specific antibody resists heating at 56°C. for 30 minutes (120). Titers of over 1:16 are considered significant (4). Complement-fixation tests are also used. When acquired toxoplasmosis is suspected, two blood specimens should be taken at intervals to check on a rising titer. When congenital toxoplasmosis is suspected, specimens from both mother and infant should be tested.

Dye test antibodies appear early and probably persist for life, whereas complement-fixing antibodies develop more slowly and tend to disappear. Thus early in active infections, and for some months, the dye test may be strongly positive and the complement-fixation test negative.

Trichinosis

c. Diagnosis

Skin Test. The intracutaneous test is particularly useful in mild cases which manifest only vague symptoms (39). The antigen is prepared by the technic of Bachman, as used by Sawitz, and is described by Faust (39).

The stock antigen is diluted 1:50 to secure a 1:5000 dilution, and the dilution is kept on ice until used. In the test 0.1 ml. is injected intra-cutaneously on one forearm and an equal amount of the solution lacking the antigen, on the other forearm. In case of infection, even subclinical, an immediate reaction appears, reaching its maximum in about 10 minutes and beginning to fade in about 15 to 20 minutes. Although false positives are not common, it is desirable to supplement the skin test with a precipitin test.

Precipitin Test. The procedure of Roth (39) employs about 100 sterile living *T. spiralis,* obtained by digestion of muscle of infected laboratory animals. The larvae are placed in a sterile, hollow-ground slide in 0.5 ml. of the patient's serum; the preparation is covered by a cover glass and incubated at 37°C. for 24 hours. In a positive test bubbles and granules of precipitate appear around the mouths of the larvae. This test becomes positive 10 to 20 days after symptoms first appear. It is claimed to be more sensitive and accurate than other serological tests for trichina infection.

Complement Fixation. This has been employed in trichinosis, but according to Faust (39), it is not so satisfactory as the intracutaneous and precipitin tests.

According to the American Public Health Association (5), the immunological tests may aid in diagnosis but are in themselves conclusive.

E. IMMUNIZATION REQUIRED FOR FOREIGN TRAVEL

Certain diseases which have either been eradicated or made very rare in the United States are still common in many parts of the world, and American citizens who desire to travel abroad would do well to protect themselves by immunization, when this is available, against the possibility of infection. This applies not only to diseases such as smallpox, yellow fever, and cholera, but to "childhood" diseases such as diphtheria, since it is not uncommon for adult Americans to contract these diseases abroad.

In addition to personal protection, the American who plans to travel must be aware that many countries require, or many require in case an outbreak of some disease threatens, evidence of vaccination against one or more diseases. Travelers whose certificates of vaccination are not in order may be subjected to surveillance or even to isolation for a period up to 14 days.

Finally, a certificate of vaccination against smallpox within three years is required *for re-entry* into the United States, and of course for the entry of foreign nationals, except in the case of persons arriving from certain areas (see below).

Immunization requirements of the various countries of course change from time to time. State and local health departments are kept informed of changes in the immunization requirements, and should be consulted when any doubt arises in a specific case. Physicians who do immunizations and others interested in this question will find it convenient to have sent them the little booklet *Immunization Information for International Travel*, published by the U. S. Department of Health, Education, and Welfare, U. S. Public Health Service. Copies of this booklet may be purchased from the Superintendent of Documents, Government Printing Office, Washington 25, D. C., at cost of thirty-five cents each.

Documents. The International Certificates of Vaccination ("yellow card") form is the only one accepted for foreign travel. The old International Certificate of Inoculation and Vaccination form remains valid, however, until the vaccinations recorded on it have expired. In some cases this is longer than indicated on the old form; for instance, the yellow fever vaccination is valid for six years although the form states only four years.

In the United States, each traveler receives the International Certificates of Vaccination form along with his passport application, from the clerk of the court in his district or from passport agencies of the Department of State in Boston, Chicago, New Orleans, San Francisco, and Washington, D. C. The form may also be obtained from travel agencies, ticket offices, local and state health departments, and offices of the United States Public Health Service. The certificate may be purchased from the Superintendent of Documents, U. S. Government Printing Office, Washington, D. C., at five cents a copy.

The information for each vaccination certificate required for the trip must be completed and signed by the doctor making the vaccination. Smallpox and cholera certificates must then be authenticated by a stamp approved by the health administration of the country in which the vaccination is performed. In the United States, the approval stamp as called for in the international certificate form may be any one of the following:

1. The stamp or seal of state or local health departments of the area in which the vaccinating physician practices.

2. The stamp of yellow fever vaccination designated by the Public Health Service.

3. The stamp of the Department of Defense.

4. The impression seal of the Public Health Service or a stamp authorized by the USPHS.

Whenever the yellow fever vaccination certificate is required it must be one issued by a yellow fever vaccination center designated by the national government to give this vaccination. A list of such centers, with addresses and clinic hours, in the United States will be found in the

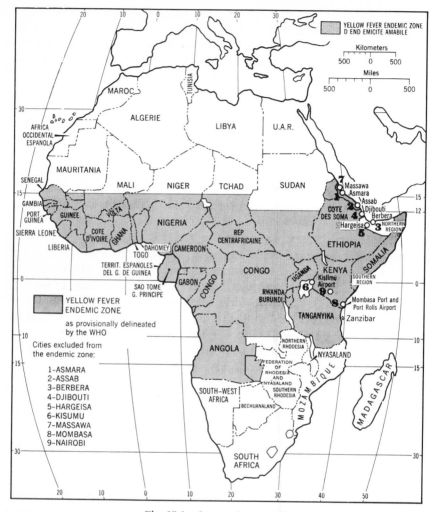

Fig. 15-1. See caption, p. 665.

booklet *Immunization Information for International Travel* already referred to.

Military personnel and their dependents, traveling under the authority or sponsorship of the Armed Forces or as members of the crew of vessels and aircraft to foreign countries beyond North America must have, in addition to the military immunization record, an International Certificate of Vaccination form completed by a medical officer.   Military per-

Fig. 15-1. Areas of the world where yellow fever was endemic in 1953.

sonnel on active duty will be issued the Department of Defense immunization certificate, DD Form 737.

Details of immunization required by the various foreign countries will be found in the booklet published by the U.S. Department of Health. We may summarize the more important points here:

1. Smallpox. A certificate of vaccination against smallpox within three years is required *for re-entry* into the United States, except from Canada and a few near-by places. This certificate *must* be in the form of the International Certificates of Vaccination ("yellow card").

Evidence of vaccination within three years of arrival is required by most foreign countries. The countries of western Europe do not normally require vaccination but do so occasionally when there is an outbreak.

The smallpox vaccination certificate is valid for a period of three years, beginning 8 days after the date of a successful primary vaccination, or on the date of revaccination.

2. Typhoid and paratyphoid. Vaccination is not required legally for foreign travel or for re-entry into the United States, but is practically essential for personal protection. Inoculation with triple typhoid vaccine (TAB) is advised for international travelers. The risk is minimal in the U. S. A., Canada, Great Britain, and Northwest Europe.

3. Tetanus. This also is not a legal requirement, but is strongly recommended for personal protection. See page 630.

4. Diphtheria. Immunization or a recall injection is strongly recommended for travelers in continental Europe as well as other foreign countries where, as is usual, the prevalence of diphtheria considerably exceeds its prevalence in this country. See page 615.

5. Plague. Vaccination to plague is not required by any country, but some authorities recommend it for those traveling to endemic areas such as certain parts of India, Burma, Java, China, Madagascar, and South, Central, and East Africa. See page 625.

6. Epidemic typhus. Vaccination against typhus is not required by any country, but is recommended for travelers to many areas of the world. Details will be found in the booklet *Immunization Information for International Travel,* or by consulting local or state health departments, or any office of the U. S. Public Health Service.

7. Cholera. Vaccination against cholera is *mandatory* for travel to or through many areas of the world, and is strongly recommended for travelers to or through a number of other areas. Details will be found in the booklet *Immunization Information for International Travel,* or by consulting local or state health departments, or any office of the U. S. Public Health Service.

The cholera vaccination certificate is valid for a period of six months, beginning 6 days after the first injection of the vaccine, or date of a revaccination within such period of six months.

8. Yellow fever. Travelers who, within 6 days of their arrival, have come from or passed through an area which is considered infected with yellow fever are required to present a valid certificate of vaccination against yellow fever. Areas of the world where yellow fever was considered endemic in 1953 are shown in Fig. 15-1.

Yellow fever vaccination is strongly recommended for travelers to or through a number of other areas. Details may be obtained by consulting the booklet *Immunization Information for International Travel*, local or state health departments, or any office of the U. S. Public Health Service. For procedure of obtaining this immunization, see p. 358.

9. Poliomyelitis. This vaccination is recommended for all international travel.

References

1. Adiseshan, R., C. G. Pandit, and K. V. Venkatraman, *Ind. J. Med. Res.*, **35**, 131 (1947).
2. Alexander, H. E., in *Bacterial and Mycotic Infections of Man*, R. J. Dubos and J. G. Hirsch, eds., Lippincott, Philadelphia, 1965.
3. Do Amaral, A., *Bull. Antivenin Inst. Am.*, **1**, 61 (1927).
4. American Academy of Pediatrics, Report of the Committee of the Control of Infectious Diseases, 1964.
5. American Public Health Association, *Control of Communicable Diseases in Man*, New York, 1965.
6. Anderson, G. W., and W. I. Reinhardt, *J. Infect. Diseases*, **57**, 136 (1935).
7. Avery, O. T., and H. J. Morgan, *J. Exptl. Med.*, **42**, 347 (1925).
8. Avery, O. T., and J. M. Neill, *J. Exptl. Med.*, **42**, 355 (1925).
9. Bedson, S. P., *Brit. J. Exptl. Pathol.*, **19**, 353 (1938).
10. Beeson, P. B., in *Textbook of Medicine*, R. L. Cecil and R. F. Loeb, eds., Saunders, Philadelphia, 1955.
11. Berberian, D. A., *Trans. Roy. Soc. Trop. Med. Hyg.*, **33**, 87 (1939).
12. Bernkopf, H., and I. J. Kligler, *J. Immunol.*, **32**, 451 (1937).
13. Bousfield, G., *Practical Guide to the Schick Test*, Churchill, London, 1929.
14. Bradford, W. L., in *Bacterial and Mycotic Infections of Man*, R. J. Dubos, ed., Lippincott, Philadelphia, 1952.
15. Bunch, C. P., *et al.*, *J. Immunol.*, **39**, 427 (1940).
16. Burnet, F. M., *Viruses and Man*, Penguin Books, Melbourne, 1953.
17. Callender, G. R., and G. F. Luippold, *J. Am. Med. Assoc.*, **123**, 319 (1943).
18. Calmette, A., *L'Infection Bacillaire et la Tuberculose*, 3rd ed., Masson, Paris, 1928.
19. Cameron, G. C. W., and J. Gibbard, *J. Immunol.*, **40**, 47 (1941).
20. Casals, J., and L. V. Brown, *Proc. Soc. Exptl. Biol. Med.*, **83**, 170 (1953).
20a. Castaneda, M. R., *J. Immunol.*, **50**, 179 (1945).
21. Cecil, R. L., and H. F. Vaughan, *J. Exptl. Med.*, **29**, 457 (1919).
22. Cheever, F. S., in *A Textbook of Medicine*, R. L. Cecil and R. F. Loeb, eds., Saunders, Philadelphia, 1955.
23. Chumakov, M. P., *K itogam izucheniya i massovogo primeneniya v 1959g. zhivo oslablennoi vaktsiny protivpoliomielita*, Vestn. Akad. Med. Nauk. USSR, **15**, 30–45 (1960) (Russian).
24. Cohn, E. J., *et al.*, *J. Clin. Invest.*, **33**, 417 (1944).

25. Cole, R., and A. G. Kuttner, *J. Exptl. Med.*, **44**, 855 (1926).
26. Cox, H. R., in *Viral and Rickettsial Infections in Man*, T. M. Rivers, ed., Lippincott, Philadelphia, 1952.
27. Craigie, J., and W. J. Tulloch, *Med. Res. Council (Brit.) Spec. Rept. Ser.*, No. **156** (1931).
28. Dahlstrom and Difs, cited in *Bacterial and Mycotic Infections of Man*, R. J. Dubos, ed., Lippincott, Philadelphia, 1951.
28a. Dalrymple-Champneys, W., *Brucella Infection and Undulant Fever in Man*, Oxford University Press, London, 1960.
29. Dick, G. F., and G. H. Dick, *Scarlet Fever*, Year Book, Chicago, 1938.
30. Dubos, R. J., *The Bacterial Cell in Its Relation to Problems of Virulence, Immunity and Chemotherapy*, Harvard University Press, Cambridge, 1945.
31. Dubos, R. J., personal communication, 1946.
32. Eagle, H., in *Bacterial and Mycotic Infections of Man*, R. J. Dubos, ed., Lippincott, Philadelphia, 1952.
33. Edsall, G., *New Engl. J. Med.*, **241**, 18, 60, 99 (1949).
34. Edsall, G., *Am. J. Public Health*, **42**, 393 (1952).
34a. Edsall, G., *J. Am. Med. Assoc.*, **171**, 417 (1959).
35. Elberg, S., in *Bacterial and Mycotic Infections of Man*, R. J. Dubos and J. G. Hirsch, eds., Lippincott, Philadelphia 1965.
36. Enders, J. F., in *Viral and Rickettsial Infections of Man*, F. L. Horsfall and I. Tamm, eds., Lippincott, Philadelphia, 1965.
37. Enders, J. F., *et al.*, *J. Exptl. Med.*, **81**, 119–135 (1945).
38. Evans, D. G., *Lancet*, **I**, 529–531 (1942).
39. Faust, E. C., *Animal Agents and Vectors of Human Diseases*, Lea, Philadelphia, 1955.
40. Feemster, R. F., *et al.*, *New Engl. J. Med.*, **207**, 82 (1932).
41. Feldman, H. A., *Am. J. Trop. Med. Hyg.*, **2**, 420 (1953).
42. Felix, Z., *Z. Immunitätsforsch.*, **39**, 127 (1924).
43. Felix, A., and R. M. Pitt, *J. Pathol. Bacteriol.*, **38**, 409 (1934); *Lancet*, **II**, 186 (1934).
44. Felton, L. D., W. D. Sutliff, and B. F. Steele, *J. Infect. Diseases*, **56**, 101 (1935).
45. Foshay, L., *J. Infect. Diseases*, **51**, 286 (1932).
46. Foshay, L., *Medicine*, **19**, 1 (1940).
47. Fox, J. P., *Proc. VI Intern. Congr. Microbiol., Rome, 1953*.
48. Fromm, G., *Der Hautartzt*, **5**, 543–548 (1954).
49. Goebel, W. F., *J. Exptl. Med.*, **68**, 469 (1938).
50. Goebel, W. F., *J. Exptl. Med.*, **72**, 33 (1940).
51. Goebel, W. F., *et al.*, *J. Exptl. Med.*, **81**, 315–358 (1945).
52. Gross, P. A. M., D. Gitlin, and C. A. Janeway, *New Engl. J. Med.*, **260**, 172 (1959).
53. Hall, W. W., *U. S. Naval Med. Bull.*, **35**, 33 (1937).
54. Hammon, W. McD., *et al.*, *J. Am. Med. Assoc.*, **151**, 1272 (1953).
55. Hansel, F. K., *Clinical Allergy*, Mosby, St. Louis, 1953.
56. *Harvard School of Public Health Symposium, Virus and Rickettsial Diseases*, Harvard University Press, Cambridge, 1940.
57. Heidelberger, M., personal communication, 1946.
58. Heidelberger, M., *J. Exptl. Med.*, **83**, 303 (1946).
59. Heidelberger, M., *et al.*, *J. Immunol.*, **53**, 109 (1946).
60. Henle, G., *et al.*, *J. Immunol.*, **66**, 535 (1951).
61. Holt, L. B., *Developments in Diphtheria Prophylaxis*, Heinemann, London, 1950.

62. Hooker, S. B., *J. Infect. Diseases*, **45**, 255 (1929).
63. Horsfall, F. L., and I. Tamm, eds., *Viral and Rickettsial Infections of Man*, Lippincott, Philadelphia, 1965.
63a. Hudson, E. H., *Non-Venereal Syphilis*, E. and S. Livingstone, London, 1958.
64. Hutyra, F., and J. Marek, *Spezielle Pathologie und Therapie der Haustiere*, Jena, 1910.
65. Ipsen, J., *J. Immunol.*, **54**, 325 (1946).
66. Irvine, K. N., B. C. G., *Vaccination in Theory and Practice*, Charles C Thomas, Springfield, Illinois, 1949.
67. Janeway, C. A., *New Engl. J. Med.*, **221**, 339 (1939).
68. Janeway, C. A., *New Engl. J. Med.*, **224**, 813 (1939).
69. Jenner, E., *An Inquiry into the Causes and Effects of the Variolae Vacciniae, a disease discovered in some of the western counties of England, particularly Gloucestershire and known by the name of the cowpox*, S. Low, London, 1798.
70. Johnson, H. N., in *Viral and Rickettsial Infections of Man*, T. M. Rivers, ed., Lippincott, Philadelphia, 1952.
71. Katzin, B., and H. Most, *Bull. U. S. Army Med. Dept.*, **6**, 613 (1946).
72. Kelser, R. A., and H. W. Schoening, *Manual of Veterinary Bacteriology*, Williams and Wilkins, Baltimore, 1948.
73. de Kock, G. v. d. W., *Abstr. Trop. Vet. Bull.*, **12**, 136 (1924).
74. Koprowski, H., in *The Dynamics of Virus and Rickettsial Infections*, F. W. Hartman, F. L. Horsfall, and V. G. Kidd, eds., Blakiston, New York, 1954.
75. Kunkel, L. O., *Harvey Lecture Ser.*, **28**, 56 (1932–1933).
76. Lennette, E. H., in *The Dynamics of Virus and Rickettsial Infections*, F. W. Hartman, F. L. Horsfall, and J. G. Kidd, eds., Blakiston, New York, 1954.
77. Lowell, F. C., *Boston Med. Quart.*, **5**, 50 (1954).
78. MacCallum, F. O., in *The Dynamics of Virus and Rickettsial Infections*, F. W. Hartman, F. L. Horsfall, and J. G. Kidd, eds., Blakiston, New York, 1954.
79. Mackenzie, R. D., *J. Pathol. Bacteriol.*, **40**, 65 (1935).
80. MacLeod, C. M., in *Bacterial and Mycotic Infections of Man*, R. J. Dubos, ed., Lippincott, Philadelphia, 1952.
81. MacLeod, C. M., *et al.*, *J. Exptl. Med.*, **82**, 445 (1945).
82. Maynard, G. D., *Publ. S. African Inst. Med. Res.*, **1** [1] (1913).
83. McDermott, W., in *Textbooks of Medicine*, R. L. Cecil and R. F. Loeb, eds., Saunders, Philadelphia, 1955.
84. McGee, L. C., J. E. Andes, C. A. Plume, and S. H. Hinton, *J. Am. Med. Assoc.*, **124**, 555 (1944).
85. McGuinness, A. C., J. G. Armstrong, and H. M. Felton, *J. Pediat.*, **24**, 249 (1944).
86. McKinnon, N. E., and M. A. Ross, *Can. Public Health J.*, **24**, 496 (1933).
87. Meyer, K. F., in *Bacterial and Mycotic Infections of Man*, R. J. Dubos and J. G. Hirsch, eds., Lippincott, Philadelphia, 1965.
88. Meyer, K. F., in *Viral and Rickettsial Infections of Man*, F. L. Horsfall and I. Tamm, eds., Lippincott, Philadelphia, 1965.
89. Meyer, K. F., in *The Dynamics of Virus and Rickettsial Infections*, F. W. Hartman, F. L. Horsfall, and J. G. Kidd, eds., Blakiston, New York, 1954.
90. Meyer, K. F., and B. Eddie, *Proc. Soc. Exptl. Biol. Med.*, **30**, 483 (1932–1933).
91. Michiels, J., and B. Schick, *Z. Kinderheilk*, **5**, 255 (1913).
92. Middlebrook, G., in *Bacterial and Mycotic Infections of Man*, R. J. Dubos and J. G. Hirsch, eds., Lippincott, Philadelphia, 1965.

93. Moloney, P. J., and C. J. Fraser, *Am. J. Public Health*, **17**, 1027 (1927).
94. Morgan, H. R., in *Bacterial and Mycotic Infections of Man*, R. J. Dubos, ed., Lippincott, Philadelphia, 1952.
95. Morgan, W. T. J., and J. Schütze, *Lancet*, **II**, 284 (1943).
96. Mueller, J. H., L. R. Seidman, and P. A. Miller, *J. Clin. Invest.*, **22**, 325–328 (1943).
97. Nelson, R. A., *et al.*, *Am. J. Syphilis, Gonorrhea, Vener. Diseases*, **34**, 101 (1950).
98. Olitsky, P. K., and J. Casals, in *Viral and Rickettsial Infections of Man*, T. M. Rivers, ed., Lippincott, Philadelphia, 1952.
99. Pappenheimer, A. M., *et al.*, *Am. J. Hyg.*, **52**, 323 (1950).
100. Parish, H. V., and D. A. Cannon, *Antisera, Toxoids, Vaccines, and Tuberculins in Prophylaxis and Treatment*, Williams and Wilkins, Baltimore, 1962.
101. Parish, H. J., *Brit. Med. J.*, **II**, 631 (1955).
102. Paul, J. R., and W. W. Bunnell, *Am. J. Med. Sci.*, **183**, 90 (1932).
103. Perlman, E., F. Binkley, and W. F. Goebel, *J. Exptl. Med.*, **81**, 349–358 (1945).
104. Prausnitz, C., and H. Kustner, *Centr. Bakteriol. Parasitenk.*, **86**, 160 (1921).
105. Raffel, S., *Immunity*, Appleton-Century-Crofts, New York, 1953.
106. Rake, G., in *Viral and Rickettsial Diseases of Man*, T. M. Rivers, ed., Lippincott, Philadelphia, 1952.
107. Ramon, G., *Rev. immunol.*, **1**, 37 (1935).
108. Reed, G. B., in *Bacterial and Mycotic Infections of Man*, R. J. Dubos, ed., Lippincott, Philadelphia, 1952.
109. Rivers, T. M., *Viruses and Virus Diseases*, Stanford University Press, San Francisco, 1939.
110. Rivers, T. M., ed., *Viral and Rickettsial Infections of Man*, Lippincott, Philadelphia, 1952.
111. Rivers, T. M., E. Haagen, and R. S. Muckenfuss, *J. Exptl. Med.*, **50**, 673 (1929).
112. Ross, F., and W. M., Stanley, *J. Gen. Physiol.*, **22**, 165 (1938).
113. Rous, P., P. D. McMaster, and S. S. Hudack, *J. Exptl. Med.*, **61**, 657 (1935).
114. Ruge, H., H. Knothe, and O. Otten, *Zeit. f. Hygiene*, **144**, 359–371 (1958).
115. Sabin, A. B., in *Viral and Rickettsial Infections of Man*, T. M. Rivers, ed., Lippincott, Philadelphia, 1952.
116. Sabin, A. B., *Am. J. Diseases Children*, **86**, 301 (1953).
117. Sabin, A. B., *Ohio State Med. J.*, **49**, 603 (1953).
118. Sabin, A. B., and H. A. Feldman, *Science*, **108**, 660 (1948).
119. Sabin, A. B., and R. W. Schlesinger, *Science*, **101**, 640 (1945).
120. Sabin, A. B. *et al.*, *J. Am. Med. Assoc.*, **150**, 1063 (1952).
121. Salk, J. E., *Am. J. Public Health*, **45**, 285 (1955).
122. Sawyer, W. A., *Harvey Lectures Ser.*, **30**, 66 (1934–1935).
123. Scamman, C. L., and B. White, *New Engl. J. Med.*, **198**, 839 (1928).
124. Schick, B., *Münch. med. Worchschr.*, **60**, 2608 (1913).
125. Shaw, L. W., A. Howell, and E. S. Weiss, *Public Health Repts. (U. S.)*, **65**, 583 (1950).
126. Smadel, J. E., in *Viral and Rickettsial Infections of Man*, F. L. Horsfall and I. Tamm, eds., Lippincott, Philadelphia, 1965.
127. Smadel, J. E., and M. J. Wall, *J. Exptl. Med.*, **72**, 389 (1940).
128. Smillie, W. F., *N. Y. State J. Med.*, **38**, 1485 (1938).
129. Smith C. E., *et al.*, *Am. Rev. Tuberc.*, **57**, 330 (1948).
130. Snyder, J. C., in *Viral and Rickettsial Infections of Man*, T. M. Rivers, ed., Lippincott, Philadelphia, 1952.

131. Snyder, J. C., in *Communicable Diseases,* F. H. Top, ed., Mosby, St. Louis, 1955.
131a. Stafford, E. S., *J. Am. Med. Assoc.,* **173,** 539 (1960).
132. Stillman E. G., and K. Goodner, *J. Exptl. Med.,* **58,** 195 (1933).
133. Swift, H. F., in *Bacterial and Mycotic Infections of Man,* R. J. Dubos, ed., Lippincott, Philadelphia, 1952.
134. Taylor, E. M., and P. J. Moloney, *J. Immunol.,* **37,** 223 (1939).
135. Theiler, M., in *Viral and Rickettsial Infections of Man,* T. M. Rivers, ed., Lippincott, Philadelphia, 1952.
136. Top, F. H., *Communicable and Infectious Diseases,* C. V. Mosby, St. Louis, 1964.
137. Traub, E., *J. Exptl. Med.,* **63,** 847 (1936).
138. Treffers, H. P., *Science,* **103,** 387–389 (1946).
139. Tribby, W. W., A. H. Stock, and F. B. Warner, *Military Surgeon,* **103,** 210 (1948).
140. Tuft, L., *Clinical Allergy,* Saunders, Philadelphia, 1938.
141. Underwood, E. A., *J. Hyg.,* **35,** 449 (1935).
142. Vaughan, W. T., and J. H. Black, *Practice of Allergy,* 3rd ed., Mosby, St. Louis, 1954.
143. Weil, A. J., and L. S. Gall, *J. Immunol.,* **38,** 1 (1940).
144. Weinstein, L., and M. Goldfield, *Boston Med. Quart.,* **4,** 7 (1953).
145. Weller, T. H., and C. A. Janeway, in *Bacterial and Mycotic Infections of Man,* Lippincott, Philadelphia, 1952.
146. White, J. S., *J. Egypt Public Health Assoc.,* **24,** 107 (1948).
147. Woodward, S. B., and R. F. Feemster, *New Engl. J. Med.,* **208,** 317 (1933).
148. Zinsser, H., J. F. Enders, and L. D. Fothergill, *Immunity: Principles and Application in Medicine and Public Health,* Macmillan, New York, 1939.

Mephistopheles. *Verachte nur Vernunft und Wissenschaft,*
Des Menschen allerhöchte Kraft,
Lass nur in Blend- und Zauberwerken
Dich von dem Lügengeist bestarken-
—Goethe, *Faust,* lines 1851–1854

CHAPTER 16

Laboratory and Clinical Technic

There are now a considerable number of good manuals of laboratory procedures in immunology and immunochemistry (*e.g.,* 37,25,1,28,14), and there seems little point in duplicating a lot of this material here. Following the advice of some of my students, I have, however, retained descriptions of procedures that they felt, rightly or wrongly, were either not described in the manuals referred to, or not described so adequately.

1. Apparatus

A good electric centrifuge and an electric refrigerator or cold room are perhaps the most important and essential features of a serological laboratory; a water bath is also practically indispensable. The most useful type of centrifuge will probably be found to be the Size 2 centrifuge manufactured by the International Equipment Co., which can take care of very small as well as fairly large quantities. For immunochemical work a refrigerated centrifuge is very useful. Cups plus tubes should be carefully balanced, and balanced pairs should be placed opposite each other in the machine. Centrifuge tubes holding about 100 ml., made of Pyrex glass, should be available, with a head and cups of suitable size. For smaller quantities test tubes of the "Wassermann" type, or smaller, may be used, in small cups interchangeable with the larger ones. For certain kinds of serological work, especially blood grouping, Dow metal carriers, with eight holes in each carrier, are very convenient. When the test tubes contain similar amounts and the centrifuge speed is not great, these carriers can simply be loaded and run, without the necessity of balancing. The carriers can be obtained with the eight holes lined up in two parallel rows, which is convenient for identification and recording.

Test tubes of the "Wassermann" type, roughly 100×13 mm., holding 8 to 9 ml., are suitable for a large number of tests. Occasionally larger tubes may be needed. For blood grouping tests, tubes measuring about 75×9 mm., holding about 4 ml., also without lip, are desirable. For optimal proportions determinations and for Rh blood grouping, tubes measuring 70×6 mm., holding about 1.3 ml., are desirable.

For the performance of "ring" precipitin tests, "micro" tubes specially made from semicapillary tubing are desirable to avoid waste of material (see p. 48). On occasion, graduated centrifuge tubes, holding about 15 ml., will be found useful. It is desirable if possible to have all test tubes made of Pyrex glass. For standardizing bacterial suspensions, and occasionally for measuring volumes of precipitates, the "Hopkins tube," which consists of a small, graduated tube forming the lower portion of a centrifuge tube of about 10 ml., capacity, will be found useful.

Test tube racks, adapted to holding Wassermann tubes, will be desirable. The size may depend upon the individual preference; a type holding two rows of six or eight tubes each will be found useful. For other purposes, such as blood grouping, galvanized racks similar to the "Kolmer" type, holding four rows of twelve each, are better. For some of the smaller types of tubes it may be necessary to make suitable racks or supports. Coarse-mesh galvanized wire screening may be utilized. For larger tubes, such as the large centrifuge tubes, galvanized wire baskets, preferably of the square or rectangular type, are useful.

Several types of pipets will be needed. Some of the ordinary chemical volumetric pipets, in sizes of 5, 10, and 20 ml. will be useful, but, in addition pipets of the serological type (graduated to the tip), in sizes of 1, 2, 5, 10, and (sometimes) 15 ml. will be wanted. For certain kinds of work other types, for instance, a 0.2-ml. pipet graduated in hundredths, may be desired. So-called capillary pipets ("Pasteur pipets") made by drawing out to a fine tip (about 1 mm.) capillary pieces of ordinary (7 to 8 mm.) laboratory glass tubing, used with rubber bulbs, will be almost indispensable. These are harder to make if Pyrex tubing is used, but the product is more durable.

For many kinds of work sterile pipets are needed. Before sterilization, cotton is stuffed in the upper end of the pipet, not too tightly, and the excess is burned off by quick passage through a flame. They are sterilized in the hot air oven in copper cans, preferably of rectangular or square cross section, each size in a separate can.

For sterilization of serum, etc., where heating would be deleterious, and where it is not desired to add a preservative, filters of the Berkefeld or Mandler type will be useful. The Berkefeld "N" or Mandler "ordinary" are usually suitable. These are used in connection with a sterile side arm filter flask (of Pyrex) holding about 250 ml. A water (or mechanical) pump to provide suction is almost essential (see, however, 8). Seitz filters are often more convenient, since they can be prepared rapidly, and the filter pad is discarded after each use. Sizes adapted to very small as well as quite large amounts are obtainable. When possible the kind employing positive pressure instead of suction should be used, in order to avoid foaming.

As a preservative of biological materials, "Merthiolate" (Lilly) and phenyl mercuric nitrate in a concentration of about 1:5000 to 1:15,000, are widely used. For preserving as well as marking blood grouping sera, certain dyes (acriflavine, brilliant green) have been found useful (3,42). For the preservation of erythrocytes for agglutination tests, the mixture of Rous and Turner (43) is suitable, but the newer ACD (acid citrate dextrose) mixtures are apparently even better (31,32). For material which is to be injected, phenol to 0.5 per cent has been found satisfactory, although it could be dangerous if very large amounts were injected.

It is important that all glassware be scrupulously clean. Glassware is much more easily cleaned if it is immersed in water immediately after it has been used. When infectious material has been used, 1 per cent formalin should be used. When pipets or burets become greasy inside, ordinary washing is not sufficient, and they should be soaked 24 to 48 hours in a solution of sulfuric acid and dichromate (for instance, 100 g. potassium dichromate, 1 l. sulfuric acid, 200 ml. water). Cloudy glassware should never be used, unless it is ascertained (by treatment with this "cleaning" solution) that the cloudiness is due merely to etching of the glass.

Two types of syringe will be needed, the Luer all-glass (Pyrex) in sizes of 2, 5, 10, 20, 30, and 50 ml., and the "tuberculin" 1-ml. syringe. Schick-test syringes (1.0 ml. graduated in tenths with graduations encircling the syringe) are better than the tuberculin type for all except the most minute measured injections. Needles of various sizes will be needed, as shown in Table 16-1. Stainless steel needles are the best on the whole; they may be sterilized by boiling or autoclaving. Platinum needles, although harder to keep sharp, are preferred by some workers who make many injections in the course of a single day. The ends of platinum needles can be sterilized by heating to redness in a flame, a procedure which is rapid and sometimes convenient; it would of course destroy the temper of steel needles. Thus the same needle, if sterilized by boiling in the morning, may be used for skin tests throughout the day. However, this procedure, or the use of the same syringe with change of needles each time is not now considered a safe procedure (2.37). It it is feasible, individual sterilized syringes and needles should be used for all clinical work.

Disposable test tubes, syringes, and needles are routinely used in the author's laboratory.

For injecting or bleeding guinea pigs, a holder consisting of a board with numerous holes in it, plus a carrier holding a cross bar for the head, is useful. The animal's legs are tied down with loops of rawhide. This holder is described and illustrated by Coca (10).

TABLE 16-1

Types of Hypodermic Needles Needed for Different Purposes

Purpose	Length, inches	Gage
Subcutaneous or intraabdominal injection of viscous material, and bleeding rabbits from the heart	1.25	18
Other subcutaneous or intraabdominal injections in animals	1	20
Single intravenous injection into rabbits	0.75	23
Intracutaneous injection into human beings, or repeated intravenous injection into rabbits	0.50	25, 26, 27
Intracutaneous injection into guinea pigs	0.50	27, 28
Bleeding sheep from the jugular or large dogs from the heart	3.50	14
Bleeding human beings from the arm veins	1	18, 20
Subcutaneous injection of large volumes into guinea pigs	1	23
Intramuscular injection of human beings	1.50	21

For rabbits various holders have been recommended, from a plain towel to a box with a sliding cover which has a notch for the neck, in which the animal is placed with the head outside (10). The present writer has found it perfectly feasible, and on the whole simpler, to hold the rabbit on the lap (which is protected by a towel or thick laboratory coat) while drawing blood from the ear or injecting into the ear veins. The animals soon become accustomed to sitting quietly during these procedures, which cannot be very painful. In this way a single person can carry out the operation. For drawing blood from the heart an assistant is necessary; an assistant is also helpful when injecting intraabdominally, although this too can be accomplished by one person who knows how to hold the animal between the knees. The assistant holds the animal firmly by the hind feet in the left hand, and holds front feet and neck in the right hand, using his knees to prevent motions by the animal.

2. Technic of Injection and Bleeding of Animals

Rabbits are the animals mainly used for the production of experimental antisera, and serum containing antibodies (antiserum) from rabbits possesses advantages (lower molecular weight, lower solubility = greater precipitating power) over that from horses, and possibly over that from chickens, which are sometimes used.   Other animals, such as guinea pigs, are too small, and furnish too little blood, for common use as precipitin producers, and may not produce precipitating antibodies so well anyway.

A number of rabbits (three to five) should be given each type of antigen used, as one or more may die during the injections, and not all rabbits produce good antisera to any given antigen.   It is probably best to inject the antigen intravenously (except in antitoxin production in the horse), using other methods only as supplementary to this.

Before starting the injection a syringe (a 2-ml. or 5-ml. type is suitable) and needles (probably 25-gage is best although there are a few who prefer larger sizes) are boiled 15 minutes to sterilize them.   Modern syringes may be boiled assembled.

The injection is made into the external marginal vein of the rabbit's ear.   During this procedure many rabbits will sit quietly in the operator's lap; others may require a "rabbit box" or rolling in a towel.   If the vein is hard to see, or if difficulty is experienced by the operator in inserting the needle into the vein, a *little* xylene may be rubbed on the ear with cotton, then washed off with alcohol.   (In all cases a little alcohol, by laying the fur, makes the vein more visible, and by its use the necessity of shaving the ear is avoided.)   If the vein does not come up, a little rubbing with dry cotton will now bring it up.   The xylene and rubbing, essential for bleeding, are not usually necessary for injecting. The needle is inserted into the vein, in the same direction as the circulation (towards the heart), the ear and needle held with the left hand so that the thumb is over the point of entry, and the antigen injected, slowly at first.   Resistance or visible distention of the tissue around the vein indicates that the needle is not in the vein.   Any injection into the perivascular tissue is likely to destroy the future usefulness of the vein for injection.

One ear (right or left) is always used for the injection, the other being reserved for bleeding.   Injections at the beginning of a course are made near the tip of the ear; bleedings begin near the root.

In some cases intraabdominal injections are desirable.   The rabbit is held, belly outwards, between the operator's knees, and the head and forefeet are held with the left hand.   Enough alcohol to wet a small area of fur is dropped on the belly, the (20-gage) needle of the already charged syringe is inserted, first through the skin, then through the abdominal wall, and the injection is made with the right hand. When dealing with infectious material, scrupulous asepsis should be observed.

3. Titration of Toxin and Antitoxin

For the principles on which these titrations are based, the reader is referred to Chapters 2 and 6, pages 102 and 322. The Ramon flocculation titration will be described on page 681, under the optimal proportions titration. The technic here described is from an old bulletin written by Rosenau (41). See also reference (46). The methods used are still rather typical and a brief account is presented here partly because of their historical importance.

The measurement of the minimum lethal dose (MLD) is one of the oldest biological measurements. When Ehrlich originally defined it, he was probably influenced more by his knowledge of the reproducible reactions of chemistry than his more recent acquaintance with the variability in the response of animals. Consequently his original definition, which seemed to imply that it was enough to test a few guinea pigs with slightly different doses, and obtain the MLD by noting which guinea pig died in 4 days, seems a little optimistic in light of later knowledge. Nevertheless, in some respects Ehrlich built better than he knew, for the response of guinea pigs to diphtheria toxin, although to be sure some individual variations in animals is found, is remarkably uniform. For this reason, all laboratories today still make use of some modification of Ehrlich's original technic, and determine MLD's and not LD50's, which the biometrician might recommend as being better. Those who have actual experience in this work believe that in the case of diphtheria toxin, determination of MLD's is actually more efficient in the use of animals than an LD50 determination would be. Consequently it will be interesting to see how the MLD of diphtheria toxin has traditionally been, and to a large extent still is, determined, before we pass on to the study of toxins and infectious agents, where the response in individual animals is more variable and where we shall see the advantages of determining the LD50 as our unit of potency.

First, preliminary measurements of the MLD and L_+ dose of the toxin are made.

When a standardized toxin is available, unknown antitoxic sera may be titrated in terms of it, remembering that the toxin is the less stable reagent. An example of such a titration is given in Table 16-2.

TABLE 16-2

Standardization of an Unknown Serum

Test dose		
Amount of toxin solution, ml. (1 L+)	Amount of antiserum, ml.	Effect on animal
0.29	1/500	Lives
0.29	1/600	Lives
0.29	1/700	Lives
0.29	1/800	Dies in 8 days
0.29	1/900	Dies in 4 days
0.29	1/1000	Dies in 2 days

This experiment, according to the original Ehrlich standard, would indicate that the antiserum contains one antitoxin unit in 1/900 of a milliliter, or 900 units per milliliter. Others prefer to base the labeled strength on the amount which just results in survival; the above serum, on that basis, would be marked as containing 700 units per milliliter.

It is clear that procedures such as this, subject to unavoidable variation in animals and employing rather coarse steps in the titration, cannot be highly accurate, but the method has one important advantage over the Ramon flocculation titration, which otherwise might replace it, in that it gives a direct indication of the actual protective power of the serum, which is of course the all-important factor in therapeutic sera.

4. Diluting Fluid

In many serological procedures the directions call at one point or another for dilution of one of the reagents. Unless something else is expressly specified, the dilutions are made with a 0.9 per cent (0.15M) solution of sodium chloride, usually referred to as saline, or physiological salt solution.

5. Optimum Proportions Determination

The significance of this determination has been discussed in Chapters 2 and 6. We may repeat that it is a convenient way to estimate antibody concentrations roughly.

Unless something is known about the strength of the serum it is usually necessary first to locate the optimum proportions point approximately by a rough test. The original technic of Dean and Webb (11) has been modified by a number of workers; the technic described in (4) will be given here.

Prepare in Wassermann tubes serial dilutions (successively 1:2 or 1:3) of the antigen, starting with a solution of known concentration. Either make these dilutions so as to leave 0.5 ml. in each tube, or transfer 0.5 ml. of each to a series of tubes as the dilutions are being made. Dilute enough serum for the rough test 1:5 or 1:10, depending on its probable strength. Have ready a little rack of small tubes of 1-ml. capacity (see page 674) in a water bath at 37°C. (or if greater speed is desired, at 40° or 45°C.), each tube being one-third immersed in the water. With a 1-ml. pipet add 0.5 ml. of the diluted serum to the highest dilution of the antigen, immediately mix by brief shaking, then immediately remove the mixture from the original tube and transfer to one of the 1-ml. tubes, using a capillary pipet with a long, not too fine tip. This insures thorough mixing. Record the time, to the nearest quarter-minute. Proceed similarly with the other antigen dilutions, using the same capillary pipet each time, and going from the higher dilutions to the lower (from weak to strong antigen).

Observe the tubes continuously. Cloudiness will begin to appear in the tubes that are going to flocculate, usually within a few minutes. Watch for the point at which individual particles just become visible to the unaided eye (this point varies with different observers, but is more or less consistent for any one individual). Record the time of participation in each tube, until four or more tubes have flocculated, or it is clear they are not going to.

The optimal proportions point may be expected to lie somewhere between the values indicated by the two most rapid tubes. From the antigen and antibody dilutions present in these tubes, it may be calculated what would be a suitable dilution of antigen and antibody for the "fine test." The serum dilution should be such that flocculation at the opti-

TABLE 16-3

Determination of Optimal Proportions Point

	Volumes, ml.								
Diluted antigen	0.5	0.4	0.35	0.30	0.25	0.20	0.17	0.15	0.12
Saline	—	0.1	0.15	0.20	0.25	0.30	0.33	0.35	0.38
Diluted serum	0.5	0.5	0.5	0.5	0.5	0.5	0.5	0.5	0.5
Time of particulation, min.	15	6.5	3	2.5	3	5	13.5	—	—

The diluted antigen and saline are mixed first, then the diluted serum added to one tube at a time, beginning at the right; the time each mixture is placed in the water bath is recorded. The time of particulation is similarly recorded for each tube.

mum may be expected to take place in 5 to 10 minutes. Make sufficient diluted antigen and diluted serum for the following procedure.

In each of a series of Wassermann tubes place the amounts of the antigen dilution shown in Table 16-3, and add the indicated volumes of saline to bring the total in each case to 0.5 ml. Then add to each tube in turn 0.5 ml. of the diluted serum, beginning with the weakest antigen, and mixing, transferring, and timing as before. If the dilutions used were the correct ones, one tube, not at either end of the series, will show most rapid flocculation, or occasionally two or more tubes will run a "dead heat." If the fourth tube from the left in Table 15-11, for instance, was most rapid, when we used a 1:400 dilution of stock antigen and a 1:10 dilution of antiserum, we should calculate that the optimal ratio of antigen to serum dilution was $0.5/0.3 \times 400/10 = 66.7$.

From a knowledge of the actual concentration of the stock antigen, it may be calculated how many milligrams of antigen, or antigen nitrogen, react optimally with 1 ml. of serum. For example, if in the above case, where we find an optimal ratio of 66.7, we had started with a stock solution containing 1.25 mg. of protein nitrogen per milliliter, we should calculate that 1 ml. of antiserum reacts optimally with $1/_{66.7} \times 1.25 = 0.019$ mg. of protein nitrogen. Or conversely, that to react with 1 mg. of antigen nitrogen, $66.7/1.25 = 53.4$ ml. of serum would be needed.

6. Ramon Titration

This is essentially the same titration, and is historically earlier, but need not be described in so much detail, since the Dean and Webb titration just described is more generally useful when rabbit sera are being studied. In the Ramon titration, constant dilutions of antigen are tested with varying dilutions of serum (see above, Chapter 6, page 362).

The amount of toxin which gives most rapid flocculation with one standard unit of antitoxin is first determined. This amount is designated

TABLE 16-4

Ramon Titration of Antitoxin

	Amounts of reagents, ml.								
Serum, dil. 1:5	0.07	0.08	0.09	0.10	0.11	0.12	0.13	0.14	0.15
Toxin	1.0	1.0	1.0	1.0	1.0	1.0	1.0	1.0	1.0
Time of floccu- lation, min.	—	—	120	40	19	15	20	45	—

If the toxin contained 15 L_f units per milliliter, we may calculate that 1 ml. of the above serum would neutralize $1/0.12 \times 5 \times 15 = 624$ L_f units of toxin.

as the L_f unit. Then unknown antisera can be titrated against this standardized toxin, remembering that the toxin will gradually change in
strength and consequently will need restandardization at intervals. Ordinary toxin is stable for flocculation tests for at least several years, if kept
cold. It may be less stable as judged by *in vivo* tests.

A sample titration is shown in Table 16-4. Descriptions of the technic
of the Ramon titration may be found in papers by Ramon (40) and
Glenny and Okell (12).

7. Preparation of Synthetic Antigens

The following example of the coupling of diazotized arsanilic acid with
the proteins of horse serum may be taken as typical of methods of preparing chemically modified antigens.

Weigh out 1 g. of arsanilic acid for each gram of protein *nitrogen* present in the amount of serum it is desired to use (the amount for pure proteins, if the tyrosine and histidine content is known, can be calculated
more precisely by the formula of Boyd and Hooker (5). For three typical
proteins the amounts of arsanilic theoretically needed for 1 g. of protein
nitrogen varied from 0.81 to 1.25 g. One gram of arsanilic acid dissolves
in about 70 ml. of water, with the addition of 1.2 ml. of concentrated
hydrochloric acid. Cool in a freezing bath (ice and salt), diazotize by the
addition of the requisite amount (about 9 ml.) of cold $0.5N$ sodium nitrite solution, using starch-iodide paper as the indicator. Allow to stand
about 30 minutes before the final test with the paper. Add 1 g. of urea,
mix, and allow to stand 10 minutes. Pour the mixture into the cold
serum, add enough cold alkali (sodium hydroxide or trisodium phosphate) to make the mixture slightly alkaline to litmus, allow to stand in
the icebox overnight. Coupling, as shown by the development of a red
color, should begin within a few minutes, and should be complete next
morning.

Proteins coupled with arsanilic acid can usually be precipitated easily
by the cautious addition of hydrochloric acid, and this fact may be utilized
for purification. The proper amount may be determined by trials with
1-ml. samples of the mixture, or the concentrated acid may be added
drop by drop with shaking until the maximum precipitate is formed.
Other modified proteins, not precipitable in this way, may be purified by
adding sodium or ammonium sulfate, preferably the former because it
contains no nitrogen, in conjunction with enough acid to bring the protein
near its (often rather acid) isoelectric point. Filter off the precipitate on
paper, or centrifuge it down, and remove liquid. Mix thoroughly with

water, than cautiously add alkali to bring the material into solution, being careful to crush all lumps with a stirring rod. Filter. Repeat the precipitation, solution, and filtration two or three times. If the protein is to be injected, the final solution should have salt added to make it isotonic and should be sterilized by passage through a Berkefeld or Seitz filter.

Purification of such conjugated antigens can also be effected by repeated precipitation with alcohol in the cold, followed by a final dialysis to remove residual alcohol.

8. Specific Inhibition

The principle of the inhibition of serological reactions by the appropriate haptens has been discussed on page (162). If the inhibitive power of a number of related haptens is to be compared, it is best to do the inhibition in a quantitative manner, using definite amounts of hapten. It is convenient to make solutions of the various haptens $0.02M$ of $0.01M$, and use successive dilutions of these. The dilutions may increase successively by a factor of 2, or in very fine work, 1.5.

A fixed amount of each of the hapten dilutions is mixed with a constant volume of serum. After a preliminary incubation period (which may be unnecessary), these are now tested by the usual precipitin technic, against an appropriate dilution of the appropriate antigen. To make the test more delicate, the antiserum may be diluted 1:4 or 1:8, and the gelatin technic of Hanks (13) used. This is illustrated in the following experiment (23) on the inhibitive power of various derivatives of strychnine against an antiserum prepared by injecting hemocyanin coupled with diazotized aminostrychnine.

A roughly optimal concentration of monoaminostrychnineazocasein, about 20 μg. of nitrogen per milliliter, was prepared in 5 per cent gelatin in saline solution. A column of this mixture, about 0.2 ml., allowed to harden in tubes of 6 mm. bore, was overlayered with 0.2 ml. of a solution containing 0.025 ml. of pooled antisera and an amount (1.0 to 0.017) micromoles) of one of the substances tested for inhibitive capacity. The tubes were then kept in the incubator at 37°C. for 5 hours; reactions were recorded at hourly intervals, and after overnight refrigeration. With the lengthening of time of incubation, increasingly larger amounts of inhibitors are required to prevent the appearance of a visible precipitate at the interface. Uninhibited serum gave a prompt clouding at the interface. Typical results are shown in Table 16-5.

In general, we may expect the results obtained with haptens H, H', H", and G, where H' is closely related chemically to H, H" less closely

TABLE 16-5

Typical Results Obtained in an Inhibition Experiment (23) Precipitation of Casein–Strychnine Compound by Antistrychnine Serum Mixed with Various Substances

Test substance (dissolved as the hydrochloride)	Micromoles of test substance										
	1.00	0.67	0.44	0.30	0.20	0.13	0.088	0.058	0.039	0.026	0.01
Strychnine[a]			—	—	—	—	—	—	t	±	+
Mononitro-strychnine[a]			—	—	—	—	—	—	t	+	+
Dinitro-strychnine[a]			C	C	C	C	C	+	+	+	+
Monoamino-strychnnine	—	—	—	—	—	—	t	t	+	+	
Diamino-strychnine	—	—	—	—	—	—	—	t	t	t	
Brucine[a]	C	C	—	—	—	—	t	±	+	+	
Morphine	+	+	+	+	+	+	+	+	+	+	+
Quinine	+	+	+	+	+	+	+	+	+	+	+
Tryptophane	+	+	+	+	+	+	+	+	+	+	+
Nicotinic acid	+	+	+	+	+	+	+	+	+	+	+

C indicates a cloudiness of the supernatant, which developed in mixtures of the particular test substance with antiserum or with normal serum. + indicates precipitation at interface, — absence of precipitation, t trace.

[a] Indicates that the substances so designated were actually used in amounts 1.14 times greater than stated. Because of the limited quantitative precision of the test this difference is not significant.

related, and G unrelated, to give results similar to those in Table 16-5. This is shown schematically in Table 16-6.

Another way of comparing the inhibiting powers of different haptens is to use constant concentrations (preferably expressed as molarities) of haptens against successive dilutions of the antiserum. In this case, again

TABLE 16-6

Precipitation Reaction of Anti-H Antibody and H Antigen, in Presence of Hapten[a]

Hapten	Dilution of hapten					
	1:2	1:4	1:8	1:16	1:32	1:64
H	0	0	0	0	+	+±
H′	0	0	±	+	++	++
H″	0	±	+	++	++	++
G	++	++	++	++	++	++

[a] ++ = Strong reaction. Other symbols as in Table 16-5.

TABLE 16-7

Precipitation Reaction of Anti-H Antibody and H Antigen
in Presence of Hapten[a]

Hapten	Dilution of antiserum					
	1:2	1:4	1:8	1:16	5:32	1:64
H	+	0	0	0	0	0
H'	++	+	±	0	0	0
H"	++	++	+	+	±	0
G	++	++	++	++	+	±

[a] Symbols as in Table 16-6.

using the hypothetical haptens H, H', H", and G, we might obtain the sort of result shown in Table 16-7.

Instead of trying to find the antibody concentration which is completely inhibited by a given concentration of hapten, or the hapten concentration which will completely inhibit a given concentration of antibody, it is more accurate to measure the amount of precipitate produced under the various conditions, and estimate the amount of hapten which gives just 50 per cent inhibition.

9. Analysis of Specific Precipitates

If the precipitates are made in the part of the range where all the antigen is precipitated, the composition of the precipitate can be determined by analyzing it for nitrogen. The value obtained, minus the nitrogen contained in the antigen (if any), gives the antibody nitrogen, and the quotient gives the ratio of antibody to antigen (in terms of nitrogen) in the precipitate. In the case of nitrogen-free carbohydrates no correction for antigen nitrogen is required. If the antigen is not all precipitated, it is necessary either to have some method of measuring the residual antigen in the supernatant (see 17,18,26) or to use an antigen containing some characteristic making it possible to measure it independently of nitrogen determinations. This method was first applied by Wu and his collaborators (44,45) to the cases where the antigen consisted of hemoglobin and iodoalbumin, respectively. Heidelberger and Kendall (16,17) made use of colorimetric estimation of a dye-antigen; Kurotchkin and Kratze (27) estimated a carbohydrate antigen by determination as reducing sugar. Artificial antigens containing arsenic have been used (15,21,34).

Of the natural protein antigens, the hemocyanins are particularly suitable for such studies, since they are very good antigens, unlike hemoglobin, and contain copper which can be used for their estimation in pre-cipitates (22,33).

The nitrogen in the precipitates may be determined by the micro-Kjeldahl method of Parnas and Wagner (38). The copper may be deter-mined by a modified method combining certain features of the methods of Locke, Main, and Rosbash (30) and McFarlane (35). More delicate methods of determining copper have since been developed.

It is convenient to make the precipitates for nitrogen analysis so that they will contain a total of about 1 mg. of nitrogen. If the ratio of anti-body to antigen in the equivalence zone is not already known, it may be estimated roughly for the first experiments from the theoretical relation with molecular weight of the antigen proposed by Boyd and Hooker (5,6).

It is desirable, if sufficient serum is available, to do all the analyses in duplicate or triplicate. The antigen and antibody are mixed in gradu-ated, conical (15-ml.) centrifuge tubes and incubated in a water bath at 37°C. until flocculation occurs, then stored overnight at 1.7°C., centri-fuged at 2500 rpm for 5 minutes, and the supernatant removed with a capillary pipet. The precipitates are washed three times with small amounts of 0.15M NaCl, being resuspended thoroughly each time, and are then ready for analysis.

Micro-Kjeldahl Determinations

Not only in the analysis of precipitates, but in connection with many other procedures of the immunochemical laboratory, the determination of protein is necessary. Various colorimetric and spectrometric methods, some of which will be described later, are very useful, but these are all ultimately based upon protein determinations which depend upon the fact that proteins contain about 16 per cent nitrogen. The micro-Kjeldahl method is very satisfactory for this purpose.

A weighed or measured sample estimated to contain about 1 mg. of nitrogen (6 mg. of protein) is placed on a micro-Kjeldahl flask, and there is added 2 ml. sulfuric acid solution saturated with copper sulfate.* Add a few large crystals of potassium sulfate (about 1 g.), and a glass bead or boiling stone.

Digest in the hood or preferably in the racks specially manufactured for this purpose (see illustration in 24), placing the flask at a 45° angle

* This solution is prepared by adding about 40 ml. saturated $CuSO_4$ solution in water to a 9-pound bottle of low nitrogen CP reagent sulfuric acid. Add the solution in 10-ml. portions with thorough mixing. Excess anhydrous $CuSO_4$ will settle out. Decant and use supernatant.

over the flame and bringing the acid to and maintaining it at a gentle boil. After the water is driven off charring usually occurs. Continue boiling until the liquid is again clear (it will be light blue in color), and all charred material destroyed.

After the digestion is finished, the acid mixture is allowed to cool, then diluted with about 10 ml. of water. It may then be transferred to the micro-Kjeldahl distilling apparatus (see illustration in 24), made alkaline, and the ammonia distilled off into boric acid.

Before using the distilling apparatus it is steamed out for 5 minutes with a micro-Kjeldahl flask containing distilled water and alkali. If the distillate is neutral to methyl red, a blank is run as follows: Put a 125-ml. Erlenmeyer flask containing 5 ml. of the boric acid-indicator solution* and 5 ml. of water under the condenser, with the tip of the condenser barely touching the surface of the liquid. Place a micro-Kjeldahl flask containing 10 ml. of water on the distilling apparatus, run in 9 ml. of alkali,† replace the flame under the steam generator, and immediately raise the flask of boric acid until the tip of the condenser touches the bottom, tipping the flask so the condenser tip is covered as deeply as possible. Distil 6 minutes, then lower the Erlenmeyer flask, rinse off the tip of the condenser and remove the flame. After all the water condensed in the trap of the distillation apparatus has returned to the Kjeldahl flask, replace the flame and distil for 1 minute more, but leave the tip of the condenser above the surface of the liquid. The blank is used as a color standard with which to compare the color obtained in titrating unknown runs. It should be faintly red in color. If it is satisfactory, another Erlenmeyer with boric acid and water is put under the condenser and one of the diluted digested unknowns put in the distilling apparatus. Distillation is as in the blank run. The ammonia distilled over into the boric acid will turn the indicator yellow.

The distillates are titrated with $N/70$ HCl to the point where their color just matches the blank. If the $N/70$ HCl is exactly $N/70$, the calculations are very simple, as the number of milligrams of nitrogen is equal to the number of milliliters of HCl used $\times$ 0.2; the error in the micro-Kjeldahl procedure is about ± 0.01 mg. N.

The procedure just described has been in satisfactory use in the author's laboratory for over 30 years, and is virtually identical with that described by Kabat and Mayer (29), who also describe certain alternatives and modifications.

* Two milliliters of a saturated solution of twice recrystallized methyl red in alcohol is added to 100 ml. saturated boric acid solution. Five milliliters of this are mixed with 5 ml. of water for each analysis.

† Saturated NaOH solution, decanted or filtered from Na_2CO_3.

Biuret Method

The protein content of precipitates and solutions can also be estimated by the quantitative biuret method of Levin and Brauer (29), determining the color developed in the photoelectric colorimeter. This has the advantages of being faster and of not requiring preliminary digestion of the protein.

Amounts should be chosen so as to give galvanometer readings in the vicinity of 50. The precipitates are then dissolved in 3 ml. of 0.2N NaOH, and 0.15M NaCl is added to give a total volume of 6 ml. Four milliliters of the biuret reagent are now added. This reagent is made by mixing together 1500 ml. concentrated NH_4OH, 2500 ml. distilled water, 1000 ml. of saturated NaOH, and 8.75 g. of $CuSO_4 \cdot 5H_2O$ dissolved in the minimum amount of distilled water. The above materials are thoroughly cooled before mixing. Readings are made in the colorimeter with filter 540 mμ. From determinations over a wide range of known protein concentrations using a stock solution analyzed by Kjeldahl, a standard curve on semilogarithmic graph paper is constructed, showing the relation between protein concentrations and galvanometer readings. From the smoothed curve it is convenient to construct a compact table showing the conversion of galvanometer readings to nitrogen, and keep this handy, for example, pasted into the back of a notebook.

Use of Phenol Reagent

Determination of protein by quantitative measurement of the color developed with the Folin-Ciocalteu phenol reagent is even more sensitive (19,20), and has the other advantages of the biuret method. For the analysis of precipitates, proceed as follows:

The precipitates are dissolved by adding 0.1N NaOH to the 1 ml. mark. Three milliliters of 0.15M NaCl, 6 ml. of 12.5 per cent Na_2CO_3, and 1 ml. of 0.1 per cent $CuSO_4 \cdot 5H_2O$ are then added to each tube. After standing for 1 hour 1 ml. of Folin-Ciocalteu phenol improved reagent freshly diluted 1:3 with distilled water is added. This reagent is available commercially. The readings are made 20 to 30 minutes later in the colorimeter at 660 mμ. Optical density is converted to protein concentration by means of a standard curve, as above.

In both analytical procedures, the color is developed in centrifuge tubes and the solutions are poured into colorimeter tubes before readings are made.

The Folin-Ciocalteu method is about 60 times as sensitive as the biuret method, thus making it an excellent procedure when only small amounts of material are available. We have found that the Folin-Ciocalteu method reads optimally with 0.02 mg. N total, whereas the biuret method requires 1.13 mg. N total.

Any proportion of reagents may be selected arbitrarily as a reference point, and other mixtures expressed in terms of this, or the optimal proportions point or the equivalence point (p. 356) may be determined and used for this purpose. Then mixtures containing proportionately less or more antibody might be expressed as being made with, say, 70 per cent, or 150 per cent, of the optimal antibody (33).

The analytical results may be reduced to some convenient standard, such as the yield from 1 ml. of serum, or from 1 mg. of antigen nitrogen, and from a knowledge of the nitrogen/copper ratio in the hemocyanin, the copper figures translated into equivalent antigen nitrogen. By subtracting this from the total, the antibody nitrogen is obtained, and the ratio gives the ratio of antibody nitrogen to antigen nitrogen in the precipitate. Since the per cent of nitrogen in the antibody and in antigen

TABLE 16-8

Protein Nitrogen Estimated by Biuret Method in Specific Precipitates Made with a Substance and Lima Bean Lectin Mixed in Various Proportions

L = lectin.   For other abbreviations, see text

Active A substance − 33% of crude A substance

	Added				Calculated				
Fract. opt. L.	Crude A sub., mg.	Lectin 8(2), ml.	Precipitated N, mg.		Active A sub./ml. L, mg.	Protein ppt./ ml.	N L, mg.	Protein N ppt./ mg. active A., mg.	
0.50	22.50	2.02	0.978	0.858	3.71	0.484	0.425	0.130	0.114
0.60	22.50	2.43	1.434	1.338	3.09	4.590	0.551	0.191	0.178
0.67	10.00	1.20	0.760	0.744	2.78	0.633	0.620	0.228	0.223
			0.758	0.714	—	0.632	0.595	0:227	0.214
0.70	10.00	1.26	0.942	0.864	2.65	0.748	0.686	0.283	0.259
0.80	7.50	1.08	1.009	0.954	2.31	0.934	0.883	0.404	0.383
0.90	7.50	1.21	1.130	1.139	2.07	0.934	0.941	0.452	0.456
1.00	5.00	0.90	0.924	0.924	1.85	1.027	1.027	0.554	0.554
			0.924	—	—	1.027	—	0.554	—
1.33	5.00	1.20	1.216	1.147	1.39	0.013	0.956	0.730	0.688
1.67	5.00	1.50	1.407	1.379	1.11	0.938	0.919	0.844	0.827
2.00	5.00	1.80	1.524	1.497	0.926	0.847	0.832	0.914	0.898
3.00	1.67	0.90	0.532	0.547	0.618	0.591	0.608	0.957	0.984
4.00	2.50	1.80	0.858	0.840	0.463	0.477	0.467	1.030	1.008
4.50	2.50	2.02	0.804	—	0.413	0.398	—	0.965	—
5.00	1.77	1.50	0.527	0.527	0.370	0.351	0.351	0.946	0.946
			0.533	—	—	0.355	—	0.957	—

usually do not differ much, the ratio by nitrogen is very nearly the ratio by weight of antibody to antigen. Different ratios are to be expected for each mixture of antiserum and antigen in which the proportions of the reagents differ (see Fig. 6-15a on p. 352).

Another example of such calculations from the raw analytical results is shown in Table 16-8, which shows actual amounts added and recovered, and calculated amounts on basis of fixed amount of antigen and on basis of fixed amount of the other reagent. In this instance the other reagent

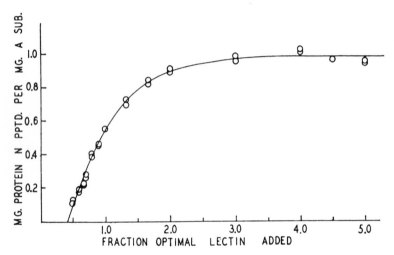

Fig. 16-1. Protein nitrogen precipitated per mg. A substance when various fractions and multiples of optimal proportions amount of lectin were added.

was not a true antibody, but a plant protein having a high degree of specificity for the antigen; its behavior imitates that of an antibody very closely (7).

A graph of the analytical results obtained in this experiment is shown in Fig. 16-1.

10. Acetyl Determination

In immunochemical work concerned with bacterial products and with blood grouping, determination of acetyl groups is often important. I am indebted to Dr. E. E. Baker, Professor of Microbiology at Boston University School of Medicine, for permission to reproduce directions for the procedures used in his laboratory. The first is essentially that given by Kabat and Mayer (33), but with fuller details at some essential points.

a. Total Acetyl

This method determines both easily hydrolyzable O-acetyl

$$(-\overset{\displaystyle |}{\underset{\displaystyle O}{\text{C}}}-\text{O}-\overset{\displaystyle \|}{\underset{\displaystyle}{\text{C}}}-\text{CH}_3)$$ and difficultly hydrolyzable N-acetyl $$(-\overset{\displaystyle |}{\underset{\displaystyle H}{\text{N}}}-\overset{\displaystyle \|}{\underset{\displaystyle O}{\text{C}}}-\text{CH}_3).$$

A solution of the sample, containing from 1 to 5 mg. of acetyl per 20 ml., is placed in a flask containing 5 g. of p-toluene sulfonic acid. The mixture is refluxed for 2 hours in a bath of boiling saturated NaCl solution. It is important that the p-toluene sulfonic acid be of high quality and give a *clear colorless* solution. After refluxing the mixture is transferred quantitatively to a 100-ml. micro-Kjeldahl flask and the liberated acetic acid steam-distilled. A Bunsen burner should be placed under the distilling flask and the flame adjusted so that the volume of the sample remains constant (concentration of the sample will result in excessive decomposition of the p-toluene sulfonic acid; dilution with condensed steam may lead to low recovery).

Successive 100-ml. portions of distillate are collected and heated to boiling under reflux while a stream of CO_2-free air is bubbled through to remove the CO_2. It seems desirable to continue boiling for 5 minutes in order to remove all the volatile decomposition products of the p-toluene sulfonic acid. After boiling the samples are cooled, with CO_2-free air still passing through the solution, and finally titrated with $N/70$ NaOH. Successive portions are titrated until a consistent blank is obtained. As a rule four or five portions will be required. The acetyl content is calculated as

$$\text{Mg. acetyl} = \frac{\text{ml. } N/70 \text{ NaOH}}{70} \times 43$$

This method will give acetyl contents of N-acetylglucosamine and pentaacetyl glucose which are within 1 per cent of the theoretical.

b. Easily Hydrolyzable Acetyl

This method is adapted from Pippen, McCready, and Owens (39). It determines only the O-linked acetyl. A weighed sample containing 3–10 mg. of acetyl is dissolved in 25 ml. of 0.1N NaOH and allowed to stand 2 to 24 hours at room temperature. The sample is then diluted to 50 ml. and 20 ml. aliquots are placed in Kjeldahl flasks together with 20-ml. amounts of Clark's magnesium sulfate–sulfuric acid solution (100

g. $MgSO_4$ and 1.5 g. concentrated H_2SO_4 diluted to 180 ml. with water). The distillation is carried out as in method (a). The successive distillates are titrated with $N/70$ NaOH without boiling or treatment with CO_2-free air. The percentage of acetyl in the sample is calculated as above. This method will give results for the acetyl content of pentaacetyl glucose within 1 per cent of the theoretical. None of the acetyl of N acetyl glucosamine is split off by this procedure. The time of hydrolysis can be anywhere within the limits given; overnight is convenient.

c. Difficultly Hydrolyzable Acetyl(N-Acetyl)

This is calculated as the difference between the total acetyl and the easily hydrolyzable acetyl.

References

1. Ackroyd, J. F., ed., *Immunological Methods,* F. A. Davis, Philadelphia, 1964.
2. American Academy of Pediatrics, *Report of the Committee on the Control of Infectious Diseases,* 1955.
3. Boyd, W. C., *J. Immunol.,* **37,** 65 (1939).
4. Boyd, W. C., *J. Exptl. Med.,* **74,** 369 (1941).
5. Boyd, W. C., and S. B. Hooker, *J. Biol. Chem.,* **104,** 329 (1934).
6. Boyd, W. C., and S. B. Hooker, *J. Gen. Physiol.,* **22,** 281 (1939).
7. Boyd, W. C., E. G. Shapleigh, and M. H. McMaster, *Arch. Biochem. and Biophys.,* **55,** 226 (1955).
8. Brown, E. A., and N. Benotti, *Science,* **93,** 23 (1941).
9. Campbell, D. H., J. S. Garvey, N. E. Cremer, and D. H. Sussdorf, *Methods in Immunology,* W. A. Benjamin, New York, 1963.
10. Coca, A. F., *Essentials of Immunology,* Williams and Wilkins, Baltimore, 1925.
11. Dean, H. R., and R. A. Webb, *J. Pathol. Bacteriol.,* **29,** 473 (1926).
12. Glenny, A. T., and C. C. Okell, *J. Pathol. Bacteriol.,* **27,** 187 (1924).
13. Hanks, J. H., *J. Immunol.,* **28,** 95 (1935).
14. Harris, A. H., and M. B. Coleman, *Diagnostic Procedures and Reagents,* 4th ed., American Public Health Assoc., Inc., New York, 1963.
15. Haurowitz, F., and F. Brenl, *Z. Physiol. Chem.,* **214,** 111 (1933).
16. Heidelberger, M., and F. E. Kendall, *Science,* **72,** 252 (1930).
17. Heidelberger, M., and F. E. Kendall, *J. Exptl. Med.,* **62,** 467 (1935).
18. Heidelberger, M., and F. E. Kendall, *J. Exptl. Med.,* **62,** 697 (1935).
19. Heidelberger, M., and C. F. C. MacPherson, *Science,* **97,** 405 (1943).
20. Heidelberger, M., and C. F. C. MacPherson, *Science,* **98,** 63 (1943).
21. Hooker, S. B., and W. C. Boyd, *J. Immunol.,* **23,** 465 (1932).
22. Hooker, S. B., and W. C. Boyd, *J. Immunol.,* **30,** 33 (1936).
23. Hooker, S. B., and W. C. Boyd, *J. Immunol.,* **38,** 479 (1940).
24. Kabat, E. A., and M. M. Mayer, *Experimental Immunochemistry,* Charles C Thomas, Springfield, Illinois, 1948.
25. Kabat, E. A., and M. M. Mayer, *Experimental Immunochemistry,* 2nd ed., Charles C Thomas, Springfield, Illinois, 1961.

26. Kolchin, B. S., and I. F. Klein, *J. Immunol.*, **41**, 429 (1941).
27. Kurotchkin, T. J., and C. O. Kratze, *Chinese Med. J.*, **46**, 387 (1932).
28. Kwapinski, J. B., *Methods of Serological Research*, Wiley, New York, 1965.
29. Levin, R., and R. W. Brauer, *J. Lab. Clin. Med.*, **38**, 474 (1951).
30. Locke, A., E. R. Main, and D. O. Rosbash, *J. Clin. Invest.*, **11**, 527 (1932).
31. Loutit, J. F., and P. L. Mollison, *Brit. Med. J.*, **2**, 744 (1943).
32. Loutit, J. F., P. L. Mollison, and I. M. Young, *Quart. J. Exptl. Physiol.*, **32**, 183 (1943).
33. Malkiel, S., and W. C. Boyd, *J. Exptl. Med.*, **66**, 383 (1937).
34. Marrack, J., and F. C. Smith, *Brit. J. Exptl. Pathol.*, **12**, 182 (1931).
35. McFarlane, W. D., *Biochem. J. (London)*, **26**, 1022 (1932).
36. Mueller, J. H., *J. Immunol.*, **42**, 343 (1941).
37. Parish, H. J., *Antisera, Toxoids, Vaccines and Tuberculins in Prophylaxis and Treatment*, Williams and Wilkins, Baltimore, 1954.
38. Parnas, J. K., and R. Wagner, *Biochem.*, **125**, 253 (1921).
39. Pizzi, M., *Human Biol.*, **22**, 151 (1950).
40. Ramon, G., *Compt. rend. soc. biol.*, **86**, 661, 711, 813 (1922).
41. Rosenau, M. J., *U.S. Public Health Service, Hyg. Lab. Bull.*, No. **21**, April, 1905.
42. Rosenthal, L., *J. Lab. Clin. Med.*, **16**, 1123 (1931).
43. Rous, P., and J. R. Turner, *J. Exptl. Med.*, **23**, 219 (1916).
44. Wu, H., L. H. Cheng, and C. P. Li, *Proc. Soc. Exptl. Biol. Med.*, **25**, 853 (1927).
45. Wu, H., P. P. T. Sah, and C. P. Li, *Proc. Exptl. Biol. Med.*, **26**, 373 (1929).
46. Zinsser, H., J. F. Enders, and L. D. Fothergill, *Immunity: Principles and Application in Medicine and Public Health*, Macmillan, New York, 1939.

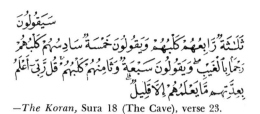

ثَلَثَةٌ رَّابِعُهُمْ كَلْبُهُمْ وَيَقُولُونَ خَمْسَةٌ سَادِسُهُمْ كَلْبُهُمْ رَجْمًا بِالْغَيْبِ وَيَقُولُونَ سَبْعَةٌ وَثَامِنُهُمْ كَلْبُهُمْ قُل رَّبِّى أَعْلَمُ بِعِدَّتِهِم مَّا يَعْلَمُهُمْ إِلَّا قَلِيلٌ

—*The Koran*, Sura 18 (The Cave), verse 23.

CHAPTER 17

Quantitation and Statistical Methods in Immunology

Statistical methods are often called for in evaluating the results of quantitative determinations in immunology, and such methods will be discussed in this final chapter.

To have a concrete example, let us recall that in many cases the only practical way of estimating the potency of a toxic or infectious preparation, or the protective power of an antiserum, is by the injection of graded doses into test animals (see 33). To interpret the results of such an experiment properly, or at any rate to extract from the figures all the information they are capable of furnishing us relative to the questions we asked, statistical methods must often be used.

1. Basic Statistical Principles

If we were testing a protective serum, and found that one moderate dose would protect every animal given it against several lethal doses of a toxic or infectious agent, even when the tests included hundreds of animals, it is clear that we should be justified in concluding without further ado that the serum had a high protective power. But considerations of time and expense usually prevent us from using really large numbers of animals in an experiment, and the results in any case are seldom so dramatic and satisfying as these hypothetical ones. More probably, we shall find ourselves carrying out experiments in which not all the treated animals are protected, and not all the controls die. Even if our problem is one of the simplest possible sort, *i.e.,* simply to

decide if one preparation is more potent than another, we have to decide
when to conclude that the results indicate a significant difference in
potency, and what degree of confidence we are justified in feeling in
them. In planning an experiment, we must decide in advance, on the
basis of the expected behavior of the reagents and our knowledge of
statistical principles, how many animals will be required to give a satisfactory answer to the question we are asking.

The procedure is always to compare the actual results with those to
be expected on the basis of pure chance. That is, we assume provisionally
that the treatment has made no difference in the life expectation of the
treated animals, and therefore the most likely result of the experiment
would be that equal numbers of both the treated and the control groups
would die. But it is possible, also by pure chance, for more of the controls
than of the treated group to die. If nothing but chance is operating, we
can calculate mathematically how frequently this would happen.

Suppose that we know accurately, from experiments with large numbers
of animals, that a certain dose of a toxin (or whatever agent we are using)
will kill just 30 per cent of our animals. We express this by saying that
the probability of death $= 0.3$. Since the animal must either live or die,
the probability of living $= 1.0 - 0.3 = 0.7$. We may symbolize the
chance of death by p, and the chance of living by q; we shall always
have: $p + q = 1$.

Suppose our experiment includes only two animals, which we may refer
to as A and B. The chance that A will die is p. In the absence of dis-
turbing influences, the chance that B will also die is $p \times p = p^2$. Similarly we may calculate the chances of the other possible outcomes:

> A lives and B lives: q^2
> A lives, B dies: pq
> A dies, B lives: pq
> A and B both die: p^2

Therefore we obtain:

> chance of 2 deaths: p^2
> chance of 1 death: $2pq$
> chance of no death: q^2

These values are the successive terms of the binomial expansion of
$(p + q)^2 = p^2 + 2\,pq + q^2$, and it is easy to show that when more than
two animals are involved, the chances of the various outcomes are calculated similarly, from the expression $(p + q)^n$, when $n =$ the number of

animals. We can now compare these frequencies, predicted on the basis of pure chance, with the observed results.

If n is at all large the computations become laborious, but fortunately, since we are usually not interested in the actual probability of each possible result, but only wish to know if a given observed result is likely or unlikely, we can make use of a short cut. If n is large, the curve obtained by plotting against the probability of each possible outcome (0, 1, 2, 3, etc., deaths), the *number* of deaths, is the normal curve of error, or probability curve, which has a known formula. We know that this curve has a certain simple function, called the standard deviation, and represented by σ, which has this property: if we lay off distances equal to σ on each side of the center (mean) of the probability curve, and draw lines, these lines include between them about two-thirds of the area under the curve; or in other words, the probability of a result represented by a point outside these lines is only about one-third (see Fig. 17-1).

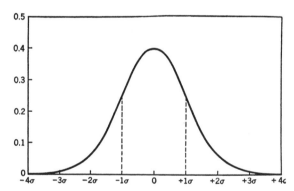

Fig. 17-1. Probability curve, showing portion of area included by line drawn through $+\sigma$ and $-\sigma$ (σ being the standard deviation).

We may calculate also the probability of results corresponding to deviations from the mean corresponding to 2σ, 3σ, or any other multiple we like. Therefore, if we observe a given deviation in an experiment (that is, our observed result is not the one predicted as most probable on the basis of pure chance), we may calculate, or determine from tables, just how probable it is, if it is assumed to be one of the rare, but possible, chance outcomes. This probability is never zero. Just how small it must be before we decide that the result is too *improbable* for the result to be solely due to chance, is a matter of individual taste and may depend also upon the type of experiment. We might be more readily convinced, for instance, in an experiment on the protective effect of an antiserum, than in an experiment apparently demonstrating the existence of telepathy or clairvoyance. If we do not believe the departure from expectation is due to chance, we consequently conclude, if we think the experiment was properly designed, that the experimental treatment is responsible for the deviation, and that the preparation we are testing is not without effect. In biological experiments in general it has proved satisfactory to consider as significant an experiment showing a deviation of as much as 2σ, which would be expected on the basis of pure chance only about once in 20 times. This will mean that we shall be led to follow up a false indication once in every 20 experiments, but has the advantage that we shall not miss a lead into a valuable investigation so often as if we set our standard of significance higher and required a larger deviation.

When the probabilities p and q are known, σ may be calculated very simply from the relation, $\sigma = \sqrt{npq}$. Thus in the hypothetical experiment above, if we treated 20 animals, σ would equal $\sqrt{20 \times 0.3 \times 0.7} = 2.05$. Since this gives for 2σ the value of 4.1, this means that in such an experiment we should consider a result significant if the deaths observed differed from the true average number of deaths, six, by more than four; that is, if only one or none of the animals die we should be led to follow up the experiment with a more elaborate one in the hope of proving that the treatment really had protective value. Tables for evaluating such tests will be found in references given below.

2. Estimation of Standard Error

In the majority of experiments we do not know the true expectations, p and q; consequently we cannot calculate σ from them, and must *estimate* it from the data of the experiment itself. This is possible, if the setup includes controls. The size of σ, and therefore the magnitude of the deviation which we must find to consider it significant, will depend upon the number of animals used. Details of such calculations will be found in reference (46). We shall not give any examples here, for other methods will prove better adapted to our purposes.

It should be pointed out that σ as we thus calculate it is merely the standard error of response, and if the response is to be used to predict the proper dose of an antitoxin, for instance, other factors enter into the estimate of the error. One of the most important of these is the slope of the dosage–mortality curve (in its straight-line form) (see below).

If the number of animals is small, as it usually is, there is a better way than the above of measuring the significance of any difference in mortality between treated and control animals. This is called the χ^2 test, and is based on a rather simple calculation from the data, which can be made without any understanding of the mathematical theory, which is not presented here.

3. The χ^2 Test

The χ^2 (chi-square) test was specifically designed to test whether an observed distribution of individuals with two (or more) different histories into two (or more) different categories can be due solely to chance. For example, we have two groups of soldiers, some inoculated against typhoid, and some not (two different histories). Some of the soldiers get typhoid and some do not (two different categories). If the distribution we find could be due merely to chance, then obviously we are not justified in saying the inoculations protected against typhoid. If it could not be due to chance, then perhaps the inoculations did help.

A classical example of such a study is provided by the results collected by the British Antityphoid Committee and analyzed by Greenwood and Yule. The results were subjected to the chi-square test by the great British statistician R. A. Fisher, and his figures are used here (18). The numbers of soldiers who were inoculated and were attacked by typhoid, and the numbers of those who were not, are shown in Table 17-1, also the corresponding figures for the non-inoculated troops.

TABLE 17-1
Typhoid Incidence in Inoculated and Uninoculated Troops (18)

	Attacked	Not attacked	Total
Inoculated	56	6,759	6,815
Not inoculated	272	11,396	11,668
Totals	328	18,155	18,483

It will be seen that the *proportion* of attacked individuals is somewhat higher in the uninoculated troops (about 2.2 per cent as opposed to about 0.8 per cent). Could this big a difference be due to chance? To compute chi-square so as to answer this question, we first calculate the numbers to be expected in the attacked and non-attacked categories if the inoculations had no effect. A total of 18,483 persons were studied. Of these 328 came down with typhoid. If the inoculations are ineffective, we should calculate that 328/18,483 of both groups would get the disease. Thus we expect $328/18,483 \times 6,815 = 120.94$ of the inoculated to get typhoid, and $328/18,483 \times 11,668 = 207.06$ of the uninoculated to suc-

TABLE 17-2

Expected Typhoid Incidence in Inoculated and Uninoculated Troops (18)

	Attacked	Not attacked	Total
Inoculated	120.94	6,694.06	6,815
Not inoculated	207.06	11,460.94	11,668
Totals	328	18,155	18,483

cumb. The calculations for the unattacked are performed similarly. This gives us Table 17-2.

Chi-square is calculated from these figures as follows: Take in each case the difference between the observed and the expected number and square it. Divide this square by the expected number. Add all these quotients. These operations are shown in Table 17-3. Note that in 2×2

TABLE 17-3

Calculation of χ^2 from Tables 17-1 and 17-2

$$120.94 - 56 = 64.94$$
$$6,759 - 6,694.06 = 64.94$$
$$272 - 207.06 = 64.94$$
$$11,460.94 - 11,396 = 64.94$$
$$(64.94)^2/120.94 = 34.7$$
$$(64.94)^2/6,694.06 = 0.6$$
$$(64.94)^2/207.06 = 20.3$$
$$(64.94)^2/11,460.94 = 0.4$$
$$\text{Total} = \chi^2 = 56.234$$

tables all the differences are the same (a good check on our arithmetic).

Whether a value of chi-square of 56.234 is significant or not can be ascertained by examination of tables such as those given by Fisher (18), Fisher and Yates (19), Pearson (39), or Pearson and Hartley (39a) taking into account the number of degrees of freedom (DF), which in 2×2 tables such as Table 17-1 is always one. The number of degrees of freedom in a given case can always be found by noticing how many of the "cells" of the table could be filled in arbitrarily and still leave enough empty cells so that, by filling in the empty cells properly, the original marginal totals would remain the same. (There are four cells in a 2×2 table, six in a 3×2 table, etc.) It is clear that in a 2×2 table only one cell can thus be filled in arbitrarily. We thus have $\chi_{(1)}^2 = 56.234$.

The subscript (1) in the above expression refers to the number of degrees of freedom, following an increasingly popular convention. The expression $\chi_{(2)}^2$ would symbolize chi-square for two degrees of freedom, and so on.

Fisher's Table III shows that as chi-square increases the probability that the observed distribution could be due to chance decreases rapidly. For $\chi_{(1)}^2 = 6.635$ the probability is 0.01, so we see that the probability of our result is much less than 0.01, and Fisher says that "the observations are clearly opposed to the hypothesis of independence" (*i.e.*, to the hypothesis that there is no significant difference in the incidence of typhoid in the two groups).

The reader might like to know just *how* improbable the observed distribution is. This can be found from a nomogram (9), of which Fig. 17-2 is an extended version.

If an index line, such as a stretched thread or a line ruled on some flat transparent material is used to connect the calculated values of χ^2 on the right-hand scale with the appropriate number of degrees of freedom (*DF*) on the middle scale, the point at which the index line crosses the left-hand scale gives the value of the probability (*P*).

Connecting 56.2 on the chi-square scale with 1 on the *DF* scale, we find on the *P* scale a probability of about 10^{-13}. This is such a low probability that it hardly has any meaning, except to enable us to state that the results are overwhelmingly significant. (It is about the same as the probability that if you toss a coin 43 times, heads will come up every time.)

The nomogram of Fig. 17-2 is quicker and more convenient to use than tables, and has a number of other advantages. It gives larger values of *DF* and chi-square than do most tables, thus enabling cases where these occur to be handled directly without any approximate calculations. It gives much lower values of the probability than are to be found in any table, for experience has shown that although a knowledge of the exact values of the very low probabilities is in no way necessary to establish that the results are significant, many workers would like estimates of the probabilities in such cases, and would cite them if they were available.

Now comes the question of the interpretation of the above result. A probability of 10^{-13} is so low that we are certainly justified in believing that the discrepancy between the proportions in the various categories of the table did not arise by accidents of sampling. We can state that there is a highly significant deviation from the proportions to be expected on the basis of chance. This much the chi-square test tells us. But what we wanted to know was whether the antityphoid inoculations had conferred a significant degree of protection against typhoid fever. Does the chi-square test tell us that?

The answer is, that the chi-square test does not tell us this directly, but it might tell us that the inoculations conferred a good degree of protection, *provided* the inoculated and control groups were exactly alike in all other respects. This means they should have been drawn at random

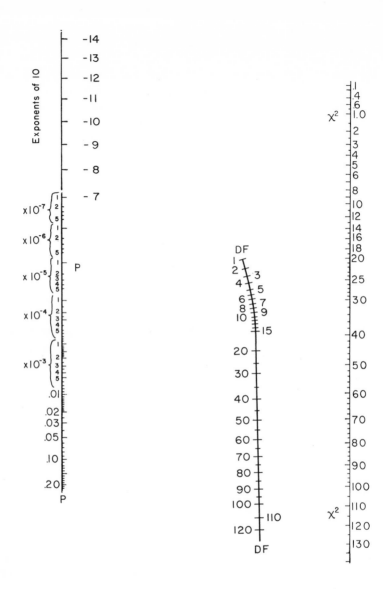

Fig. 17-2. Nomogram for calculating the probability of a found value of chi-square for various numbers of degrees of freedom (9), extended beyond the original range of P by use of the relations

$$\log_e P = -\,^1\!/_2\ \chi^2_{(2)}$$

$$\chi^2_{(1)} = (D/\sigma)^2$$

(D/σ) as in Fisher's Table 1 (18). For values of $P < 10^{-9}$, interpolation in the National Bureau of Standards' *Tables of the Error Function and its Derivative*, Washington 1954, was resorted to.

from the same social and economic classes of the population, and from areas with a similar prevalence of typhoid, so that we may suppose they had been equally exposed to typhoid infection in the past, and had had equal amounts of previous inoculation, if any, and that their native resistance, as determined by physique, diet, general health, etc., was on the whole the same. *Furthermore,* since we said the two groups must be exactly alike in *all* respects, this means that the degree of exposure of the two groups to typhoid infection after the inoculations were made must be known to have been the same.

These considerations show some of the practical difficulties of interpreting experiments to which the chi-square test is applicable, for it is immediately obvious that it is unlikely that the two groups were really as exactly alike as required, and in fact examination of the original protocols provides good reasons for believing that they were not. The data we have just finished analyzing are therefore a better example of how to do a chi-square test than they are of the efficiency of antityphoid inoculation, and they have been presented here precisely for the former purpose. We now know that the degree of protection afforded by even modern antityphoid inoculation is far from perfect (p. 636), and the vaccines in use when the above data were collected were not equal to our present vaccines, containing as they did no Vi antigen and in some cases apparently no "O" antigen.

If the numbers involved are small, so that the number expected in any class is less than ten, a "correction for continuity" should be applied to the simple calculations just outlined, for greatest accuracy. This is particularly desirable if the results appear to be just barely significant (probability slightly less than 0.05). A method of making this correction is given by Fisher and Yates (19).

Application of the χ^2 test to immunological experiments, even to some of the results which have been published as showing the advantage of some certain mode of treatment, sometimes gives surprising results. For instance, if of 73 animals given a serum only 28 died, whereas of 13 controls 9 died, it is probable that some workers would consider that a definite effect of the serum was indicated. Actually, however, accurate application of the χ^2 test shows that the results are below our usual level of significance (19).

4. Measurement of Effective Dose

The simple procedure of Ehrlich (42), with slight modifications, still suffices to estimate the minimum lethal dose (MLD) of diphtheria toxin with adequate accuracy. But the reproducibility of response of the animals to similar doses of toxin seen in this procedure is far from typical of the results generally observed when a group of animals are treated with a biological reagent. Rather more typical, unfortunately, are data of the sort shown in Table 17-4, which show the results of an experiment of

TABLE 17-4
Animal Titration of a Toxin

Dose, mg.	Mice used (n)	Lived	Died	Per cent mortality
0.0625	5	4	1	20
0.125	5	3	2	40
0.25	5	4	1	20
0.5	5	0	5	100
1.0	5	1	4	80
2.0	5	0	5	100
4.0	5	0	5	100

Irwin and Cheeseman (24) designed to determine the toxicity for mice of a preparation of a toxic preparation from *S. typhimurium*.

Here there is abundant evidence of nonuniformity of response on the part of the animals. A dose of 0.5 mg. killed all the mice in the fourth group, and might perhaps be considered the MLD, except that a dose twice as big, given to the fifth group, killed only four of the group. Futhermore, a dose only $1/8$ as large, given to the first group, killed one animal, and a dose $1/4$ as large killed two out of five. Evidently individual animals, although chosen to be as similar as possible, respond differently to the same dose. Just what is the MLD of this toxin for mice? It is pretty obvious that this question can hardly be answered on the basis of the present data, which are unfortunately quite typical; in fact nine repetitions of this experiment by Irwin and Cheeseman yielded in every case data of the same general sort. Is it possible to conclude anything at all of a quantitative nature from such an experiment?

The answer to this latter question is an affirmative, but it turns out that we shall do much better, in terms of amounts of quantitative information we get out of a given number of mice, to inquire, not what is the MLD of the toxin, but rather what dose will kill on the average just 50 per cent of them (20). This unit, in analogy with the MLD, is usually called the LD50.

If instead of a toxin, we were testing a protective serum, we should try to determine the dose which would just save 50 per cent of the animals, each of which was "challenged" with a fatal dose of the agent against which the serum was supposed to protect. This dose of serum might be known as the ED50, meaning the dose effective for 50 per cent of the animals. It is apparent that in determining it we have to make use of one or several MLD of the toxic or infectious agent, and it might be supposed that the uncertainties which we have just discussed in the determination of this MLD might affect the ED50 estimated for the serum, and also it might make a difference how many MLD's we used for a challenge. This supposition is correct, and we shall return to the question.

5. Fifty Per Cent End Point

The experimental determination of the LD50 of a toxin involves administering different doses to several groups of animals, and observing the numbers of animals in each group which are killed on or before a certain day after the inoculations. It is customary to give doses which increase in some logarithmic ratio (*e.g.*, are successively doubled), and to give each dose to each of the several animals which make up the experimental group for that dose. It used to be planned to have the doses vary sufficiently so as to cover the complete range from no deaths to 100 per cent kill, but this is not the most economical use of the animals, and if the approximate toxicity of the preparation is known the animals should be divided into several equal groups, each receiving a dose supposed to be near, somewhat above, and somewhat below the 50 per cent end point, making fairly certain that in some groups the mortality will be more, and in other groups less, than 50 per cent. Before this can be done, however, it is necessary to have some idea of the toxicity, as from a preliminary "orientation" experiment. Such experiments are likely to cover pretty much the whole mortality range. The experiment of Irwin and Cheeseman (Table 17-4) is an example of such an experiment .

Looking at Table 17-4, we see that it is certainly not easy to determine the LD50 by inspection. Since the number used in each group was 5, it was a course impossible for any dose to kill exactly 50 per cent of the animals. Of the actual doses, 0.125 mg. came closest to doing this, but the results of the other doses indicate that 0.125 can hardly be the true LD50. We evidently need to calculate the LD50 from the information provided by the experiment as a whole. How shall we do it?

A number of methods of calculating 50 per cent end points from such data have been proposed (8,14,24,41,6,26,36,27), but for practical purposes one of them has far greater utility than any other. This procedure is the simple one of making a graph of the data, fitting a curve to it by inspection, and reading off the LD50 from this curve.

However, it will not do to make a simple plot of mortality against dosage on ordinary graph paper, for the relation between mortality and dosage is not a linear one, which means it is difficult to fit actual data such as those of Table 17-4 with an ideal curve that will summarize the information contained in the data. It is necessary instead to plot the data in such a way that the theoretical relation between mortality and dosage is a straight line. After this has been done, drawing in the best-fitting line, and reading off from it the dosage corresponding to 50 per cent mortality, become easy. Again, more than one way of plotting the data so as to obtain a straight line exists, but we shall discuss only three of them here. The simplest, if the materials are available, consists in plotting the data on logarithmic probability paper, which is graph paper ruled in such a way that the percentage scale expands more and more in either direction from the 50 per cent ordinate, and the dosage scale is logarithmic. If we plot the above data on such paper, draw in the best-fitting line by eye, and note the dosage corresponding to the intersection of this line with the 50 per cent ordinate, we obtain an LD50 of 0.25 mg. (There is no way of plotting points corresponding to 100 per cent on probability paper, since at mortality 100 and 0 per cent the scale stretches away to infinity. This does not greatly matter, for as we shall see below, the statistical weight to be given such points is small. Actually, there is a way of using these points, which will be described below.)

If probability paper is not available, the same result may be achieved by plotting, not the observed mortalities, but certain functions of them called probits (short for probability units), using semilogarithmic graph paper, and plotting the doses on the logarithmic scale (36). Then we may proceed to draw in the best-fitting line and read off the intersection as before. We note that a mortality of 50 per cent corresponds to a probit of 5.00. Probits corresponding to other percentages are found in tables in the various papers and books referred to. The conversion may be made with sufficient accuracy for the present purpose by use of the chart* of Fig. 17-3. More accurate values will be found in the references.

Even if only ordinary graph paper is available, it is still simple to solve our problem graphically. We plot the probits corresponding to the mortality percentages against the logarithms of the doses, looking up these latter values in any table of logarithms or even on a slide rule. If

---

* Examples of other charts that have been proposed for use in connection with such problems will be found in references (28, 31, and 32).

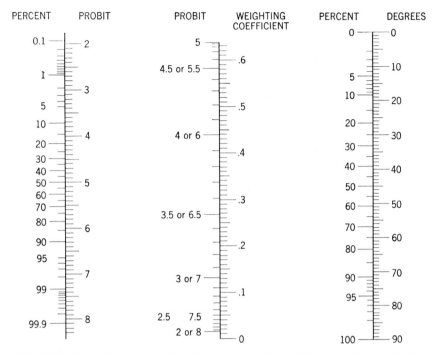

Fig. 17-3. Charts for converting per cents to probits (left-hand portion), obtaining weighting factor for probits (middle portion), and converting per cents to angles (right-hand portion). Since in each case there is a fixed correspondence between the two values, no stretched thread or movable index line is needed to read this chart.

the doses were successively doubled, as in the present example, we may simply plot the powers of 2 by which the basic dose is multiplied. Such a graph is shown in Fig. 17-4. We let dose $= 0.3125 \times 2^x$, where 0.03125 is the basic dose and x is the quantity we call the "dose metameter."

This graphical method, in addition to being simple and quick has other important advantages (14). It is just as easy and satisfactory to use when the dosages are not equally spaced or do not cover the whole range, and when the numbers of animals tested are not equal for all dosages. It is also just as adaptable to estimating other properties of the dose-response relationship, such as the LD90, and forms a convenient beginning for the more accurate maximum likelihood analysis by probits, should a more precise estimate be required.

Again we have not plotted the points corresponding to 100 per cent mortality (suggested by arrows pointing upward), for a probit corresponding to 0 or 100 per cent has no meaning. However, it has been shown

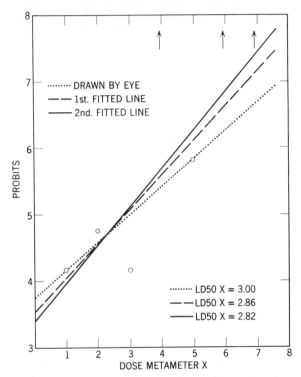

Fig. 17-4. Graph of mortality data from toxin titration (Table 17-4). Probits plotted against dose metameter x, where dose $= 0.3125 \times 2^x$. Arrows indicate that no probits for the mortality at these dosages (100 per cent mortality) exist. Dotted line drawn by eye, dashed line obtained by maximum likelihood adjustments, solid line obtained by second round of maximum likelihood adjustments.

that the contribution of such points to the final result is slight, and we shall not greatly impair the accuracy of our estimate if we ignore them. In case it is thought necessary to take account of them, it may be assumed that in such instances $1/4$ of an animal responded or failed to respond. In our case this would mean that where 5 animals died we should calculate a mortality of 4.75/5.00 or 95 per cent. However, if such points are plotted, it should be kept in mind in drawing an empirical line that they have only about a third as much weight in influencing the final results as do points nearer the 50 per cent region. To avoid decisions as to weight, we have omitted the 100 per cent points in Fig. 17-4. The line, which shows the relation between mortality and dosage, is called the mortality–dosage regression line.

From Fig. 17-4 we find that the intersection of our empirical line with the ordinate 5.00 corresponds to $x = 3.00$, which means an LD50 of $0.03125 \times 2^3 = 0.25$ mg., which is the same as that read directly from the more convenient probability paper. Following Finney (14) we shall let m stand for the value of x corresponding to the LD50.

The data used to obtain this estimate are poor and inadequate, so it is easy to see that we cannot have much confidence that we have hit the true LD50 exactly on the head. If we had used more animals or had done the experiment with different animals, we might have got quite a different result. How different, we do not know. In other words, we have estimated the 50 per cent end point, but have provided no "yard-stick" to enable us to judge how close to the true end point our estimate may be.

To obtain an accurate estimate of the size of the region within which we may reasonably expect the true end point to lie, we should need an accurate estimate of the standard error of our estimate. This can be obtained only by calculations which will at the same time estimate more accurately the LD50. In certain types of work we may want to make these calculations, but for many purposes they will be unnecessary. If we do not wish to go on, a rough estimate of the standard error of m may be obtained from the following formula:

$$s_m = \frac{1}{b\sqrt{pnw}},$$

where s_m means the estimate of the standard error of the dose metameter x, b is the slope of the fitted line, p is the number of points upon which the line is based, n is the average number of animals in each group, and w is the average weight of an observation, which depends upon the response to be expected at each dose (not the observed response). This expected response is the percentage mortality, at each dose, predicted from the straight line fitted to the data. In our case, since we have not plotted per cents but probits, we read the expected probits from the line marked "drawn by eye." We find, for the seven doses used, expected probits of 4.15, 4.57, 5.00, 5.40, 5.85, 6.25, and 6.67. The weights to be assigned to expected percentages or probits can be found with sufficient accuracy for our present purposes from Fig. 17-3. We obtain weights of 0.49, 0.60, 0.64, 0.60, 0.49, 0.35, and 0.22; average 0.48.

To obtain the slope of the line drawn by eye, we note that as the abscissas (does metameter) go from 1 to 6, the ordinates (probits) go from 4.15 to 6.25. The slope, therefore, is

$$b = \frac{6.25 - 4.15}{6 - 1} = 0.42.$$

The number of points, p, is 7, the number of animals in each group, n, is 5, and therefore we find

$$s_m = \frac{1}{0.42\sqrt{7 \times 5 \times 0.48}} = 0.58.$$

This means that we estimate for the LD50 that $x = m = 3.00 \pm 0.58$. (We find by more precise (maximum likelihood) calculations that the best estimate of m is 2.82 ± 0.47.) These standard errors apply to the dose metameter, and the dose goes up by powers of 2 of the dose metameter. This standard error is therefore not strictly applicable to the estimated LD50, and various dubious calculations are sometimes resorted to in order to obtain one which is (pp. 711 and 727). But in fact such a directly applicable error is not needed. What we are interested in are the "confidence limits" within which we may suppose the true LD50 to lie, and we have to get these from s_m. From the theory of the normal distribution it is known that 95 per cent of results should fall within limits of ± 1.96 standard errors,* and 99 per cent within 2.576 standards errors. We have $1.96 \times 0.58 = 1.14$. This means that we may state that 95 per cent of our results should lie between $0.03125 \times 2^{3} - {}^{1.14}$ and $0.03125 \times 2^{3} + {}^{1.14}$, or between our estimated LD50 multiplied by $2^{1.14}$ and our estimated LD50 divided by $2^{1.14}$. Now $2^{1.14} = 2.20$, and $1/2.20 = 0.45$, so we should expect 95 per cent of our estimates to lie between 220 and 45 per cent of our estimated LD50, or between 0.55 and 0.11 mg. We should expect 99 per cent to lie between 0.70 and 0.089 mg. (More precise estimates obtained by the maximum likelihood method are, 95 per cent limits, 0.422 to 0.116 mg., 99 per cent limits, 0.514 to 0.095 mg.) It is apparent that our approximate methods, making use of a line merely fitted by eye, have given results of fair accuracy, probably of sufficient accuracy for most purposes. They have somewhat overestimated the breadth of the confidence interval, which is probably good rather than

---

* Strictly speaking, this is true only if there is no significant "heterogeneity," as tested by χ^2, in fit of our line to the data; otherwise the standard error must be multiplied by "t," which depends upon the required level of significance and the number of "degrees of freedom" used in estimating the standard deviation (8,14). I have chosen to ignore this complication in such an elementary exposition. Those who intend to use such methods will do well to do considerable further reading, for example, in the sources cited here. (For the record, it may be mentioned that the χ^2 test in the present case shows no significant heterogeneity.)

bad. In general this approximate method would *underestimate* the confidence interval, and this should be kept in mind in order that we should not let it inspire us with false confidence in results obtained by it.

Instead of probits, the values obtained from the "angle transformation" may be plotted, as in the method of Knudsen and Curtis (27). The angle transformation, suggested by R. A. Fisher (15), also has the property of converting the dosage mortality curve, when dosage is plotted logarithmically, into a straight line, and has the further advantage that all points are of equal weight (except for percentages at or very near 0 or 100). The transformation may be carried out by means of the formula

$$a = \arcsin \sqrt{\bar{p}}$$

where arcsin means "the angle whose sine is" and p is the proportional response *(e.g.,* if the percentage mortality at a point is 20 per cent, $p = 0.20$). Much more convenient than the formula is Fig. 17-3. Tables also exist which give the conversion of per cents into angles.

Plotting the data of Table 17-4, after transforming the percentage mortalities to angles, and using the powers of 2 as abscissae, as before, enables us to draw in an estimated regression line by eye. The x value corresponding to the intersection of the 45-degree ordinate with this line enables us to estimate the dose metameter of the LD50 and thence the LD50. Results very similar to those obtained from the probit graph are obtained in this case; $m = 3$, LD50 $= 0.25$ mg.

The standard error of this estimated LD50 can be estimated roughly on the basis of the following formulas

$$V_m = \frac{S(Y - y)^2}{b^2(p - 2)Sn}$$

and

$$s_m = \sqrt{V_m}$$

where V_m stands for the estimated variance of the dose metameter of the LD50 and s_m the standard error, $S(Y - y)^2$ is the sum of the squares of the deviations of points from the fitted line (omitting angles of 0 and 90, which correspond to responses of 0 or 100 per cent), b is the slope of the fitted line, p the number of points upon which it is based (again omitting angles of 0 and 90), and Sn is the total number of animals used at doses giving the responses not 0 or 100 per cent. In the present case we have

$$V_m = \frac{0^2 + 3.5^2 + 18.3^2 + 0^2}{9.16^2 \times 2 \times 20} = 0.104$$

$$s_m = 0.32.$$

The crude estimate in this case underestimates the standard error, and confidence limits from this estimate would be too narrow.

As already mentioned, there exist many other ways of estimating 50 per cent end points. One of the most used of these is the method of Reed and Muench (41), which proceeds to add mortalities and survivals for the various groups of animals, and computes the 50 per cent end point from the cumulative mortalities and survivals which bracket the 50 per cent point. The method is fairly simple (although not as simple as the above method of drawing a straight line on a graph) and, probably because the accumulation of mortalities and survivals gives the experimenter a comfortable feeling that more animals have been used than is actually the case, has been very popular. Nevertheless, it suffers from grave disadvantages, and although given in the first two editions of this book, will not be described here. Certain workers will doubtless continue to use it no matter what is said, but these persons, being already familiar with the method, will not require a new description of it, and others not familiar with it might be tempted to use it were it presented.

One of the original disadvantages of the Reed and Muench method was that there was no way of making an estimate of the standard error of the LD50 estimated by this method, leaving uncertain the limits within which the true LD50 would be expected to lie. However, an approximate method of estimating the standard error* has since been proposed (40).

The second disadvantage is that the Reed and Muench method does not always give results as good as those obtainable by the simple method of drawing in a line by inspection. The method of accumulating deaths and survivals looks as if it would take due account of the results at all doses, but it does not actually do so. For good data, all methods of estimation are likely to lead to much the same result, but for the sort of data which are unfortunately common in immunology this may not be so. For example, for the above data, the Reed and Muench method leads to an LD50 of 0.27 mg., which is actually not as close to the maximum likelihood value of 0.221 as was our result of 0.25 obtained by eye.

---

* It may be noted that the method of estimating the standard error proposed by Irwin and Cheeseman (24), described in the first two editions of this book, does not start with an estimate of the LD50 obtained by the Reed-Muench method, but uses the method of Kärber (26). It may sometimes give an acceptable result, but nevertheless, although it involves a fair amount of calculation, it is only a make-shift. It is doubtful if any such way-stations between graphical approximations and accurate computations are worth stopping at. It may be mentioned that Irwin and Cheeseman found for the data of Table 17-4 results equivalent to $m = 2.90$, $s_m = 0.43$. The Reed and Muench method gives $m = 3.11$. These may be compared with the maximum likelihood method value of $m = 2.82$ (p. 715).

The third disadvantage of the Reed and Muench method is that not only may it inspire false confidence by its apparent use of more animals than were actually used, it may with very bad data actually make it possible to estimate an end point where no end point ought to be. For instance, consider the data in Table 17-5, taken by Batson (2) from a recent publication in a recognized scientific journal. By means of the Reed and Muench method it can be calculated that the LD50 of the virus was a dilution of $10^{-1.7}$. But Batson points out that this value means nothing. A dose approximately 5 times as great (10^{-1}) killed only 10 per cent of the mice, and diluting the virus 100,000-fold $(10^{-1}$ to $10^{-6})$ practically *tripled* the mortality rate! Clearly, these data contain no evidence of any relationship between dosage and mortality, and any attempt to estimate an LD50 is a waste of time. The Reed and Muench method, of course, was never intended to be used with such data.

Three other approximate methods of calculating end points may be mentioned: the method of extreme lethal dosages (20), Behren's method (6), and Kärber's method (26). They have, among other drawbacks, the disadvantage that the test animals must be distributed more or less evenly over wide ranges of dosages, in order to ensure having zero or complete response at the extremes. Finney (14) pointed out that this is very wasteful, and that if previous experience or preliminary trials give any clue to the value of the LD50, by concentrating on dosages nearer to the LD50, observations of much greater weight are obtained, and a correspondingly more precise estimate of the LD50 obtained.

6. Method of Probits

If the estimate of the LD50 obtained by the graphical method described above is not considered accurate enough, an improved estimate can be obtained by the method of maximum likelihood applied to probits (8, 14). This procedure apparently seems difficult and complicated to many workers, but with a little practice it can be rapidly and accurately carried through. Probably few of the readers of the present book are likely to attempt it, but since if they do they will want detailed directions, and since it requires the use of tables which it would be out of place to reproduce here, it seems better to refer such ambitious readers to publications (14,8,19,35) in which the method is described and the requisite tables can be found. Of the references given here, it is probable that the book by Finney (14) would be the most useful to beginners having need for routine use of the probit method.

As an illustration of the application of the probit method to immunological data, we show in Table 17-6 the outline calculations for the

TABLE 17-5

Deaths Among Serum-Protected and Control Mice Challenged with Various Dilutions of a Virus Suspension. Numbers Indicate Deaths/Total Mice

Mice	Virus dilutions									LD50	N.I.[a]
	10^{-1}	10^{-2}	10^{-3}	10^{-4}	10^{-5}	10^{-6}	10^{-7}	10^{-8}	10^{-9}		
Serum protected	1/10	2/8	2/9	3/9	3/9	3/9	0/8	0/7	—	$10^{-1.7}$	
Controls	—	—	—	8/8	8/8	8/8	7/8	2/8	0/7	$10^{-7.6}$	790,000

[a] Neutralization index.

data of Table 17-4, starting with expected probits (Y) read off from the line drawn by eye in Fig. 17-4. It will be recalled that the number in each group (n) was 5. The weighting coefficients (w) and working probits (y) are found in Tables 4 and IV of Finney's book. The rest of the calculation is given without explanation, merely to give an idea of the amount of computation required. The symbol S indicates sum.

TABLE 17-6

Maximum Likelihood Estimation of LD50 by Method of Probits

Data from Table 17-4

Per cent mor- tality	Dose met- ameter x	Expected probit Y	nw	Working probit y	nwx	nwy
20	1	4.16	2.95	4.16	2.95	12.272
40	2	4.57	2.98	4.76	5.96	14.185
20	3	5.00	3.19	4.25	9.57	13.558
100	4	5.42	2.99	6.31	11.96	18.867
80	5	5.84	2.95	5.84	14.75	17.228
100	6	6.25	1.77	6.83	10.62	12.089
100	7	6.67	1.09	7.07	7.63	7.706
Totals			17.92		63.44	95.905

$$\bar{x} = 3.5402 \qquad\qquad \bar{y} = 5.3518$$

$Snwx^2$	$Snwxy$
282.30	369.400
224.59	339.521
57.71	29.879

$(Snwx)^2 = 4024.6336 \qquad\qquad (Snwx)(Snwy) = 6084.2132$

$(Snwx)^2/Snw = 224.59 \qquad\qquad (Snwx)(Snwy)/Snw = 339.321$

$Snwx^2 - (Snwx)^2/Snw = Snw(x - \bar{x})^2$

$Snwxy - (Snwx)(Snwy)/Snw = Snw(x - \bar{x})(y - \bar{y})$

$b = Snw(x - \bar{x})(y - \bar{y})/Snw(x - \bar{x}^2)^2 = 29.879/57.71$

$Y = \bar{y} + b(x - \bar{x}) = 3.519 + 0.518x$

For LD50 $Y = 5.00$, $x = m = 2.859$

$V_m = (1/0.518^2)(1/17.92 + 0.481^2/57.71) = 0.223$

$s_x = 0.472$

The variance of the estimated LD50, or rather the variance of the value of x corresponding to the LD50, is given by the formula

$$V_m = \frac{1}{b^2} \frac{(m - \bar{x}^2)}{Snw(x - \bar{x})^2} + \frac{1}{Snw}.$$

The standard error σ is the square root of V_m.
Since we put

$$\text{dose} = 0.03125 \times 2^x,$$

we have from Table 17-6

$$\text{LD50} = 0.03125 \times 2^{2.86} = 0.227.$$

Another round of calculations altered this to 0.221 (for $m = 2.82$), with a standard error S_m of 0.473.

The confidence limits for the LD50 can be estimated with sufficient accuracy for our purposes from the s_m, although a strictly accurate computation of the limits is somewhat more complicated (8,14) and leads to somewhat wider limits. We may take the 95 per cent limits to be as before between $0.03125 \times 2^{2.82 \ + \ 1.96(0.472)}$ and $0.3125 \times 2^{2.82 \ - \ 19.6(0.472)}$, which means 0.221×1.91 and $0.221 \div 1.91$.

The 95 per cent limits are between 191 and 52 per cent of the estimated LD50, or between 0.422 and 0.116 mg. The 99 per cent limits are between 0.514 and 0.095 mg.

The change in the regression line introduced by these two rounds of maximum likelihood calculations is indicated by the dashed and solid lines in Fig. 17-4. The increase in slope in the adjusted lines is due to the influence of the 100 per cent points which were not plotted.

The limited number of animals used, and their variability of response, do not permit a more precise knowledge of the whereabouts of the LD50. It is doubtful if in such cases the application of any methods of calculations more accurate than the graphical methods described is worth while. The application of the more elaborate and exact methods might well be reserved, in general, for more precise data obtained with more animals.

It is of interest to note that nine other exactly similar assays of the same preparation (24), also computed by the method of probits, gave the following estimated LD50's: 0.148, 0.246, 0.126, 0.274, 0.453, 0.276, 0.145, 0.470, 0.174, with a mean of 0.230. The 95 per cent limits, in per cents of the estimated LD50's, were for these other nine assays 60-167, 60-166, 62-163, 68-147, 65-155, 56-180, 56-177, 61-165.

One objection to the method of probits which is often mentioned may be discussed here, which is that the calculations require a prohibitive amount of time. The present author, who is far from being an expert in such matters, found that the calculations summarized in Table 17-6, using a piece of graph paper, a ruler, Finney's book, and a desk computer, required just 35 minutes by the clock. It was thus possible to do two rounds of calculations, of which the latter resulted in an adjustment amounting to less than one-tenth of a standard deviation, in a little over an hour. For data which were hard to obtain, or which might throw light on an important question, this could hardly seem a disproportionate outlay of time.

An advantage, already mentioned, of the method of probits over certain other methods is that it is not necessary that the data cover the entire dosage–mortality range.

7. Graded Response

Although death is certainly an all-or-none phenomenon, the response to toxins and antitoxins is often far from being all-or-none. Some animals may succumb promptly to a toxin, some after a longer or shorter time, some may recover after illness of greater or less severity, and some may show no symptoms. It is clear that if we treat the response in such cases as all-or-none we are throwing away some of the information which the experiment could provide. Ipsen *et al.* (23) reported experiments on the assay of the immunizing potency of tetanus toxoid where it was possible to draw conclusions from the grade of response of various animals, whereas in several of the assays the all-or-none response alone left the results inconclusive.

In order to make use of the grades of response in titrating an immunological preparation, it is necessary to devise a numerical scoring system. Ipsen used the following record to grade the immunity of his mice, which were challenged with several lethal doses of tetanus toxin:

Symptom	Score
Death within 2 days	0
Death within 3 and 4 days	2
Death within 5 and 7 days	3
Survival on 7th day with tetanus	4
Survival with no tetanus	5

These scores were chosen so that the mean scores of groups of mice would show an approximately linear relation to the logarithm of the dose of toxoid. This made it unnecessary to make use of any transformation such as the probit transformation. Consequently the responses could be plotted against doses on semilogarithmic paper, or against the logarithms of doses on ordinary graph paper, and a straight line drawn in by eye or fitted by the method of least squares. As an example we may consider the assay of tetanus toxoid shown in Table 17-7.

TABLE 17-7

Assay of Tetanus Toxoid. Animals Immunized
12-14-'51, Challenged 12-28-'51 (23)

Dose of toxoid, ml.	No. of mice	Dead on day after challenge							Survivors		Sum of scores
		1	2	3	4	5	6	7	With tet.	No. tet.	
0.0125	6	—	—	—	—	1	—	—	—	5	33
0.0125	6	—	—	—	—	—	—	—	1	5	34
0.00625	6	—	1	2	—	—	—	—	1	2	20
0.00625	6	—	2	—	—	1	—	—	—	3	21
0.003125	6	—	3	1	—	—	—	—	2	—	10
0.003125	6	—	1	1	—	—	—	—	3	1	20
0.00156	6	—	4	1	1	—	—	—	—	—	4
0.00156	6	—	4	—	—	—	1	—	1	—	7

This is taken from a larger series reported by Ipsen *et al.* (23). The results are plotted in Fig. 17-5. The line drawn by eye and that fitted by least squares would hardly be distinguishable, and only the latter is shown.

From the graph we can interpolate the value of the dose metameter x (dose in milliliters $= 0.000781 \times 2^x$) for any particular score desired. Ipsen chose for purposes of comparison a mean score of 3 (total score 18 for 6 mice), which would not differ much from the ED50. For $y = 18$ we find $x = m = 2.43$, giving an ED (S_3) of 0.00421 ml. of toxoid. To estimate the confidence limits of this ED50 we need an estimate for the $s_y/b\sqrt{n}$, when s_m is the estimated standard deviation of m, s_y is the estimated standard deviation of y, b the slope of the fitted line, and n the number of points. (The slope is found as in the example on p. 709.) The standard deviation s_y is estimated by the formula

$$s_y = \sqrt{\frac{S(y - Y)^2}{n - 2}},$$

where y is the observed value of the score and Y the value calculated from the fitted line.

In the present case we find, approximately

$$s_y = 3.53; \qquad b = 8.95; \qquad n = 2.83;$$

therefore $s_m = 0.139$.

From this we estimate the 95 per cent limits for the ED (S_3) to be 0.00508 to 0.00349.

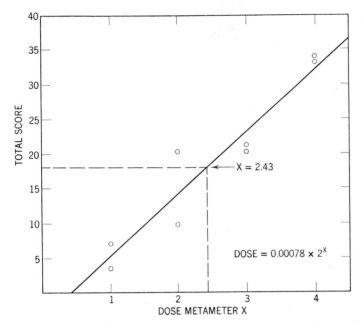

Fig. 17-5. Estimation of ED(S_3) of a tetanus toxoid by method of graded response (23). Total score for each group of six mice plotted against dose metameter x, where dose = 0.000781×2^x ml. toxoid. Dotted lines show intersection of total score of 18 (average score = 3.00) and fitted line, and corresponding value of dose metameter.

It should be realized that this value of s_m, and consequently these limits, like the ED(S_3), are merely estimates, and that if accurate values are required a line should be fitted accurately and the standard error computed by methods such as those used by Ipsen *et al.* in the article referred to.

One of the first contributions of Ipsen (21) to this subject was a re-examination of the old question of the determination of the MLD of toxins. The method of Ehrlich, as originally defined, was an all-or-none method making no use of the information obtainable from the grades of response. But it had long been evident that not merely the fact of the death of a guinea pig, but also the time required for it to die, contributes valuable information towards the estimation of the minimum lethal dose, and some not very successful attempts had been made to utilize this information. One of the difficulties was that the curve of death time, plotted against dose, is not a straight line, and neither is the curve of log death time plotted against log dose. Ipsen perceived that by taking advantage of knowledge accumulated from a great many experiments with toxin and any particular species of animal it would be possible to find a function of the death time as a linear function of the logarithm of the dose. This function, which Ipsen called $f(T)$, is shown in Table 17-8.

TABLE 17-8

Function $[f(T)]$ of Death Time (T) of Guinea Pigs Giving Linear Relation to Logarithm of Dose of Diphtheria Toxin [from Ipsen (21)]

T, hours	$f(T)$ (= log D/d)	T, hours	$f(T)$ (= log D/d)
15	3.254	40	0.498
16	2.604	48	4.353
18	2.045	56	0.260
20	1.628	64	0.198
22	1.442	72	0.155
24	1.196	80	0.124
28	0.927	96	0.085
32	0.792	120	0.042
36	0.602	144	0.035

In order to set up such a table it was necessary to have some starting dose which was not zero (since the logarithm of zero is minus infinity), such as a dose known to produce no symptoms, or the dose which would kill just half the animals (the time of observations being supposed so long as to be immaterial). Ipsen chose the latter in the present case, and represented this "asymptotic" dose by d. The actual dose is represented by D, and the function $f(T)$ is just the logarithm of D/d, or

$$f(T) = \log (D/d)$$

so that

$$\log d = \log D - f(T).$$

This enables us to compute a log d for each animal that dies in a reasonable observation period, and compute the mean of all these. Since from the original definition the MLD is the dose which decreases the survival time of the average guinea pig to 4 days (96 hours), the logarithm of the MLD is obtained by adding log 96 to log d.

The method can be illustrated (22) by applying it to the data of Table 17-9.

From Table 17-10 we find the mean log d [= mean log $D - f(T)$] to be -2.336. By adding to this the log of 96, we find the log of the MLD to be -2.256, which corresponds to 0.0055 ml. of toxin, instead of the 0.005 estimated by the traditional method (42).

The standard deviation of the values in the last column of Table 17-10 is found to be 0.118, and the standard deviation of the mean (obtained by dividing by the square root of the number of observations) is 0.0417.

TABLE 17-9
Determination of the MLD of Toxin (42)

Dose, ml.	Result
0.03	Death in 1.5 days
0.02	Death in 1.5 days
0.01	Death in 2 days
0.008	Death in 3 days
0.006	Death in 3.5 days
0.005	Death in 4 days = MLD
0.004	Death in 6 days
0.003	Death in 8 days
0.002	Late paralysis
0.001	Well in 16 days

TABLE 17-10

Dose, ml.	D death in		$\log D$	$f(T)$[a]	$\log D - f(T)$
	Days	Hours			
0.03	1.5	36	−1.52	0.60	−2.12
0.02	1.5	36	−1.70	0.60	−2.30
0.01	2	48	−2.00	0.35	−2.35
0.008	3	72	−2.10	0.16	−2.26
0.006	3.5	84	−2.22	0.11	−2.33
0.005	4	96	−2.30	0.08	−2.38
0.004	6	144	−2.60	0.04	−2.44
0.003	8	196	−2.52	0.01	−2.51
				Sum	−18.69

[a] From Table 17-8.

Since the standard deviation of a variable plus a constant is just the standard deviation of the variable, we have

$$\log \text{MLD} = -2.256 \pm 0.0417.$$

The 95 per cent confidence limits of this estimate are found by multiplying the standard error by the factor t, which can be found in Fisher's tables. For a probability of 0.05 and seven degrees of freedom, $t = 2.365$, so that the 95 per cent confidence limits of this estimate are −2.256 + (2.365 × 0.0417) and −2.256 − (2.365 × 0.0417), or since the antilogarithm of 2.365 × 0.0417 is 1.255, it is seen that the MLD can be considered to be known within about 26 per cent, which, considering how few animals were used, is surprisingly close. As Ipsen aptly says (21), few workers would ever want to know the MLD with an accuracy much greater than this.

Since t for $P = 0.05$ approaches 1.96 for larger numbers, we can calculate that if we desired to know the MLD to an accuracy of 10 per cent, for instance, we should have

$$0.118/\sqrt{n} = \log (1.10)/1.96,$$

where n is the number of animals needed. This gives $n = 31.2$, suggesting that we should need to use about 32 animals.

8. Comparisons of Potency

It is undoubtedly valuable to have confidence limits for end points, and we are justifiably suspicious of end points not accompanied by such estimates. Nevertheless, their meaning and value must not be exaggerated. They suggest limits within which we may expect the true end point to lie, if our experiment were a typical one in regard to all the possible variations. But this is seldom true. If factors which can vary and which would affect the result happened to be constant in our particular experiment, our estimate of the standard error and the confidence limits may be much too small. Therefore confidence limits do not, and cannot, successfully specify the limits of the estimated ED50 which will be obtained by a repeat trial. The results are affected by errors the nature of which may be unknown to us, depending upon the resistance of the particular lot of animals employed, which varies from laboratory to laboratory, upon their food, upon their sex, and many other factors. Any one determination of an end point is a measure of the

TABLE 17-11

ED50 Values and 95 Per Cent Confidence Limits of Repeated Mouse-Protection Potency Assays on Typhoid Vaccine MTV-1, Calculated By Bliss' Method (3)

Assay no.	ED50, ml.	Confidence limits, ml.
1	0.025	0.016–0.039
2	Data unsuitable for calculations	
3	0.209	0.077–0.565
4	0.093	0.059–0.147

material tested, of the animals employed, and of the complex "conditions of the experiment." For example, Batson (3) performed potency assays on a vaccine once a week for four consecutive weeks (Table 17-11). In each case the assay was carried out in as nearly the same manner as practicable, yet the results of the second trial were unsatisfactory for analysis and the ED50's obtained on the third and fourth trials were well outside the confidence limits estimated from the results of the first assay.

Some of the factors leading to such variation are discussed by Batson (3), who points out that a good deal of the time spent on elaborate calculation of end points might better be spent ensuring the validity and reliability of the original observations and in identifying and eliminating, as far as possible, the sources of variation.

9. Simultaneous Titrations

One way in which much of the effect of such variation can be eliminated consists in determining the potency of a preparation in comparison with a standard. Then if we use the same stock of animals for both, and do both experiments at the same time, keeping all conditions as comparable as possible, we may get a determination of *relative* potency which is much more accurate than any individual end point estimation.

Nevertheless, we are essentially comparing two estimates of potency, and each of these is subject to error. It is clear therefore that our estimate of relative potency will be subject to error.

If we knew the standard error σ exactly (instead of having only an estimate s of it, as is usual), we could calculate the uncertainty of the ratio of two LD50 values, making use of the fact that the standard error σ_D of the sum or difference of two quantities is equal to $\sqrt{(\sigma^2_1 + \sigma^2_2)}$. Suppose we had the following two values:

Preparation	log LD50	σ
A	1.127	0.105
B	1.669	0.129

The difference in the logs is 0.542, and $\sigma_D = \sqrt{0.105^2 + 0.129^2} = 0.166$.

The antilog of 0.542 is 3.48. Therefore we should estimate that preparation A is 3.48 times as strong as B. The uncertainty of this estimate is expressed as before, by calculating

$$\text{antilog } (1.96 \times 0.166) = 2.11.$$

The chances are 95 out of 100 that the true ratio of potencies is between 47 and 211 per cent of our estimate, that is, the true ratio of potencies lies between 1.65 and 7.35. This serves to illustrate the high degree of uncertainty which may attend comparisons of potency arrived at by tests on small numbers of experimental animals.

In actual practice we do not know the true standard errors, σ_1 and σ_2, but merely have estimates of them, s_1 and s_2, and we have to estimate the uncertainty of a relative potency from these. In practice this is very hazardous, for not only are the true standard errors unknown, but the LD50's as estimated are subject to other uncertainties which these standard errors do not reflect.

If the unknown preparation is tested at the same time as a standard preparation, and the experiment scored as an all-or-none phenomenon, we can obtain the relative potencies by plotting the probits of the mortalities, due to the two preparations, against the logarithm of the dosages, as above, and estimating the LD50 for each preparation. The ratio of the reciprocals of the LD50 values then gives an estimate of the relative potencies of the two preparations, which will be fairly reliable if the two dosage–response curves are parallel. As an illustration we may consider an assay reported by Batson, Brown, and Oberstein (5), shown in Table 17-12. From these data Batson *et al.* estimated graphically that the ED 50

TABLE 17-12

Typhoid Vaccine Mouse Protection Potency Assay (5) Numbers
Indicate Survivors/Total Animals 72 Hours after Challenge

Unknown vaccine		Standard vaccine	
Low dose (0.015 ml.)	High dose (0.15 ml.)	Low dose (0.015 ml.)	High dose (0.15 ml.)
6/20	16/20	4/20	14/20

All mice challenged i.p. with 1000 *S. typhosa* in 5 per cent mucin 6 days following immunization.

of the unknown was 0.0365 and that of the standard 0.0625. The relative potency of the unknown is therefore

$$0.0625/0.0365 = 171 \text{ per cent.}$$

In actual practice it is unnecessary to determine the separate ED50's. If the dosage–response curves are parallel (and if they are not parallel an attempt is made to adjust them so they will be parallel), the horizontal distance between them is m, and the log of the ratio of the potencies. For the above data we find $m = 0.2336$, so that the relative potency of the unknown is antilog $0.2336 = 1.71$. The standard error of m can be approximated by means of the formula (8)

$$s_m = (1/b) \sqrt{2/N_s + 2/N_u},$$

where b is the slope of the lines, and N_s and N_u are the numbers of animals responding in the range of probits 3.5 to 6.5, with the standard and with the unknown, respectively. For the above data we find

$$s_m = (1/1.36) \sqrt{(2/40 + 2/40)} = 0.233.$$

The 95 per cent limits of the relative potency would be estimated as before as $171 \times$ antilog (1.96×0.233) and $171 \div$ antilog (1.96×0.233), or 500 to 58 per cent. It will be seen that although the unknown seems stronger than the standard, and may in fact be five times as strong, it is also consistent with the data to consider it may possibly be weaker. This again illustrates the uncertainty of comparisons of potency based on the numbers of animals typically employed in immunological assays.

For the two-dose ("four point") assay it is possible to do these calculations without making a graph of the data, by use of the following formula

$$\text{Relative potency} = \text{antilog } (2 + iV/W),$$

where the relative potency of the unknown to the standard is expressed in per cent, $i = \log$ ratio doses, *i.e.*, $\log$ (high dose/low dose), and $V = U_L - S_L + U_H - S_H$ and $W = S_H - S_L + U_H - U_L$ and U_H response to high dose of the unknown, U_L response to low dose of the unknown, S_H response to high dose of the standard, and S_L response to low dose of the standard, and U_H, U_L, S_H, and S_L are all expressed in probits. Applying this to the data of Table 17-12, we obtain

$$i = \log 10 = 1 \qquad V = 4.48 - 4.16 + 5.84 - 5.52 = 0.64$$
$$W = 5.52 - 4.16 + 5.84 - 4.48 = 2.72$$
$$\text{potency} = \text{antilog } [2 + (1) (0.64)/2.72] = 171 \text{ per cent, as before.}$$

This calculation will correct for absence of strict parallelism in the two regression lines, but if the divergence from parallelism is great the result should be received with some reserve.

For a four-point assay, if the regression lines are reasonably parallel, this calculation of the relative potency will give the same result as the graphical method, and is as good as any that can be made. The standard error, of course, is only an approximation, and if more than two doses were used the relative potency, obtained graphically, is also only an approximation. For more reliable estimates the more elaborate formal methods should be used.

The method of Knudsen and Curtis (27) is preferred by some workers, especially for assays in which only two doses were used ("four-point assays"). It proceeds in a very similar way to the method of probits just given, but has the advantage that a more accurate estimate can be made of the standard error.

The Knudsen-Curtis method makes use of the angle transformation

$$a = \arcsin \sqrt{p}$$

where a is the transformed response in degrees, p is the proportional response, and arcsin means the angle whose sine is the value of $\sqrt{p}$ in question. This transformation can be effected by tables found in books such as Fisher and Yates (19), or by Fig. 17-3.

The equation for estimating relative potency by the Knudsen-Curtis method is the same as that used above for probits

$$\text{Relative potency} = \text{antilog } (2 + iV/W),$$

where the symbols have the same meaning as before, but U_L, U_H, S_L, and S_H, from which V and W are calculated, are expressed in angles. For the data of Table 15-25 we obtain

$$V = 33.2 - 26.6 + 63.4 - 56.8 = 13.2;$$
$$W = 56.8 - 26.6 + 63.4 - 33.2 = 60.4;$$

$\text{Relative potency} = \text{antilog } [2 + (1)(13.2)/(60.4)] = \text{antilog } (2.2185)$
$$= 165 \text{ per cent.}$$

The confidence limits of this estimate can be found from the standard error of the log ratio of potency, which is given by the formula

$$V_m = (s_m)^2 = \frac{i^2(57.3)^2}{n} \times \frac{W^2 + V^2}{W^2},$$

where n = the number of mice at each dose. In the present case we have

$$(s_m)^2 = \frac{(1)^2(57.3)^2}{20} \times \frac{(60.4)^2 + (13.2)^2}{(60.4)^4} = 0.0471;$$

$$(s_m)^2 = \sqrt{0.0471} = .0.217.$$

The 95 per cent confidence limits are, as before,

$$165 \times 2.66 \quad \text{and} \quad 165 \div 2.66$$

or 440 and 62 per cent.

It is seen that our crude estimate of the confidence limits was not too far off, and tended to exaggerate the range somewhat, which is of course a good thing for an approximate method to do.

There is a tendency for immunologists to want a standard error which applies directly to relative potency in per cent. Such a standard error can be computed, but this calculation is attended with pitfalls which should be mentioned.

The formula is (8.3)

Standard error $= (2.303)$ (s_m) (relative potency in per cent).

In the present case we have

Standard error $= (2.30)$ (0.217) $(165) = 82.5$ per cent.

Therefore we might say that the relative potency of the unknown is 165 ± 82.5 per cent.

But what does this mean? A standard error applies only to a parameter which is normally distributed. If the relative potency estimates are normally distributed with standard error 82.5, then 95 per cent of the estimates would be expected to lie between $165 + 1.96 \times 82.5$ and $165 - 1.96 \times 82.5$, or between 326 and 4 per cent. This does not agree at all with our previous estimate of the 95 per cent limits. It is in fact not right, for since the estimates of the *logarithm* of the relative potency are approximately normally distributed, the relative potency itself, which is the antilogarithm, cannot be normally distributed. By assuming that it is, we have made a serious mistake, and not estimated the upper confidence limit high enough, and have estimated the lower limit too low. The standard error for the relative potency we have calculated evidently cannot be used to estimate confidence limits, and in fact can have hardly any other function than a purely decorative one. A standard error which has some significance can under some circumstances be calculated from the above formula for the relative potency, but this should not be attempted when the standard error of the dose metameter, s_m, is greater than 10 per cent of the log of the relative potency (when this comes out as a ratio) or 10 per cent of the log relative potency minus 2 (when the relative potency comes out in per cent) (8).

As an example of the formal application of exact methods to the comparison of potency, we may take the data of Lockhart (34), who compared the virulence for mice of two strains of *Salmonella typhimurium* (Table 17-13).

This example is interesting because it illustrates the increase in power and precision of our research methods which modern statistics have made

TABLE 17-13
Mortality of Mice Produced by Intraperitoneal
Injection of Various Doses of *Salmonella Typhimurium*

Dose	Number of mice in each group	Mortality per cent strain A52	Mortality per cent strain Ellinger
10,000,000	25	92	96
100,000	25	48	88
1,000	25	44	56
10	25	16	24

possible. Thirty years ago, Topley and Wilson (46), who referred to these data, stated that although we can feel fairly confident that the Ellinger strain is more virulent than the A 52 strain, it is impossible to express the results in any numerical ratio. Dr. C. I. Bliss (7), whom the present author consulted in connection with this problem, pointed out that, on the contrary, merely by an application of the method of the probit-maximum likelihood, the relative virulence of the Ellinger strain could be calculated to be 30 times that of the A 52. Dr. Bliss' calculations are shown in Table 17-14.

It is true that the uncertainty in the estimate of relative virulence here is great (the 95 per cent confidence limits are from 350 to 2.5), but this is because of the very flat slope of the dosage-mortality curve. Bliss points out that anyone doing new experiments with such material would probably find it advantageous to see if some other method of conducting the test might lead to a marked steepening of the curve. Be that as it may, the fact remains that we have verified that the Ellinger strain is more virulent than the A 52, and have found a numerical estimate of the ratio of virulence. As in many similar cases, the standard error warns us to be cautious about taking this ratio too literally.

If a *graded* response is recorded and plotted according to a numerical scale, comparison between an unknown preparation and a standard is also possible, and this method sometimes enables information to be obtained from experiments where the mere record of the death or survival of the animals would be inconclusive. Ispen *et al.* (23) reported a large-scale experiment in which tetanus toxoids were compared by this method in different laboratories. The logarithm of the relative potency was given, as in the above titrations, by the horizontal distance between the two reaction curves. The slope of these curves was found to differ for the results of different laboratories, and seemed to be dependent on the relative immunizability of the mice. The reaction curves for unknown and standard could be drawn parallel for any given laboratory.

In Fig. 17-6 are shown the results of a comparison by the method of graded response of the immunizing effectiveness of two toxoids (23). The lines were drawn parallel, with the average slope found in 6 such assays in that laboratory. The distance between two lines, Δx, = 3.2, so we estimate that toxoid B is $2^{3.2} = 9.2$ times as effective as A. From the errors found in the series of assays of which this was a part, we may estimate that the 95 per cent limits for the relative potency of B and A as determined by this assay are 14.6 to 5.8. The mean of 8 different assays in 6 different laboratories gave a relative potency of B to A of 8.0.

The results of the study of Ispen *et al.* indicate again the necessity of including a reference standard in an assay to control the variations of the mouse populations used (variations of 15-fold in immunizability were observed between different laboratories). It was found that when this was done the precision of the comparisons of potency in the various laboratories were all about the same, such that a toxoid with a "true" potency of 100 would be ascribed potencies between 63 and 160 in 95 cases out of 100.

Details of the calculation involved in such comparisons of potency will be found in the paper by Ipsen *et al.* (23).

10. Size of Challenge Dose

If we are testing the immunizing effect of an antigen, we shall challenge our animals, after a suitable interval, with a dose of the infectious microorganism, or with a toxic product of this organism. We shall certainly want to use at least one infectious or one lethal dose, but there is the difficulty that some animals are more resistant than others, so we generally use several such doses. We have already quoted one worker who merely reports that he challenged his animals with "several lethal doses" of a toxin. Does it make no difference how many lethal doses we use?

The answer to this question is; of course it makes a difference, but if we are sensible and choose a suitable number of MLD's any comparative results we obtain will probably still be valid. However, an incorrect choice of the challenge dose can diminish considerably the apparent difference in response to an antigen. It is important to use a challenge dose of such a size that the mortality in each group of animals is definite, yet not 100 per cent in either.

11. Increasing the Accuracy of Assays

The standard errors of all the comparisons of potency we have discussed are relatively large, and the confidence limits correspondingly

TABLE 17-14

Comparison of Virulence of Two Strains of Bacteria (Table 17-13) by Method of Probits (Bliss)

Strain of bacteria	Observations		Computation of provisional curves			Expected probit, Y	Working probit, y	Computation of corrected curves		
	Log dose, x	Per cent dead	Empirical probit, Y'	Coefficient				Weighting coefficient, w	wx	wy
				X	XY'					
A 52 (S)	1	16	4.01	−3	−12.03	3.88	4.01	9.9	9.9	39.699
	3	44	4.85	−1	− 4.85	4.66	4.85	15.3	45.9	74.205
	5	48	4.95	1	4.95	5.45	4.91	14.8	74.0	72.668
	7	92	6.41	3	19.23	6.23	6.41	9.0	63.0	57.690
Total	16		20.22	0	7.30			49.0	192.8	244.262
Ellinger (U)	1	24	4.29	−3	−12.87	4.41	4.30	14.0	14.0	60.200
	3	56	5.15	−1	− 5.15	5.20	5.15	15.7	47.1	80.855
	5	88	6.18	1	6.18	5.99	6.16	11.0	55.0	67.760
	7	96	6.75	3	20.25	6.77	6.75	4.7	32.9	31.725
Total	16	—	22.37	0	8.41			45.4	149.0	240.540

(continued)

TABLE 17-14 (continued)

Provisional Curves

Combined slope: $b_c = \dfrac{2S(XY')}{INS(X^2)} = \dfrac{2(7.30 + 8.41)}{(2)(2)(20)} = 0.393$.

Means: $\bar{Y}'_s = 5.055,\ \bar{Y}_u = 5.592,\ \bar{x} = 4.$

Expected probits: $Y_s = 5.055 + 0.393\,(x - 4);\ Y_u = 5.592 + 0.393\,(x - 4).$

Calculation of Corrected Curves and of Relative Potency

	S	U	S + U
$\bar{x}$	3.934694	3.281938	
$\bar{y}$	4.984939	5.298238	
$[wx^2]$	199.9910	171.5912	371.5822
$[wxy]$	68.3878	74.2026	142.5904
b	0.34195	0.43244	0.38374
$[wy^2]$	28.049	32.370	60.419
χ^2	4.663	0.282	5.702, $n = 5$

$$m = 3.9347 - 3.2819 - 2.6062(4.9849 - 5.2982) = 1.4692$$

$$s_m = 2.6062 \sqrt{\frac{1}{49.0} + \frac{1}{45.4} + \frac{(4.985 - 5.298)^2 2.6062}{142.59}} = 0.5481$$

Relative potency = antilog m = 29.5, determined within limits of 2.5 and 350 at $P = 0.95$.

In this table, I stands for the interval in logarithms between successive doses, and N, which ordinarily stands for the number of animals in a group, refers in this case (each probit being taken as one) to the fact that there is one value on each dose of the standard (S) and one on each dose of the "unknown" (U), and thus equals 2. The letter S has been used here as the sign for summation. The meaning of the other symbols will be clear from the table itself.

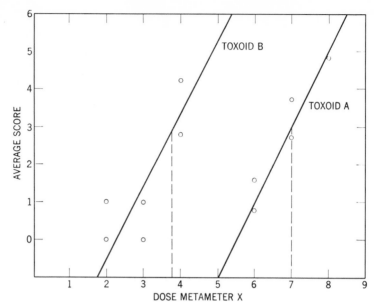

Fig. 17-6. Comparison of potency of two toxoids (see text).

wide. For certain kinds of work it might be desired to obtain estimates with smaller standard errors and more narrow confidence limits. Since the standard error is in general inversely proportional to the square root of the number of animals used, it is easy to see that for any given assay procedure we can diminish the standard error by a factor of $\sqrt{2} = 1.41$ by using twice as many animals. We can cut the standard error to $1/2$ the value found by using four times as many animals. If we do this, the factor by which we multiply and divide the estimated potency to obtain the confidence limits is reduced to the square root of its previous value, since antilog $1.96\sigma/2 =$ antilog $(1/2)$ $(1.96\sigma) = \sqrt{\text{antilog } 1.96\sigma}$. For example, in the assay discussed above (data of Table 17-12), we found a standard error s_m of 0.217, and estimated relative potency of 165 per cent, and confidence limits of 440 and 62 per cent. If we had used four times as many animals, we might have hoped to find a standard error of only 0.108, and our 95 per cent confidence limits would then be obtained by multiplying and dividing the estimate of the relative potency, which we assume to be the same, instead of by 2.66 by, $\sqrt{2.66} = 1.63$. The new confidence limits would be 270 and 101 per cent. We should obviously be happier with the new limits, but we must weigh our potentially increased happiness against the hard economic fact that it would require

$4 \times 80 = 320$ animals to attain it. And to cut the standard error in half once more, and make our confidence limits 211 and 129 per cent, would require 1280 animals. It is clear that we shall have to get along with something less than certainty in such experiments. The problems of how much accuracy we need, and how much accuracy we can afford to get, will have to be weighed together in each practical situation which arises.

It may be doubted if in many real situations we should really wish to increase the numbers of animals by anything like the amount suggested by this argument (4), for it is far from certain that such calculated confidence limits mean enough to be worth so much trouble and expense. Batson (4) states that if one really wanted to know the relative potency with greater accuracy, it would be preferable, not to go from 80 to 1280 animals just to reduce the confidence limits, but rather to run six or so tests using 80 animals in each. The geometric mean potency would then begin to have some actual reliability.

An excellent review of statistical methods as applied to microbiological problems has been published by Stearman (43).

12. Design of Experiments

Now we have just seen that if we wish to divide our standard error by a factor of 1.41 (or multiply it by 0.707) with the resulting improvements in the confidence limits of our estimates, we can do so by the expedient of using twice as many animals as before and doing the experiment in the same old way. But larger numbers of animals may not be so uniform as our smaller batches were, and besides we may not be able to afford the larger numbers, or not be able to afford the expense of housing, feeding, and injecting them. It thus comes as information not to be lightly ignored if somebody tells us we can substantially cut down the standard error, without increasing the number of animals used at all, merely by doing the experiment in a different way. This is where experimental design comes into the picture. It is a subject which the experimental immunologist will do well to study thoroughly.

Suppose, for example, that we have done an assay, using increasing doses of a toxin, and using six mice in each group with the following percentage mortalities: 0, 17, 50, 83, 100. From this experiment we might possibly get an LD50 of 1.00 mg., with confidence limits 2.46 to 0.41 mg. Now suppose we had instead divided our mice into two equal groups, and adjusted the doses so that we obtained mortalities of 40 and 60 per cent in the two groups. Because of the concentration of our animals at two points having relatively great weight statistically, our standard error might now be only 0.707 times that obtained previously, and if we again obtained an end point of 1.00 mg., our new confidence limits would be 1.87 to 0.53. By simply replanning the experiment we have produced the same effect as if we had doubled the number of animals.

This hypothetical example does not by any means exhaust the possible improvements which can be made in experiments by careful planning. Part of the standard error is due to variability in response of the animals, and not all of this variability is beyond our control. We should do well to try to analyze the causes of this variability, and to consider means of diminishing it. As already suggested, this involves the use of one stock of animals, perhaps all of the same sex for any given assay, all possible uniformity in food and housing, and precisely reproducible treatments. Variations in factors which might be considered unimportant may have a considerable effect. For instance, Batson (3) found that differences between lots of hog gastric mucin in which the microorganisms were suspended for the challenge had significant effects on the mortality. A typhoid vaccine had a considerably greater apparent potency when the challenge organisms were suspended in one lot of mucin than when they were suspended in another.

When all variables we can think of have been made as similar for the experimental and control animals, or the two lots of experimental animals, as we know how, there will still remain numerous and potent sources of variability.

Part of the procedure of experimentation involves the avoidance of any element of unconscious bias on the part of the experimenter, and of systematic variations of susceptibility in certain groups of animals, by the introduction of a random element into the make-up of the experiment. In so far as possible, animals are assigned to groups, and groups to treatments, by the use of dice, shuffled cards, random numbers, or some such device. Arrangements such as randomized blocks and Latin squares enable duplication to be avoided. The details of such arrangements will be found in Fisher (17), Bliss (18), Cochran and Cox (13), Mather (35), and elsewhere. We can give but the merest outline here.

In the type of experiment known as randomized blocks, or randomized groups, we use equal sized groups with as many individuals in each group as there are different doses under test. In each group one individual is assigned to each dose. Thus each group provides a "replicate" of each dosage trial. Differences between the groups, due to the differences in food or laboratory environment, or other causes, do not bias the mean response to each treatment, since each group is represented equally at all dosage levels. Any differences in response due to differences between groups can then be eliminated from the estimate of the experimental error. Treatments are assigned at random (as determined by dice, cards, or random numbers) to the individuals in each group.

The ideal experiment, we were taught in high school physics, is one in which the experimenter investigates the effect of changing only one thing at a time, keeping everything else exactly the same. Fisher (17) states that this ideal experiment probably never takes place, except conceptually when simple principles of physics are being demonstrated. When actual research is being done, we often do not know what all the influences on the outcome of an experiment are, and can never be sure we have kept them all constant. The modern technic of experiment, Fisher points out, is to vary a number of factors which we think influence the outcome of the experiment, but to vary them in a controlled, independent way so that the effects of the different factors can be analyzed separately. This technic is capable of giving much more information from one experiment than the older technic, and will in addition tell us if there is significant "interaction" between two or more factors, which the older technic would not.

The subject of design of experiments has its own large literature and is too specialized to be gone into in more detail here. The interested reader may consult books such as those of Bliss (8), Fisher (17), Burn (11), and Mather (35). It is a study which will pay large dividends to the experimental immunologist, even larger than will attention to those elementary principles of statistical analysis which have been outlined above.

Aspects of experimental design wihch are not statistical in nature are also important. More than one way of trying for an answer to a question may exist, and one may be better than another. We might be led to try one instead of the other because of some intuitive feeling as to the relation between the thing we want to measure and the thing we can observe. This feeling may or may not be correct. For example, there are two quite different laboratory procedures which may be used to assay the potency of a vaccine or an antiserum. In the first, which is more commonly used, we administer the protective agent to a number of animals and later give groups of these treated animals progressively increasing doses of the infectious agent. From the proportions of survivors we can estimate the potency of the protective agent as the number of LD50's against which 50 per cent of the animals are protected.

An alternative procedure is to administer graded doses of the immunizing agent to different groups of animals, followed by the same challenge dose of the infectious agent. Here we should express the effectiveness of the immunizing agent in terms of the ED50, the amount required to protect 50 per cent of the animals against the particular challenge dose used.

Underlying the first procedure is the hypothesis that the size of the challenge dose which an animal can resist after immunization is directly related to the potency of the immunizing agent. Underlying the second procedure is the hypothesis that the amount of immunizing agent required to protect a certain proportion of the animals against a particular challenge dose is directly related to the potency of the product. There is no particular *a priori* reason to prefer one of these hypotheses to the other.

Batson (3) first predicted, then confirmed, by actual experiments that the graded immunizing dose-constant challenge method gave much better estimates of relative potency for two antisera than did the constant dose-graded challenge method. The constant immunizing dose-graded challenge method yielded very uncertain results, because of the low slope of the dosage–response regression lines. Evidently the assumption that the size of the challenge dose against which an antiserum will protect is directly related to its potency is not correct, at least in this case. This is a conclusion we could never have been able to draw from theory alone.

13. Interpretation of Results of Assays

Suppose we have completed an assay of a new immunizing agent or protective serum. We have compared it with a standard preparation of known efficacy, and it compares well in potency. If large numbers of animals have been used, and the unknown and standard have been run concurrently on animals of the same stock, we may even be able to state that the unknown is not less than 60 per cent as effective as the standard, and not more than 160 per cent effective. By using larger number of animals we can still further narrow these limits, and put on the label of our preparation that it contains so many units of activity. Does this mean that the physician can rely upon these figures as an indication of the effectiveness of the preparation under the only circumstances in which he wants to use it, namely, in human immunization or treatment?

The answer to this question is unfortunately only a very qualified yes. Unless the unknown is a preparation of exactly the same sort of material, neither more nor less impure, treated in exactly the same way, we cannot be confident that the relative potency as determined in animals will apply to man.

For several reasons, the possession of a high efficacy in animal tests may not be any guarantee of effectiveness of a preparation in man. In the first place, just as different animal strains differ in susceptibility and immunizability, so do different species differ, only more so. The capsular polysaccharides of pneumococcus will immunize men and mice against pneumonia, but not guinea pigs or rabbits. Even when the agent is effective against more than one species, considerable differences in degree of effectiveness may exist. The only way to find out if this is the case is to assay a preparation against animals and test it carefully in man. This latter is a very difficult procedure. Another difficulty is that we may have tested the protective action of our agent in animals by using some inappropriate route of administration of the challenge dose. An agent might protect all right against interacerebral inoculation of a bacillus into mice, but be relatively ineffective against human infection by the oral route. It is important not to draw any more conclusions from an experiment than it actually warrants.

It is apparent that many pitfalls exist in the problem of standardizing vaccines and serums for human use. We have been able to suggest only some of them here. Nevertheless, in the face of the impossibility of doing all the assays directly on human subjects, animal assays will continue to be used, and indeed will certainly continue to be one of the most valuable tools of the laboratories supplying serums and biologicals.

14. Rank Methods

In some types of immunological experiment it is not only impossible to record the result as all-or-none, but it is difficult or impossible to give the various results a numerical score so the outcome of the experiment can be treated as a problem in graded response. If the results can nevertheless be compared quantitatively with one another, and arranged by inspection in order of development of the phenomenon or effect being studied, it is possible to apply statistical methods in evaluating the experiment.

As a simple example of the application of such methods, we may mention the work of Stinebring and Flick (45), who were studying the *in vitro* tuberculin reaction. It was desired to test *(1)* if tuberculin [actually PPD (see p. 232) was used] has an inhibiting effect on the migration *in vitro* of large wandering cells from splenic fragments from tuberculin-sensitive guinea pigs, and *(2)* if hemolytically active complement were necessary for this inhibition reaction.

Fragments of spleen from tuberculin-sensitive guinea pigs were washed in Hank's solution and planted in chicken plasma in tubes, two explants per tube. After the plasma had clotted, supernatant fluids containing or not containing guinea pig complement and containing or not containing

PPD were added.   The tubes were randomized before these supernatants
were added.   After 48 hours' incubation, the tubes, identified only by
number, were arranged by inspection in order of amount of migration,
with those showing the best migration placed first and those showing
the worst migration placed last.   In an experiment in which 10 tubes
with PPD were compared with 10 tubes without PPD (all containing
complement), the following ranks were assigned (44):

	PPD	No PPD
	10	1
	12	2
	13	3
	14	4
	15	5
	16	6
	17	7
	18	8
	19	9
	20	11
Total rank	154	56

Now it may be calculated that there is a probability of about 5 per
cent of getting one rank total as low as, or lower than, $9N^2/10 - 3N/2
+ 3$, where N is the number of pairs compared in rank (in this
case $N = 10$) (37,48).   From this calculation, we obtain 78 as the
rank total which our lower rank total may equal or fall below in 5 per cent
of the cases merely by chance.   Clearly our observed rank total for the
tubes without PPD is significantly lower than could reasonably be
ascribed to chance.   The observed value of 56 is even significant at the
1 per cent level, for it may be calculated that the rank total which our
value may be as low as, or lower than, in 1 per cent of the cases, is

$$4N^2/5 - 9,$$

which in our case $= 71$ (actually only one other possible outcome of the
experiment could have led to a lower total rank than was actually
found).

Therefore, although we have not *measured* anything, we can state
with confidence that PPD inhibits the migration of tuberculin-sensitive
splenic large wandering cells *in vitro*.

When tubes with complement and tubes without complement (all
containing PPD) were compared, the following ranks were assigned:

With Complement	Without Complement
1	6
2	9
3	10
4	11
5	12
7	14
8	15
13	16
18	17
19	20
Rank total 80	130

Here it is seen that the lower rank total is not so low as the value of 78 required for 5 per cent significance (although it is not far from it), and we are obliged to say that the experiment does not disprove the null hypothesis that complement plays no role in the *in vitro* tuberculin reaction. Stinebring and Flick concluded that they had failed to demonstrate that there is such an effect.

Rank methods can also be applied when the numbers in the two groups are not equal (47), and the reader will find examples of other applications of rank methods in the following references (37,48,29).

Another appliction of ranking methods may be made in the case where the treated and control animals fall into categories which have a natural order. In such cases rank methods may reveal a significant trend when the χ^2 test, which takes no account of the order in which categories are arranged, would show no significant difference between the two groups.

Suppose, for example, we have a group of patients with hay fever, whom we have treated by injections of pollen extracts or in some other way which is supposed to decrease their symptoms. The autumn following the treatment we question the treated patients, and a group of untreated patients who serve as controls, as to their hay fever symptoms during the summer. It is difficult to quantitate the severity of the symptoms of such an ailment, and perhaps the best we can do, on the basis of the patients' verbal descriptions, is to arrange the symptoms or lack of them into four categories: no symptoms, mild symptoms, moderate symptoms, and severe symptoms. Suppose the numbers of patients reporting symptoms falling into these categories are as shown in the table (see following page).

	No Symptoms	Mild Symptoms	Moderate Symptoms	Severe Symptoms	Totals
Treated patients	15	13	20	20	68
Untreated (controls)	6	5	16	27	54

It looks as if our treatment has mitigated the symptoms somewhat, but will the data stand statistical examination? If we apply the χ^2 test, we find $\chi^2 = 7.383$, which for 3 degrees of freedom, is not significant [we find from tables such as those of Fisher (18) or Fisher and Yates (19) that for 3 degrees of freedom χ^2 has to be 7.815 or over to be significant at the 5 per cent level].

If, however, we calculate a statistic designated as t from these data, making use of the fact that the categories are arranged in order of increasing severity of symptoms, we find $t = 7.216$. According to a table of χ^2, the use of which is appropriate, with *one* degree of freedom, this value is significant at the 5 per cent level, in fact significant even at the 1 per cent level. It seems safe to conclude that our hypothetical treatment has done our patients some good, even if the effect was merely psychological. Details of making such calculations will be found in Wilcoxon (48), White (47), Kruskall and Wallis (29), and Bross (10).

15. Application to the Precipitin Test

If the precipitin test is carried out quantitatively, and the amount of precipitate from a given mixture of antigen and serum estimated by methods such as the microkjeldahl or biuret (see Chapter 16), it may be desired to answer the question: is the average amount of precipitate from equivalent mixtures of different antisera with the same antigen, or different antigens with the same antiserum, significantly different or not?

A typical example of such data was treated by Hooker and Boyd (20a). These investigators made nitrogen determinations of quadruplicate precipitates made at the equivalence point (see p. 353) with three antisera to native crystalline ovalbumin and one pool of antisera to ovalbumin coupled with diazotized arsanilic acid and iodosulfanilic acid, with the results shown in Table 17-15.

Application of the "t" test (Fisher (18), Sections 24 and 24.1 and Table IV) showed that the mean of four determinations with the antibody to the modified ovalbumin differed significantly from the means obtained

TABLE 17-15

Means of Determinations of Antibody–Antigen Ratios (R) for Different Sera (20a)

Antiserum no.	Antigen injected	Mean $R(M)$	σ_M
610	Native ovalbumin	9.98	0.17
671-2-3	Native ovalbumin	9.67	0.13
717-8-9	Native ovalbumin	9.99	0.06
621-2	Modified ovalbumin	8.72	0.07

"t" for comparison of first three means and fourth mean $= ca.$ 6, $n = 6$, $P < 0.01$.

with the antibody to the native ovalbumin, but that the means obtained with the three antisera to native ovalbumin did not differ significantly from each other.

16. Statistics and Inhibition Tests

Many of the procedures that immunologists euphemistically call "titrations" are only semiquantitative at best, and it is difficult or impossible to apply statistical methods with any confidence to results so obtained. Inhibition tests provide a good example of this.

There are two basically different ways of doing "quantitative" inhibition tests with haptens (see p. 684). Either the hapten or the antiserum may be kept constant in concentration, and the other used in serial dilutions. Suppose we consider tests in which the hapten is diluted.

From such an experiment we shall obtain readings of the strength of some serological reaction, such as precipitation or agglutination, as a function of the concentration of the hapten, which would usually diluted 1:12, 1:4, etc. If the degree to which the (partially) inhibited serological reaction has taken place can be estimated quantitatively, the concentration of hapten that reduces this to 50 per cent of the value obtainable with the same antigen and antiserum without hapten can be estimated. This would be called the 50 per cent inhibiting dose.

If several such series of quantitative measurements are carried out, it is possible to obtain a mean (average) estimate of the 50 per cent inhibiting dose and, from the standard deviation of this mean, an estimate of its reliability. When such standard errors are calculated they tend to be rather large, for the quantitative precipitin technique is not as reproducible as the measurements of inorganic quantitative analysis or physical chemistry are. For this and a variety of other reasons, standard errors are not usually calculated for such estimates: (a) The necessary determinations would require too great an outlay of the experimenter's time and of an antibody that may be in short supply. (b) The goal of such experiments is not usually an estimate of the actual inhibiting dose of any one particular hapten, but an estimate of the relative inhibiting power of two different haptens; in other words, a ratio. It is quickly found that attempts to calculate the standard error of a ratio from the standard errors of the two numbers involved leads one into Higher Statistics.

It might seem to the nonserologist that in the simple type of inhibition study shown schematically in Tables 16-5 and 16-6 statistical methods could be applied and would be helpful, but this is not generally the case either. To begin with, inhibition experiments are ordinarily interpreted as if inhibition were an all-or-none phenomenon. Thus from the first line of Table 16-5 we conclude that for complete inhibition (tube 4, counting from the left) of the amount of serum used in the experiment 1/16 of the amount of hapten H contained in a unit volume of stock solution is sufficient. But for all we know the amount of hapten in tube 4 may be anywhere from 1.02 to 1.98 times the minimal inhibiting dose (MID) of H. If tube 4 contains 1.02 MID, then tube 5 in turn contains only 0.51 MID, and the unavoidable accidental variations in experimental conditions are not likely to cause tube 5 to give a negative reading, though they well might make tube 4 positive. But if tube 4 contains 1.98 MID, which is equally possible, then tube 5 would contain 0.99 MID, and a slight variation in the conditions of the experiment might mean that tube 5 would read negative instead of positive. Thus in different experiments our estimate of the smallest amount of hapten that will completely inhibit a given amount of antiserum might vary from 1.0 to 2.0 to 0.5 mM. An experimenter is likely to feel that he is wasting his time in averaging numbers like 1.0, 2.0, and 0.5, not to speak of trying to estimate a standard deviation and a standard error of the resulting mean.

Also, it must be realized that, just as the results with hapten H might vary from 1.0 to 2.0 to 0.5 mM, so the results with hapten H' might vary from 0.25 to 0.5 to 0.125 mM. It is expected that the variations in estimated MID's of the two haptens will generally go in the same direction; indeed, this is one of the reasons for running all the tests simultaneously, but it is apparent that the ratio of the apparent MID's *might* vary from 16 to 1.

In the second place, the all-or-none interpretation of inhibition experiments is an oversimplification. The experiment summarized in the first line of Table 17-5 actually yields more information than is contained in the mere statement that tubes 1 to 4 are negative and tubes 5, 6, etc., are positive. The strength of the reaction in the first tube to the right of the last negative tube also contributes information, for the reaction can vary from weak to strong. Taking the simple point of view, for example, we should estimate from Table 2-2 that hapten H' is only one-fourth as effective an inhibitor as hapten H, for it takes four times as much to produce complete inhibition. But if we take account of the fact that the next tube after complete inhibition gives a reaction of $+$ in the case of hapten H and only $\pm$ in the case of H', it is clear that H' is actually somewhat more than one-fourth as effective as H'. But how much more? It is hard to put such things into numerical terms. It is possible to invent codes for the translation of such readings into quantitative terms, or appropriate numerical scores may be found by statistical methods [see, for example, Fisher (18), Section 49.2, Example 46.2]. In general, however, such treatments of the results of inhibition tests have not been found to extract enough extra information from the results to justify the calculations involved.

Recognizing, therefore, that the results of inhibition experiments are only semiquantitative at best, serologists who are attempting to compare the inhibitory power of two different haptens do not generally attempt to make quantitative estimates, but are content to say merely that hapten H is more effective, for this particular serum, than H' is. Some tend to rely on the old rule of thumb, which is pretty well borne out in practice, that a difference in the results obtained with two haptens is significant if the difference in their inhibiting capacity differs rather consistently, from one experiment to another, by two tubes (ordinarily meaning a four-fold difference in effective concentrations). If the results do not differ by this much, one may suspect a difference in the effectiveness of the two haptens, without venturing a confident opinion. Even such a difference, however, arbitrarily judged to be "nonsignificant," may be of value as a guide to further experiments.

References

2. Batson, H. C., *Statistical Methods in Medical Research*, unpublished manuscript, 1950.
3. Batson, H. C., *J. Immunol.*, **66**, 737 (1951).
4. Batson, H. C., personal communication, 1954.
5. Batson, H. C., M. Brown, and M. Oberstein, *U. S. Public Health Repts.*, **66**, 789 (1951).
6. Behrens, B., *Arch. exptl. Pathol. u. Pharmakol.*, **140**, 237 (1929).
7. Bliss, C. I., personal communication, 1942.
8. Bliss, C. I., *The Statistics of Bioassay*, Academic Press, New York, 1952.
9. Boyd, W. C., *J. Am. Statistical Assoc.*, **60**, 344 (1965).
10. Bross, I. D. J., *Federation Proc.*, **13**, 815 (1954).
11. Burn, J. H., D. J. Finney, and L. G. Goodwin, *Biological Standardization*, Oxford University Press, London, 1950.

12. Campbell, D. H., J. S. Garvey, N. E. Cremor, and D. H. Sussdorf, *Methods in Immunology*, W. A. Benjamin, New York, 1963.
13. Cochran, W. G., and G. M. Cox, *Experimental Design*, Wiley, New York, 1950.
14. Finney, D. J., *Probit Analysis*, Cambridge University Press, Cambridge, 1952.
15. Fisher, R. A., *Proc. Roy. Soc. Edinburg*, **42**, 321 (1921–22).
16. Fisher, R. A., *Statistical Methods for Research Workers*, Oliver and Boyd, Edinburgh, 1950.
17. Fisher, R. A., *The Design of Experiments*, Oliver and Boyd, Edinburgh, 1942.
18. Fisher, R. A., *Statistical Methods for Research Workers*, 12th ed., Oliver and Boyd, Edinburgh, 1958.
19. Fisher, R. A., and F. Yates, *Statistical Tables for Biological, Agricultural, and Medical Research*, 2nd ed., Oliver and Boyd, Edinburgh, 1943.
20. Gaddum, J. H., *Med. Res. Council (Brit.), Spec. Rept. Ser.*, No. **183** (1933).
20a. Hooker, S. B., and W. C. Boyd, *Proc. Soc. Exp. Biol. Med.*, **32**, 1104 (1935).
21. Ipsen, J., *Contribution to the Theory of Biological Standardization*, Nyt Nordisk Forlag Arnold Busck, Copenhagen, 1941.
22. Ipsen, J., personal communication, 1955.
23. Ipsen, J., *et al.*, *J. Immunol.*, **70**, 171 (1953).
24. Irwin, J. O., and E. A. Cheeseman, *J. Hyg.*, **39**, 574 (1939).
26. Kärber, G., *Arch. exptl. Pathol. u. Pharmakol.*, **162**, 480 (1931).
27. Knudsen, L. F., and J. M. Curtis, *J. Am. Statistical Assoc.*, **42**, 282 (1947).
28. Koch, W., and D. Kaplan, *J. Immunol.*, **65**, 7 (1950).
29. Kruskall, W. H., and W. A. Wallis, *J. Am. Statistical Assoc.*, **47**, 583 (1952).
31. Litchfield, J. T., *J. Pharmacol. Exptl. Therap.*, **97**, 399 (1949).
32. Litchfield, J. T., and F. Wilcoxon, *J. Pharmacol. Exptl. Therap.*, **96**, 99 (1949).
33. Little, P. A., *J. Immunol.*, **47**, 97 (1943).
34. Lockhart, L. P., *J. Hyg.*, **25**, 50 (1926).
35. Mather, K., *Statistical Analysis in Biology*, Interscience, New York, 1947.
36. Miller, L. C., and M. L. Tainter, *Proc. Soc. Exptl. Biol. Med.*, **57**, 261 (1944).
37. Moroney, M. J., *Facts from Figures*, Penguin, London, 1956.
39. Pearson, K., *Tables for Statisticians and Biometricians*, University College of London Biometrical Laboratory, London, 1930.
39a. Pearson, E. S., and H. O. Hartley, eds., *Biometrical Tables for Statisticians. I.*, Cambridge University Press, London, 1962.
40. Pizzi, M., *Human Biol.*, **22**, 151 (1950).
41. Reed, L. J., and H. Muench, *Am. J. Hyg.*, **27**, 493 (1938).
42. Rosenau, M. J., *U. S. Public Health Service, Hyg. Lab. Bull.*, No. **21**, April (1905).
43. Stearman, R. L., *Bacteriol. Rev.*, **19**, 160 (1955).
44. Stinebring, W. R., personal communication, 1954.
45. Stinebring, W. R., and J. A. Flick, *Federation Proc.*, **13**, 513 (1954).
46. Topley, W. W. C., and G. S. Wilson, *The Principles of Bacteriology and Immunity*, 5th ed., G. S. Wilson and A. A. Miles, eds., Williams and Wilkins, Baltimore, 1964.
47. White, C., *Biometrics*, **8**, 33 (1952).
48. Wilcoxon F., *Biometrics*, **1**, 80 (1945).

Appendix

Translation (by the present writer) of Quotations for Chapters 2, 5, 6, 8, 12, 13, 14, 15, 16, and 17

Chapter 2. Now no machine is capable of choice, except in accord with precise predetermined criteria written into its program.

Chapter 5. She used to write with blood in the albums of tender maids.

Chapter 6. I saw a young shepard, twisting, choking, turning, with a face distorted, from whose mouth a heavy black snake hung.
Have I ever seen so much loathing and pale horror on *one* face? He had probably been asleep? Then the snake crept into his mouth—there bit itself fast.

Chapter 8. One man's meat is another man's poison (literally, "What is food for one may be fierce poison for others").

Chapter 12. And I say to them: "Yes, I am that, when that is I and all is mine and the totality of things is mine."

Chapter 13. And the forepart turning back and trying to bite itself, that by its bite it might stop the burning pain of the wound that struck it.

Chapter 14. Besides, since there is pain when bodies of matter are attacked by some force through the living flesh and limbs, and they tremble in their interior dwellings, when they move back to their place there comes soothing delight.

Chapter 15. The good master said to me, "You had best not be seen until I am ready. Crouch behind a rock, so as to have some protection. And whatever attack may be made on me, do not fear. I know these matters: I have been through this once before."

Chapter 16. Just have contempt for reason and science, the highest strength of man, allow yourself to be strengthened in illusion and magic by the Spirit of Lies—

Chapter 17. (Some) will say: They were three, their dog the fourth, and (some) say: Five, their dog the sixth (making wild guesses) and (some) say: seven, and their dog the eighth. Say (O Mohammed): My Lord knows their numbers best, None know them but a few.

745

INDEX

A